ELECTROMECHANICAL POWER CONVERSION

McGraw-Hill Electrical and Electronic Engineering Series

FREDERICK EMMONS TERMAN, *Consulting Editor*
W. W. HARMAN AND J. G. TRUXAL, *Associate Consulting Editors*

AHRENDT AND SAVANT · Servomechanism Practice
ANGELO · Electronic Circuits
ASELTINE · Transform Method in Linear System Analysis
ATWATER · Introduction to Microwave Theory
BAILEY AND GAULT · Alternating-current Machinery
BERANEK · Acoustics
BRACEWELL · Transform Methods in Linear Systems
BRENNER AND JAVID · Analysis of Electric Circuits
BROWN · Analysis of Linear Time-invariant Systems
BRUNS AND SAUNDERS · Analysis of Feedback Control Systems
CAGE · Theory and Application of Industrial Electronics
CAUER · Synthesis of Linear Communication Networks
CHEN · The Analysis of Linear Systems
CHEN · Linear Network Design and Synthesis
CHIRLIAN · Analysis and Design of Electronic Circuits
CHIRLIAN AND ZEMANIAN · Electronics
CLEMENT AND JOHNSON · Electrical Engineering Science
COTE AND OAKES · Linear Vacuum-tube and Transistor Circuits
CUCCIA · Harmonics, Sidebands, and Transients in Communication Engineering
CUNNINGHAM · Introduction to Nonlinear Analysis
EASTMAN · Fundamentals of Vacuum Tubes
EVANS · Control-system Dynamics
FEINSTEIN · Foundations of Information Theory
FITZGERALD AND HIGGINBOTHAM · Basic Electrical Engineering
FITZGERALD AND KINGSLEY · Electric Machinery
FRANK · Electrical Measurement Analysis
FRIEDLAND, WING, AND ASH · Principles of Linear Networks
GEPPERT · Basic Electron Tubes
GHAUSI · Principles and Design of Linear Active Circuits
GHOSE · Microwave Circuit Theory and Analysis
GREINER · Semiconductor Devices and Applications
HAMMOND · Electrical Engineering
HANCOCK · An Introduction to the Principles of Communication Theory
HAPPELL AND HESSELBERTH · Engineering Electronics
HARMAN · Fundamentals of Electronic Motion
HARMAN · Principles of the Statistical Theory of Communication
HARMAN AND LYTLE · Electrical and Mechanical Networks
HARRINGTON · Introduction to Electromagnetic Engineering
HARRINGTON · Time-harmonic Electromagnetic Fields

HAYASHI · Nonlinear Oscillations in Physical Systems
HAYT · Engineering Electromagnetics
HAYT AND KEMMERLY · Engineering Circuit Analysis
HILL · Electronics in Engineering
JAVID AND BRENNER · Analysis, Transmission, and Filtering of Signals
JAVID AND BROWN · Field Analysis and Electromagnetics
JOHNSON · Transmission Lines and Networks
KOENIG AND BLACKWELL · Electromechanical System Theory
KRAUS · Antennas
KRAUS · Electromagnetics
KUH AND PEDERSON · Principles of Circuit Synthesis
LEDLEY · Digital Computer and Control Engineering
LEPAGE · Analysis of Alternating-current Circuits
LEPAGE AND SEELY · General Network Analysis
LEVI AND PANZER · Electromechanical Power Conversion
LEY, LUTZ, AND REHBERG · Linear Circuit Analysis
LINVILL AND GIBBONS · Transistors and Active Circuits
LITTAUER · Pulse Electronics
LYNCH AND TRUXAL · Introductory System Analysis
LYNCH AND TRUXAL · Principles of Electronic Instrumentation
LYNCH AND TRUXAL · Signals and Systems in Electrical Engineering
MEISEL · Principles of Electromechanical-energy Conversion
MILLMAN · Vacuum-tube and Semiconductor Electronics
MILLMAN AND SEELY · Electronics
MILLMAN AND TAUB · Pulse and Digital Circuits
MILLMAN AND TAUB · Pulse, Digital, and Switching Waveforms
MISHKIN AND BRAUN · Adaptive Control Systems
MOORE · Traveling-wave Engineering
NANAVATI · An Introduction to Semiconductor Electronics
PETTIT · Electronic Switching, Timing, and Pulse Circuits
PETTIT AND MCWHORTER · Electronic Amplifier Circuits
PFEIFFER · Linear Systems Analysis
REZA · An Introduction to Information Theory
REZA AND SEELY · Modern Network Analysis
ROGERS · Introduction to Electric Fields
RUSTON AND BORDOGNA · Electric Networks: Functions, Filters, Analysis
RYDER · Engineering Electronics
SCHWARTZ · Information Transmission, Modulation, and Noise
SCHWARZ AND FRIEDLAND · Linear Systems
SEELY · Electromechanical Energy Conversion
SEELY · Electron-tube Circuits
SEELY · Electronic Engineering
SEELY · Introduction to Electromagnetic Fields
SEELY · Radio Electronics
SEIFERT AND STEEG · Control Systems Engineering
SISKIND · Direct-current Machinery

Skilling · Electric Transmission Lines
Skilling · Transient Electric Currents
Spangenberg · Fundamentals of Electron Devices
Spangenberg · Vacuum Tubes
Stevenson · Elements of Power System Analysis
Stewart · Fundamentals of Signal Theory
Storer · Passive Network Synthesis
Strauss · Wave Generation and Shaping
Terman · Electronic and Radio Engineering
Terman and Pettit · Electronic Measurements
Thaler · Elements of Servomechanism Theory
Thaler and Brown · Analysis and Design of Feedback Control Systems
Thaler and Pastel · Analysis and Design of Nonlinear Feedback Control Systems
Thompson · Alternating-current and Transient Circuit Analysis
Tou · Digital and Sampled-data Control Systems
Tou · Modern Control Theory
Truxal · Automatic Feedback Control System Synthesis
Valdes · The Physical Theory of Transistors
Van Bladel · Electromagnetic Fields
Weinberg · Network Analysis and Synthesis
Williams and Young · Electrical Engineering Problems

Brooklyn Polytechnic Institute Series

Angelo · Electronic Circuits
Levi and Panzer · Electromechanical Power Conversion
Lynch and Truxal · Signals and Systems in Electrical Engineering
Combining Introductory System Analysis
Principles of Electronic Instrumentation
Mishkin and Braun · Adaptive Control Systems
Schwartz · Information Transmission, Modulation, and Noise
Strauss · Wave Generation and Shaping

ELECTROMECHANICAL POWER CONVERSION

Low-frequency, Low-velocity Conversion Processes

Enrico Levi
Professor of Electrophysics

and

Marvin Panzer
Associate Professor of Electrical Engineering

POLYTECHNIC INSTITUTE OF BROOKLYN

McGraw-Hill Book Company

New York St. Louis San Francisco Toronto London Sydney

ELECTROMECHANICAL POWER CONVERSION

Library of Congress Catalog Card Number 66-14807

37363

1234567890 MP 7321069876

To Bitia and Charlotte

FOREWORD

To many electrical engineering educators, an alarming feature of the current debates on engineering education is the strong focusing of emphasis on the two aspects of materials engineering and information systems engineering. The teacher and the curriculum planner tend to overlook the entire area of energy generation, conversion, and processing. The trend is strengthened by the transition of the United States economy from its manufacturing orientation to a service emphasis.

The stress on materials and information systems within the typical electrical engineering curriculum is certainly in part the consequence of the past refusal of teachers of electrical machinery and power distribution to modify their courses to develop a relationship with the remainder of the curriculum. As the circuits and field courses evolved rapidly in the 1950s, the machinery courses often tended to become more and more detached and isolated. As the numbers of faculty members interested in electronics and electrophysics swelled under the impetus of federally sponsored research, the machinery and energy conversion work was gradually squeezed out of the undergraduate curriculum. The associated industry loudly lamented the changes, but failed to take positive steps to reverse the trend.

With an acute awareness of this educational scene and, at the same time, with an unusual appreciation of the importance of power conversion within the long-term role of electrical engineering, Professors Levi and Panzer launched the intensive course development which is now marked by publication of this book. The work is characterized by three features which seem particularly significant in broad educational terms:

1. Unlike other attempts to "modernize" machinery, it is closely associated with both fields and circuits portions of the curriculum; indeed, the course makes a major contribution in reinforcing and motivating much of the basic material in electromagnetic theory.
2. Unlike most other attempts to "modernize" machinery, this course relates closely to technical areas of major interest in modern electrical engineering research. The illustrative examples and problems vividly portray the current range of application of the basic concepts presented in the text. A large portion of the Polytechnic faculty who have taught in this required course have found that electromechanical power conversion can be an exciting subject.
3. The authors have fearlessly deviated from traditional approaches —an intrepidity and creativity which are curiously rare in the educational institutions which feed graduates into an industrial complex where these qualities are essential to success.

The significance of any novel text depends not only upon the merits of the book but also on the educational climate. As engineering education emerges from its emphasis on communications and space sciences toward concern with the problems of urban and societal engineering, the importance of the engineering of power conversion systems returns as a legitimate and essential phase of the undergraduate electrical engineering curriculum. This book represents one possible approach which we at the Polytechnic believe to be attractive, educationally significant, and intellectually stimulating for the student.

JOHN G. TRUXAL

PREFACE

The study of electromechanical power conversion has always been an integral part of education in electrical engineering. In the early days, of course, electrical engineering was largely identified with power conversion. In the last two decades, the impact of the enormous development in electronics, network theory, communications, and control has caused a sharp reduction in the attention devoted to power conversion in EE curricula. There exists also a general consensus of opinion that, although the study of power conversion is basic and desirable since the ability to convert power in a usable fashion is after all one of the very foundations of modern technology, traditional courses in transformers and rotating machines do not meet the needs of the times with regard to overall curricular requirements and stimulation of interest on the part of students and faculty.

As a consequence, there has been widespread interest in finding new approaches to the study of electromechanical power conversion and several new textbooks have appeared. Reflecting the spirit of the times, they have tended to be network-analytic in character, with emphasis on circuit models and sophisticated mathematical techniques.

This book presents a different approach which has been motivated by several factors. Foremost is the advent of the space age which has brought about a greater concern with natural phenomena in which power-conversion processes, over the whole gamut of frequencies, play such a spectacular role. These include the sustenance of the magnetic field in celestial bodies; the interaction of the geomagnetic field with the solar wind; the rise, growth, and acceleration of solar flares; the generation of cosmic rays; the excitation of Alfvén and electromagnetic waves and finally, the hydromagnetic vorticity, which according to some cosmological theories, is responsible for the formation of solar systems.

Another major factor is the rapidly developing technology of nuclear power. Power generation from fission sources is currently becoming economically competitive, and the future holds the promise of both magnetoplasma-dynamic generation and controlled thermonuclear fusion. These developments, as well as ancillary technological achievements, such as the production of gaseous materials having conductivities higher than that of copper at one extreme of the temperature scale, and the construction of large superconducting magnets at the other extreme, portend a revolution of the entire field. As a result of these accomplishments, we may expect electromechanical power conversion to be liberated (1) from the geometries and field configurations imposed by the use of rigid conductors and ferromagnetic materials and (2) from the constraint of a single mechanical degree of freedom. Moreover, we may anticipate a union of low- and high-frequency bands in a continuous range of coupled oscillatory processes.

The authors have accordingly sought to prepare a book which presents the principles of power conversion in a unified and fundamental way, permitting the inclusion of both the old and new in power conversion, and laying the groundwork for the student's understanding of and participation in future developments.

Paralleling the new technical factors outlined above, a new educational trend has recently developed, which may be characterized by the phrase "back to engineering." It stems from the realization on the part of engineering educators that a curriculum which devotes itself primarily to analytic studies without due attention to synthesis and design does a basic disservice to the training of the neophyte engineer. As Dr. Henry T. Heald* has said: "Engineering is an art of synthesis, of consolidating the gains of scientific research, and of fashioning knowledge into systems and designs that are the most effective, feasible, and economic."

These views of engineering education have motivated the authors in writing this book. As a result, the text includes the three major steps in the development of feasible and economic electromechanical power-conversion systems from basic principles, namely the fundamental field-particle interactions, the formulation of suitable physical models, and finally their application to basic design. Network representations are widely used, but they are introduced only after the physical systems have been thoroughly discussed and the operating mechanisms studied in all their aspects; the "black-box" model based solely on experimentally determined parameters is never used.

The book that has grown from these considerations starts with the study of the motion of elementary charged particles according to the Lorentz force law. These particles are next put together with increasing density to form in turn gaseous plasmas and liquid and solid conductors. The electromechanical performance of a volume element of such conducting material is then determined. These volume elements are used as the building blocks for the engineering synthesis of the active conductors, around which the fundamental types of converting units take shape. Starting with maximum uniformity and symmetry and relinquishing these attributes in ordered stages, the homopolar, synchronous, and induction converters are developed. Essentially this book covers the low-frequency, low-velocity interactions between systems of currents; a second volume will study the high-frequency, high-velocity interactions between

* Dr. Heald, then president of the Ford Foundation, made these remarks in a speech at the dedication ceremonies for the new Quadrangle for the School of Engineering and Applied Sciences of Princeton University, fall, 1962.

systems of charges using the principles established here in a dual fashion.

This book represents several years of classroom development at the Polytechnic Institute of Brooklyn and is presently being taught as a one-semester required senior course. The essential prerequisite of the course is an elementary knowledge of electromagnetic field theory. In fact, this association with EMT is a major contribution of the course to the overall curricular structure, because of the opportunity it affords the student to apply and consolidate his knowledge of field theory.

The text contains more material than can be covered at a reasonable pace in one semester, and in order to save time the instructor may deem it desirable to omit those sections dealing with illustrative applications which have been starred.

The material for Vol. 2 is presently being developed in an additional one-semester senior course.

The authors are greatly indebted to Prof. John G. Truxal for his suggestions and encouragement, to Prof. Mischa Schwartz, who has taught this course and made many valuable constructive criticisms, and to all the other colleagues, in particular Prof. P. E. Serafim and Mr. L. Birenbaum, as well as Prof. J. P. Freidberg and Mr. H. Friedman, who have read and commented on the text and have aided in the preparation of the problems.

Enrico Levi
Marvin Panzer

CONTENTS

SYMBOLS and NOTATION

Vectors are denoted by boldface roman letters, for example **B**; the same letter in lightface type B denotes either the magnitude of the vector or the value of a designated component of the vector.

Phasors are indicated either by a bar over the letter, for example $\bar{E}$, or by a dot as in $\dot{E}$. The bar identifies a "wave" phasor, i.e., a constant complex number which is associated with an exponential that is periodic in both space and time; the dot identifies a "time" phasor, i.e., a complex number that is a function of position, which is associated with an exponential that is periodic only in time.

The following lists present the notation found in this book, except for a few symbols which appear infrequently or in starred sections. Abbreviations used for the units are shown in the listing.

Capital Letters

Symbol	*Quantity*	*Unit*
A	Angstrom unit	10^{-10} m
A	area	m^2
A	vector potential	weber/m
B, B	magnetic flux density	weber/m^2
C	capacitance	farad
D, D	electric flux density	coul/m^2
E, E	electric field intensity	volt/m
F, F	force	newton
H, H	magnetic field intensity	amp/m
I	current	amp
J, J	volume current density	amp/m^2
K, K	surface current density	amp/m
L	inductance	henry
$\mathcal{L}$	torque	newton-m
M	mass	kg
N, N	Poynting vector	watt/m^2
N	rate of incident particles	particle/(m^2)(sec)
N_d, N_n	rate of ionized, neutralized particles	particle/sec
P	power	watt
$\mathcal{P}$	pressure	newton/m^2
Q	fluid flow rate	m^3/sec
R	radius	m
R_0	collision radius	m
R	resistance	ohm
R_H	Hall coefficient	m^3/coul
$\mathcal{R}$	Larmor radius (gyroradius)	m
S	slip or fractional deviation from synchronous speed	—
T	temperature	°K, °C
T	time interval	sec

T	electrical period	sec
U	random energy of particle motion	joule
V	potential difference, voltage	volt
V	volume	m^3
W	work, kinetic energy	joule
X	reactance	ohm
X	normalized value of E_x	—
X_1, X_2	primary, secondary leakage reactance	ohm
$\mathfrak{X}_m$	magnetizing (gap) reactance	ohm
Y	normalized value of E_y	—
Z	ionic valence number	—
Z	impedance	ohm

Lower case Letters

Symbol	*Quantity*	*Unit*
a	thickness of active conductor	m
$\mathbf{a}$	acceleration	m/sec^2
b	length of active conductor	m
c	velocity of light in vacuum	3×10^8 m/sec
c	specific heat	joule/(m^3)(°C)
c	total number of conductors	—
d	length	m
e	elementary charge	1.60×10^{-19} coul
ev	electron volt	1.60×10^{-19} joule
$\mathbf{f}$, f	volume force density	newton/m^3
$\mathbf{f}_m$	mechanical volume force density	newton/m^3
f	frequency	cycle/sec
$\mathbf{g}$	acceleration of gravity	9.81 m/sec^2
g	gap length in magnetic circuit	m
h	heat transfer coefficient	watt/(°K)(m^2)
h	magnetic mirror distance	m
k	Boltzmann constant	1.38×10^{-23} joule/°K
k_d, k_p	distribution, pitch factors	—
$\mathbf{l}$	directed length	m
ℓ	volume torque density	newton/m^2
m	mass	kg
m	number of phases	—
n	volume particle density	particle/m^3
n	number of conductors	—
n	number of turns	—
n	revolutions/sec	sec^{-1}
n	Loschmidt number	2.7×10^{25} particles/m^3
p	volume power density	watt/m^3
p_s	surface power density	watt/m^2
p	number of pole pairs	—
q	electric charge	coul
r	radius	m
r	resistivity	ohm-m
s	slip or fractional deviation from drift velocity	—
t	time	sec

$\mathbf{u}$, u	random component of particle velocity	m/sec
$\mathbf{v}$, v	velocity	m/sec
$\mathbf{x}_0$, $\mathbf{y}_0$, $\mathbf{z}_0$	unit vectors parallel to x, y, z axes	m

Greek Letters

Symbol	*Quantity*	*Unit*
α	angle	rad
β	angle	rad
β_e	ratio of electron cyclotron frequency to collision frequency	—
γ	angle	rad
γ	conductor conductivity	mho/m
δ	power angle	rad
δ	skin depth (depth of penetration)	m
Δx, $\Delta\theta$	finite interval in x, θ	m, rad
ϵ	permittivity	farad/m
ϵ_0	permittivity of vacuum	8.85×10^{-12} farad/m
η	efficiency	—
θ	angle	rad
Θ	moment of inertia	kg-m^2
λ	angle	rad
λ	line charge density	coul/m
μ	permeability	henry/m
μ_0	permeability of free space	$4\pi \times 10^{-7}$ henry/m
ν	collision frequency	sec^{-1}
ξ	mass density	kg/m^3
ρ	volume charge density	coul/m^3
σ	surface charge density	coul/m^2
σ	angle	rad
τ	time constant	sec
τ	pole pitch	m
τ	volume	m^3
ϕ	electrostatic potential	volt
φ	phase angle	rad
Φ	magnetic flux	weber
ω; ω_s	angular velocity; synchronous speed	rad/sec
ω	radian frequency	rad/sec
ω_c	cyclotron (Larmor, gyro) radian frequency	rad/sec
ω_e	electric radian frequency	rad/sec
ω_h	natural radian frequency of oscillation of synchronous converter	rad/sec

Subscripts

Compound subscripts are separated by commas; for example $\mathbf{v}_{0,n}$; $p_{s,\text{conv}}$.

Symbol	*Refers to*	*Example*
$\parallel$	component (of vector) parallel to designated reference	$\mathbf{v}_{\parallel}$, parallel component of $\mathbf{v}$

$\perp$	component (of vector) perpendicular to designated reference	$\mathbf{v}_{\perp}$, perpendicular component of $\mathbf{v}$
a	applied	$\mathfrak{L}_a$, applied torque
a	armature conductor	I_a, armature conductor current
c	conductor	I_c, conductor current
conv	converted	P_{conv}, converted power
d	developed	$\mathfrak{L}_d$, developed torque
diss	dissipated	P_{diss}, dissipated power
e	electron	m_c, electron mass
elec	electric	P_{elec}, electric power
E	electric field	v_E, drift velocity in **B** and **E** field
f	field conductor	I_f, field conductor current
g	acceleration of gravity	$\mathbf{v}_g$, drift velocity in **B** and **g** field
g	gap	r_g, gap radius
g	generating	η_g, generating conversion efficiency
i	ion	m_i, ion mass
imp	impressed component of field vector	$\mathbf{B}_{\text{imp}}$, impressed component of **B**
ind	induced component of field vector	$\mathbf{E}_{\text{ind}}$, induced component of **E**
kin	kinetic	W_{kin}, kinetic energy
l	leakage	X_l, leakage reactance
l	line-to-line	V_l, line-to-line voltage
m	magnetic	$\mathbf{F}_m$, magnetic force
m	magnetizing	X_m, per-phase magnetizing reactance
m	maximum	B_m, maximum flux density
m	motoring	η_m, motoring conversion efficiency
mech	mechanical	P_{mech}, mechanical power
n	component (of vector) normal to a designated surface	$\mathbf{v}_{o,n}$, normal component of $\mathbf{v}_0$
N.L.	no-load value	$\bar{E}_{a,\text{N.L.}}$, no load value of the (phasor) armature conductor electric field intensity
p	proton	m_p, proton mass
p.o.	pullout	$\mathfrak{L}_{\text{p.o.}}$, pull-out torque
p.u.	per-unit	$K_{\text{p.u.}}$, per-unit value of K
R	rated value	S_R, rated value of slip
s	surface	$p_{s,\text{conv}}$, converted surface power density
s.c.	short-circuit value	$p_{\text{s.c.}}$, short-circuit value of volume power density
st	stall value	p_{st}, stall value of volume power density
w	wall	v_w, wall velocity

Superscripts

Only a few superscripts are used. Unprimed, primed, and multiple-primed quantities are used to distinguish quantities measured in different reference frames. The letters α and β are used in the same way. The letter g is used to refer to a group of particles having a particular common velocity. The letter n is used to designate volume power densities normalized against their maximum values.

Other Symbols

Symbol	*Definition*
$< \ >$	average value of
$*$	conjugate complex value
$\| \ \|$	absolute value of (magnitude)
$\underline{/^{2}}_{1}$	angle from phasor 1 to phasor 2

chapter 1
INTRODUCTION

1.1 THE MEANING OF ELECTROMECHANICAL POWER CONVERSION

We conduct our lives surrounded by the complexities of a technological society. Very quickly, scientific discoveries are translated into devices that enter our everyday world and compel correspondingly rapid changes in our patterns of living. With each passing year, we generate and control increasingly larger amounts of power and develop materials of increasing subtlety to accomplish more and more ambitious tasks.

Let us pause to look about us and to inquire: What are the essential factors that have permitted us to reach our present level of technical sophistication? It may be said that our ability to convert power in a controlled fashion along with the ability to produce or refine suitable materials constitute the two fundamental skills upon which our technological culture is based. Without them, the engineering and scientific accomplishments that we possess today could not have been achieved, and man would be limited to implements operable by human or animal muscle power alone. The study of power conversion is therefore of fundamental importance in the practice of today's technology.

Power conversion is the transformation of power from one physical form into another. Examples of such transformations are everywhere around us in nature and in our technological environment. To name but two instances, the power of a waterfall derives ultimately from the thermal power of the sun through a cycle which includes evaporation of water from the sea, its fall in the form of rain, and its streaming on the surface of the earth; the mechanical power developed by electric motors derives from electric power supplied by utilities. The electric power, in turn, originates in nuclear reactions occurring either in the body of the sun or in man-made reactors.

This book deals with one particular form of power conversion from mechanical to electrical, and from electrical to mechanical—that is, *electromechanical power conversion*, which we shall abbreviate as EMPC. Mechanical power is the rate at which work is done by a force whose point of application is seen to be moving; electric power is the rate at which work is done on charges seen to be moving in electric fields. Thus, EMPC is inherently concerned with interactions between systems of charges and currents, subjected to inertial and other nonelectrical forces, and moving with respect to each other.

Further, by EMPC we refer not only to the processes taking place in machines made by men, but also to those processes occurring in nature. In the world of man-made devices, EMPC takes place in a very large number of applications. A few examples are:

1. The electric motor.
2. The turbogenerator, by means of which almost all of our electric power is produced.
3. The telephone.
4. The electromagnetic pump, used for circulating liquid metal coolant in nuclear reactors.
5. Magneto plasma-dynamic (MPD) generators, now being investigated experimentally for the production of large quantities of electric power.

In the world of nature, EMPC occurs almost everywhere that we find manifestations of electricity and magnetism: in the aurora borealis and in lightning strokes, displays that have inspired awe and excited the imagination of mankind since its earliest days. EMPC occurs in solar flares and in the sustenance of the magnetic fields of the earth and other celestial bodies; the earth's magnetic field shields us from the stream of charged particles emanating from the sun called the *solar wind.*

1.2 HISTORICAL DEVELOPMENT

Only recently has man succeeded in his attempt to understand, to reproduce, and to control the processes that underlie these natural phenomena. As shown in the chronological chart of Fig. 1.1, the first historical record of such an attempt dates back to the sixth century B.C. when Thales of Miletus produced static electricity by rubbing a piece of amber (in Greek, ηλεκτρον, electron) with a dry cloth. However, more than two thousand years elapsed before the first electrostatic generator was built by Otto von Guericke in 1640. Earlier, in 1600, William Gilbert had published a major scientific treatise covering both aspects of EMPC, the force interaction between electric charges and between magnets. In so doing, Gilbert apparently recognized the association between

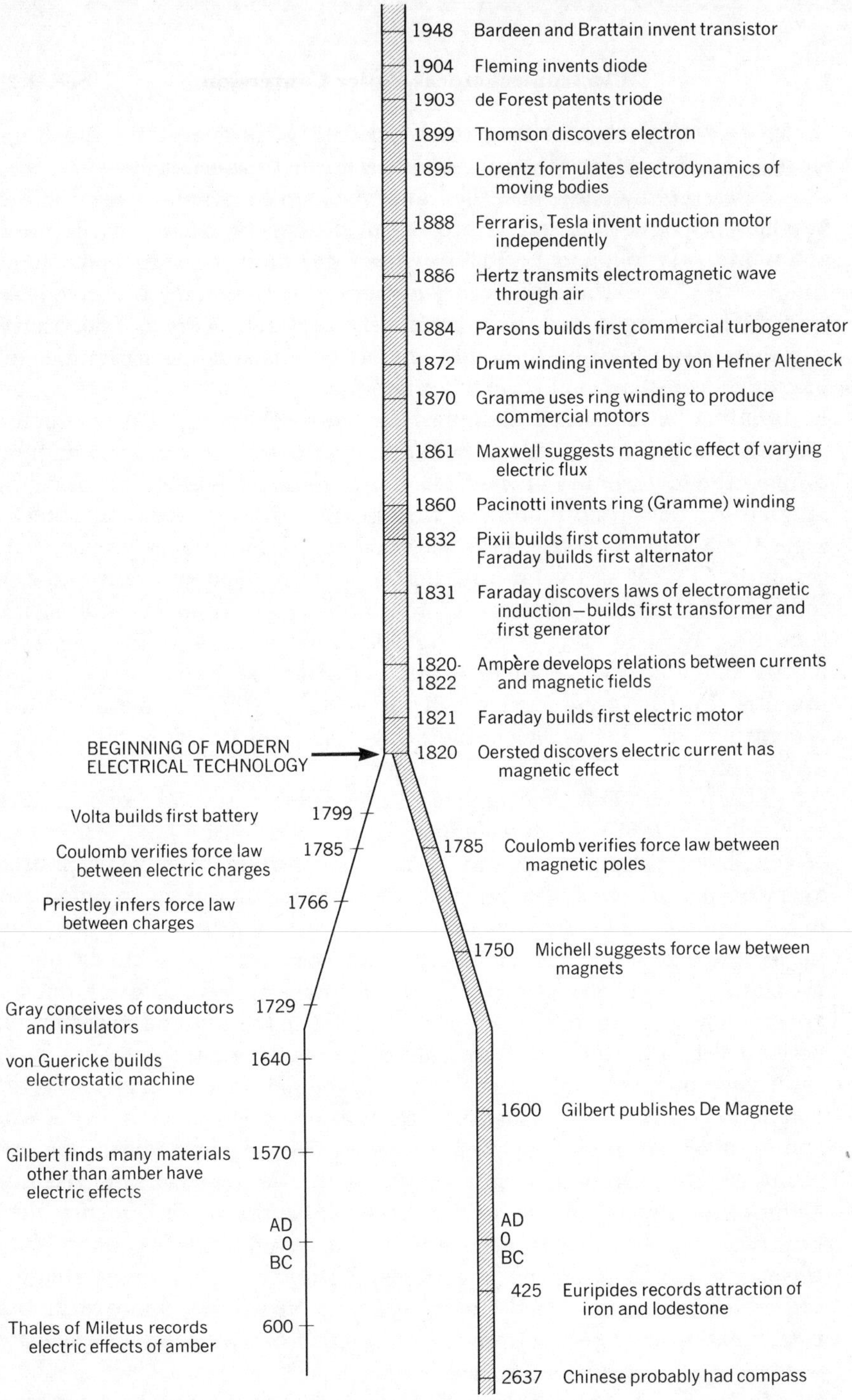

Fig. 1.1 Chronological chart illustrating rapidity of development of electrical technology.

electricity, for which he coined the word, and *magnetism*, after which he entitled his book "De Magnete, Magneticisque Corporibus."

With the modern scientific approach well established, progress became very rapid. The development of the electric battery by Galvani and Volta was followed in 1820 by the vital discovery of Oersted and Ampère of the relation between the electric current and the magnetic field. This merged the two previously distinct fields of electricity and magnetism and led to a spate of inventions starting with Michael Faraday's construction of the first electromagnetic motor in 1821. Ten years later Faraday used a similar structure consisting of a conductor moving in a uniform magnetic field and operated it as a generator, thus proving the reversibility of the EMPC process. In 1832 he built the first alternator. It consisted of a coil with many turns of fine wire rotating in a magnetic field, so as to expose the wires to opposite polarity every half revolution. This is by far the most important generator type in use today. At that time, however, there were no applications for alternating currents. As a result, during the next 50 years, these converters were mostly operated in conjunction with an array of mechanical switches invented by Hippolyte Pixii which served the purpose of rectifier when generating and inverter when motoring. We call this switching device a *commutator*.

The most notable development during these years was the invention by Pacinotti (1860) and the commercial exploitation by Gramme (1870) of converters having a large number of coils symmetrically distributed over the periphery of the gap which separates the stationary and the rotating parts. This construction afforded better utilization of the converter and a smoother rectified current and paved the way for the development of polyphase systems. Concurrently the work by Faraday, Henry, and Poggendorff on electromagnetic induction and transformer action led to a better understanding of alternating quantities.

The crowning achievement in the development of converters of the magnetic type was the almost simultaneous invention by Galileo Ferraris and Nicola Tesla of the induction motor in 1888. An immediate practical result was the acceptance of a-c systems for the transmission and distribution of electric power. Of no less moment and consequence than the discovery itself was the underlying theory of a *rotating field*. This theory, which is based on the fundamental principles enunciated by Maxwell and Lorentz, leads to the unifying viewpoint, adopted in this book, that EMPC results from the interaction of waves having the same wavelength and traveling with the same speed.

In the years that followed the invention of the induction converter, EMPC took a different turn. The development of communication systems by means of telegraph, telephone, and radio had created the need for converters operating at high frequencies. In the '80s of the last century Thomas A. Edison discovered that a unidirectional current could be made to pass across the empty space between the hot filament of an electric lamp and another metallic conductor. The discovery of the electron by J. J. Thomson in 1899 gave a clue to the nature of this effect. Commercial applications followed quickly; in 1904 J. A. Fleming invented the diode, and 1907 Lee de Forest patented the triode.

The low inertia of the electrons and the low reactance of the associated circuits made the electron tubes ideally suited for high frequencies. However, within three decades their limitations had become apparent. To meet the demand for ever-increasing frequencies and power levels, a better understanding of the electron dynamics was required. The papers of F. B. Llewellyn in 1941 summarize the results of these studies. The new devices which emerged fall into three major categories: the klystron, the magnetron, and the traveling-wave tube. While these converters are mainly used for the purpose of generation and amplification of microwaves, the same principles and structures are applied to the motoring mode of operation in high-energy-particle accelerators.

It thus appears that during the first half of this century the research effort was mainly concentrated on the high-frequency aspects of EMPC and that the high- and low-frequency technologies constituted completely separate and divergent fields of interest. The last decade, however, has seen a reversal of this trend. As contributory factors one can mention:

1. Automation, which joins communication and mechanical actuation in a single system and thus creates the need for components capable of operating over a wide band of frequencies.
2. The controlled thermonuclear effort aimed at tapping the practically unlimited resources of energy stored in the isotopes of hydrogen found in the sea, by means of the interaction between hot plasmas and electromagnetic fields.
3. The advent of the space age, which has not only brought about a better understanding of the EMPC processes taking place in interplanetary regions but has also prompted increased effort in the development and integration of power sources, electronic and control equipment, and electric thrusters.
4. The availability of superconducting magnets, ferrites, and gaseous conductors, which eliminate the constraints imposed by the magnetic path on the geometry, the frequency, and the number of mechanical degrees of freedom of power converters.

Thus the modern engineer must be familiar with all the aspects of the EMPC field. In its technological applications the power ranges from microwatts in communications, instrumentation, and control to thousands of megawatts in electric-power generation, a range of over 15 orders of magnitude. Frequency, as well as speed, spans comparable ranges. Frequency varies from direct current and fractions of a cycle per second in control applications to gigacycles per second in electronic amplifiers utilizing wave-electron interaction; speed varies from well below sonic in rotating machinery to almost the speed of light in high-energy-particle accelerators.

To bring such an enormous field within grasp, it is clear that one must search for a unifying viewpoint and organize the treatment following as logical a development as possible. In the rest of this chapter we will attempt to outline the viewpoint and the order of presentation adopted.

1.3 SURVEY OF THE EMPC FIELD

In Sec. 1.1 we mentioned that EMPC is concerned with two types of interactions: (1) interactions between charges and (2) interactions between currents. The EMPC field thus splits naturally into two major domains.

To the first domain, that of charge interaction, belong most of the manifestations of electricity in the lower atmosphere and all the high-frequency devices developed in this century. However, converters based on the interaction between charges have few applications in the low-frequency domain. In fact, when seen from the electric terminals such a converter looks like a capacitance and therefore has a high input impedance at low frequencies. For this reason electrostatic converters are suited only for applications where high voltage is either desirable, as in the Van de Graaff generator, or unobjectionable, as in outer space where the high vacuum eliminates the danger of breakdown.

On the other hand, the domain where the interaction occurs between currents then includes the majority of the conversion processes taking place in astrophysical situations and in man-made devices at low frequency. In fact, the EMPC processes resulting from the interaction between currents in electrically neutral systems require the motion of positive as well as negative charges. Since positive ions are much heavier than electrons, their dynamical response is too sluggish to be of any import in the high-frequency range. These low-frequency processes may also be described as low-velocity processes, since velocity and frequency are related by a proportionality factor, a characteristic length such as the excursion in an oscillatory process or a wavelength in a traveling wave.

From another viewpoint we may classify EMPC processes according to the state of the materials involved, whether solid, liquid, or gaseous. Again we find that the presence of the heavy positive ions precludes the use in EMPC of the solid and liquid states at very high frequency. On the other hand, we find that at low frequency and therefore at low velocity, the gaseous state offers very little technical advantage over the other two states. Moreover, a gas flowing at low velocity in a duct of constant cross section behaves and can be treated analytically as a solid. The reason is that the characteristic property of gases, i.e., the susceptibility to volume changes or compressibility, produces effects which become appreciable only at velocities approaching the speed of sound. This makes the low-frequency, low-velocity domain of EMPC the simpler to understand and therefore the first to be studied.

1.4 SCOPE OF THIS VOLUME

(a) Organization

We observe that by starting with the low-frequency, low-velocity domain we will be following the sequence in which the technology of EMPC was developed. As a matter of fact, since the historical development represents the evolution of human thought, it has an inherent compatibility with our learning processes. Consequently, we shall parallel this development in our study of EMPC as far as the actual converter types are concerned.

The historical development, however, cannot give us the underlying theory or the unifying viewpoint since this comes only with "hindsight." Although in this volume we will be concerned primarily with interacting systems of low-frequency currents flowing in conductors that either are rigid or can be treated as such, we must prepare the background for the study of interacting systems of charges and compressible media.

In order to formulate a coherent approach we must take a comprehensive look at the whole EMPC field, and seek the unifying fundamental mechanisms in the many devices we intend to study, even though these devices differ widely in form and exterior appearance. Fortunately, we find that these mechanisms are not many in number and furthermore possess certain intrinsic symmetries. For instance, the interaction between charges and currents are dual aspects of the same electromagnetic phenomenon. Recognition of this fact will permit us in Vol. 2 to reduce the analysis of all types of electrostatic converters with rigid structures to the enunciation of a few transformation rules, and then apply all the knowledge accumulated while studying the magnetic devices.

Our approach to EMPC in this book can be characterized by the single phrase *unified fundamental engineering*. The purpose is to:

1. *Unify* by presenting the basic principles in a coherent treatment which permits the understanding of a wide variety of natural phenomena and technological applications.

2. Emphasize *fundamental* mechanisms rather than the devices per se, so that the reader is not only acquainted with conventional technology but is also prepared to understand and partake in new developments in the field.
3. Foster an *engineering* approach which relinquishes the "black-box" viewpoint, and its exclusive preoccupation with the ability to analyze, in favor of a physical approach which engenders the basic design as well as the analysis.

Certainly these are ambitious objectives, and they are not easy to realize. We attempt to further these objectives by arranging the text so that we start from fundamental principles and their applications to elementary systems and organize our work as a progressive synthesis, building up from the simplest cases, always beginning with configurations of maximum symmetry and uniformity, and moving to increasingly complex situations in order to achieve advantages or circumvent shortcomings which have been elicited.

(b) Content

In order to accomplish these objectives, Chap. 2 begins with a study of the motion of a single charged particle in an electromagnetic field. This early investigation reveals the basic processes involved in electromechanical power conversion and sheds some light on important events occurring in nature and on the operation of man-made devices.

Chapter 3 moves on to consider neutral aggregates of positively and negatively charged particles called *plasmas*, and the basic equations governing plasma behavior are derived. Making suitable approximations, the quantitive laws of electromechanical power conversion for a volume element of active conducting material are then deduced.

In Chap. 4, we make an engineering study of these laws and find the most effective geometric configuration for their implementation. We identify three modes of operation called *motoring*, *generating*, and *braking*, and carry out the first step in the design of a converter, the determination of the dimensions of the active conductor.

With these principles established, we move on in Chap. 5 to the first synthesis of practical converters, and study the design and operation of the *homopolar* or *acyclic* converter using both solid and gaseous conductors. We find the homopolar converter to be inherently a low-voltage, high-current device.

In seeking to overcome the low-impedance limitation of the homopolar converter, we discover in Chap. 6 the advantages arising from a *heteropolar* configuration. This leads to space and time variability, and the electromagnetic quantities take the form of traveling waves. The simplest converter employing a heteropolar structure is the *synchronous* machine, so called because of the *tie* or fixed proportionality between steady-state speed and frequency of excitation. The synchronous machine, which has considerable practical importance, is then further studied in Chaps. 7 and 8. Chapter 7 is devoted to the steady-state performance and design considerations. Chapter 8 considers the transient performance and the problem of stability, which plays an extremely important role in more complex physical situations.

To obtain greater flexibility and overcome the performance limitations of synchronous converters, we turn in Chaps. 9 and 10 to the *asynchronous* or *induction* converter. Here the synchronous tie is broken, and the result is a great increase in the range of performance characteristics, as well as the possibility of excitation from a single a-c source.

In brief, we may say that we are primarily concerned in this volume with the *interactions between systems of low-frequency currents flowing in neutral media which move relative to each other at low speed.* This category includes those applications in nature and technology which are most important from the viewpoint of converting large quantities of power.

1.5 PRINCIPLES AND PROCEDURES

(a) Lorentz Force

The common aspect of EMPC is that all the interacting systems consist of elementary charged particles which are acted upon by the Lorentz force,

$$\mathbf{F} = q(\mathbf{E} + \mathbf{v} \times \mathbf{B}) \tag{1.1}$$

where q is the charge of the particle, $\mathbf{v}$ its velocity, $\mathbf{E}$ the electric-field intensity, and $\mathbf{B}$ the magnetic flux density. In addition, in most cases of practical interest, this force overrides all other forces. This means that the motion of the particle can be determined by using Eq. (1.1) and applying Newton's law, i. e.,

$$\frac{d}{dt}(m\mathbf{v}) = \mathbf{F} = q(\mathbf{E} + \mathbf{v} \times \mathbf{B}) \tag{1.2}$$

where m is the mass of the particle.

The dynamic behavior of a single charged particle in an electromagnetic field thus displays the fundamentals of EMPC in their most elementary form. In addition, we shall find that the performance of entire converting units has many features in common with the behavior of single charged particles in similar field configurations. For these reasons we choose the Lorentz dynamical relation of Eq. (1.2) as the focal point in our treatment.

Normally we are concerned with systems containing a large number of particles. In this case, if we interpret Eq. (1.2) as describing the motion of a test particle in the ensemble, we immediately become aware of a major difficulty. The electromagnetic vectors **E** and **B** here represent unknown quantities, since the charged particles themselves contribute to the electromagnetic field. As a consequence it is, in general, necessary to solve Eq. (1.2) simultaneously with Maxwell's equations. This set of equations is inherently nonlinear; for instance, the term $q\mathbf{v} \times \mathbf{B}$ is nonlinear since **B** depends on **v**. This nonlinearity, in conjunction with the fact that very few of the electromagnetic field configurations are amenable to an exact description in closed analytical form, suffices to tell us that we can only hope to solve specific problems one at a time. Therefore we choose to build up our knowledge gradually by beginning with limiting cases which have the greatest simplicity, uniformity, and symmetry.

(b) Dynamic and Electromagnetic Phases

In our attempt to follow a rational approach to the study of EMPC we are guided by the fact that EMPC stems from the interplay of charged-particle motion and electromagnetic fields. We may then think of EMPC as exhibiting two distinct "phases," a *dynamic* and an *electromagnetic* phase, which are linked in circular causal relationship by the Lorentz and Maxwell equations, respectively. The dynamic phase is concerned with the calculation of the charged-particle motion under the action of a given electromagnetic field, and the electromagnetic phase is concerned with the calculation of fields resulting from given distributions of charged-particles velocities.

It then follows that our study will be greatly simplified by considering, insofar as possible, a succession of limiting cases in which one of these phases is trivial or the two phases are not coupled. Thus, with regard to the dynamic phase, we always study steady-state conditions, where the velocities are time-invariant, before we investigate the transient performance. Also, in connection with the spatial dependence, we consider, for the most part, systems with one degree of freedom, so that the velocity vectors have only one component. Furthermore, in this first volume, we limit ourselves to that domain in EMPC where we can neglect compressibility effects. In other words, we restrict our consideration to those systems in which the interacting currents subdivide into two groups, with all the elements of one group moving together with respect to all the elements of the other. As a result, the dynamic phase reduces to the determination of the relative velocity between the two groups, i. e., a scalar function of time only.

Similarly, in connection with the electromagnetic phase we maintain symmetry, uniformity, and time invariance of the *impressed field*, insofar as is consistent with the case at hand, and we consider a succession of situations in which the *induced field*, representing the coupling with the dynamic phase, becomes increasingly important. We begin with single particles or very rarefied gases whose motion in general does not contribute appreciably to the prevailing field. Next we consider a unique case, that of the homopolar converter, where the effect of the collective motion of the particles is large, but does not contribute to the field component which is relevant to the power-conversion process. Finally, before we proceed to the most general case, we study synchronous devices where at least one of the field components can be specified independently of the dynamic phase.

This succession of limiting cases not only forms a logical sequence which makes clear the nature of the power-conversion process and the role of the various physical mechanisms involved, but also presents the most important types of existing and proposed power converters in context.

(c) Simplified Electromagnetic Model

As we progress with our study, we eventually reach a point where the mutual interdependence of the dynamic and electromagnetic phases must be given full consideration. We may then simplify the problem of representing the electromagnetic phase by abstaining from consideration of radiation effects, as we have simplified the dynamic phase by abstaining from consideration of sonic propagation effects. Thus in the low-speed, low-frequency, and charge-neutrality domain of EMPC we can avail ourselves of a simplified electromagnetic model.[1]† We refer to the model which historically evolved before the introduction by Maxwell of the displacement current. In Appendix A we show that the set of equations

$$\nabla \times \mathbf{E} = -\frac{\partial \mathbf{B}}{\partial t} \tag{1.3a}$$

$$\nabla \times \mathbf{B} = \mu \mathbf{J} \tag{1.3b}$$

$$\nabla \cdot \mathbf{B} = 0 \tag{1.3c}$$

with $\epsilon_0 = 0$, $\mathbf{D} = 0$, $\rho = 0$, adequately describes the interactions which interest us in this volume.

(d) Transformation of Reference Frames

Once the idealization process has been completed and we have formulated our simplified model of the physical situation under consideration, we proceed with the analysis. Here again the labor that is entailed strongly depends on the viewpoint taken. A classical example which illustrates the importance of the choice of an appropriate frame of

† Superscript numbers refer to references at the end of the chapter.

reference is given by the solar system. The motion of the planets makes very little sense when referred to a frame of reference attached to the earth but acquires great order and symmetry when viewed from a frame of reference attached to the sun.

Recognition of the latter made it possible for Newton to derive his gravitational laws and opened the way for modern scientific progress.

The same underlying relativistic concept, namely, that the measure of velocity depends on the selection of the reference frame, is very important in EMPC. This comes about not only because motion is essential, but also because the measure of the electromagnetic quantities varies with the frame of reference. We thus exploit this fact to simplify the analysis of the problem at hand. For instance, when dealing with periodic structures, choice of a reference frame attached to the traveling wave makes all quantities, and in particular the magnetic flux density, time-invariant. This not only eliminates time as a variable in the problem but also makes an important component of the electric field vanish.

REFERENCES

1. Blank, A. A., K. O. Friedrichs, and H. Grad: Theory of Maxwell's Equations without Displacement Current, *AEC Res. and Develop. Rept.*, NYU-6486, Nov. 1, 1957.

chapter 2
THE DYNAMICS OF CHARGED PARTICLES IN ELECTRIC AND MAGNETIC FIELDS

2.1 INTRODUCTION

Following the approach outlined in Chap. 1, we shall begin our study of power conversion by considering in this chapter the behavior of a single particle in an electromagnetic field. The basic relationships will be formulated in a general way, although the examples and applications will mostly be limited to uniform fields which do not vary with time.

Our initial steps will be to state the force law and the power and energy relationships and to determine the free motion of the charged particle. We shall note and be particularly concerned with the fact that the evaluation of power and kinetic energy yields different results in coordinate reference frames which are in relative motion. This serves to introduce the idea of the "subjective" character of the measurements of some physical quantities in different reference frames. Later we find that among these quantities are the electric and magnetic fields, and we determine the transformation laws which the electromagnetic field components satisfy when measured in frames that are in relative motion.

By studying the motion of individual charged particles in electric and magnetic fields we learn how the interaction of these particles and fields leads to the definition of the power-conversion modes which characterize the operation of physical devices.

The theoretical principles which we establish are illustrated by examples and applications, such as astrophysical situations and the ion and plasma rocket motors now under development, as well as devices of a proven character such as the mass spectrometer.

2.2 ELECTRIC FORCE ON A CHARGED PARTICLE

Consider a charged particle with mass m and electric charge q. In the presence of other material bodies and charges this particle experiences forces of two types: (1) a gravitational force which is proportional to the mass m and (2) an electromagnetic force which is proportional to the charge q. Of these two forces, the gravitational force is relatively so weak that in most practical applications it can be neglected, as we shall see later in this section.

The electromagnetic force, in general, consists of two components: one is a function of position only and serves to define the electric-field intensity $\mathbf{E}$; the other is a function of both the position and the velocity of the particle and serves to define the magnetic flux density $\mathbf{B}$. We consider first situations in which $\mathbf{B}$ is zero. The electromagnetic force acting on the charge can then be written as

$$\mathbf{F}_e = q\mathbf{E} \tag{2.1}$$

where $\mathbf{F}_e$ is the vector force on the particle and $\mathbf{E}$ is the electric-field intensity prevailing at the position of the particle, due to the presence of other charges. Equation (2.1) may also be used to define the electric field at a point as the force per-unit test charge at that point, or more precisely as

$$\mathbf{E} = \lim_{\delta q \to 0} \frac{\delta \mathbf{F}_e}{\delta q} \tag{2.2}$$

If free to move, a particle subjected to the electric force will accelerate and acquire velocity. Throughout this book we shall restrict ourselves to situations in which the velocities of the charged particles are small enough, as compared with the velocity of light, so that relativistic effects, such as increase in mass and electromagnetic radiation, may be neglected. In this case the motion is adequately described by Newton's law:

$$\mathbf{F}_e = q\mathbf{E} = \frac{d}{dt}(m\mathbf{v}) = m\frac{d\mathbf{v}}{dt} = m\mathbf{a} \tag{2.3}$$

Equation (2.3), which holds for an inertial reference frame, tells us that the particle experiences an acceleration $\mathbf{a}$ of magnitude $|q\mathbf{E}/m|$ in the direction of the electric field.

It is instructive to consider some numerical values for typical particles. In the case of the electron,

$$q_e = -e = -1.60 \times 10^{-19} \text{ coul}$$
$$m_e = 9.11 \times 10^{-31} \text{ kg}$$
$$\frac{e}{m_e} = 1.76 \times 10^{11} \text{ coul/kg}$$

This large ratio of charge to mass for the electron results in extremely large accelerations, even in relatively weak fields. For example, if the magnitude of **E** is 1 volt/m, the acceleration is 1.76×10^{11} m/sec², or approximately 18 *billion* times g, the acceleration of gravity on the surface of the earth. Even the proton, with a charge of $+e$ and a mass of approximately $1{,}837m_e$, has an acceleration of almost 10 million g. It is therefore apparent that the effect of gravitational forces on charged particles is negligible in most instances.

2.3 POWER AND ENERGY RELATIONS

(a) Mechanical Power

Whenever the point of application of a force **F** moves with velocity **v**, the force gives rise to mechanical work at a rate given by the mechanical power $\mathbf{F} \cdot \mathbf{v}$. This is the case when a charged particle experiences an electric field. As a result of the force $\mathbf{F}_e$, as given by Eq. (2.1), acting on the particle, mechanical power is either being delivered to or developed by the particle, depending on whether $\mathbf{F} \cdot \mathbf{v}$ is positive or negative.

An important point to note, in connection with the evaluation of power, is that such an evaluation is subjective, yielding a result which is entirely dependent on the frame of reference of the observer. This condition comes about because of the velocity term **v**, which is clearly different when measured in two frames of reference moving with respect to each other. Thus observers who calculate with respect to each of these reference frames quite correctly evaluate different powers when observing a given force acting on a given point of application. In particular, for an observer fixed to the point of application of the force, the velocity and hence the power vanish! Thus power is *not an invariant quantity* when going from one system of reference to another in relative motion.

The subjective character of power is illustrated by the following example.

EXAMPLE 2.1

A certain boat attains a speed of 20 mph in still water when the engine runs at its rated power of 100 kw; by rated power we mean the continuous full-load level suggested by the manufacturer and so stated on his nameplate.

The boat services two stations along a river which are located 40 miles apart. With the engine developing rated power at all times, twice as much fuel is consumed in the upstream run as in the downstream run. Compute the average mechanical power and the work performed in propelling the boat during both runs, as evaluated by an observer standing on the river shore.

Solution

We shall use two frames of reference in relative motion: a frame fixed to the shore (shore reference frame) and a frame at rest with respect to the stream (stream reference frame). Using primes to denote quantities referred to the shore reference frame, and subscripts u and d for upstream and downstream, respectively, we let

v_b = speed of boat in still water = speed of boat in stream reference frame
v'_u = upstream speed, shore reference frame
v'_d = downstream speed, shore reference frame
v'_s = speed of stream, shore reference frame

It follows that $v'_u = v_b - v'_s$, $v'_d = v_b + v'_s$.

The engine power $P_e = 100$ kw represents the work done per second in overcoming the resistance of the water to the motion of the boat; thus P_e must be the power measured in the stream reference frame. If F is the thrust developed by the propeller,

$$P_e = Fv_b$$

The fuel consumption is a measure of the work done by the engine as viewed in the stream reference frame. Since power is constant, the work is simply power × time. The fact that the upstream fuel consumption is twice that in the downstream run thus means that (1) the work done in the upstream run is twice that in the downstream run, and (2) the time t_u to make the upstream run is twice the time t_d to make the downstream run,

$$t_u = 2t_d$$

If L is the distance between stations,

$$v'_u = \frac{L}{t_u} = \frac{L}{2t_d} = \tfrac{1}{2}v'_d$$

so that

$$v_b - v'_s = \tfrac{1}{2}(v_b + v'_s)$$

or

$$v'_s = \frac{v_b}{3}$$

The upstream power in the shore reference frame is

$$P'_u = Fv'_u = F\left(v_b - \frac{v_b}{3}\right) = \tfrac{2}{3}Fv_b = \tfrac{2}{3}P_e$$

Similarly the downstream power is

$$P'_d = Fv'_d = F\left(v_b + \frac{v_b}{3}\right) = \tfrac{4}{3}Fv_b = \tfrac{4}{3}P_e$$

Thus $P'_u = 66.7$ kw and $P'_d = 133.3$ kw. The work done upstream is

$$W'_u = P'_u t_u = \frac{P'_u L}{v'_u} = FL$$

The work done downstream is

$$W'_d = P'_d t_d = \frac{P'_d L}{v'_d} = FL$$

Consequently, the work done in the upstream run is the same as that done in the downstream run, from the viewpoint of a shore observer who sees the same thrust times distance in either case. This work is

$$FL = \frac{P_e}{v_b}L = \frac{100 \times 10^3 \times 40}{20/3{,}600} = 7.20 \times 10^8 \text{ joules}$$

(Note that no unit conversion is required for length since L/v_b has the dimensions of time only.)

Since relative motion between systems of electric charges and currents is the necessary condition for electromechanical power conversion, it is extremely important to take early notice of the fact that some observable quantities may measure differently in different reference frames. This is particularly true because such quantities include the electromagnetic field vectors, which, as we shall later see, take on values which vary with the frame of reference. It follows that many of the relations that we shall use are correct and meaningful only for that reference frame in which *all* quantities are measured.

It must not be thought that the variation in physical quantities from one reference frame to another is necessarily a source of difficulty in analyzing and understanding the problem at hand. Once we pay due attention to the details and are consistent in expressing the relevant quantities, we can take advantage of the arbitrariness in the choice of the reference frames, so as to simplify our calculations and gain better physical insight. Our Example 2.1 presented previously is perhaps too simple to demonstrate fully the advantages that can be derived by this procedure. However, subsequent examples will make this quite clear.

(b) Electric Power

We now return to the electric force and the power associated with it. Of course, the mechanical power must be continuously balanced with power in *electrical* form from the sources of the electric field. We are reminded of this fact by the equation which results from taking the dot product of Eq. (2.1) with **v**:

$$\mathbf{F}_e \cdot \mathbf{v} = q\mathbf{E} \cdot \mathbf{v} \tag{2.4}$$

In this relation the right-hand side can easily be interpreted as the *electric power*, familiarly defined as the product of voltage V and current I. To do this, we consider the particle moving an infinitesimal distance from point A to point B, as illustrated in Fig. 2.1, in the infinitesimal time dt.

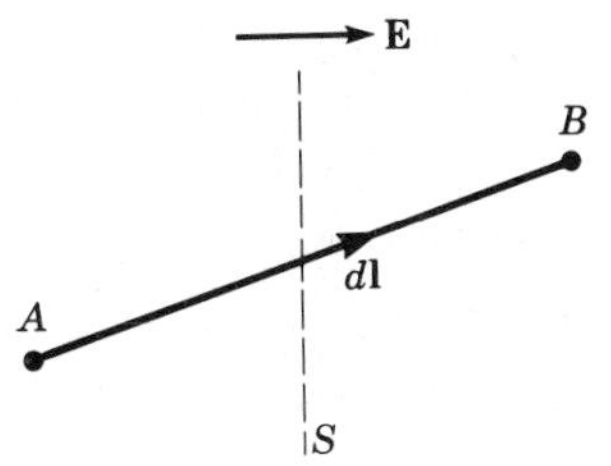

Fig. 2.1 Evaluation of the electric power.

Then $\mathbf{v} = d\mathbf{l}/dt$ and the expression for the electric power may be rewritten as follows:

$$q\mathbf{E} \cdot \mathbf{v} = q\mathbf{E} \cdot \frac{d\mathbf{l}}{dt} = (\mathbf{E} \cdot d\mathbf{l}) \frac{q}{dt} \tag{2.5}$$

The potential difference from A to B in the presence of the field $\mathbf{E}$ is then $\mathbf{E} \cdot d\mathbf{l}$, and the current through a surface S separating A and B is q/dt. Therefore the product of the small voltage $\mathbf{E} \cdot d\mathbf{l}$ and the large current q/dt gives the finite electric power $q\mathbf{E} \cdot \mathbf{v}$, as we see from Eq. (2.5).

We can conclude that Eq. (2.4) represents the power balance

$$\begin{pmatrix}\text{Mechanical power absorbed} \\ \text{by charged particle}\end{pmatrix} = \begin{pmatrix}\text{electric power delivered by} \\ \text{sources of electric field}\end{pmatrix}$$

and thus establishes the fundamental relation in electromechanical power conversion.

(c) Energy Conservation in an Electrostatic Field

Simple energy relations obtain for the special case where $\mathbf{E}$ is time-invariant. It is then possible to define an electrostatic potential ϕ such that

$$\mathbf{E} = -\operatorname{grad} \phi = -\nabla \phi \tag{2.6}$$

Using this definition and the definition of $\mathbf{v} = d\mathbf{l}/dt$, we can rewrite Eq. (2.4) as

$$\mathbf{F} \cdot \mathbf{v} = -q \frac{d\mathbf{l}}{dt} \cdot \nabla \phi = -q \frac{d\mathbf{l} \cdot \nabla \phi}{dt} \tag{2.7}$$

From the definition of the gradient, the quantity $d\mathbf{l} \cdot \nabla \phi$ is precisely the change $d\phi$ encountered in the displacement $d\mathbf{l}$, so that Eq. (2.7) becomes

$$\mathbf{F} \cdot \mathbf{v} = -q \frac{d\phi}{dt} \tag{2.8}$$

We can then integrate Eq. (2.8) with respect to time and obtain

$$\int_1^2 \mathbf{F} \cdot \mathbf{v}\, dt = \int_1^2 \mathbf{F} \cdot d\mathbf{l} = -\int_1^2 q\, d\phi = q(\phi_1 - \phi_2) \tag{2.9}$$

The significance of Eq. (2.9) is, of course, that the mechanical work delivered to the charged particle is equal to the decrease of the potential energy of the particle in the electric field.

In the particular case where the particle is completely free to move in the electric field, all the electric force goes into accelerating the particle and Eq. (2.3) applies. Consequently, we may write

$$\begin{aligned}\int_1^2 \mathbf{F} \cdot \mathbf{v}\, dt &= \int_1^2 m\, d\mathbf{v} \cdot \mathbf{v} = \int_1^2 \frac{m}{2}\, d(\mathbf{v} \cdot \mathbf{v}) \\ &= \frac{m}{2} \int_1^2 d(v^2) = \frac{m}{2} (v_2^2 - v_1^2)\end{aligned} \tag{2.10}$$

so that in this case Eq. (2.9) becomes

$$\frac{m}{2}(v_2^2 - v_1^2) = q(\phi_1 - \phi_2) \tag{2.11}$$

Equation (2.11) is, of course, a statement of the conservation of energy, the fact that the increase of the kinetic energy of the freely moving particle is equal to the loss of potential energy of the particle by virtue of its change of position in the electrostatic field, without regard to the actual path traversed. This is an extremely useful principle to apply in the study of motion of charged particles in electrostatic fields, and we shall illustrate its use in the example subsequently given in Sec. 2.4.

(d) The Electron Volt

In addition to its other uses, Eq. (2.11) also serves to suggest the definition of an energy unit which has become conventional in charged-particle studies. This is the *electron volt*, abbreviated ev, which is simply defined as the kinetic energy acquired by one electron falling through an electrostatic potential difference of one volt. According to Eq. (2.11), this amount of energy is

$$1 \text{ ev} = 1.60 \times 10^{-19} \times 1 = 1.60 \times 10^{-19} \text{ joule} \tag{2.12}$$

Also in common use are the units

$$\begin{aligned} 1 \text{ Mev} &= 10^6 \text{ ev} \\ 1 \text{ Bev} &= 10^9 \text{ ev} \end{aligned} \tag{2.13}$$

2.4 FREE MOTION IN A UNIFORM ELECTROSTATIC FIELD

As a first step in the study of the dynamic response of material bodies in impressed electromagnetic fields, we consider the free motion of a particle in a uniform electrostatic field. In order to determine the path, we need to know the position and velocity at a particular moment, which we may choose as the origin of time $t = 0$. Let us denote the known velocity at that moment by $\mathbf{v}_0$. We may then resolve $\mathbf{v}_0$ into components parallel and perpendicular to the field intensity $\mathbf{E}$ denoted respectively by $\mathbf{v}_{0,\parallel}$ and $\mathbf{v}_{0,\perp}$. The component $\mathbf{v}_{0,\perp}$ is then unaffected, because there is no force in its direction, but the velocity in the field direction experiences an acceleration $\mathbf{a} = q\mathbf{E}/m$ which is constant in time. Thus the equations for the velocity components are

$$\begin{aligned} \mathbf{v}_\perp &= \mathbf{v}_{0,\perp} \\ \mathbf{v}_\parallel &= \mathbf{v}_{0,\parallel} + \frac{q}{m}\mathbf{E}t \end{aligned} \tag{2.14}$$

The resolution of $\mathbf{v}$ into these components is shown in Fig. 2.2.

The above results are strictly analogous to those for the velocity of a point mass projected into a uniform gravitational field, with $q\mathbf{E}/m$ equivalent to the acceleration of gravity **g**. Thus the path of the charged particle must be a parabola in the plane of $\mathbf{v}_0$ and **E**, and the usual formulas involving distance, velocity, and time for uniformly accelerated motion apply here directly. If we set up in this plane a coordinate reference frame with the y axis parallel to **E** and the x axis perpendicular to **E**

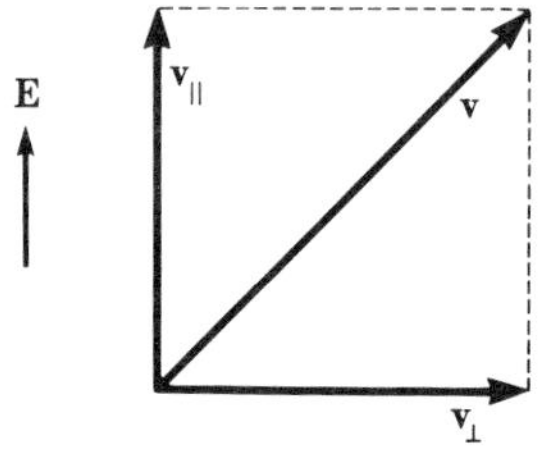

Fig. 2.2 Resolution of **v** into components parallel and perpendicular to **E**.

and if we denote by $\mathbf{x}_0$ and $\mathbf{y}_0$ the unit vectors along the x and y axes, respectively, then Eq. (2.14) may be written as

$$\begin{aligned} \mathbf{v}_\perp &= v_x\mathbf{x}_0 = v_{0,x}\mathbf{x}_0 \\ \mathbf{v}_\parallel &= v_y\mathbf{y}_0 = \left(v_{0,y} + \frac{q}{m}E_y t\right)\mathbf{y}_0 = \left(v_{0,y} + \frac{q}{m}Et\right)\mathbf{y}_0 \end{aligned} \tag{2.15}$$

In Eq. (2.15) we have employed the scalar symbol E to represent the *magnitude* of the vector **E**. This is a convention which we shall frequently use.

Integration of Eq. (2.15) in time immediately leads to the x and y coordinates of the particle. Thus we obtain

$$\begin{aligned} x &= v_{0,x}t \\ y &= v_{0,y}t + \frac{q}{2m}Et^2 \end{aligned} \tag{2.16}$$

and

$$y = \frac{v_{0,y}}{v_{0,x}}x + \frac{q}{2m}E\left(\frac{x}{v_{0,x}}\right)^2$$

It is clear from Eq. (2.16) that the particle trajectory is a parabola whose axis is parallel to the y axis (or **E**) and displaced from the origin by the distance $x = -mv_{0,x}v_{0,y}/qE$, as shown in Fig. 2.3.

Let us now calculate the kinetic energy of the particle. This is, of course, given by

$$W_{\text{kin}} = \tfrac{1}{2}m|\mathbf{v}|^2 = \tfrac{1}{2}mv^2 \tag{2.17a}$$

and since $v^2 = v_x^2 + v_y^2$,

$$W_{\text{kin}} = \tfrac{1}{2}mv_x^2 + \tfrac{1}{2}mv_y^2 = W_{\text{kin},x} + W_{\text{kin},y} \tag{2.17b}$$

Equation (2.17*b*) breaks down the total kinetic energy into terms separately associated with each component of velocity; thus $\frac{1}{2}mv_x^2$ is called the *x-associated kinetic energy* $W_{\text{kin},x}$, and similarly for y (of course, for an arbitrary orientation of the coordinate axes there will be, in general, three components). It is often convenient to work with the component-associated kinetic energies.

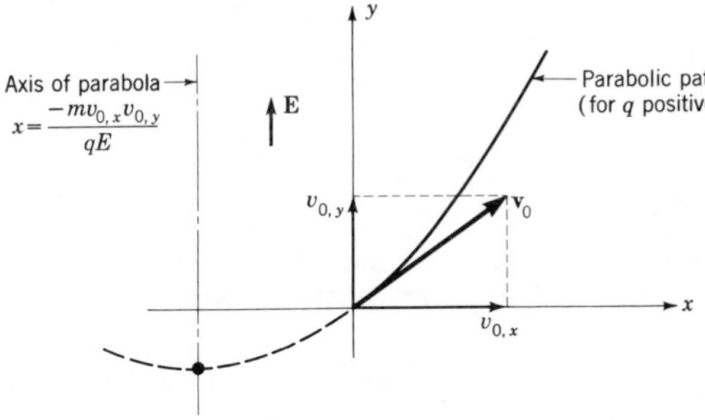

Fig. 2.3 Charged-particle trajectory in uniform electrostatic field.

In our case, then, we have, from Eq. (2.15),

$$W_{\text{kin},x} = \tfrac{1}{2}mv_x^2 = \tfrac{1}{2}mv_{0,x}^2 \tag{2.18a}$$

$$W_{\text{kin},y} = \tfrac{1}{2}mv_y^2 = \tfrac{1}{2}m\left[v_{0,y}^2 + \frac{2q}{m}E\left(v_{0,y}t + \frac{q}{2m}Et^2\right)\right] \tag{2.18b}$$

By using Eq. (2.16) for the y coordinate as a function of time, Eq. (2.18*b*) can be rewritten

$$W_{\text{kin},y} = \tfrac{1}{2}m\left(v_{0,y}^2 + \frac{2qE}{m}y\right) = \tfrac{1}{2}mv_{0,y}^2 + qEy \tag{2.19}$$

Thus we see that the x-associated kinetic energy is constant, whereas the y-associated kinetic energy contains the term qEy and so increases linearly with y. From Fig. 2.3 it is clear why this should be so. As we move in the direction of the y axis, we are moving in the direction of **E** and so giving up electric potential and electric potential energy. In fact, Ey is the potential difference, and so qEy is the decrease in potential energy, as well as the increase in kinetic energy. This energy balance, of course, agrees precisely with Eq. (2.11), the equation of the conservation of energy. When we move along the x axis, on the other hand, the electric potential is constant, and so the x-associated kinetic energy is likewise constant.

We now pause to consider an example which illustrates free motion in a uniform E field, the electron-volt energy unit, and energy balance.

Example 2.2

A 1,000-ev electron is injected into a uniform electric field with a velocity component in the direction of **E**. For convenience, we select the y axis in the **E** direction and the origin at the point of injection. In this reference frame, $\mathbf{v}_0$ makes an angle

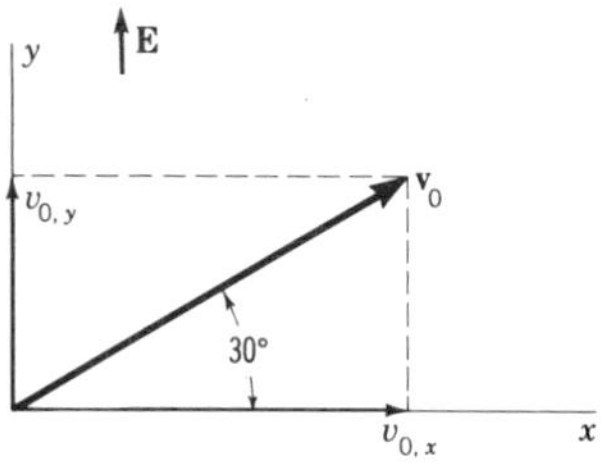

of 30° with the x axis, as shown in the figure. What must the value of **E** be in order that the electron return to the x axis 3 cm from the origin?

Solution

The path is a parabola as shown. The particle reaches its zenith when $x = x_r/2$. Its average vertical velocity in the time from injection to zenith is $v_{0,y}/2$ since the ver-

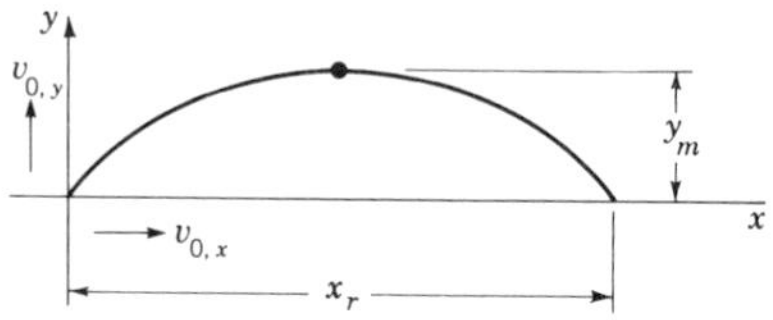

tical velocity varies linearly with time because of the constant acceleration. Thus we have

$$t_{\text{zenith}} = \frac{y_m}{v_{0,y}/2} = \frac{x_r/2}{v_{0,x}} \qquad \text{or} \qquad y_m = \frac{x_r v_{0,y}}{4v_{0,x}} = \frac{x_r}{4}\tan 30^\circ$$

Therefore

$$y_m = \frac{3}{4}\frac{\sqrt{3}}{3} = \frac{\sqrt{3}}{4} \text{ cm}$$

Now the initial y-associated kinetic energy is

$$W_{\text{kin},y} = \tfrac{1}{2}mv_{0,y}^2 = \tfrac{1}{2}m(v \sin 30^\circ)^2 = W_{\text{kin,total}} \sin^2 30^\circ$$
$$= 1{,}000 \text{ ev} \times \tfrac{1}{4} = 250 \text{ ev}$$

At the zenith $v_y = 0$, and so all the initial $W_{\text{kin},y} = 250$ ev has been lost. Thus, in going from origin to zenith there must be a potential energy increase of 250 ev. Since our particle is a single electron, the potential difference from origin to zenith is 250 volts. Therefore

$$E = \frac{250}{y_m} = \frac{250}{(\sqrt{3}/4) \times 10^{-2}} = 5.77 \times 10^4 \text{ volts/m}$$

As an alternative procedure in solving this problem, we can use the results of our previous analysis as deduced from Eq. (2.16). Here $q = -e$, and so the axis of the parabola has the coordinate

$$x = +\frac{mv_{0,x}v_{0,y}}{eE}$$

This coordinate is clearly $x_r/2$, so that

$$E = \frac{2mv_{0,x}v_{0,y}}{ex_r} = \frac{\frac{1}{2}mv_0^2}{e}\frac{4 \sin 30° \cos 30°}{x_r}$$

$$= 1{,}000\,\frac{4 \times \frac{1}{2} \times (\sqrt{3}/2)}{3 \times 10^{-2}} = \frac{1{,}000}{\sqrt{3} \times 10^{-2}} = 5.77 \times 10^4 \text{ volts/m}$$

(a) Ion-gun Rocket Motor

An interesting application of charged-particle motion in electric fields is the ion-gun rocket motor which has been proposed for space propulsion;

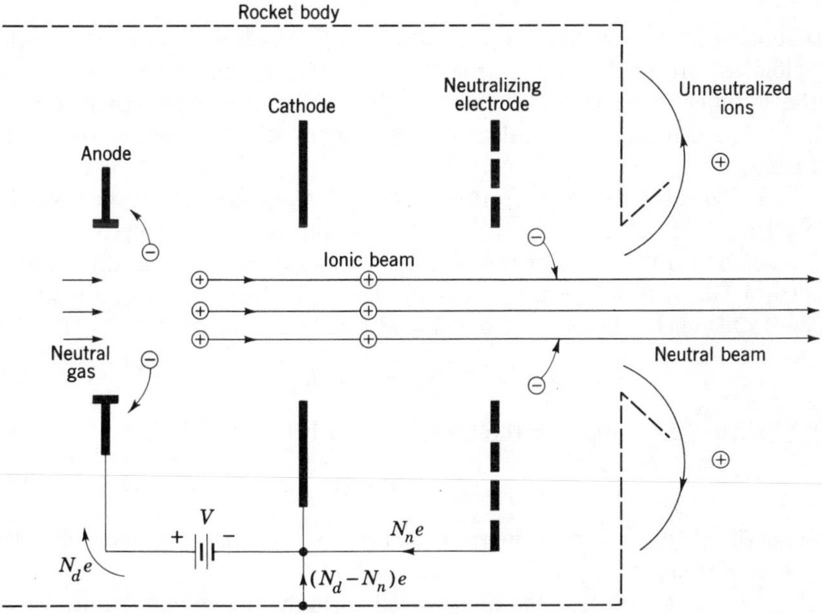

Fig. 2.4 Principle of ion-gun rocket motor.

it is illustrated in Fig. 2.4. Although we are not concerned here with the theory of rockets, it should be noted that the interest in this unconventional rocket motor arises from the fact that the velocities which the exhaust gases attain in rockets employing chemical reactions are too low for efficient operation in interplanetary missions, whereas it is very easy to achieve high-velocity particles by electrostatic acceleration, as we have previously noted. This device is, in fact, under intensive development at the present time.[1-3] There are many problems still to be solved, particularly those requiring space-environment testing. We shall not study this motor in great detail, as we are primarily interested in the basic principles of operation. These are illustrated in Fig. 2.4.

A low-velocity stream of easily ionizable gas (such as cesium, with a first ionization potential† of 3.87 volts) is dissociated into electrons and ions in the vicinity of an electrode, the anode, which is held at a positive potential with respect to an open-cathode structure. The electrons are attracted to the anode, whereas the ions are accelerated by the electric field toward the negative cathode. Essentially all of this ion beam passes through the cathode into a region of zero applied field between the cathode and the neutralizing electrode. Assuming that we have single ionization only, these ions have the kinetic energy

$$\tfrac{1}{2}m_i v_i^2 = eV$$

where m_i is the ion mass and v_i the ion speed after acceleration (initial velocities are negligible). Finally, most of the ions are neutralized by thermionically emitted electrons at a neutralizing electrode placed downstream, resulting in a neutral exhaust beam which provides the rocket thrust.

If N_d is the number of atoms that ionize per second, all the resulting electrons are attracted to the anode, causing a current flow $N_d e$ amp in the anode lead. If N_n of the N_d ions per second are successfully neutralized, a current of $N_n e$ amp flows in the neutralizing electrode lead, and the total mechanical power developed by the motor is

$$P = N_n(\tfrac{1}{2}m_i v_i^2) = N_n eV \tag{2.20}$$

The thrust developed by the motor is clearly

$$F = N_n m_i v_i \tag{2.21}$$

since the thrust is the momentum carried by the amount of gas exhausted per-unit time.

The ions that are not neutralized in flight do *not* contribute to the overall electromechanical power conversion. In fact, they are eventually recaptured by the external field which builds up as a consequence of the accumulation of negative charge on the rocket structure, and thus contribute a current $(N_d - N_n)e$ which makes its way back to the anode, as shown in the figure. It will be noted that the power delivered by the voltage source V is $N_d eV$, which exceeds the useful power $N_n eV$ by the amount $(N_d - N_n)eV$. This excess power goes into heating the rocket body, by virtue of the impact of the recaptured unneutralized ions. These are brought to standstill and then accelerated back to the rocket by the external field which, in effect, provides a retarding potential source of V volts. Since the eventual development goal includes almost com-

† The first ionization potential of an element corresponds to the energy required to free the outermost electron from an atom of the element.

plete neutralization, the inefficiency represented by the power loss $(N_d - N_n)eV$ is, however, not of any practical consequence.

2.5 MOTION IN A BOUNDED ELECTROSTATIC FIELD

(a) Electrostatic Deflection of an Electron Beam

It is obvious that the perfectly uniform field is not realizable; any field is only approximately uniform over a bounded region in space. In many cases, the necessity for analyzing the motion of a particle in non-uniform fields may arise. In these instances, it may be possible to approximate the results without appreciable error by using a "piecewise-homogeneous" technique in which the actual field is replaced by an approximation based on the assumption that the field variation occurs in

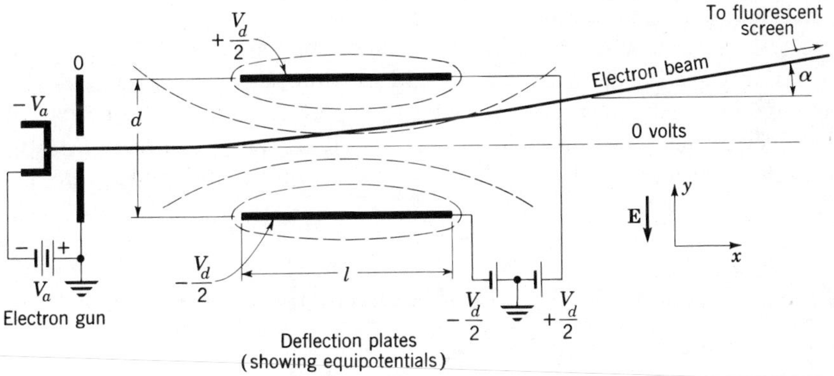

Fig. 2.5 Electrostatic deflection in cathode-ray tube.

discrete steps only at the sharp boundaries of properly delineated regions of space. This technique has many other applications with which the reader may already be familiar. Such are, for instance, the "staircase approximation" of time functions and the "piecewise linearization" of the characteristics of nonlinear elements in circuit analysis.

As a practical example of the application of this technique, consider the motion of an electron through the deflection plates of a cathode-ray tube, as shown in Fig. 2.5. The electrons are emitted from a thermionic cathode and are accelerated in the axial direction toward an anode provided with a central hole. In falling through the potential difference V_a between cathode and anode, they acquire a horizontal velocity v_0 by the time they pass through the anode hole. Since the region between anode and deflection plates is relatively field-free, this velocity is maintained until they reach the deflection plates.

We assume that a balanced source of direct voltage V_d is connected across the deflection plates as shown, causing an electric-field intensity $|\mathbf{E}| = V_d/d$ directed downward. Since the fringing field outside a parallel-plate capacitor drops off rapidly as we move away from the confines of the plates, we will make the approximation that the **E** field suddenly disappears outside the plates and is uniform inside.

We now desire to relate the deflection of the electron beam to the parameters of the system. Under our approximation of the piecewise-homogeneous electric field, the horizontal velocity v_x is constant at the value v_0 throughout the deflection and thereafter, and the vertical velocity v_y is also constant after deflection. Consequently, the path of the electrons after deflection is a straight line rotated by an angle α from the horizontal, such that $\tan \alpha$ is the ratio of the vertical to horizontal component of velocity. To find α, then, we need only find the vertical component of velocity acquired by the electrons in passing through the deflection plates, as follows.

We choose x and y axes in the plane of the paper, with the positive y axis upward as shown. The origin of time $t = 0$ is chosen at the instant the electron enters the deflection plates. Under the action of the electric field, the electron is accelerated in the $+y$ direction only, so that the scalar equation for the vertical component of velocity is

$$v_y = at = \frac{e}{m} Et$$

If l is the length of the plates in the x direction, the transit time t_T is

$$t_T = \frac{l}{v_0}$$

and the value of v_y after the electron leaves the plates is

$$v_y = \frac{e}{m} E \frac{l}{v_0} \qquad t \geq T$$

Thus the deflection angle α is then

$$\alpha = \tan^{-1} \frac{v_y}{v_x} = \tan^{-1} \frac{eEl}{mv_0^2} = \tan^{-1} \frac{l}{2d} \frac{V_d}{V_a} \tag{2.22a}$$

since $v_x = v_0$ throughout, $E = V_d/d$ and $mv_0^2 = 2eV_a$. Usually the angle α is small, and we can make the good approximation

$$\alpha = \tan^{-1} \frac{v_y}{v_x} \doteq \frac{v_y}{v_x} = \frac{eEl}{mv_0^2} = \frac{l}{2d} \frac{V_d}{V_a} \tag{2.22b}$$

so that the deflection is inversely proportional to the kinetic energy. With α and the screen location known, the position of the spot on the screen can be readily found.

Although the piecewise-homogeneous approximation gives reasonably good results in predicting the beam deflection, we should be careful in extending the technique without justification. For example, we might conclude, on the basis of the above analysis, that each electron hits the screen with higher kinetic energy than that initially acquired from the electron gun, "since v_y has been acquired vertically in addition to the unchanged horizontal v_0." This cannot be true since the resulting mechanical power would then require a direct-current flow through the d-c source which is connected to the open deflection plates, and this is manifestly impossible. Consequently, we cannot correctly use our piecewise-homogeneous model to calculate the final kinetic energy. Upon further study, we find that the bending of the field equipotential lines outside the plates brings the deflected electron back to its entering potential, and there is no transfer of energy from the deflection source to the electron beam. This is clearly indicated in Fig. 2.5, since the beam potential gets closer and closer to zero as it moves to the right, even though the beam is diverging from the axis.

2.6 FORCE ON A CHARGED PARTICLE MOVING IN A MAGNETOSTATIC FIELD

In the previous sections we have considered the motion of a charged particle in purely electric fields. As the next step in the development of a more general picture of the dynamics of charged particles, we shall consider the behavior of a charged particle moving in a magnetostatic field.

Experimentally we find that the force on a charged particle moving with velocity $\mathbf{v}$ with respect to a reference frame in which we measure a magnetic flux density $\mathbf{B}$ and zero electric field is given by

$$\mathbf{F}_m = q\mathbf{v} \times \mathbf{B} \tag{2.23a}$$

where $\mathbf{B}$ is the magnetic flux density at the point where the charged particle is located.

Although Eq. (2.23*a*) is an independent experimental law, it should be noted that this law is consistent with, and in fact inferable from, the expression for the force experienced by a current-carrying conductor in a magnetic field. Consider a small directed wire length $\mathbf{l}$ carrying a current I in a magnetic flux density $\mathbf{B}$, the wire being small enough so that $\mathbf{B}$ does not vary appreciably over its length. The small force on this wire is

$$\mathbf{F}_m = I\mathbf{l} \times \mathbf{B} \tag{2.23b}$$

where the positive direction of $\mathbf{l}$ is defined as the direction of flow of conventional positive current. Now if $\mathbf{v}$ is the average velocity of the charged particles which carry the current flow, and λ is the linear charge density of these particles along the wire, then

$$I = \lambda v \tag{2.24a}$$

and

$$I\mathbf{l} = \lambda v\mathbf{l} = \lambda \mathbf{v}l = \lambda l\mathbf{v}$$

$$I\mathbf{l} = q\mathbf{v} \tag{2.24b}$$

since λl is simply q, the total charge present in the length l. Using Eq. (2.24*b*), Eq. (2.23*b*) becomes

$$\mathbf{F}_m = q\mathbf{v} \times \mathbf{B} \tag{2.25}$$

which is identical with Eq. (2.23*a*). Of course, this "derivation" is not entirely conclusive since we have certainly used a most simplified model of a current-carrying wire. Without further consideration we may only say that the form of Eq. (2.25) strongly suggests applicability to a moving-point charge, as is indeed verified experimentally.

2.7 POWER AND ENERGY RELATIONS IN A MAGNETOSTATIC FIELD

Before studying the details of particle motion in the time-invariant magnetic field, it will be useful to examine the power and energy relations. To do this, we proceed as in Sec. 2.4 and find the dot product of Eq. (2.23*a*) with $\mathbf{v}$, giving

$$\mathbf{F}_m \cdot \mathbf{v} = q\mathbf{v} \times \mathbf{B} \cdot \mathbf{v} = 0 \tag{2.26}$$

where the triple scalar product $(\mathbf{v} \times \mathbf{B}) \cdot \mathbf{v}$ vanishes because it contains the vector $\mathbf{v}$ twice; i.e., since $\mathbf{v}$ is always perpendicular to $\mathbf{v} \times \mathbf{B}$. In other words the magnetic force is always at right angles to the instantaneous direction of the motion. Thus *the power due to the magnetic force is identically zero; no work is done by this force, and, consequently, the kinetic energy of the particle is constant.* This result is, of course, quite different from the one observed in the case of the electric-field force.

Even though the magnetic force does no work, it must not be thought that it "has no effect" on the motion of the charged particle. The magnetic force cannot change the particle speed, but it does change the direction of the velocity. Acting by itself on a moving particle, the magnetic force results in a characteristic free motion which we shall study next, and in concert with an electric field, the magnetic force acts as a "control force" which has a marked influence on the path and energy of the particle, as we shall see in Sec. 2.13.

2.8 FREE MOTION OF A CHARGED PARTICLE IN A UNIFORM MAGNETOSTATIC FIELD

Consider now a charged particle free to move in a magnetostatic field which is essentially uniform in the region of interest. From Eq.

(2.23*a*), the equation of motion is

$$\mathbf{F}_m = q\mathbf{v} \times \mathbf{B} = m\mathbf{a} = m\frac{d\mathbf{v}}{dt} \tag{2.27}$$

The motion that results is most conveniently considered in terms of two components, one parallel to the direction of **B**, and the other perpendicular to **B**. Note that a unit direction vector parallel to **B** is uniquely defined, but a unit direction vector perpendicular to **B** may be anywhere in a *normal plane* perpendicular to **B**.

We shall see that the motion of the charged particle consists of (1) a uniform velocity "coasting" parallel to **B** and (2) a circular trajec-

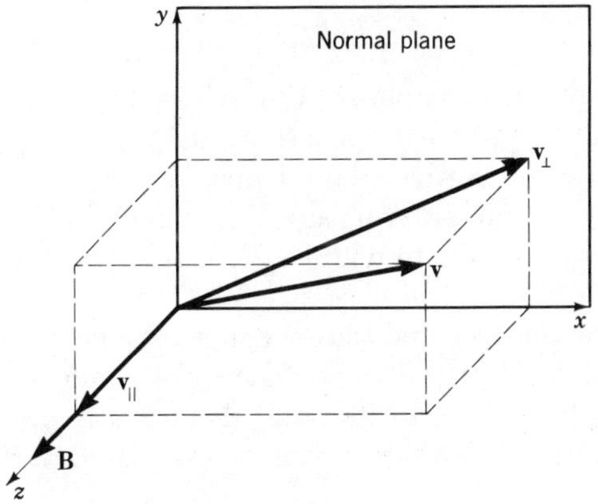

Fig. 2.6 Parallel and perpendicular components of **v**, and the normal plane.

tory with constant angular velocity in the normal plane. The combination of these motions plainly yields a total motion which is a helix of constant pitch with axis parallel to **B**.

To see how these conclusions are arrived at, we proceed as follows. First we consider **v** as a sum of parallel and perpendicular components as described above, i.e.,

$$\mathbf{v} = \mathbf{v}_\parallel + \mathbf{v}_\perp \tag{2.28}$$

This is depicted in Fig. 2.6, where the z axis has been chosen in the direction of **B**, so that the xy plane becomes the normal plane; $\mathbf{v}_\parallel$ is then always in the z direction, but $\mathbf{v}_\perp$ varies in the normal plane as the direction of **v** changes. Introducing Eq. (2.28) into (2.27), we get

$$\begin{aligned} m\frac{d\mathbf{v}_\parallel}{dt} + m\frac{d\mathbf{v}_\perp}{dt} &= q\mathbf{v}_\parallel \times \mathbf{B} + q\mathbf{v}_\perp \times \mathbf{B} \\ &= 0 + q\mathbf{v}_\perp \times \mathbf{B} \end{aligned} \tag{2.29}$$

where $q\mathbf{v}_\parallel \times \mathbf{B}$ is obviously zero. Of the terms that are left, only

$m\,d\mathbf{v}_{\parallel}/dt$ is in the parallel (z) direction; the others are in the normal xy plane, since $\mathbf{v}_{\perp}$ is always composed of x and y components only, and $\mathbf{v}_{\perp} \times \mathbf{B}$ is always perpendicular to $\mathbf{B}$. Thus, if we break (2.29) down into two equations for the parallel and perpendicular components, we obtain

$$m\frac{d\mathbf{v}_{\parallel}}{dt} = 0 \tag{2.30a}$$

$$m\frac{d\mathbf{v}_{\perp}}{dt} = q\mathbf{v}_{\perp} \times \mathbf{B} \tag{2.30b}$$

The meaning of Eq. (2.30*a*) is immediately clear; $\mathbf{v}_{\parallel}$ must be constant as time changes, or

$$\mathbf{v}_{\parallel} = \mathbf{v}_{0,\parallel} \tag{2.31}$$

where $\mathbf{v}_{0,\parallel}$ is the parallel component of the initial velocity at $t = 0$. This establishes our first statement concerning the motion.

To determine the normal plane trajectory from Eq. (2.30*b*) we can proceed formally by integration, as will be done in Sec. 2.8*a*. At this point it is more instructive to deduce the trajectory in a largely qualitative manner.

We have previously noted that the magnetic field can do no work on the moving particle; thus the kinetic energy W_{kin} must be constant with time. Let us split W_{kin} into its parallel- and perpendicular-associated parts, just as we split W_{kin} into x- and y- associated parts in Sec. 2.4:

$$W_{\text{kin}} = W_{\text{kin},\parallel} + W_{\text{kin},\perp} \tag{2.32a}$$

$$= \tfrac{1}{2}mv_{\parallel}^2 + \tfrac{1}{2}mv_{\perp}^2 \tag{2.32b}$$

Equation (2.31) tells us $\mathbf{v}_{\parallel}$ is constant, so that $W_{\text{kin},\parallel}$ is likewise constant. Since the total energy is also constant, it follows that $W_{\text{kin},\perp} = \tfrac{1}{2}mv_{\perp}^2$ is likewise constant; thus $v_{\perp}$ itself is constant. This means that the *magnitude* of $\mathbf{v}_{\perp}$ or the *speed* in the normal plane is constant, as $\mathbf{v}_{\perp}$ changes direction. Thus both vectors in the term $q\mathbf{v}_{\perp} \times \mathbf{B}$ are constant in magnitude, and Eq. (2.30*b*) then tells us that the acceleration in the normal plane is always constant in magnitude and perpendicular to the trajectory in the normal plane.

We have thus deduced that the particle trajectory in the normal plane has constant speed with a constant magnitude acceleration perpendicular to the path. The only planar trajectory that satisfies these conditions is a circle traversed with constant angular velocity. This proves our second statement concerning the motion.

We can now find the radius and angular velocity in the normal plane. First we recall that in uniform circular motion with speed $v_{\perp}$, the centripetal acceleration has a magnitude $v_{\perp}^2/\mathcal{R}$; but from Eq. (2.30*b*) this magnitude is also $|q|v_\perp B/m$. Thus

$$\frac{v_\perp^2}{\mathcal{R}} = \frac{|q|v_\perp B}{m}$$

and

$$\mathcal{R} = \frac{mv_\perp}{|q|B} \tag{2.33}$$

this radius is called the *Larmor* radius, or gyroradius.

The angular velocity of the "gyration" in the normal plane is found from

$$\omega_c = \frac{v_\perp}{\mathcal{R}} = \frac{|q|B}{m} \tag{2.34}$$

This angular velocity and the corresponding radian frequency are called the *cyclotron* radian frequency or, in short, cyclotron frequency; sometimes the terms Larmor frequency and gyrofrequency are used. The

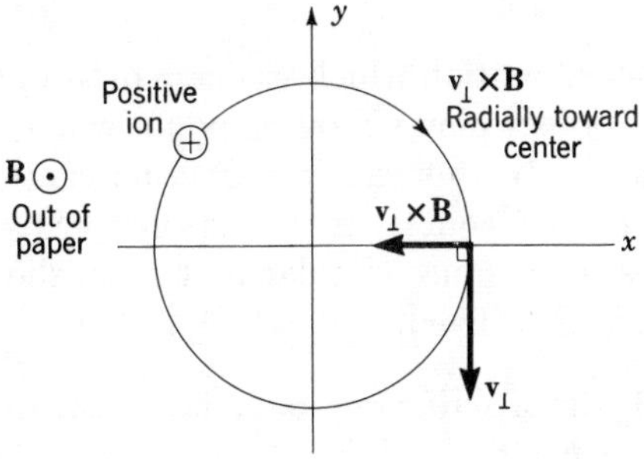

Fig. 2.7 Motion in the normal plane.

Larmor radius and the cyclotron frequency are important parameters in the behavior of ionized gases.

The motion in the normal plane is pictured in Fig. 2.7 for a positive charge, with the origin selected as the center of the circle. We note that if we impart a vector character to the angular velocity by giving it a direction along the axis of rotation (in the right-handed sense), the resulting vector is opposite to the direction of **B**. Thus we may write

$$\boldsymbol{\omega}_c = -\frac{q}{m}\mathbf{B} \tag{2.35}$$

Plainly Eq. (2.35) holds true for either plus or minus charges, since the direction of $\boldsymbol{\omega}_c$ reverses as the sign of q is changed.

The gyrating charge in effect constitutes a current "flowing" around the circle of gyration. As seen in Fig. 2.7, the direction of this current is such as to set up a magnetic field which opposes the impressed magnetic flux density **B**. This, then, is another interpretation of the minus sign in Eq. (2.35); it signifies that the field of the resulting gyration always opposes the impressed **B**.

It is instructive at this point to consider some representative numbers. In the mks system, we measure B in webers per square meter. A flux density of 1 weber/m^2 is, however, quite large; the saturation levels of most ferromagnetic materials are under $B = 2$ mks units. As a result, B is frequently measured in gauss, where 10^4 gauss $= 1$ weber/m^2. For $B = 1$ gauss $= 10^{-4}$ mks, we have for an electron

$$\omega_c = 1.76 \times 10^{11} \times 10^{-4} = 1.76 \times 10^7 \text{ rad/(sec)(gauss)} \tag{2.36}$$

Thus, even for weak magnetic fields the cyclotron frequency is very high. The radius $\mathcal{R}$, for fixed ω_c, is directly proportional to $v_\perp$. For example, an electron in a field of one gauss moving with $v_\perp = \frac{1}{10}c$ (where $c = 3 \times 10^8$ m/sec, the velocity of light) has $\mathcal{R} = v_\perp/\omega_c = 1.70$ m. At the same velocity in a field of 1 weber/m^2, the radius is $\mathcal{R} = 0.17$ millimeter.

The overall helical motion which we have determined can be thought of as a circular gyration around a moving point, which is called the *guiding center* of the particle. In this case the guiding center moves uniformly along a **B** flux line. Of course, in the special case $v_{0,\parallel} = 0$, the total motion degenerates to the pure circular motion in the normal plane, and the guiding center is then fixed.

(a) Formal Analysis of Charged-particle Motion in a Uniform Magnetostatic Field

In the previous section we have informally studied the motion of a charged particle in a uniform magnetostatic field, and have found it to be a helix of constant pitch coaxial with the field lines, with radius and angular velocity given by Eqs. (2.33) and (2.34). The same results are, of course, obtainable in a perfectly formal way through the solutions of the differential equations of motion. We shall outline this procedure, leaving the completion of the details as an exercise for the reader.

Returning to Eqs. (2.30*a*) and (2.30*b*) and writing these in terms of the x, y, z components of the coordinate reference frame of Fig. 2.6, we get

$$\begin{aligned} \frac{dv_z}{dt} &= 0 \\ \frac{dv_y}{dt} &= \frac{-qB}{m} v_x \\ \frac{dv_x}{dt} &= \frac{+qB}{m} v_y \end{aligned} \tag{2.37}$$

In Eq. (2.34) we defined ω_c as $|q|B/m$; this can also be written as

$\pm\omega_c = qB/m$, choosing the upper sign for $q > 0$ and vice versa. Using ω_c, and introducing boundary conditions by specifying that $\mathbf{v}$ is known to have the components $v_{0,x}$, $v_{0,y}$, $v_{0,z}$ at $t = 0$, Eqs. (2.37) are readily solved to give

$$
\begin{aligned}
v_z &= v_{0,z} \\
v_y &= -v_{0,x} \sin(\pm\,\omega_c t) + v_{0,y} \cos \omega_c t \\
v_x &= v_{0,y} \sin(\pm\,\omega_c t) + v_{0,x} \cos \omega_c t
\end{aligned}
\tag{2.38}
$$

This is, of course, the expected result, since we have here a case of simple harmonic motion in the xy plane and a uniform velocity along the z axis. Note also that Eq. (2.38) demonstrate the constancy of $v_\perp$ and v, since

$$
\begin{aligned}
\mathbf{v}_\perp &= v_x\mathbf{x}_0 + v_y\mathbf{y}_0 \\
\mathbf{v}_\perp{}^2 &= v_x{}^2 + v_y{}^2 = v_{0,x}^2 + v_{0,y}^2 \\
\mathbf{v} &= \mathbf{v}_\perp + v_z\mathbf{z}_0 \\
v^2 &= v_\perp{}^2 + v_z{}^2 = v_{0,x}^2 + v_{0,y}^2 + v_{0,z}^2
\end{aligned}
\tag{2.39}
$$

Now if we further specify that the position of the particle is (x_0,y_0,z_0) at $t = 0$, Eq. (2.38) may be integrated and the time t eliminated to give the equation for the trajectory in the normal xy plane. The result is

$$
\left(x - x_0 \mp \frac{v_{0,y}}{\omega_c}\right)^2 + \left(y - y_0 \pm \frac{v_{0,x}}{\omega_c}\right)^2 = \frac{v_\perp{}^2}{\omega_c{}^2}
\tag{2.40}
$$

This is plainly a circle of radius $\mathcal{R} = v_\perp/\omega_c$, as expected. If we now shift to polar coordinates (r,θ) in the xy plane with an origin at the center of the circle given in Eq. (2.40), we readily find that $d\theta/dt = \mp\omega_c$, where the minus sign is chosen for a positive charge and vice versa. Thus we see that ω_c is indeed the actual angular velocity of the gyrating particle; and the signs indicate that, for $q > 0$, the particle is moving clockwise as viewed from the positive z axis. This is, of course, consistent with the direction of $\mathbf{B}$ and the direction of the force $q\mathbf{v} \times \mathbf{B}$, as shown in Fig. 2.7. We have thus formally obtained all the results determined in the previous section.

2.9 MOTION IN A BOUNDED MAGNETOSTATIC FIELD

(a) Magnetic Deflection of a Particle Beam

Much in the following chapters will be devoted to power converters of the magnetic type in which the magnetic fields are not uniform. We are therefore interested in acquiring an early understanding of the motion of charged particles in such fields. For this purpose it is expedient to proceed, as we have previously done in the electrostatic case, by approximating the variation of the field by a piecewise-homogeneous model. In the interest of simplicity, we shall consider the transition from a field-free region to a region of homogeneous magnetic field, where the boundary is a plane.

As a practical example, we consider first the magnetic-deflection scheme used in ordinary kinescopes in TV receiving sets and in one version of the mass spectrometer.†

As shown in Fig. 2.8, a beam of charged particles passes through a small gap between two magnetic pole pieces, oriented so that **B** in the gap is normal to the plane of the paper. We shall make the approximation

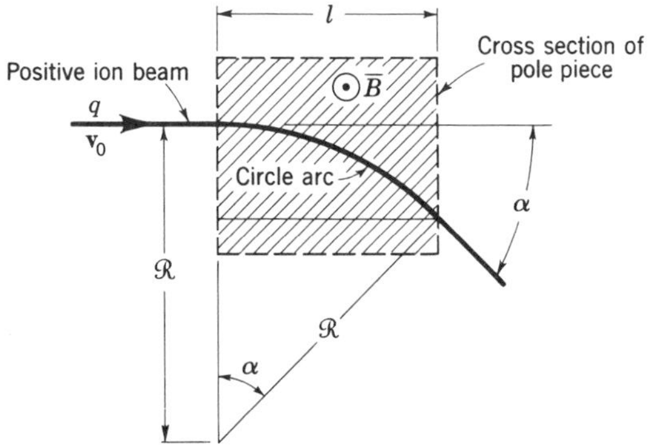

Fig. 2.8 Magnetic deflection.

that the field within the pole pieces is uniform, and drops abruptly to zero outside.

Thus, when in the gap the particles move in a circle arc with radius given by Eq. (2.33), $\mathcal{R} = mv_0/|q|B$, whereas outside the gap the particles move in straight lines tangent to this circle arc. Calling the length of the pole pieces in the $\mathbf{v}_0$ direction l, we see from the geometry of Fig. 2.8 that the deflection angle α is given by

$$\alpha = \sin^{-1}\frac{l}{\mathcal{R}} = \sin^{-1}\frac{l|q|B}{mv_0} \tag{2.41}$$

In these applications the length l is usually much less than the radius $\mathcal{R}$, so that we make the approximation

$$\alpha \doteq \frac{l}{\mathcal{R}} = \frac{l|q|B}{mv_0} \tag{2.42}$$

† The mass spectrometer is a device employed to separate charged particles having equal charge but different masses, as, for example, chemical isotopes.

It follows that the deflection of each particle is inversely proportional to its momentum.

We have seen in Sec. 2.5 that the electrostatic deflection of charged particles is inversely proportional to their kinetic energy. By combining electrostatic with magnetic deflection it is then possible to isolate particles having the same charge-to-mass ratio from a group of particles differing in charge, mass, and velocity.

(b) Magnetic "Mirrors" and "Walls"

In the deflection scheme just studied the particle succeeds in crossing the pole piece because its length l is small compared with the gyroradius

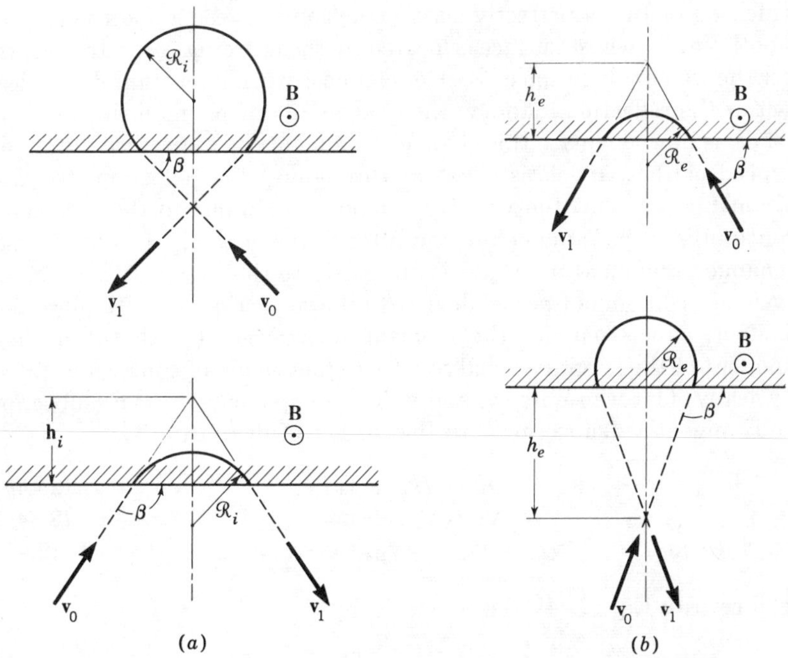

Fig. 2.9 Particle reflection by magnetic wall: (*a*) Ion; (*b*) electron.

$\mathcal{R}$. If, on the other hand, the extent of the region of nonzero **B** is larger than $2\mathcal{R}$, the particle turns around toward the field boundary and is expelled back into the field-free region. This situation is pictured in Fig. 2.9 for both ions and electrons. Here we see from the symmetry that the *angle of incidence* is equal to the *angle of reflection*; also the outgoing speed is equal to the incoming speed. Consequently, we may picture the incident and reflected trajectories outside the field as light rays and represent the effect of the field as a reflection from a "mirror" situated at a distance h from the boundary. Since we know the particle trajectory inside the field to be an arc of a circle tangent to the entering velocity vector, we can readily deduce from the geometry that

$$h = \pm \frac{\mathcal{R} \sin^2 \beta}{\cos \beta} = \frac{mv \sin^2 \beta}{qB \cos \beta} \tag{2.43}$$

where the angle β is the angle by which the incoming $\mathbf{v}$ vector must be rotated in a positive sense to bring it into coincidence with the wall, when we view the normal plane from the side in which we see $\mathbf{B}$ point toward us. Note that a positive h locates the mirror outside the field region, and a negative h inside.

Instead of using the optical analogy, we might use a mechanical one in which we picture a perfectly elastic collision between a point mass and a smooth "wall" whose surface is located by the coordinate h. In fact, we prefer the wall analogy since it better emphasizes an important dynamical aspect of the reflection, namely, the change in particle momentum.

Let us now calculate this change in momentum. First we note that the speed of the particle is constant throughout the reflection; we also see from Fig. 2.9 that the velocity component parallel to the surface of discontinuity is the same before and after the reflection. It follows that the change in momentum $\Delta(m\mathbf{v})$ is due solely to the change in the sign of the velocity component perpendicular to the surface of discontinuity, and is, in fact, equal to twice the momentum associated with the normal component of the leaving velocity. These facts may, of course, be stated analytically: first we resolve $\mathbf{v}_0$ and $\mathbf{v}_1$ into components normal (subscript n) and tangential (subscript t) to the surface of discontinuity:

$$\mathbf{v}_0 = \mathbf{v}_{0,n} + \mathbf{v}_{0,t} \tag{2.44a}$$

$$\mathbf{v}_1 = \mathbf{v}_{1,n} + \mathbf{v}_{1,t} \tag{2.44b}$$

Next, since

$$\mathbf{v}_{1,t} = \mathbf{v}_{0,t} \qquad \mathbf{v}_{1,n} = -\mathbf{v}_{0,n} \tag{2.45}$$

we can rewrite Eq. (2.44b) as

$$\mathbf{v}_1 = -\mathbf{v}_{1,n} + \mathbf{v}_{0,t} \tag{2.46}$$

Thus the change in momentum $\Delta(m\mathbf{v})$ is

$$\begin{aligned} \Delta(m\mathbf{v}) &= m(\mathbf{v}_1 - \mathbf{v}_0) = m(-\mathbf{v}_{0,n} + \mathbf{v}_{0,t} - \mathbf{v}_{0,n} - \mathbf{v}_{0,t}) \\ &= -2m\mathbf{v}_{0,n} = +2m\mathbf{v}_{1,n} \end{aligned} \tag{2.47}$$

Since this result is exactly what we would get in the case of the purely mechanical collision of a particle and a smooth (frictionless) wall, we are correct in applying this analogy to the action of a jump discontinuity in $\mathbf{B}$ in reflecting a charged particle.

We may carry the wall analogy a step further by considering an array of charged particles (with a uniform distribution in space) impinging on the **B** discontinuity, rather than a single particle or a beam. Suppose N is the number of particles impinging on the discontinuity per-unit time and per-unit surface. From Eq. (2.47), we know that each particle undergoes a change of momentum of $-2m\mathbf{v}_{0,n}$ upon reflection from the wall; with N particles impinging on a unit area in a unit time, we have

$$-2Nm\mathbf{v}_{0,n} = \text{time rate of change of momentum per-unit wall surface} \qquad (2.48)$$

By direct analogy with the case of a gas confined by material walls, the magnitude of this rate of momentum change per-unit surface plainly is the *pressure* exerted by the impinging charged particles on the magnetic wall. Consequently, we see that a jump discontinuity in the magnetic field withstands the pressure exerted by an aggregate of charged particles in the same way that a material wall reacts to the impact of the particles of a gas. This important phenomenon thus provides the possibility of magnetic confinement or containment of charged particles. Moreover, it even suggests the possibility of driving a group of such particles in a pistonlike fashion. This is indeed feasible, as we shall see later in Sec. 2.14.

An interesting instance of particle motion in a discontinuous magnetic field is given in the example below.

Example 2.3

Data obtained by means of artificial satellites have shown that the sun ejects at all times a stream of protons and electrons called the *solar wind*. The earth is effectively shielded from this wind by the geomagnetic field which prevents penetration of this wind beyond a boundary called the *magnetospheric boundary*. Measurements taken with the Imp satellite[4] place the magnetospheric boundary in the equatorial plane at a distance of about 10 earth radii and show that the geomagnetic field intensity rises there from about zero to a value of $B = 10^{-7}$ weber/m^2.

Assuming that:

(1) The total density of electrons and protons in the solar wind near the boundary is $n_e = n_i = 9.6 \times 10^6$ particles/m^3 and the density of particles actually impinging on the wall is half as much (as will be explained in Chap. 3)

(2) The solar wind moves with a speed $v = 5 \times 10^5$ m/sec

(3) A small area on the magnetosphere can be approximated as a planar magnetic wall

Evaluate:

(*a*) The maximum depth of penetration of the solar wind into the magnetosphere when the particles impinge on the wall with near-normal incidence.

(*b*) The maximum pressure exerted by the solar wind on the magnetosphere.

Solution

(*a*) The charged particles impinging on the wall perform half a gyration and, consequently, penetrate a distance equal to a Larmor radius, as shown in the figure; thus

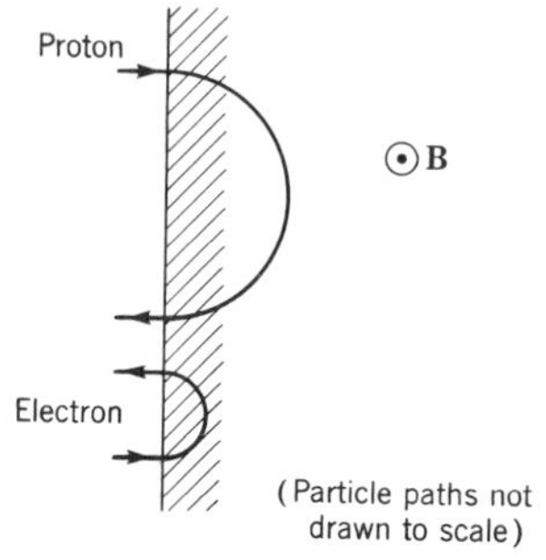

$$\mathcal{R}_e = \frac{v}{(q/m)B} = \frac{5 \times 10^5}{1.76 \times 10^{11} \times 10^{-7}} = 28.4 \text{ m}$$

for the electrons, and for the protons

$$\mathcal{R}_p = \frac{m_p}{m_e}\mathcal{R}_e = 1837 \times 28.4 = 5.2 \times 10^4 \text{ m}$$
$$= 52 \text{ km}$$

The maximum depth of penetration, 52 km, is thus due to the protons.

(*b*) The partial pressure for each species of particles is $2mNv_n$, according to Eq. (2.48), where N stands for the number or particles of each species impinging per-unit area per-unit time. This means that N is the total number of impinging particles contained in the rectangular box having the sides 1, 1, v_n. Thus $N = 1 \times 1 \times v_n \times n/2$, where n is the total particle volume density, and

$$\mathcal{P} = 2m\frac{n}{2}v_n^2 = mnv_n^2$$

Consequently, the electrons exert a pressure

$$\mathcal{P}_e = 9.11 \times 10^{-31} \times 9.6 \times 10^6 \times (5 \times 10^5)^2$$
$$= 2.19 \times 10^{-12} \text{ newton/m}^2$$

and the protons exert a pressure

$$\mathcal{P}_p = \frac{m_p}{m_e}\mathcal{P}_e = 1{,}837 \times 2.19 \times 10^{-12}$$
$$= 4.00 \times 10^{-9} \text{ newton/m}^2$$

We observe that the pressure contributed by the electrons can be neglected when the two particle species have the same density and velocity.

2.10 FORCE ON A CHARGED PARTICLE MOVING IN AN ELECTROMAGNETIC FIELD

We have thus far discussed the free motion of charged particles in regions where there exist either an electrostatic or magnetostatic field.

We proceed now to consider cases in which both fields coexist. Consider a charged particle moving with velocity $\mathbf{v}$ relative to a reference frame in which we measure an electric-field intensity $\mathbf{E}$ and a magnetic flux density $\mathbf{B}$. We find the total force on the particle simply by superposing the forces contributed by $\mathbf{E}$ and $\mathbf{B}$:

$$\mathbf{F} = q(\mathbf{E} + \mathbf{v} \times \mathbf{B}) \tag{2.49}$$

We observe in Eq. (2.49) a peculiarity which indeed should have previously caught our attention in Eq. (2.23*a*). The description of the force in terms of the charge and the electromagnetic field intensities $\mathbf{E}$ and $\mathbf{B}$ involves the velocity $\mathbf{v}$ of the particle, a quantity which is clearly dependent on the observer's frame of reference. In fact, two observers in relative motion would see the particle moving with different velocities. It follows that if the relations expressed in Eqs. (2.23*a*) and (2.49) have to be satisfied for both observers, at least one of the other quantities besides the velocity has to measure differently in the two frames of reference. Experimental evidence shows that the electric charge q is an *invariant* quantity. Likewise for velocities small as compared to the velocity of light, we know from Newtonian mechanics that the force $\mathbf{F}$ does not depend on the state of motion of the observer. We must therefore conclude that two observers in relative motion will, in general, measure different values of the electromagnetic field intensities. As we shall see in Sec. 2.11*b*, for most cases of practical interest the variation in $\mathbf{B}$ is negligible, so that it is the value of the electric field $\mathbf{E}$ that compensates for the difference in the velocity term $\mathbf{v} \times \mathbf{B}$. It is for this reason that we did not raise this point in connection with Eq. (2.23*a*), where the absence of an electric-field term makes an explanation of the situation difficult. We are, however, ready to consider it now.

2.11 TRANSFORMATION LAWS FOR THE ELECTROMAGNETIC FIELD QUANTITIES

(a) Electric Field

Consider the force observed on a single charged particle as seen from two different coordinate reference frames. In one frame, the "unprimed" frame, the particle is seen to move with velocity $\mathbf{v}$, and the field quantities $\mathbf{E}$ and $\mathbf{B}$ are measured. The other frame, the "primed" frame (denoted by a prime superscript), is fixed to the particle. An observer in the primed frame is by definition unaware of the motion of the particle, but he does detect a force $\mathbf{F}'$ acting on a stationary charge q'. Consequently, he concludes that there exists an electric field $\mathbf{E}'$, given by Eq. (2.1) as

$$\mathbf{E}' = \frac{\mathbf{F}'}{q'} \tag{2.50}$$

He may, of course, detect the presence of a magnetic field by *other means*, but this will not affect his calculation of $\mathbf{E}'$ since, for him, the particle velocity is zero.

The observer in the unprimed frame observes a force $\mathbf{F}$ and a charge q, and applies Eq. (2.49) to obtain

$$\frac{\mathbf{F}}{q} = \mathbf{E} + \mathbf{v} \times \mathbf{B} \tag{2.51}$$

However, $q = q'$, and at low velocities $\mathbf{F} = \mathbf{F}'$†, as we have noted in Sec. 2.10 just above. Thus

$$\frac{\mathbf{F}'}{q'} = \frac{\mathbf{F}}{q} \tag{2.52}$$

and from Eqs. (2.50) to (2.52) we have immediately

$$\mathbf{E}' = \mathbf{E} + \mathbf{v} \times \mathbf{B} \tag{2.53}$$

Thus the primed observer (who is at rest with respect to the charge) detects an electric field which differs from the one measured by the unprimed observer (who sees the charge moving with velocity $\mathbf{v}$) by the motional term $\mathbf{v} \times \mathbf{B}$.

Equation (2.53) has a general interpretation of great importance. Although we deduced this equation through the expedient of observing a particular point charge, the indicated relationship must nevertheless be valid regardless of how the electric field is determined. In this sense, Eq. (2.53) is a *transformation law* which enables us to relate in a perfectly general way the different values of electric-field intensity seen in two reference frames in relative motion. Interpreted as a general transformation law, Eq. (2.53) tells us that, if we measure $\mathbf{E}^\alpha$, $\mathbf{B}^\alpha$ in a reference frame α, and if we also see another reference frame β moving with velocity $\mathbf{v}^\alpha$, the electric field $\mathbf{E}^\beta$ measured in the latter frame is, from Eq. (2.53), $\mathbf{E}^\beta = \mathbf{E}^\alpha + \mathbf{v}^\alpha \times \mathbf{B}^\alpha$.

It is clear, then, that one's measure of field quantities in systems which are in relative motion is dependent on the choice of reference frame. Thus in the analysis of power-conversion devices, different approaches are possible depending on the choice of reference coordinates. This flexibility may be exploited by selecting a reference system most convenient to the application at hand, as we shall see in subsequent chapters. An interesting possibility for exploiting the transformation law is given in the following example.

† This by no means implies that $m\,d\mathbf{v}'/dt = m\,d\mathbf{v}/dt$. Instead, according to Newtonian mechanics, $m\,d\mathbf{v}'/dt = m(d\mathbf{v}/dt - d\mathbf{v}_f/dt - 2\boldsymbol{\Omega}_f \times \mathbf{v}')$, where $d\mathbf{v}_f/dt$ is the acceleration of the primed frame and $\boldsymbol{\Omega}_f$ its angular velocity. In this case $\mathbf{v}' = 0$, $\mathbf{v} = \mathbf{v}_f$, and therefore $m\,d\mathbf{v}'/dt = 0$.

Example 2.4

A proposed scheme for determining the velocity of a submarine moving with respect to the earth is to detect the electric field resulting from the motion and the earth's magnetic field. Determine the electric field E' resulting from a velocity of 20 knots if $E = 0$ and $B = 10^{-4}$ weber/m² in a frame of reference fixed to the earth, if B is perpendicular to the velocity. Do you think this scheme is easy to implement?

Solution

$$\text{Since 1 knot} = 1{,}853.2 \text{ m/hr} = \frac{1{,}853.2}{3{,}600} \text{ m/sec}$$

$$v = 20 \times \frac{1{,}853.2}{3{,}600} = 10.3 \text{ m/sec}$$

then $E' = |\mathbf{v} \times \mathbf{B}| = vB = 10.3 \times 10^{-4} = 1.03 \times 10^{-3}$ volt/m

or $E' = 10.3\ \mu\text{v/cm}$

This electric field is very small and is thus easily perturbed by stray fields which are difficult to avoid. Such a scheme would consequently be difficult to implement.

A brief discussion of this technique is given in W. R. Smythe, "Static and Dynamic Electricity," 2d ed., sec. 16.14, McGraw-Hill Book Company, New York, 1950.

(b) Magnetic Field

In the previous section we have learned that relative motion between reference frames, when a magnetic field is present, results in a difference between the electric-field values observed in the two frames. It does not take an uncommonly strong technical curiosity to set us wondering whether there should not be a dual effect, i.e., the observation of a difference between the magnetic field values, measured in two reference frames moving with respect to each other, when an electric field is present. If so, is the magnitude of this effect of significant proportions?

There are several ways in which we might go about investigating the first of these two questions, but one of the easiest is simply to focus attention on the sources of the electric field. Suppose we have an electrostatic field set up by charges fixed to a reference frame. An observer moving with respect to this frame sees these charges move with respect to him; thus he detects a *current* flow which in his terms of reference causes a magnetic field. As a consequence, we do conclude that there exists a "motional magnetic field" which is dual to the "motional electric field" of Eq. (2.53).

We may in fact set up this "experiment in concept" in a quantitative way as follows: Consider a charged parallel-plate capacitor as shown in Fig. 2.10*a* and *b*. Fringing effects may be avoided by simply taking the capacitor shown to be a small portion of a very large structure. In Fig. 2.10*a* we illustrate the situation seen by an observer in the unprimed reference frame. This observer sees a fixed positive surface charge density σ on the upper plate, and a corresponding negative density on the lower plate; as a result he measures a uniform electric flux density **D** between the plates. This **D** is normal to the plates, directed down, and of magnitude $|\mathbf{D}| = \sigma$. The observer also sees another reference frame, denoted by primes, moving to the right with velocity **v** as shown. An observer in the primed reference frame sees the picture shown in Fig. 2.10*b*. Here the positive charges on the upper plate are seen to be moving to the left with velocity $-\mathbf{v}$, and this transforms the surface charge density σ into a surface current density $\mathbf{K} = -\sigma\mathbf{v}$ moving to the left, i.e., a current of $-\sigma\mathbf{v}$ amperes per meter of length perpendicular to the paper. In the same way, he sees a surface current density of $\sigma\mathbf{v}$ moving

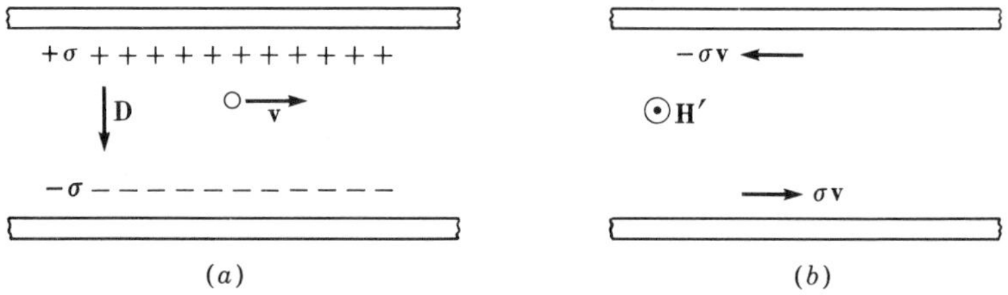

Fig. 2.10 Origin of the motion-induced magnetic field: (*a*) "Unprimed" observer's viewpoint; (*b*) "primed" observer's viewpoint.

to the right on the bottom plate. By Ampère's law and symmetry, these two current densities set up a completely uniform magnetic field intensity **H′** between the plates, pointing out of the paper and having the magnitude σv of the current densities. Since $|\mathbf{D}| = \sigma$ and **H′** is perpendicular to **v**, it is apparent that the primed observer sees a magnetic field

$$\mathbf{H}' = \mathbf{D} \times \mathbf{v} = -\mathbf{v} \times \mathbf{D} \tag{2.54}$$

The value of **H′** given by Eq. (2.54) is seen by the primed observer solely because of his motion with respect to the sources of the electrostatic field, since $\mathbf{H} = 0$ in the unprimed frame. A nonzero value of **H** must also contribute by superposition to **H′**, as is easily seen if we consider the limiting case $\mathbf{v} \to 0$. Thus the most general form for **H′** as seen by the primed observer is

$$\mathbf{H}' = \mathbf{H} - \mathbf{v} \times \mathbf{D} \tag{2.55}$$

Equation (2.55) is the general low-velocity transformation law for the magnetic field; it is the dual counterpart of Eq. (2.53). Although we have deduced it from a particular example, the result applies generally.

We turn to the second question, concerning the magnitude of the "motional magnetic field." To facilitate our inquiry, let us assume we are dealing with free space with $\mathbf{H} = 0$ and put

$$\mathbf{H}' = \frac{1}{\mu_0}\mathbf{B}' \tag{2.56}$$

$$\mathbf{D} = \epsilon_0\mathbf{E} \tag{2.57}$$

Substituting in Eq. (2.54), we get

$$\mathbf{B}' = -\mu_0\epsilon_0\mathbf{v} \times \mathbf{E} \tag{2.58}$$

However,

$$\mu_0\epsilon_0 = \frac{1}{c^2} = \frac{10^{-16}}{9}\ \text{sec}^2/\text{m}^2 \tag{2.59}$$

so that

$$\mathbf{B}' = -\frac{\mathbf{v} \times \mathbf{E}}{c^2} \tag{2.60}$$

Since we are interested in seeing how large $\mathbf{B}'$ might possibly be, we should, of course, consider extremely large values of $\mathbf{v}$ and $\mathbf{E}$. We will take $v = c/10$; this is a large velocity, yet not so large that we need be concerned with relativistic effects. The electric field is essentially limited only by practical considerations. We are, of course, making this calculation in free space, but as a representative large practical value let us take E as the dielectric breakdown strength of air, which is approximately 3×10^6 volts/m. With these values, and assuming $\mathbf{v} \cdot \mathbf{E} = 0$ in order to get the largest $\mathbf{B}'$, we find that

$$|\mathbf{B}'| = \frac{3 \times 10^7 \times 3 \times 10^6}{(3 \times 10^8)^2} = 10^{-3}\ \text{weber/m}^2$$

or $|\mathbf{B}'| = 10$ gauss.

This flux density is not at all negligible when compared, for example, with the earth's magnetic field strength, whose order of magnitude varies between $\frac{1}{10}$ and 1 gauss. However, a completely different situation prevails in most cases of practical interest as, for instance, in the most important class of power converters, i.e., rotating converters of the magnetic type, with solid conductors. There, the velocity is limited by permissible centrifugal forces to about 200 m/sec, and the electric field does not exceed 10^3 volts/m. The resultant motional flux density is

$$|\mathbf{B}'| = \frac{200 \times 10^3}{(3 \times 10^8)^2} = 2.2 \times 10^{-12}\ \text{weber/m}^2$$

This in turn has to be compared with the flux density associated with the conduction currents, which is of the order of 1 weber/m². It is therefore safe to assume that we will have little concern for the flux-density component contributed by motion and that in most technological applications we will consider $\mathbf{B}' = \mathbf{B}$.

(c) Low-speed Field-transformation Equations†

In Secs. (2.11*a*) and (2.11*b*) we have discussed the effect of relative motion between observers on the measured field intensities. In general, when both **E** and **B** exist in the unprimed frame of reference, the fields detected by an observer moving with relative velocity **v** ($v < c$) are given by Eqs. (2.53) and (2.55). Repeating Eq. (2.53), and rewriting Eq. (2.55) *for free space* by using Eqs. (2.56) and (2.57), we have

$$\mathbf{E}' = \mathbf{E} + \mathbf{v} \times \mathbf{B} \tag{2.53}$$

$$\mathbf{B}' = \mathbf{B} - \frac{\mathbf{v} \times \mathbf{E}}{c^2} \tag{2.61}$$

It is particularly interesting at this point to stop and subject these equations to a little investigation. They relate the field intensities, as measured in two reference frames which are moving with respect to each other, but it is perfectly plain that neither reference frame is privileged. Since this is the case, we must demand that these transformation equations work *either way*, so that either observer, seeing the other moving, can use the same *transformation rules* for predicting what the other observer measures. In other words, if the primed observer, seeing the unprimed observer moving with velocity $-\mathbf{v}$, uses the rules embodied in Eqs. (2.53) and (2.61), he would predict that the unprimed observer measures

$$\mathbf{E} = \mathbf{E}' - \mathbf{v} \times \mathbf{B}' \tag{2.62}$$

$$\mathbf{B} = \mathbf{B}' + \frac{\mathbf{v} \times \mathbf{E}'}{c^2} \tag{2.63}$$

The crucial question is: Are Eqs. (2.62) and (2.63) consistent with the original Eqs. (2.53) and (2.61)? They need be, or else the original equations themselves are not valid. To answer this question, we can simply solve Eqs. (2.53) and (2.61) simultaneously to get **E** and **B** as the dependent variables. If we eliminate first **B** and then **E** from (2.53) and (2.61), we get

$$\mathbf{E} = \mathbf{E}' - \mathbf{v} \times \mathbf{B}' - \frac{\mathbf{v} \times (\mathbf{v} \times \mathbf{E})}{c^2} \tag{2.64}$$

$$\mathbf{B} = \mathbf{B}' + \frac{\mathbf{v} \times \mathbf{E}'}{c^2} - \frac{\mathbf{v} \times (\mathbf{v} \times \mathbf{B})}{c^2} \tag{2.65}$$

At first glance Eqs. (2.64) and (2.65) are not identical with (2.62) and (2.63), and so we conclude we are in trouble. However, upon further inspection we see that the offending terms involving the triple products are of no greater order of magnitude than $(v^2/c^2)E$ and $(v^2/c^2)B$, respectively. Since we have assumed the small-velocity case $v < c$, these

† For a more complete discussion the reader is referred to Appendix A.

terms are indeed negligible when compared respectively with E and B, and Eqs. (2.64) and (2.65) do practically reduce to (2.62) and (2.63) as the first approximation. Thus we can indeed take Eqs. (2.53) and (2.61) as the low-speed transformation laws. The fact that these equations are not perfectly reciprocal because of small second-order terms is only symptomatic of their approximate nature. (In the relativistic formulation the reciprocity is perfect, and, in fact, one way to derive this formulation is to demand that this perfect reciprocity exist.)

To illustrate the use of the low-speed transformation laws and demonstrate their approximate nature, we consider the following example.

Example 2.5

Positive charges are uniformly distributed on an infinite straight line with a linear charge density λ^+ of 10^{-4} coul/m.

(*a*) Evaluate the electromagnetic field at a point P, situated at a distance of one meter from the line charge:

(*b*) Repeat part (*a*) when the line charge translates along its axis with a velocity of 200 m/sec with respect to the point P at which the field is evaluated.

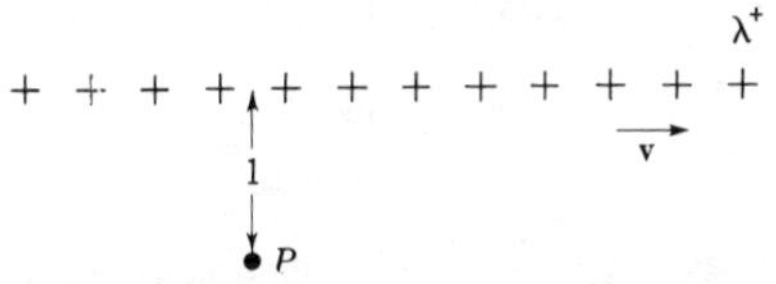

(*c*) Assume now that along the moving positive line charge of part (*b*) is placed a negative line-charge density λ^- of 10^{-4} coul/sec which is stationary with respect to the point P. Evaluate the electromagnetic field at the point P, first by superimposing the fields produced by the two line charges using the results of parts (*a*) and (*b*), and

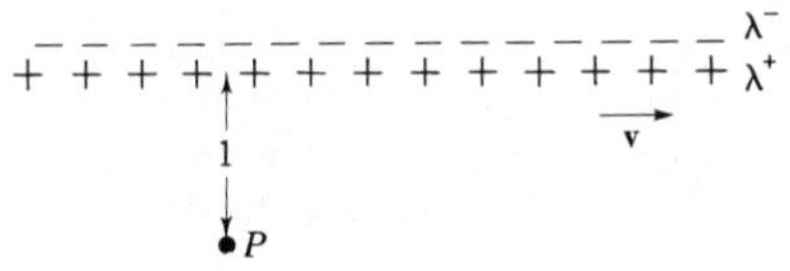

then by choosing a system of reference fixed to the positive line charge and transforming from the first result. Compare the motional electric field $\mathbf{v} \times \mathbf{B}$ obtained to the electric field evaluated in part (*b*).

Solution

(*a*) The electric-field intensity of a line charge is directed radially and has a magnitude $E = \lambda/2\pi\epsilon_0 r$, where r is the distance between the point of observation and the line charge. Thus

$$E = \frac{10^{-4}}{2\pi \times (10^{-9}/36\pi) \times 1} = 1.8 \times 10^6 \text{ volts/m}$$

and since there is no current flow, $B = 0$.

(*b*) The results of (*a*) above give E and B in a reference frame fixed to the charge. To find the field at P, we need only use the transformation laws between the reference frame fixed to the charge and the one in which P is stationary. Thus

$$E = |\mathbf{E}' - \mathbf{v} \times \mathbf{B}'| = E'$$

since B', which is the field in the frame fixed to the charge, is zero. Therefore,

$$E = 1.8 \times 10^6 \text{ volts/m}$$

Also there exists an azimuthally directed magnetic field,

$$\mathbf{H} = \mathbf{H}' + \mathbf{v} \times \mathbf{D}' = +\mathbf{v} \times \epsilon_0 \mathbf{E}'$$

so that

$$B = \mu_0 H = \mu_0 \epsilon_0 v E' = \frac{vE'}{c^2} = \frac{200}{9 \times 10^{16}} \times 1.8 \times 10^6$$
$$= 4 \times 10^{-9} \text{ weber/m}^2$$

Alternatively we may find B by saying that the translating line charge is equivalent to a current $I = \lambda v$ and $B = \mu_0 I/2\pi r$, so that

$$B = \frac{\mu_0 \lambda v}{2\pi r} = E\frac{v}{c^2} = 4 \times 10^{-9} \text{ weber/m}^2 \qquad \text{as before}$$

Note that the equivalence of these alternative approaches is indeed the method whereby we earlier deduced the magnetic field transformation law.

(*c*) By superposition of the results of (*a*) and (*b*) we obtain for the electric field at P

$$E = \frac{\lambda^+ + \lambda^-}{2\pi\epsilon_0 r} = \frac{10^{-4} - 10^{-4}}{2\pi\epsilon_0} = 0$$

so that we would conclude that the two line charges neutralize each other completely. The magnetic field is unchanged: $B = 4 \times 10^{-9}$ weber/m². By evaluation from a system of reference fixed to the positive line charge we obtain for the magnitude of the electric field at P,

$$|\mathbf{E}|_1 = |\mathbf{E}' - \mathbf{v} \times \mathbf{B}'| = |-\mathbf{v} \times \mathbf{B}| = \frac{v^2 \mu_0 \lambda}{2\pi r} = 200 \times 4 \times 10^{-9} = 8 \times 10^{-7} \text{ volt/m}$$

The disagreement between the values of E calculated in the two reference frames proves that the transformation equations we have used are only approximate. By comparing the electric field E_1 as evaluated from a moving frame with that produced by the positive charge alone we satisfy ourselves that

$$\frac{E_1}{E} = \frac{v^2 \mu_0 \lambda}{2\pi r} \frac{2\pi\epsilon_0 r}{\lambda} = \frac{v^2}{c^2}$$

In other words the electric field E_1 is indeed of second order in v/c with respect to E.

The appearance of a low-intensity electric field leads us to suspect that the neutralization between the moving positive charge and the stationary negative charge is not complete. In fact, according to the special theory of relativity, the linear charge density is increased, when viewed from an observer in relative motion with respect to the charge. The discrepancy between the intensity of the electric field as calculated in the two reference frames disappears when relativistically corrected formulas are used. It can be shown that the actual value of the electric field is about half the value obtained using $\mathbf{v} \times \mathbf{B}$ or approximately the average value between the intensities evaluated in the two reference frames.

2.12 FREE - PARTICLE MOTION IN A UNIFORM ELECTROSTATIC AND MAGNETOSTATIC FIELD

We shall next study the free motion of a charged particle in a time-invariant uniform electromagnetic field. In this case, again assuming low speeds ($v < c$), we have from Eq. (2.49)

$$m\frac{d\mathbf{v}}{dt} = q(\mathbf{E} + \mathbf{v} \times \mathbf{B}) \tag{2.66}$$

The simplest way to determine the nature of the particle motion is to resolve the velocity into convenient components, thereby reducing the motion into a few simpler types which we have already studied. The first step in this procedure is to use the direction of **B** as a reference direction, and use parallel and perpendicular components just as we did in the case of motion in a pure magnetic field in Sec. 2.8. In this way, Eq. (2.66) breaks down into

$$m\frac{d\mathbf{v}_\parallel}{dt} = q\mathbf{E}_\parallel \tag{2.67a}$$

$$m\frac{d\mathbf{v}_\perp}{dt} = q(\mathbf{E}_\perp + \mathbf{v}_\perp \times \mathbf{B}) \tag{2.67b}$$

The motion described by Eq. (2.67*a*) is a uniformly accelerated translation in the $\mathbf{E}_\parallel$ direction, i.e., along the **B** flux lines; so much for the parallel direction. The motion described by Eq. (2.67*b*) lies entirely in the normal plane, and we shall deduce the nature of this motion below.

Equation (2.67*b*) is, of course, written with respect to the original reference frame in which **E**, **v**, and **B** are observed. Suppose it were possible to find a *new* reference frame (designated by superscript primes), which translates uniformly in the normal plane with respect to the original reference frame, so chosen that $\mathbf{E}'_\perp = 0$. In such a frame, the perpendicular component of electric field is then absent, and the normal plane motion seen is simply the circular gyration in a pure magnetic field, already discussed in Sec. 2.8. If we can find this new frame, the total normal plane motion as described by Eq. (2.67*b*) is then immediately determined as the combination of the gyration in the primed frame plus the uniform translation of the primed frame itself.

We can indeed find this new reference frame. There are several ways to do this; the reader is invited to try one of his own. We shall proceed here as follows: Suppose the new frame is seen to be translating in the normal plane with velocity $\mathbf{v}_E$. Our problem is to find $\mathbf{v}_E$ such that $\mathbf{E}'_\perp = 0$. Since the transformation law as given by Eq. (2.53) is

$$\mathbf{E}'_\perp = \mathbf{E}_\perp + \mathbf{v}_E \times \mathbf{B}$$

the $\mathbf{v}_E$ which we seek is the solution of

$$\mathbf{E}_\perp + \mathbf{v}_E \times \mathbf{B} = 0 \tag{2.68}$$

Equation (2.68) can be solved either formally or by inspection. A direct formal procedure is to simply cross-multiply the entire equation with **B**. This gives

$$(\mathbf{v}_E \times \mathbf{B}) \times \mathbf{B} = -\mathbf{E}_\perp \times \mathbf{B} \tag{2.69}$$

The triple vector product may be expanded by using the identity

$$(\mathbf{Q} \times \mathbf{R}) \times \mathbf{S} = (\mathbf{Q} \cdot \mathbf{S})\mathbf{R} - (\mathbf{R} \cdot \mathbf{S})\mathbf{Q}$$

so that

$$(\mathbf{v}_E \times \mathbf{B}) \times \mathbf{B} = (\mathbf{v}_E \cdot \mathbf{B})\mathbf{B} - (\mathbf{B} \cdot \mathbf{B})\mathbf{v}_E$$
$$= 0 - B^2\mathbf{v}_E$$

and, using Eq. (2.69),

$$\mathbf{v}_E = \frac{\mathbf{E}_\perp \times \mathbf{B}}{B^2} = \frac{\mathbf{E} \times \mathbf{B}}{B^2} \tag{2.70}$$

Since **E** and **B** are time- and space-invariant, $\mathbf{v}_E$ is a constant vector perpendicular to $\mathbf{E}_\perp$ in the normal plane, with a magnitude

$$v_E = \frac{E_\perp}{B} \tag{2.71}$$

The result of Eq. (2.70) is also easily seen from inspection of Eq. (2.68). Refer to Fig. 2.11, which shows the normal plane as the plane of the paper, with an arbitrary $\mathbf{E}_\perp$. Now $\mathbf{v}_E$ is somewhere in the normal plane (since a parallel component of $\mathbf{v}_E$ contributes nothing to $\mathbf{v}_E \times \mathbf{B}$ in any case), and $\mathbf{v}_E \times \mathbf{B}$ is also in the normal plane, rotated 90° from $\mathbf{v}_E$. Since $\mathbf{v}_E \times \mathbf{B}$ must be rotated 180° from $\mathbf{E}_\perp$, it follows that $\mathbf{v}_E$ itself must be rotated 90° from $\mathbf{E}_\perp$; i.e., it is perpendicular to $\mathbf{E}_\perp$. Consequently, the direction of $\mathbf{v}_E$ must be that of $\mathbf{E}_\perp \times \mathbf{B}$, and adding the magnitude requirement, we obtain Eq. (2.70).

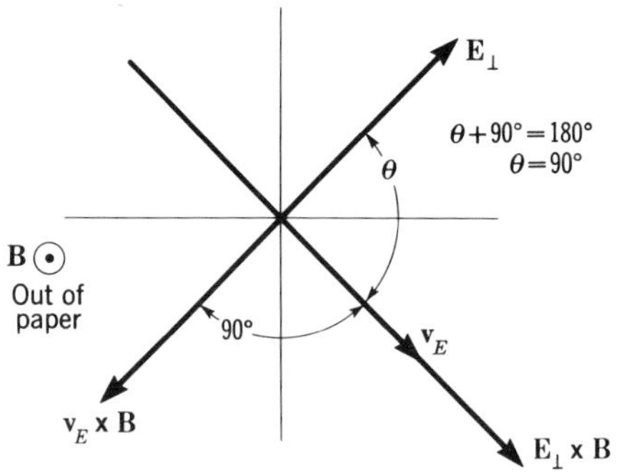

Fig. 2.11 Determination of $\mathbf{v}_E$ with an arbitrary $\mathbf{E}_\perp$.

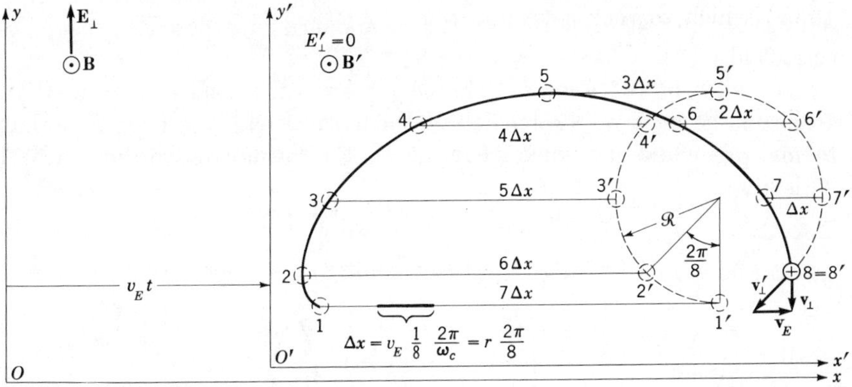

Fig. 2.12 Geometrical construction of the normal-plane trajectory of a positively charged particle in a uniform electrostatic and magnetostatic field.

The relation between the normal plane velocities seen in the two reference frames is by superposition

$$\mathbf{v}_\perp = \mathbf{v}'_\perp + \mathbf{v}_E \tag{2.72}$$

A velocity transformation such as Eq. (2.72), is only valid for speeds well below the speed of light and is often called a *Galilean velocity transformation*. Introducing Eq. (2.72) into Eq. (2.67*b*) and recalling that $\mathbf{v}_E$ does not vary with time, we obtain

$$m\frac{d\mathbf{v}'_\perp}{dt} = q(\mathbf{E}_\perp + \mathbf{v}_E \times \mathbf{B} + \mathbf{v}'_\perp \times \mathbf{B}) \tag{2.73}$$

This simplifies by virtue of Eq. (2.68) to

$$m\frac{d\mathbf{v}'_\perp}{dt} = q(\mathbf{v}'_\perp \times \mathbf{B}) \tag{2.74}$$

Equation (2.74) is, of course, what we expected, the equation for charged particle motion in a pure magnetic field; consequently, $\mathbf{v}'_\perp$ represents the tangential velocity of a circular motion with Larmor radius and cyclotron angular velocity.

In summary of the above, we have found that in a particular reference frame, which moves with a velocity $\mathbf{v}_E = (\mathbf{E} \times \mathbf{B})/B^2$, as seen in the original frame, the charged particle is seen to move in the normal plane with purely circular motion given by the Larmor radius and cyclotron angular velocity. The total motion is then, as indicated in Fig. 2.12, a combination of the gyration $\mathbf{v}'_\perp$ and the uniform progression or "drift" $\mathbf{v}_E$. The velocity $\mathbf{v}_E$ is then called the *drift velocity*, and the primed reference frame the *drift reference frame*. The subscript E is used to show that the drift is caused by the *electric* field superposed on the magnetic field.

In view of the above, a simple mechanical model can be used to generate the path of the particle in the normal plane. The path is that taken by the end of a spoke of radius $\mathcal{R}$ (the Larmor radius) on a wheel

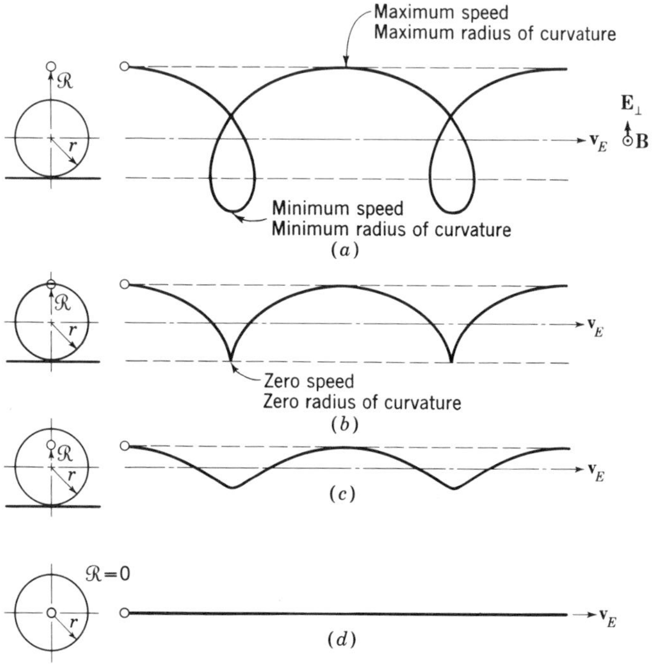

Fig. 2.13 Particle paths in the normal plane.

with radius r, rolling on a line parallel to $\mathbf{v}_E$ with angular velocity ω_c, the cyclotron radian frequency. The radius r is given by

$$r = \mathcal{R}\frac{v_E}{v'_\perp} = \frac{m}{q}\frac{E}{B^2} \tag{2.75}$$

As illustrated in Fig. 2.13, the path which results is cycloidal: the prolate cycloid (*a*) which loops back on itself for $v'_\perp > v_E$, the common cusped cycloid (*b*) for $v'_\perp = v_E$, the curtate cycloid (*c*) for $v'_\perp < v_E$, and the degenerate straight line (*d*) for $v'_\perp = 0$.

Since the magnitude of $v'_\perp$ is constant, in a given field the Larmor radius $\mathcal{R}$ and therefore the type of the trajectory are uniquely determined by the initial velocity:

$$v'_\perp = v'_{0,\perp} \tag{2.76}$$

i.e.,

$$|\mathbf{v}_\perp - \mathbf{v}_E| = |\mathbf{v}_\perp(0) - \mathbf{v}_E|$$

In particular, the cusped cycloid results from zero initial velocity, and the straight line from an initial velocity equal to the drift velocity.

The drift and cycloidal nature of the trajectory in the normal plane can indeed be anticipated from qualitative considerations. As shown in Fig. 2.14*a*, if the magnetic field is directed out of the plane of the paper, the motion of a positive particle, under the action of the $\mathbf{v} \times \mathbf{B}$ term alone, is a clockwise gyration. If now an electric field directed upward is applied, the particle will accelerate in the upward stretch of its trajectory, i.e., on the left side of its gyration, and decelerate in the downward

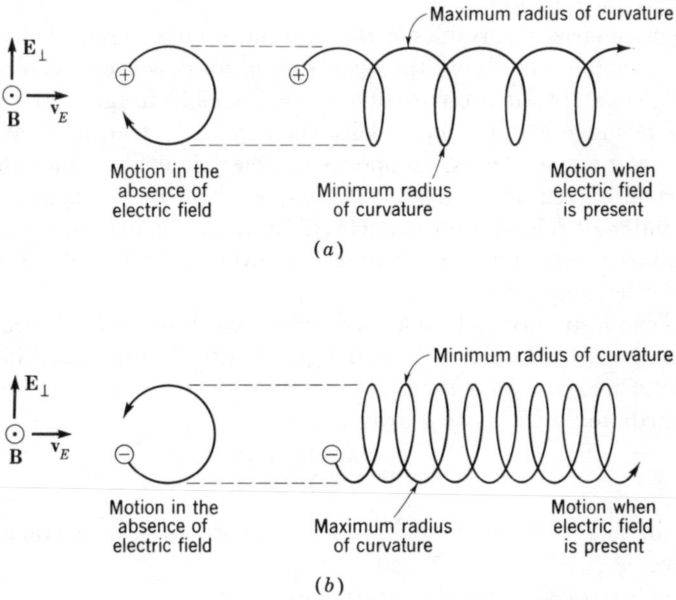

Fig. 2.14 Qualitative evolution of the trajectory in the normal plane: (*a*) Positive particle; (*b*) negative particle.

stretch to the right. As a result, the velocity on the side toward the top of the page will exceed the velocity at the bottom. Since Eq. (2.33) tells us that the Larmor radius is proportional to the tangential speed in the constant-speed case, we may anticipate that the radius of curvature of the particle's path is analogously proportional to the particle speed in the variable-speed case. Hence the radius of curvature of the particle's path in Fig. 2.14*a* is greater at the top than at the bottom. Since the particle tends to gyrate in the same direction as in the absence of $\mathbf{E}_\perp$, then if the lowest portions of the path close from right to left, loops form as shown, and the result is a drift to the right. In the event that in the lowest portions of the path the motion is from left to right as in the uppermost parts, then the path is loopless as in Fig. 2.13*c*, but the drift still occurs to the right.

For a negative particle the gyration will be counterclockwise, but the acceleration produced by the electric field will also be reversed, so that, as shown in Fig. 2.14*b* the drift will occur in the same direction as for the positive particle. This is, of course, confirmed by Eq. (2.70), which shows v_E to be independent of the charge magnitude or sign. This fact leads to the important conclusion that the motion of an equal number of positive and negative charges in the presence of a uniform electromagnetic field does not produce any direct current, and therefore any power conversion, as we shall see.

To summarize the results of this section, we have learned the fundamental principle underlying the operation of all power converters of the magnetic type: In the presence of a magnetic field, charged particles that are free to move attain such a drift velocity as to transform away the transverse or perpendicular component of electric field. Since the field-transformation relation Eq. (2.53) is independent of the particle parameters q and m, it follows that particles differing in the magnitude and sign of the charge, or in mass, all acquire the same drift velocity in a static uniform electromagnetic field.

We can also anticipate that drift will occur if other fields are substituted for the electric field. Thus, if a gravitational field is combined with a magnetic field, the force $m\mathbf{g}$ plays exactly the same role as $q\mathbf{E}$, and so we can immediately anticipate a drift velocity,

$$\mathbf{v}_g = \frac{(m/q)\mathbf{g} \times \mathbf{B}}{B^2} \tag{2.77}$$

Clearly in this instance the drift velocity is sensitive to particle charge and mass.

We next consider two illustrative examples.

Example 2.6

The magnetron is a microwave tube in which a beam of electrons moves in crossed electric and magnetic fields, as shown schematically in the figure. If the electrons

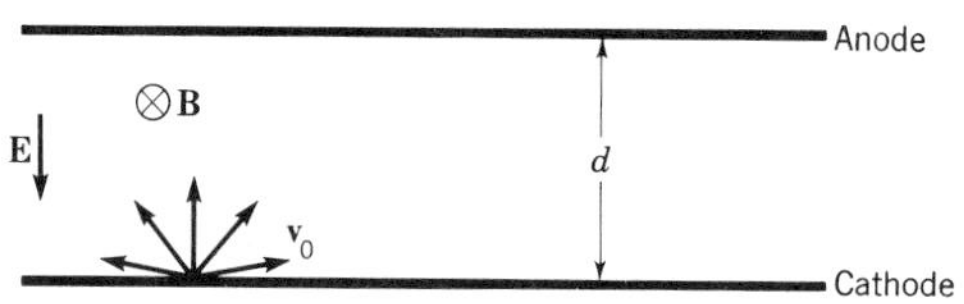

are emitted from the cathode with a kinetic energy of 0.1 ev in a random direction, what is the minimum distance d between the electrodes for the cutoff condition, i.e., such that none of the electrons can reach the anode? Assume

$$E = 10^4 \text{ volts/m} \qquad B = 10^{-1} \text{ weber/m}^2$$

Solution

For the orientation of **E** and **B** shown in the figure, $\mathbf{v}_E$ is oriented horizontally, pointing to the right. Since $\mathbf{v}'_\perp = \mathbf{v}_\perp - \mathbf{v}_E$, the maximum initial velocity in the drift reference frame is attained by those electrons emitted horizontally to the left. Moreover, these electrons also achieve the maximum height for a given initial velocity since their circular paths in the drift reference frame are tangent to the lower plate. Thus the electrons emitted horizontally to the left achieve the greatest height; and this height is $2\mathcal{R}$, where $\mathcal{R}$ is the corresponding Larmor radius. Now

$$v_0 = \sqrt{\frac{2qV}{m}} = \sqrt{2 \times 1.76 \times 10^{11} \times 10^{-1}} = 1.9 \times 10^5 \text{ m/sec}$$

$$v_E = \frac{E}{B} = \frac{10^4}{10^{-1}} = 10^5 \text{ m/sec}$$

and so the value of $v'_\perp$ for the electrons emitted horizontally to the left is

$$v'_\perp = 10^5 + 1.9 \times 10^5 = 2.9 \times 10^5 \text{ m/sec}$$

and

$$\mathcal{R} = \frac{mv'_\perp}{qB} = \frac{2.9 \times 10^5}{1.76 \times 10^{11} \times 10^{-1}} = 1.65 \times 10^{-5} \text{ m}$$

Thus no current will flow if the upper plate distance exceeds $2\mathcal{R}$ or $d > 3.3 \times 10^{-5}$ m.

Example 2.7

We have noted the possibility of normal plane drifts occurring from the action of gravity or other forces acting on charged particles in the presence of a magnetic field. Assuming that $B = 10^{-7}$ weber/m² and that the acceleration of gravity is perpendicular to **B** and equal to 1 m/sec²:

(*a*) Determine the normal plane drift velocity that the electrons and protons trapped in the Van Allen radiation belt acquire under the action of the earth's gravitational field.

(*b*) Evaluate, if possible, the value and orientation of the electric field which could eliminate this drift motion by compensating for the effect of gravity on the electrons and protons.

Solution

(*a*) From Eq. (2.77) we have

$$\begin{aligned} v_{ge} &= \frac{g}{(q/m)B} = \frac{1}{1.76 \times 10^{11} \times 10^{-7}} \\ &= 5.7 \times 10^{-5} \text{ m/sec} \qquad \text{for electrons} \\ v_{gp} &= \frac{m_p q_e}{m_e q_p} v_{ge} = -1837 \times 5.7 \times 10^{-5} \\ &= -0.125 \text{ m/sec} \qquad \text{for protons} \end{aligned}$$

It is clear that the gravitational drifts produce net electric currents, because electrons and protons have different drift velocities. It turns out that these currents encircle the earth in such a way as to strengthen the magnetic field interior to the Van Allen belt and weaken the exterior field.

(*b*) It is clear that a single electric field cannot compensate for the gravitational drift of *both* electrons and protons, because $\mathbf{v}_g$ is particle-sensitive whereas $\mathbf{v}_E$ is not.

2.13 POWER CONVERSION IN A UNIFORM ELECTROSTATIC AND MAGNETOSTATIC FIELD

We shall now determine the power converted from electrical into mechanical form in the case of free motion of a charged particle in space- and time-invariant electric and magnetic fields. We obtain this converted power P_{conv} by taking the dot product of Eq. (2.49) with $\mathbf{v}$:

$$P_{\text{conv}} = \mathbf{F} \cdot \mathbf{v} = q(\mathbf{E} + \mathbf{v} \times \mathbf{B}) \cdot \mathbf{v} = q\mathbf{E} \cdot \mathbf{v} \tag{2.78}$$

Expressing the particle velocity in terms of its components parallel and perpendicular to $\mathbf{B}$, Eq. (2.78) can be written as

$$\begin{aligned} P_{\text{conv}} &= q\mathbf{E} \cdot (\mathbf{v}_{\parallel} + \mathbf{v}_{\perp}) \\ &= q(\mathbf{E}_{\parallel} \cdot \mathbf{v}_{\parallel} + \mathbf{E}_{\perp} \cdot \mathbf{v}_{\perp}) \end{aligned} \tag{2.79}$$

Introducing Eq. (2.72) and observing from Eq. (2.70) that $\mathbf{v}_E$ is perpendicular to $\mathbf{E}_{\perp}$, Eq. (2.79) reduces to

$$P_{\text{conv}} = q\mathbf{E}_{\parallel} \cdot \mathbf{v}_{\parallel} + q\mathbf{E}_{\perp} \cdot \mathbf{v}'_{\perp} \tag{2.80}$$

Since the particle moves in the direction of $\mathbf{B}$, according to Eq. (2.67a), with constant acceleration $(q/m)\mathbf{E}_{\parallel}$, the power contributed by the parallel component of $\mathbf{E}$ is

$$P_{\text{conv}\parallel} = q\mathbf{E}_{\parallel} \cdot \left(\frac{q}{m}\,\mathbf{E}_{\parallel} t + \mathbf{v}_{0,\parallel}\right) \tag{2.81}$$

and is therefore the same as though the magnetic field were not present. As we shall see in the next chapter, systems containing positive and negative particles with equal densities cannot utilize this component of power for the purpose of electromechanical power conversion. With this in mind, the power component $q\mathbf{E}_{\perp} \cdot \mathbf{v}'_{\perp}$ associated with $\mathbf{E}_{\perp}$ assumes particular importance.

As shown in Secs. 2.12 and 2.8a, the velocity $\mathbf{v}'_{\perp}$ is a vector of constant magnitude $v'_{\perp} = v'_{0,\perp} = |\mathbf{v}_{0,\perp} - \mathbf{v}_E|$ rotating with angular velocity $\mp\omega_c$. It follows, then, that the power contributed by the perpendicular component of $\mathbf{E}$ is

$$P_{\text{conv},\perp} = qE_{\perp}v'_{\perp} \cos \angle_{\mathbf{E}_{\perp}}^{\mathbf{v}_{\perp}} = qE_{\perp}v'_{0,\perp} \cos(\mp\omega_c t + \gamma) \tag{2.82}$$

where as shown in Fig. 2.15, γ is the angle by which $\mathbf{v}'_{\perp}$ leads $\mathbf{E}_{\perp}$ at $t = 0$, when the normal plane is viewed from the side in which $\mathbf{B}$ points toward us, and $(\mp\omega_c t + \gamma)$ is similarly the angle between $\mathbf{v}'_{\perp}$ and $\mathbf{E}_{\perp}$ at any time t. Note that the sign prefixing $\omega_c t$ is chosen as negative for $q > 0$ and vice versa, as we have explained in Sec. 2.8a.

A study of Eq. (2.82) leads us to realize that serious limitations for electromechanical power conversion also occur in connection with the component of **E** perpendicular to **B**. First we notice that $P_{\text{conv},\perp}$ vanishes if ever the particle attains a velocity $\mathbf{v}_\perp = \mathbf{v}_E$ so that $v'_\perp$ vanishes. This clearly results from the fact that for this value of $\mathbf{v}_\perp$, the particle is at standstill in the drift reference frame. In other words, no force is acting on the particle, in this inertial reference frame. Since force is invariant under low-speed coordinate transformation, the force is also zero in the original reference frame, so that the power vanishes.

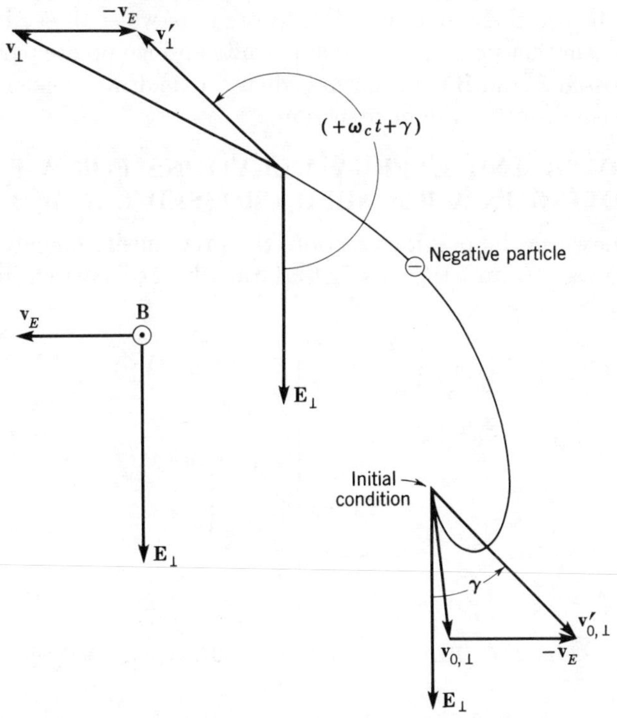

Fig. 2.15 Definition of the angle γ.

In addition, we notice that the power converted alternates in time with radian frequency ω_c. Therefore even when $v'_\perp \neq 0$, the power converted vanishes *on the average* over a gyration period. This stems from the fact that the average force on the particle vanishes over a gyration period. These limitations in power conversion are then quite general and do not depend on a particular choice of the reference frame, because they derive from the vanishing of the *force*.

The average power can also be zero even in the case of an incomplete gyration period if the particle excursion is symmetrical with respect to $\mathbf{E}_\perp$. This corresponds to a symmetrical variation of the argument

$(\mp \omega_c t + \gamma)$ of the cosine function in Eq. (2.82) around 90°, i.e., a variation such that $\mathbf{v}'_\perp$ on the average is at right angles to $\mathbf{E}_\perp$.

We conclude that Eq. (2.82) does not leave us much choice; its import is that in crossed **E** and **B** fields conversion of a nonvanishing amount of energy takes place only if the particle performs an asymmetrical fractional number of gyrations. This is exactly what does occur in multiparticle systems, when the particles collide between themselves at random and are prevented from performing an integer number of gyrations before their motion is interrupted, as we shall see in the next chapter. Another possibility which permits an incomplete particle gyration in crossed **E** and **B** fields occurs when the fields are *bounded;* we consider this condition in the next section.

2.14 POWER AND ENERGY RELATIONS FOR A PARTICLE MOVING IN A BOUNDED CROSSED E AND B FIELD

As shown in the previous section, the prerequisite for power conversion in crossed **E** and **B** fields is that the charged particle perform an

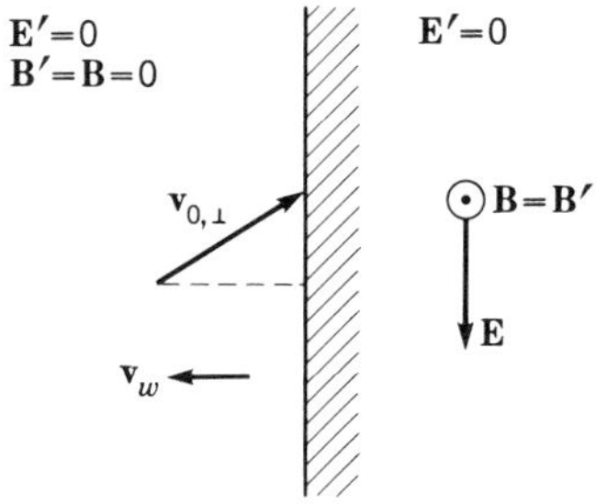

Fig. 2.16 Particle impinging on moving magnetic wall.

oscillation in the direction of $\mathbf{E}_\perp$, which is incomplete and asymmetrical with respect to $\mathbf{E}_\perp$. As we have done before, we shall illustrate this point by studying the case of a sharp discontinuity in the field region or a bounded field. In particular, we shall consider a case of great practical interest. This introduces the mechanism responsible for power conversion in a major class of devices which will be studied in later chapters. We refer to the case where the boundary of the field region is a "wavefront" or "moving magnetic wall," as shown in Fig. 2.16. Here there is a step discontinuity in **B**, with $\mathbf{B} = 0$ on the left and **B** out of the paper on the right. We assume that conditions are such that in a reference frame attached to the interface, the electric field vanishes everywhere; denoting this frame by prime superscripts, then $\mathbf{E}' = 0$. In another unprimed reference frame, the interface is seen to move with a velocity $\mathbf{v}_w$. In this unprimed reference frame the magnetic flux density **B** is given by the transformation law, Eq. (2.63),

$$\mathbf{B} = \mathbf{B}' + \mu_0\epsilon_0\mathbf{v}_w \times \mathbf{E}' \doteq \mathbf{B}' \tag{2.83a}$$

It is therefore zero to the left of the interface, finite and out of the paper to the right of the interface. The electric field **E** is given by the transformation law, Eq. (2.62),

$$\mathbf{E} = \mathbf{E}' - \mathbf{v}_w \times \mathbf{B}' = 0 - \mathbf{v}_w \times \mathbf{B} \tag{2.83b}$$

so that $\mathbf{E} = 0$ to the left of the interface and $\mathbf{E} = -\mathbf{v}_w \times \mathbf{B}$ to the right of the interface.

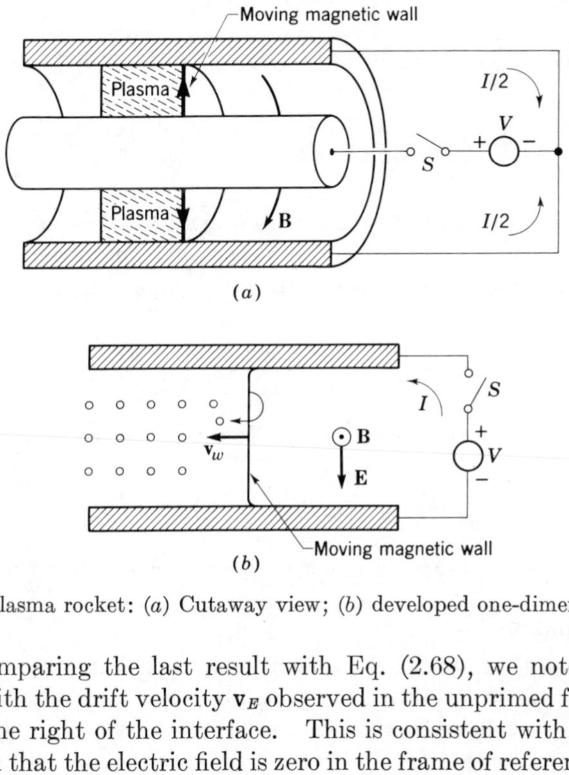

Fig. 2.17 Plasma rocket: (*a*) Cutaway view; (*b*) developed one-dimensional model.

By comparing the last result with Eq. (2.68), we note that $\mathbf{v}_w$ is identical with the drift velocity $\mathbf{v}_E$ observed in the unprimed frame for the region to the right of the interface. This is consistent with the original assumption that the electric field is zero in the frame of reference attached to the interface. An example in which such a situation arises in its simplest form, is the plasma gun or rocket,[5,6] proposed for space propulsion and schematically shown in Fig. 2.17. This device consists of a pair of parallel electrodes between which small clouds of an ionized gas, or plasma, are periodically injected. For reasons that will be explained in the next chapter, on closing of the switch a magnetic wall forms near the source of electric power. This wall progresses toward the left with a velocity $\mathbf{v}_w$ such that the desired condition Eq. (2.83) is satisfied. In its motion the magnetic wall scoops up the charged particles and propels them to the left.

Suppose we now observe a charged particle impinging on the wall from the left with a normal-plane velocity component $\mathbf{v}_{0,\perp}$ in the unprimed reference frame. As can be seen from the viewpoint of the wall (drift) reference frame, the particle will penetrate the wall and be reflected back to the left. Let us find the change of kinetic energy experienced by the particle under these circumstances. Counting time from the instant the particle strikes the wall, and letting T be the total time the particle spends inside the magnetic wall, the energy converted in kinetic form is, from Eq. (2.82),

$$\Delta W_{\text{kin}} = \int_0^T P_{\text{conv},\perp}\,dt = qE_\perp v'_{0,\perp} \int_0^T \cos\,(\mp\omega_c t + \gamma)\,dt$$
$$= \frac{qE_\perp v'_{0,\perp}}{\mp\omega_c} [\sin\,(\mp\omega_c T + \gamma) - \sin\gamma] \tag{2.84}$$

where we follow the sign convention established in Sec. 2.8*a*. We also know that in the primed reference frame the angle of incidence is equal to the angle of reflection. This means that the angle of gyration within the wall is

$$\mp\omega_c T = -2\gamma + \begin{cases} 0 \\ +2\pi \end{cases} \tag{2.85}$$

as shown in Fig. 2.18. Combining Eqs. (2.84) and (2.85), we find

$$\Delta W_{\text{kin}} = \frac{-2qE_\perp v'_{0,\perp}}{\mp\omega_c} \sin\gamma \tag{2.86}$$

It is clear that the converted kinetic energy is maximum when the particle is normally incident on the wall, since ΔW_{kin} in Eq. (2.86) takes on a maximum value for $\sin\gamma = 1$ or $\gamma = \pi/2$.

It is interesting to look further into the details of the wall-particle collision. In the wall reference frame, the normal component of the incident particle velocity is $\mathbf{v}'_{0,n}$, where $\mathbf{v}'_{0,n} = \mathbf{v}'_{0,\perp}\,|\sin\gamma|$; upon reflection, the normal component simply reverses direction so that the change in particle momentum for the reflection is, in the wall reference frame

$$\Delta(m\mathbf{v}') = -2m\mathbf{v}'_{0,\perp}\,|\sin\gamma| = -2m\mathbf{v}'_{0,n} = +2m\mathbf{v}'_{1,n} \tag{2.87}$$

Let us compare the details of the reflection in both reference frames. If $\mathbf{v}_{0,n}$ and $\mathbf{v}_{1,n}$ are the wall-normal components of velocity in the unprimed reference frame before and after collision, respectively, we have from the

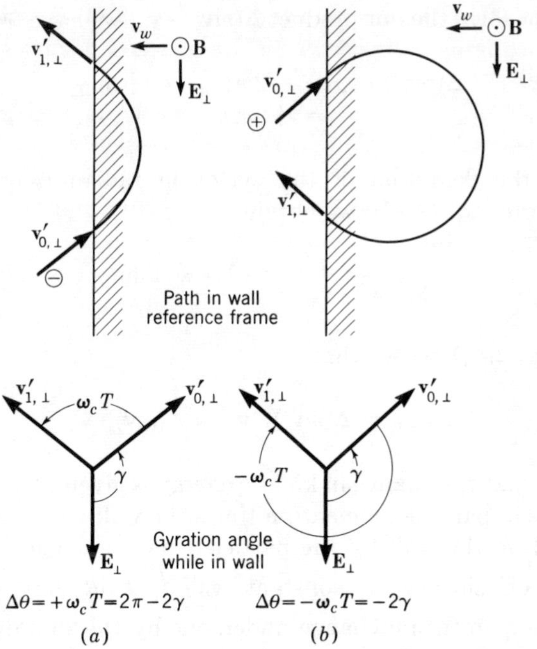

Fig. 2.18 Particle reflection by moving magnetic wall: (*a*) Negative charge; (*b*) positive charge.

Galilean coordinate transformation

$$\begin{aligned} \mathbf{v}_{0,n} &= \mathbf{v}'_{0,n} + \mathbf{v}_w \\ \mathbf{v}_{1,n} &= -\mathbf{v}'_{0,n} + \mathbf{v}_w \end{aligned} \tag{2.88}$$

From these two equations we see from addition and subtraction that

$$\mathbf{v}_{1,n} = -\mathbf{v}_{0,n} + 2\mathbf{v}_w \tag{2.89}$$

$$\Delta(m\mathbf{v}) = m(\mathbf{v}_{1,n} - \mathbf{v}_{0,n}) = -2m\mathbf{v}'_{0,n} = +2m\mathbf{v}'_{1,n} \tag{2.90}$$

and from Eq. (2.87),

$$\Delta(m\mathbf{v}) = \Delta(m\mathbf{v}') \tag{2.91}$$

Equation (2.89) tells us that the reflected velocity in the unprimed frame consists not only of the reversed initial velocity but also of a component equal to twice the wall velocity as seen in the unprimed frame; and Eq. (2.91) tells us that the change of momentum is invariant to the change of reference frame. This is, of course, expected, since momentum is related to force by an integration in time, and both force and time are invariant in the low-speed transformation between reference frames.

If we now form the dot product $\Delta(m\mathbf{v}') \cdot \mathbf{v}_w$, we have from Eq. (2.87)

$$\begin{aligned} \Delta(m\mathbf{v}') \cdot \mathbf{v}_w &= -2m(\mathbf{v}_0' \cdot \mathbf{v}_w)\,|\sin\gamma| \\ &= +2mv_0'v_w \sin\gamma \end{aligned} \tag{2.92}$$

Introducing the definition of the cyclotron radian frequency ω_c and $v_w = E_\perp/B$ into Eq. (2.92), we obtain

$$\Delta(m\mathbf{v}') \cdot \mathbf{v}_w = \frac{-2qEv_{0,\perp}' \sin\gamma}{\mp\omega_c} \tag{2.93a}$$

and from Eq. (2.86) we see that

$$\Delta W_{\text{kin}} = \Delta(m\mathbf{v}') \cdot \mathbf{v}_w = \Delta(m\mathbf{v}) \cdot \mathbf{v}_w \tag{2.93b}$$

We conclude that the change in kinetic energy is given by the dot product of the change in particle momentum times the wall velocity. If $\mathbf{f}_w$ is the force exerted on the wall by the particle, the work done on the wall is $\int_0^T \mathbf{v}_w \cdot \mathbf{f}_w\, dt$ or, since $\mathbf{v}_w$ is constant, $\mathbf{v}_w \cdot \int_0^T \mathbf{f}_w\, dt$; but $\int_0^T \mathbf{f}_w\, dt$ is by definition the momentum change undergone by the wall during the particle reflection. Since the momentum is conserved, the work done on the wall is also

$$\mathbf{v}_w \cdot [-\Delta(m\mathbf{v})] = -\mathbf{v}_w \cdot \Delta(m\mathbf{v})$$

Thus we see that the work done on the wall is the negative of the increase of kinetic energy of the particle, which is another indication that the collision is perfectly elastic.

Next we express the work done by the wall in terms of electrical quantities. Using the Larmor radius $\mathcal{R} = v_{0,\perp}'/\omega_c$, we can rewrite Eq. (2.86) as

$$\Delta W_{\text{kin}} = \pm qE_\perp(2\mathcal{R}\sin\gamma) \tag{2.94a}$$

where we recognize that $2\mathcal{R}_L \sin\gamma$ is the distance traveled by the particle in the direction of the constant electric field $\mathbf{E}_\perp$. Therefore we find

$$\Delta W_{\text{kin}} = q \int_{\text{injection}}^{\text{ejection}} \mathbf{E}_\perp \cdot d\mathbf{l} \tag{2.94b}$$

as we would indeed expect.

Note that since the distance traveled in the direction of $\mathbf{E}_\perp$ is proportional to the Larmor radius, the charged particles acquire energy in proportion to their mass, so that the energy level of the ions is raised preferentially over that of the electrons. This is important, for example, in research directed toward the achievement of controlled thermonuclear fusion.[7] In fact, by repeated acceleration of the ions trapped between rapidly converging magnetic walls, ionic temperatures in the million-degree range have been already attained in the "pinch" and "mirror" machines. This mechanism has also been postulated by Fermi and others to explain the origin of the highly energetic cosmic rays; it is illustrated in the following example.

Example 2.8

It is estimated that in order to achieve economic thermonuclear fusion, deuterons† have to be accelerated to energies of the order of 40 Kev.[8] Evaluate the number of reflections required if the deuterons are accelerated by means of repeated reflection in rapidly convergent walls, as shown in the figure. Assume that in the frame of reference in which the deuterons are initially at rest, the electric and magnetic fields measure inside the walls.

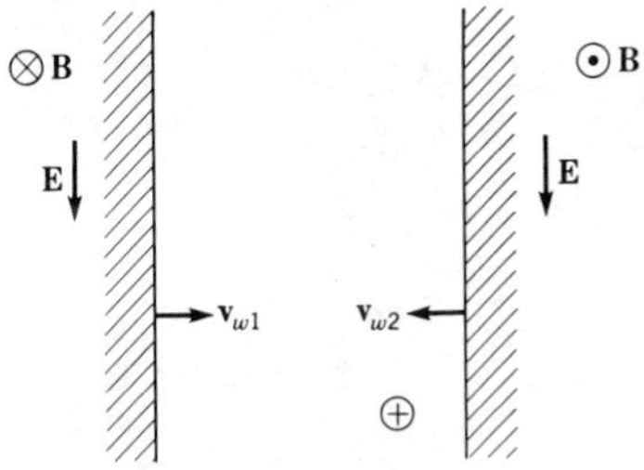

$$E = 10^6 \text{ volts/m} \qquad B = 10 \text{ webers/m}^2$$

Solution

The velocity corresponding to 40 Kev is for deuterons with a mass of $2 \times 1{,}837 m_e$

$$v_D = \sqrt{\frac{2 \times eV}{2 \times 1{,}837 m_e}} = \sqrt{\frac{2 \times 4 \times 10^4 \times 1.76 \times 10^{11}}{2 \times 1{,}837}}$$

$$= 1.96 \times 10^6 \text{ m/sec}$$

According to Eq. (2.89), at each reflection the deuteron acquires a velocity component equal to twice the velocity of the wall. These cumulatively increase the speed so that after N reflections the speed is $2v_wN$. To achieve a speed v_D, then,

$$N = \frac{v_D}{2v_w}$$

or, since $v_w = E/B$,

$$N = \frac{v_D}{2}\frac{B}{E} = \frac{1.96 \times 10^6}{2}\frac{10}{10^6} \doteq 10$$

† The deuteron is the positive ion created by stripping deuterium, the hydrogen isotope with an atomic weight of 2, of its orbital electron.

(a) Motoring and Generating Action

We have so far illustrated in Figs. 2.16 to 2.18 cases in which the charged particle gains energy from the magnetic wall, although our formulation of the energy interchange has been perfectly general. The conversion of power from electromagnetic into mechanical form we define as *motoring* action. We can also find cases in which charged particles

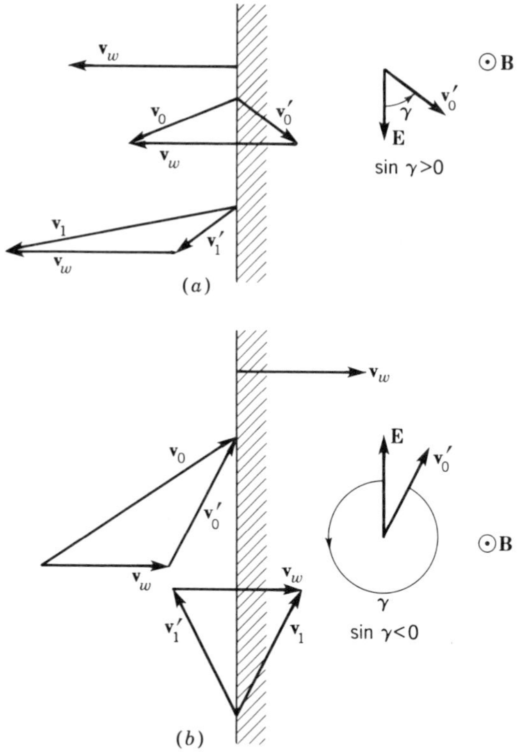

Fig. 2.19 Asynchronous motoring and generating action: (*a*) Motoring; (*b*) generating.

give up kinetic energy during the reflection, energy that is absorbed by the sources of the electromagnetic field; these are cases of *generating* action.

Motoring action always occurs, as we have seen, when wall and particle approach each other from opposite directions. If, on the other hand, wall and particle are moving in the same direction, as shown in Fig. 2.19, motoring occurs when the wall overtakes the particle, and generating occurs where the particle overtakes the wall.

Analytically, motoring and generating action are distinguished in Eq. (2.86) by the sign of sin γ, i.e., by the quadrant of γ. If $\sin\gamma > 0$ (γ in first or second quadrants), motoring action occurs; if, on the other hand, $\sin\gamma < 0$ (γ in the third or fourth quadrants), generating action occurs. These circumstances are shown in Fig. 2.19.

In both the motoring and generating cases discussed above the wall-particle interaction has been characterized by the fact that $v'_{0,n} \neq 0$; i.e., there is a relative normal component of initial velocity with either "head-on" or "overtaking" collision. This type of interaction can be called *asynchronous*, meaning that initially wall and particle do not move with the same normal velocity. It may appear that the asynchronous

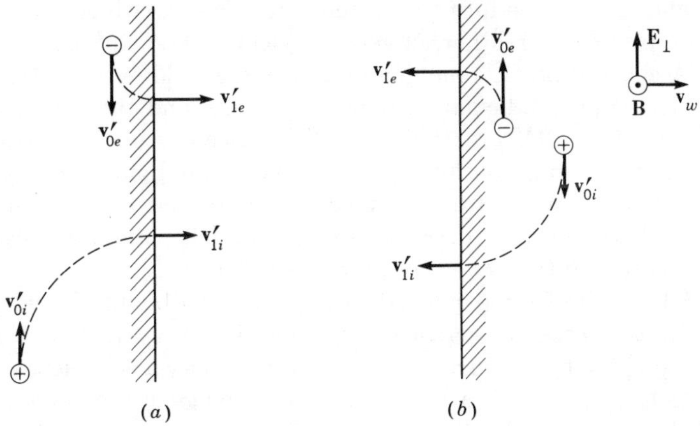

Fig. 2.20 Synchronous interaction: (*a*) Motoring; (*b*) generating.

interaction is a necessary condition for power conversion, but this is not the case. There exists another condition which is operative in a large class of power converters, in which the initial velocities of wall and particle differ only in the tangential component, as shown in Fig. 2.20. In this case the particles are injected parallel to the interface within the wall, in such a way as to prevent them from performing a complete gyration. As in the asynchronous case, motoring action occurs when the particles are ejected in front of the traveling wall, and generating action when they are ejected behind. The amount of power converted is now a function of the initial position of the particle with respect to the interface. The power converted is maximum when the initial distance from the interface is $\mathcal{R}$ and the particle undergoes a 90° deflection (as shown in Fig. 2.20), and clearly vanishes when the particle is injected at the interface or at a distance equal to or greater than $2\mathcal{R}$. This type of interaction is called *synchronous*.

2.15 SUMMARY

We have studied in this chapter the motions that charged particles perform when they experience an electromagnetic field. The major points that have been brought to light are the following:

1. An electric field exerts a force on a charged particle which exceeds by far the earth's gravitational force. The rate of work done by the electric force equals the power delivered by the sources of the electric field. In the free motion of a particle in an electrostatic field, energy is conserved: the gain in the kinetic energy corresponds to a loss of potential energy. Measurements of power and energy performed in reference frames which move with respect to each other, in general, yield different results.
2. A charged particle moving in a magnetic field experiences a force that is perpendicular to both its velocity and the magnetic field intensity. This force deflects the trajectory of the particle but produces no power and does not change the kinetic energy of the particle. When free to move in a pure and uniform magnetic field, the particle describes in the normal plane a circular orbit whose radius is inversely proportional to B.
3. The orbit of the particle does not close in a bounded field region. In this case the particle trajectory is simply deflected as is a light ray by a mirror. This deflection has mechanical implications because it is accompanied by a change in the momentum of the particle. The bounded field region thus assumes the aspect of a magnetic wall on which the impinging particles exert a pressure.
4. In combined electric and magnetic fields, the force exerted on a charged particle (for $v \ll c$) does not measure differently, when going from one reference frame to another in relative motion. However, the electric and magnetic components of this force change. This proves that the individual components of the electromagnetic field are not invariant to a transformation of frame of reference. This property has much greater practical importance for the electric than for the magnetic field.
5. When the electromagnetic field is constant in space and time, there always exists a frame of reference in which the component of electric field perpendicular to the magnetic field vanishes. The same is often true in the case of a "moving" wavefront. The velocity with which this frame moves with respect to the frame in which one measures $\mathbf{E}$ and $\mathbf{B}$ is $\mathbf{v}_E = (\mathbf{E} \times \mathbf{B})/B^2$ and is called the *drift velocity*. Consideration of problems in the drift frame intro-

duces great simplification in the analysis. For instance, the free motion of a charged particle in crossed **E** and **B** fields can be determined as a circular motion in the drift frame superposed on a translation with drift velocity. The resultant trajectory in the normal plane is a cycloid.

6. The presence of a component of **B** perpendicular to **E** sets constraints on the power-conversion process. The drift component of the particle motion is perpendicular to **E** and its contribution to the converted power is therefore identically zero. The gyration component oscillates in the direction of **E**, and its contribution to the power vanishes on the average. For net power conversion, the orbits must be incomplete and asymmetrical with respect to **E**.
7. A magnetic wall which is seen to be moving satisfies the conditions for power conversion. Depending on whether or not the particles gain or lose kinetic energy during the collision with the wall, we distinguish between the motoring or generating action. Both asynchronous and synchronous modes of power conversion are possible: the first is characterized by a nonzero normal component of velocity of the impinging particles relative to the wall, and the second by tangential injection within the wall proper.

REFERENCES

1. Stuhlinger, Ernst: "Ion Propulsion for Space Flight," McGraw-Hill Book Company, New York, 1964.
2. Kaufman, H. R.: One-dimensional Analysis of Ion Rockets, *NASA Tech. Note* D-261, March, 1960.
3. Giannini, Gabriel: Electrical Propulsion in Space, *Sci. Am.*, vol. 204, no. 3 (March, 1961).
4. Ness, N. F., C. S. Scearce, and J. B. Seek: Initial Results of the IMP-1 Magnetic Field Experiment, *Goddard Space Flight Center Rept.* X-612-64-95, presented at COSPAR, May, 1964.
5. Corliss, William R.: "Propulsion Systems for Space Flight," McGraw-Hill Book Company, New York, 1960.
6. Kunen, A. E., and W. McIlroy: The Electromagnetic Pinch Effect for Space Propulsion, in A. B. Cambel and J. B. Ferm (eds.), "Dynamics of Conducting Gases," Northwestern University Press, Evanston, Ill., 1960.
7. Rose, David J., and Melville Clark, Jr.: "Plasmas and Controlled Fusion," MIT Press and John Wiley & Sons, Inc., New York, 1961.
8. Thomson, W. B.: "An Introduction to Plasma Physics," Pergamon Press, New York, and Addison-Wesley Publishing Company, Inc., Reading, Mass., 1962.

PROBLEMS

2.1 Two regions of space are separated by a double layer of charge with a surface charge density of $\sigma = 10^{-6}$ coul/m². What separation d is required between the two layers in order to prevent electrons with energies up to 100 ev from escaping from region I into region II?

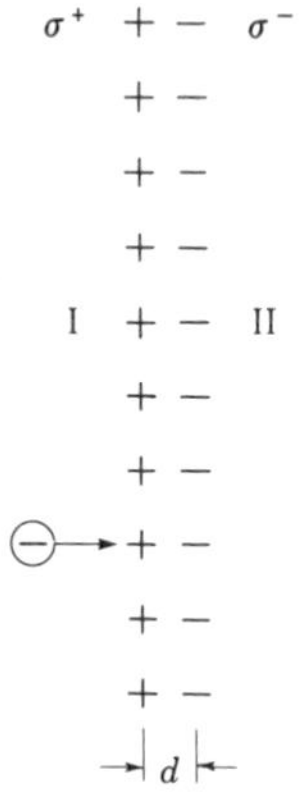

2.2 A proton is injected into the field of the parallel-plate capacitor with an initial energy of 700 ev at an angle of 45° as shown.

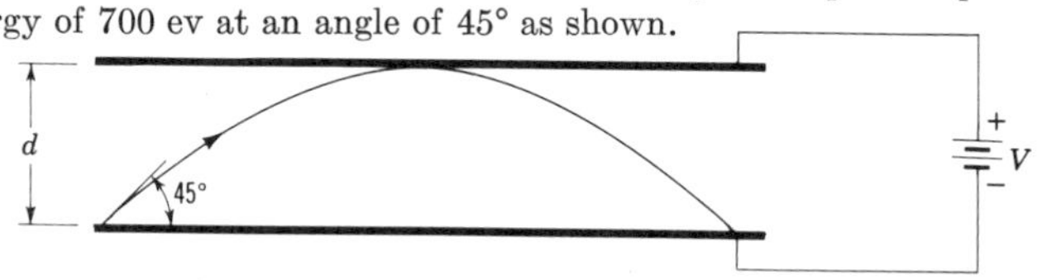

(*a*) What must the voltage V be in order that the proton follow a grazing incidence path (just missing the upper plate)?

(*b*) For this value of V, how far from the entrance point does the proton return to the lower plate (in terms of d)?

2.3 It is desired to design an ionic rocket to develop a thrust:

$$T = Mv_f = 0.2 \text{ newton}$$

and a power

$$P = \frac{Mv_f^2}{2} = 0.1 \text{ Mw}$$

where M is the mass of the fuel used in one second and v_f is its exhaust velocity with respect to the rocket. If the fuel consists of protons find:

(*a*) N = number of protons ejected per second.

(*b*) V = accelerating potential.

Assume 99 percent neutralization.

2.4 The figure shows an arrangement for investigating the velocity distribution of a flow of electrons of differing velocities. When the collector potential V is negative,

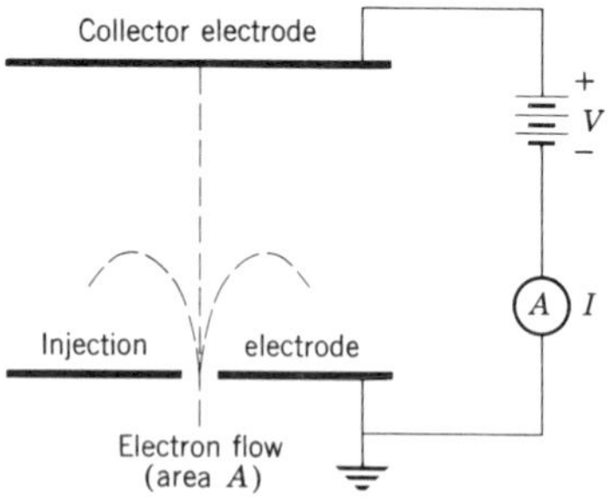

the current I changes as V is varied, since all injected electrons which have kinetic energies less than $e|V|$ cannot reach the collector. There is thus a *cutoff velocity* $v_{c.o.} = \sqrt{2(e/m)|V|}$. If n is the number of electrons (per-unit volume) in the flow, which possess a velocity v at injection, show that the *velocity spectrum* dn/dv is related to the slope of the observed curve of I vs. V by $(dn/dv)|_{v=v_{c.o.}} = (m/Ae^2)(dI/dV)$. (Assume that the electrons which possess a given velocity are uniformly distributed over the area A of the electron flow). Also, sketch dn/dv vs. v corresponding to the I-V curve shown. [The arrangement described here is essentially the one-dimensional model of a Langmuir probe when the electron source is a *plasma* (Chap. 3)].

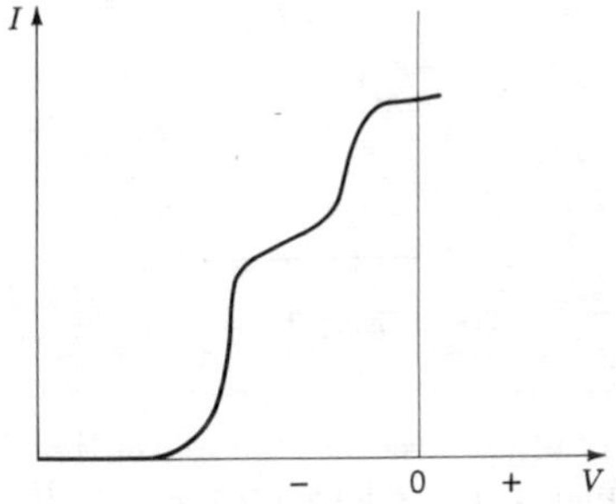

2.5 The trajectory of an electron passing through the deflection plates of a cathode-ray tube is shown in the figure. Determine the magnitude of the initial,

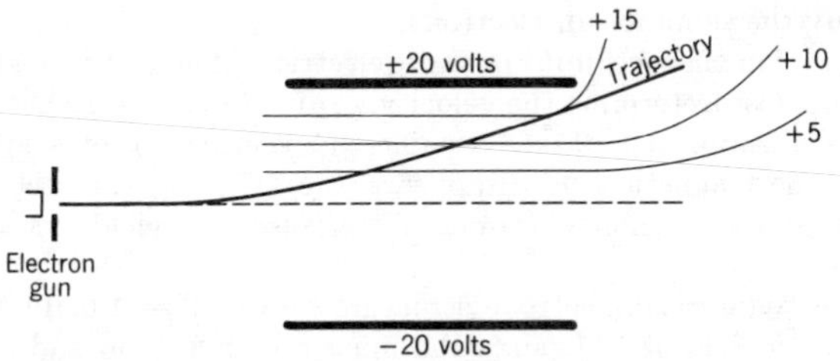

the maximum, and the final velocity of the electron when the cathode and anode of the electron gun are maintained at 0 and −70 volts, respectively, and the initial velocity of the electron as it leaves the cathode is negligible.

2.6 Determine the path of a charged particle in a uniform magnetostatic field by setting up and solving the differential equations of motion with respect to a rectangular coordinate frame (as outlined in the text).

2.7 Physicists measure the response of a particle to a magnetic field by its *magnetic rigidity*, that is, the ratio of momentum to charge. Particles of a given rigidity and initial trajectory suffer identical deflections in a magnetic field. The earth's magnetic field thus acts as an energy-spectrum analyzer for cosmic radiation. Taking for the magnetic flux density in the space between the magnetospheric boundary and the surface of the earth an equivalent uniform value $B = 5 \times 10^{-6}$ weber/m², determine the order of magnitude of the cutoff rigidity for particles which impinge normally on the magnetosphere in the equatorial plane.

The radius of the magnetosphere is approximately $10 \times r_e$, where r_e, the earth radius, is according to the original definition of the meter, $(40 \times 10^6)/2\pi$ m.

2.8 Assuming for the interplanetary magnetic field an average value of $B = 3 \times 10^{-9}$ weber/m², determine the Larmor radius of the following cosmic-ray particles:

(*a*) α particle with 200 Mev energy.

(*b*) Nickel nucleus with 2.5 Bev energy.

(*c*) High-energy particle with a rigidity $mv/q = 10^9$ newtons/amp.

2.9 An electron beam is focused by a longitudinal uniform magnetic field as shown. The effect of **B** is to cause electrons that have off-axis velocity components

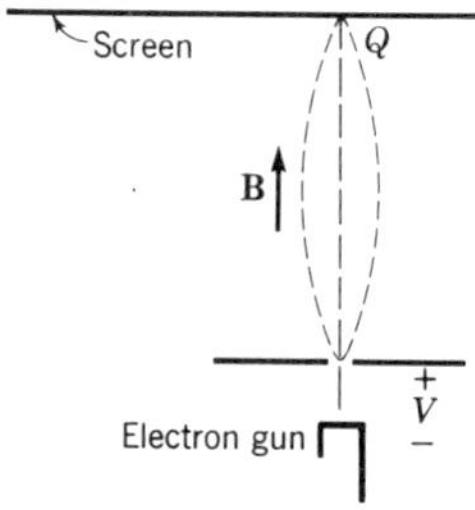

to move in a helix. If B is adjusted so that the transit time from the gun anode to the screen is an integer multiple of the cyclotron period, the diverging beam is focused.

Knowing that a minimum magnetic flux density $B = 2.5 \times 10^{-3}$ weber/m² is required for focusing at Q when $V = 900$ volts, determine the minimum and the next higher values of B required when the accelerating potential drop V is reduced to 400 volts. Assume that the axial component of velocity at the output of the electron gun is essentially the same for all electrons.

2.10 In a region of space uniform static electric and magnetic fields are "crossed" (perpendicular). (*a*) Determine the velocity $\mathbf{v}_E$ of a moving reference frame in which the electric field disappears. (*b*) Determine the velocity $\mathbf{v}_H$ of a moving reference frame in which the magnetic field disappears. (*c*) What is the relation between v_E and v_H? Can both reference frames *simultaneously* yield valid low-velocity approximations?

2.11 In the cylindrical electrode structure shown, $V = 1{,}000$ volts, B is a uniform axial magnetic field of 100 gauss, the inner radius is 1 cm and the outer radius

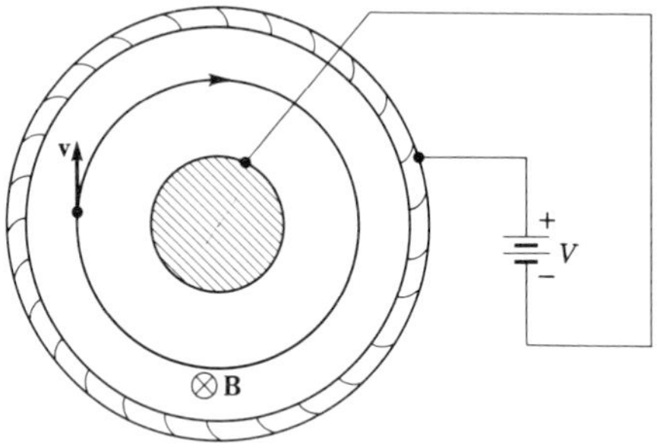

2.72 cm. An electron moves clockwise on a circular orbit with a radius of 2 cm. Find the electron velocity v.

2.12 The figure shows the form of a mass spectrograph used by Thomson to study charged-particle parameters.

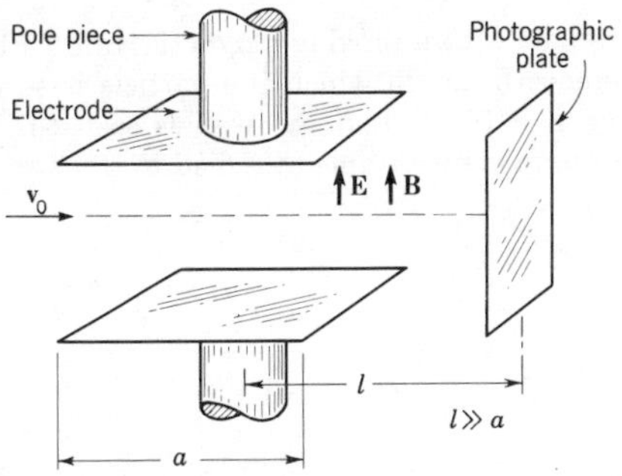

Thomson Mass Spectrograph

(*a*) Determine the lines traced on the plate by identical charged particles with different velocities.

(*b*) Express the velocity v_0 and charge-to-mass ratio of the particles in terms of the coordinates x, y at which they strike the plate and the values of E, B, a, l, assuming $l \gg a$.

2.13 A 10-ev electron is moving in a uniform magnetic field of intensity $B = 1$ weber/m^2.

(*a*) Evaluate the linear electric charge density λ which in the absence of the magnetic field would produce the same motion.

(*b*) Repeat part (*a*) for a 10-ev proton moving in a field $B = 1$ weber/m^2.

2.14 An electron hits a magnetic wall with an energy of 75 ev and an angle of incidence of $\pi/4$ as shown.

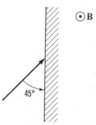

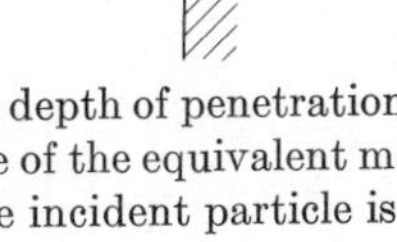

(*a*) Calculate the maximum depth of penetration into the field if $B = 1$ weber/m^2.

(*b*) Calculate h, the distance of the equivalent magnetic mirror from the interface.

(*c*) Repeat (*a*) and (*b*) if the incident particle is a proton of the same energy and angle of incidence.

(*d*) Assume now a different situation: An observer who sees the particles moving as above before collision also detects a motion of the wall perpendicular to its surface and toward the particles with velocity 10^6 m/sec. Calculate the energy gained by the electron and proton in the collision with the wall.

2.15 Solar flares are believed to originate in the trapping of particles between rapidly convergent magnetic walls and their subsequent acceleration.

(*a*) Evaluate the velocity of the walls if the charged particles initially at rest and reflected when the walls are 10^4 m apart reach the opposite wall after 6 sec.

(*b*) Evaluate the pressure exerted by the particles at their first reflection when their density in front of the wall is 10^{17} particles per cubic meter, if the particles are protons.

2.16 A proton interacts with a moving magnetic wall. Find the instantaneous electric power in a reference frame in which the particle is seen to move before the collision with a velocity $\mathbf{v} = 10^7\ \mathbf{x}_0$ and the wall is seen to move with a velocity $\mathbf{v}_w = -3 \times 10^7 \mathbf{x}_0$, if in the reference frame attached to the wall $\mathbf{E}' = 0$ and $\mathbf{B}' = 0.7$ weber/m^2.

chapter 3
MULTIPARTICLE SYSTEMS: THE MAGNETOPLASMA-DYNAMICAL EQUATIONS

3.1 INTRODUCTION

In the preceding chapter, we investigated the electrodynamics of single charged particles in an electromagnetic field. Among other important facts, we noted that a charged particle is acted upon by the force $q(\mathbf{E} + \mathbf{v} \times \mathbf{B})$, the so-called *Lorentz* force, of which only the electric-field term contributes to electromechanical power conversion.

Our purpose in this chapter is to build the structure of fundamental information further toward the subsequent development of the physical power-conversion devices themselves. We need, therefore, to extend our study of the single particle to conducting media, in which we generally find extremely large numbers of charged particles, both positive and negative, as well as uncharged or neutral particles.

In such multiparticle systems, the charged particles interact with one another, and the motion of each particle is to some extent determined by the position and velocity of all the other particles. This particle interaction involves long-range effects, since all charged particles contribute to the total quantities, as well as short-range effects due to binary collisions between two particles. To describe the dynamic performance of such a system, we shall use a macroscopic picture in terms of average quantities to take care of long-range effects, and introduce additional force terms to account for the local or microscopic interaction between neighboring particles. In this way we obtain independent equations of motion for electrons and ions, which are applicable to fully ionized gases, and with slight modifications which account for nuclear- and electron-spin interactions, to conduction in liquids and solids as well.

In order to express the relationships contained in the particle equations as a set of external characteristics, i.e., in terms of variables more amenable to direct measurement, we recast the particle equations in terms of the total current density and the velocity of the center of mass. We then find that, in striking contrast to the result for media consisting of charges of the same sign, in the case of multiparticle conducting media which are electrically neutral, the resultant force associated with the electric field vanishes and *only the magnetic* field serves as the means of electromechanical power conversion.

Since the electrically neutral case with very large electron density is specifically the subject of interest here, we make approximations appropriate to this case and simplify our overall equations. The result consists of two equations, one a generalized Ohm's law and the other a Newton's equation of motion. These now constitute the fundamental laws, the underlying theoretical foundation for all electromechanical power-conversion devices employing conducting media.

3.2 IONIZED GASES; PLASMAS

A natural example of a system with many charged particles is a gas in which at least some of the atoms have been ionized, giving rise to free electrons, positive ions, neutral atoms, and to a lesser extent, negative ions resulting from associations of electrons and neutral atoms. Because of the attractive force which positive and negative charges exert on each other, an ionized gas naturally tends toward a state of electrical neutrality. A region in an ionized gas where the volume density of negative charge is essentially equal to the volume density of positive charge, thus resulting in zero *space charge*, is called a *plasma*.

Ionized gases and plasmas form the major constituent of stars and interstellar space. On earth they constitute the active current-carrying media in a large number of devices such as thyratrons, ignitrons, mercury-arc rectifiers, electric-arc welders, and circuit breakers. Moreover, they play a key part in contemplated future schemes for power conversion which are now the subject of considerable research and which we shall discuss in subsequent chapters. It is clear, then, that ionized gases and plasmas are of practical importance, and offer a very interesting field of study per se; but a fact of greater significance from our viewpoint is that they represent, physically as well as logically, a transition phase from single charged particles to liquid and solid conductors. In fact, they afford us the unique opportunity of developing the elements of power conversion discussed in the previous chapter into the principles governing the performance of all electric machines, by simply including in our considerations an increasing volume density of both positive- and negative-charged particles.

3.3 MACROSCOPIC DESCRIPTION OF SYSTEMS OF INTERACTING PARTICLES

(a) Simplifying Assumptions

A rigorous derivation of the complete equations which govern the dynamics of an ionized gas is not only a formidable task, but one that has little practical value, because such equations, once derived, are too complicated to be easily solved. It is far more useful to make simplifying assumptions and derive approximate equations, which being limited in scope, display only the salient features of the physical situations under consideration.

We shall accordingly make the following assumptions:

1. The gas is fully ionized and so consists exclusively of charged particles.
2. There are only two species of particles: all the negative particles are electrons and all the positive ions are identical in charge and mass.
3. Compressibility effects, which show up as variations in the number of particles per-unit volume, are neglected.
4. The gas is allowed to flow only in channels or ducts of constant cross section.

These assumptions are satisfied, as a first approximation at least, by the kind of material media which are of interest to power conversion. In addition, they do not impose very severe restrictions on the validity of the equations that ensue.

For instance, as we shall see, the presence of neutral particles makes practically no difference, even when they exceed in number the ionized particles by one order of magnitude. Similarly a certain amount of impurities can be tolerated or easily accounted for. As for the assumption of incompressibility, its impact is that the natural modes of wave propagation which depend on compressibility effects, the *sonic* waves, are neglected. This means that we assume "infinite" propagation velocity. The resulting equations are then accurate only for velocities much smaller than the velocity of sound in the medium, which is of the order 10^3m/sec in solids and liquids and 10^4m/sec in gaseous plasmas. Note that the procedure is entirely analogous to our previous neglect of radiation and relativistic effects, which restricted us to velocities much smaller than that of light. Leaving out compressibility effects now means that our equations will be valid only for power conversion at subsonic velocities. Moreover, at these velocities the effect introduced by the divergence of channels with variable cross section is truly of second order.

(b) Long-range Interactions

We begin our development of an analytic description of multiparticle systems with some considerations of a general nature.

It is clear at the outset that the equations of the previous chapter which describe single-particle motion do indeed apply to *each* of the particles as long as we do not pack the particles so tightly that the classical model breaks down. Even if we observe this precaution, however, there still are certain obstacles to overcome. The trouble lies simply in the determination of the electromagnetic field to which each particle is exposed. This field is contributed by *all* the other charged particles, near and far, as well as by the sources external to the ionized gas; as a result, the description of this total field becomes hopelessly complex if we attempt to account for the motion of each and every particle.

In this situation it is necessary to limit the scope of the analytical description and be satisfied with a less detailed representation. We thus relinquish the individual particle as the object of our consideration, in favor of a coarser unit, the ensemble of all the particles contained in a small volume element. Of course, in so doing we must replace the exact positions and velocities of the particles by statistical averages and find an appropriate formulation to represent the forces acting upon the ensemble.

A major step in furthering the *macroscopic* description is to break down the total electromagnetic field into two parts. These are (1) the *average* field which characterizes *long-range* interactions of the particles and (2) the *local* field which characterizes their *short-range* interactions.

To clarify the meaning of this partition we consider a specific particle as a probe charge. The very large number of charged particles that are relatively far from the probe contribute a force component acting on the probe which is not appreciably changed by a small displacement or velocity increment of either an individual remote charge or the probe charge itself. It thus follows that, with regard to long-range interactions, it is not important to assign an exact value for the position and velocity of each particle; an *average* will do. This implies that the particles lose their discreteness and are "smeared" into a continuum which is characterized by charge and current densities. The interaction force originating from and acting upon these densities is then properly expressed by the *average field* of classical electromagnetic theory.

If we now turn to the dynamical effect of these long-range interactions, we observe that all the particles neighboring the probe charge experience essentially the same force and undergo the same rate of change of momentum, thus adding further justification to the "smearing" of the discrete particles into a continuum. This continuum is then additionally characterized by fluid-dynamic quantities, the mass and momentum densities.

The picture which thus emerges from a consideration of the long-range interactions only, is one of essentially continuous charge and mass distributions where the field and dynamical variables are expressed in terms of average quantities.

(c) Short-range Interactions

We next consider the nature of the short-range or local interactions. As we know, the Coulomb forces of interaction between two particles are inversely proportional to their distance and increase very rapidly as the two particles come closer. The result of such an encounter between two particles is that the so-called *binary interaction force* may well exceed the background force which arises from the ensemble of the remote particles; in this event we find a rapid change in the velocity and a marked deflection in the trajectory of the two particles involved. These effects are strongly dependent on the relative velocities of the particles, and in a system with many particles are practically unpredictable. We can simulate the situation for a group of particles of identical charge and mass by picturing billiard balls on the surface of a table colliding and scattering one another in all possible directions in a random fashion. Since our particles behave in this very way, the name *collision* is appropriately given to these encounters. The binary collisions thus cause a probe charge to sense rapidly fluctuating microfields which vary in a random way. Clearly this behavior is quite different from that brought about by long-range interactions, and so merits its separate treatment.

As we have noted previously, our *entire* analysis must be based on a macroscopic model in order to be feasible. The long-range interactions lead to average values which are inherently macroscopic, but the forces arising from collisions are essentially microscopic and random. What can we do to portray the short-range interactions in a macroscopic fashion? The answer is that, rather than represent the forces in terms of equivalent electromagnetic microfields, we choose to describe their dynamical effect directly by representing them as average momentum rates, taking due account of the statistical properties of the particle random motions. We shall see that, in terms of these average rates of change of momentum, the primary collision effects will appear as pressure gradients and drag forces which may be added as macroscopic correction terms to the collision-free equations of motion.

3.4 COLLISION - FREE MODEL OF A PLASMA

(a) Applicability of the Model

As a result of our discussions above, we can conclude that:

1. If the collision effect is absent or negligible, the average field term suffices and the equations of motion are directly inferable from that of a single particle.

2. When the collision effects are significant and must be accounted for, we avoid writing complex expressions for the microscopic or local field by simply adding appropriate terms to the equations of motion already derived for the collision-free case.

In view of the foregoing, it is logical to first develop the equations neglecting collisions, and then later return to the collision effects, which are discussed in Sec. 3.6. It should also be noted that for the purposes of electromechanical power conversion, the transfer of energy from orderly to disorderly motion represents an undesirable dissipative loss, so that we prefer media in which collisions may be neglected or at least do not play a predominant role. Thus the collision-free model is not only a logical step, but in many instances a practical one as well. For example, collisions may be neglected if the gas is rare enough so that the maximum excursion of any particle around its average position is small compared to the average interparticle distance; and this may occur with particles either gyrating in a strong magnetic field (since the gyroradius mv/qB decreases as B increases) or oscillating in a high-frequency, low-intensity electric field [since the maximum excursion of the particle can be shown to be $(q/m)(E_{\max}/\omega^2)$]. In a way, this is also the case in a solid conductor at very low temperatures, where the thermal vibrations of the ions about their mean positions in the crystalline lattice are negligible. Also, binary collisions may be neglected in the case of highly energetic charged particles; in this instance an extremely close approach is required to get enough Coulomb force to cause appreciable deflection, and the probability of this happening is small.

(b) Derivation of the Equations

We proceed now to derive the equations which are valid when the close-range binary encounters and collisions with external walls are negligible. Under these conditions neighboring particles are acted upon by similar forces and in response to these forces perform similar motions. It is therefore meaningful to write the equations in terms of the density of particles n and the average values of $\mathbf{v}$, $\mathbf{E}$, and $\mathbf{B}$. For the sake of simplicity we shall retain the previous symbols, which now denote *average* values of the variables. We will use the subscripts i and e to indicate ions and electrons, respectively.

Although the ions and electrons are interspersed, we may consider the forces acting on these two species of particles individually and subsequently combine the results to obtain overall relationships. We consider a volume element $\delta\tau$, small enough so that the average field quantities do not vary appreciably within its confines. If n_i is their density, the number of ions contained in this volume is $n_i\,\delta\tau$, and the mass of these ions is $m_i n_i \,\delta\tau$. The momentum associated with this mass element which moves with a velocity $\mathbf{v}_i$, is $m_i n_i \mathbf{v}_i \,\delta\tau$. If we neglect compressibility, we are in effect considering n_i constant, so that the rate of change of this momentum is the inertial force $\delta\mathbf{f}_{i,\text{inertial}}$ given by

$$\delta\mathbf{f}_{i,\,\text{inertial}} = m_i n_i \frac{\partial \mathbf{v}_i}{\partial t}\,\delta\tau \tag{3.1}$$

where the partial derivative is used since, in general, $\mathbf{v}_i$ may vary in space as well as in time. Now, if Z is the ion valence number q_i/e, the total charge of the ions in $\delta\tau$ is $+Zen_i\,\delta\tau$, so that the total force applied to this "charge" by the electric and magnetic fields is $\delta\mathbf{f}_{i,\text{field}}$, where

$$\delta\mathbf{f}_{i,\text{field}} = Zen_i\,\delta\tau(\mathbf{E} + \mathbf{v}_i \times \mathbf{B}) \tag{3.2}$$

Since these are the only forces acting in the collision-free model, the equation of motion for the ions considered as a separate fluid becomes

$$m_i n_i \frac{\partial \mathbf{v}_i}{\partial t} = Zen_i(\mathbf{E} + \mathbf{v}_i \times \mathbf{B}) \tag{3.3}$$

where $\delta\tau$ has been canceled. The ion density n_i is retained, since it is the only factor that makes this equation distinguishable from that of a single particle.

In exactly the same way, we write the equation for the electron fluid,

$$m_e n_e \frac{\partial \mathbf{v}_e}{\partial t} = -en_e(\mathbf{E} + \mathbf{v}_e \times \mathbf{B}) \tag{3.4}$$

Equations (3.3) and (3.4) above provide the desired mathematical description for the dynamical behavior of collision-free, fully ionized gases. Before proceeding to develop more complicated models, we will pause to discuss in the next sections the physical implications contained in these equations, giving particular emphasis to the features that distinguish between the behavior of collectives of particles and single particles.

3.5 REACTION OF MATTER TO APPLIED ELECTRIC AND MAGNETIC FIELDS

We have previously noted in Sec. 3.3 that the **E** and **B** which appear in the collision-free model [Eqs. (3.3) and (3.4)] are average or macroscopic values which include all sources, internal as well as external. Once we define **E** and **B** in this way, the extension of the equation of motion for a single particle to a collisionless, incompressible, fully ionized gas is, as we have seen, a simple step indeed. This is natural, since the neglect of the local or microscopic field eliminates the very mechanism that is responsible for making a particle behave differently from its neighbors in the volume element $\delta\tau$. We must be careful, however, not to let the apparent simplicity of this procedure obscure the consequences of the definition of the average or macroscopic fields. For example, the formal similarity of the equations for the single particle and the collision-free multiparticle system does not mean that the motion of the gas as whole duplicates the motion of a single particle in vacuum under the action of the electric and magnetic fields resulting from an identical distribution of sources outside the gas. Of course, the point is—and although it has been said before, we cannot emphasize this too strongly—that the average field quantities in the equations for the collision-free multiparticle model are the *total* or *resultant* values which are contributed to not only by the external sources, but by the charges and motion of the particles themselves. In the case of a single particle or a very tenuous gas, the field due to sources outside the medium, which we will call the *impressed* field is essentially the same as the resultant field, whereas in the multiparticle case these fields differ greatly as the particle density and the extent of the medium increase.

This phenomenon of the perturbation of the impressed field by the redistribution or motion of the charged particles may be termed "the reaction of matter to applied fields." It is universally encountered, since it evidences the forces exerted on the material medium and is therefore instrumental in electromechanical power conversion. Its practical consequence is the necessity for simultaneously formulating and solving the electromagnetic field equations along with the dynamical equations of motion in order to be able to determine the actual particle motions. This requirement for relating the macroscopic **E** and **B** to the sources arising from the dynamical response of the active medium, as well as to the external or impressed sources, in fact constitutes a central problem in the analysis of power-conversion devices, and one of the objectives of this book will be the accurate evaluation of the reaction of *induced* field components and their effects.

(a) An Example of Induced Charges

The reader may be familiar with one situation in which the induced fields produce a marked effect. We refer to the limitation which space charges impose on the current flow in vacuum tubes according to the Child-Langmuir law. Another more appropriate example which shows how far-reaching the effects of the induced electric field can be is the flow of a plasma across a uniform magnetic field, as discussed below.

We have seen in Sec. 2.8 that the motion of a charged particle in a plane perpendicular to a uniform **B** field is a gyration around a line of force. Consequently, the particle cannot progress continuously *across* the flux lines of the field; in effect, the particle is leashed to the flux lines. If we were to extrapolate this result to an assemblage of charged particles, we could be led to suspect that a "blob" of plasma or a "plasmoid" would similarly be leashed to the field flux lines. Experimental evidence, however, shows that this plasmoid can freely move across the field.

The apparent contradiction here is readily explained in terms of the reaction field. We consider, for example, a plasmoid immersed in a homogeneous magnetic field **B** and initially at standstill with respect to a

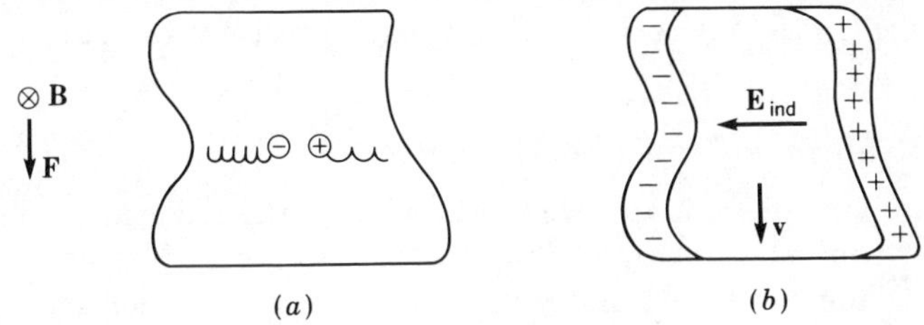

Fig. 3.1 Motion of a plasma across a uniform magnetic field.

frame of reference in which **E** is zero. The plasmoid is set in motion by some external force **F** of nonelectrical nature, such as gravity. This force acting on the electrons and ions of the plasma will cause them to drift according to the equation

$$m\frac{d\mathbf{v}}{dt} = \mathbf{F} + q\mathbf{v} \times \mathbf{B} \tag{3.5}$$

with a drift velocity

$$\mathbf{v}_F = \frac{(\mathbf{F}/q) \times \mathbf{B}}{B^2} \tag{3.6}$$

As mentioned in Sec. 2.12, this drift occurs perpendicularly to the force and in opposite directions for the electrons and ions, when **F** is nonelectrical in character. Because of this drift the electrons and ions tend to separate as shown in Fig. 3.1*a*. Since there are many particles present, this separation is manifested only at the boundary, where it constitutes a buildup of space charge. This charge produces an electrostatic field $\mathbf{E}_{\text{ind}}$, as shown in Fig. 3.1*b*. As a result the plasmoid can now move freely through the magnetic field because the induced charges in the plasma provide an electrostatic field which, as will be proved in Chap 4, is

$$\mathbf{E} = \mathbf{E}_{\text{ind}} = -\mathbf{v} \times \mathbf{B} \tag{3.7}$$

Thus **v** takes on the character of the drift velocity $\mathbf{v}_E$.

Since the drift $\mathbf{v}_F$ is proportional to $\mathbf{F}$, the buildup of charge ceases as soon as the force is removed. As a result, from this point on, the induced electric field then remains constant. Since $\mathbf{B}$ is also constant, we see from Eq. (3.7) that the plasmoid continues, as it should, in its state of motion with constant velocity. This proves that the uniform magnetic field exerts no restraining action on a plasma which is finite in extent.

An alternative viewpoint of the same effect can be taken in a frame of reference fixed to the center of mass of the plasmoid. Here the trajectories of the particles are the same as though the particles were acted upon by $\mathbf{B}$ and $\mathbf{F}$ only. In particular, they become circular as soon as the plasmoid acceleration vanishes. An observer would then conclude that in the plasmoid frame of reference there is no electric field ($\mathbf{E}' = 0$). However, $\mathbf{E}' = \mathbf{E} + \mathbf{v} \times \mathbf{B}$, so that we get precisely the same result as before.

(b) An Example of Induced Currents

In the previous example we have seen how the induced component of $\mathbf{E}$ arising from space charges affects the motion of a plasma. Here we turn our attention to the induced component of flux density $\mathbf{B}_{\text{ind}}$ as it arises from distribution of currents in the plasma. For this purpose we again consider a situation introduced in Chap. 2, the reflection of charged particles by a magnetic wall, and compute the resulting current flow and its associated magnetic field.

We recall from Sec. 2.14 that the reflection of the charged particles by a magnetic wall produces a net translation of the particles parallel to the wall equal to $2\mathcal{R}\,|\sin\gamma| = 2\mathcal{R}\sin\beta$, where, according to Sec. 2.9*b*, β is the angle of the incoming velocity vector seen in a reference frame attached to the wall, and $\mathcal{R}$ is the gyroradius. The electrons and ions move in opposite directions, as shown in Fig. 3.2, and their translations parallel to the wall contribute additive components to a current which flows at the surface of the wall within a boundary layer of thickness less than the greater Larmor diameter. Since this boundary layer is relatively thin, we shall approximate the actual current flow by a concentrated *surface* current.

Let us calculate the current due to the ions. If we consider a portion of the magnetic wall which extends a unit length in the direction of $\mathbf{B}$, we can evaluate the current flowing per unit length, simply by counting all the ions which cross a control surface S perpendicular to the wall in one second. From Fig. 3.3*a* it is apparent that this surface is crossed by all the ions that penetrate the wall-plasma interface within a strip of width $2\mathcal{R}_i \sin\beta_i$ in one second.

If N_i is the number of ions impinging on a unit area of the wall per second, the current produced by these particles is then, from Eqs. (2.33)

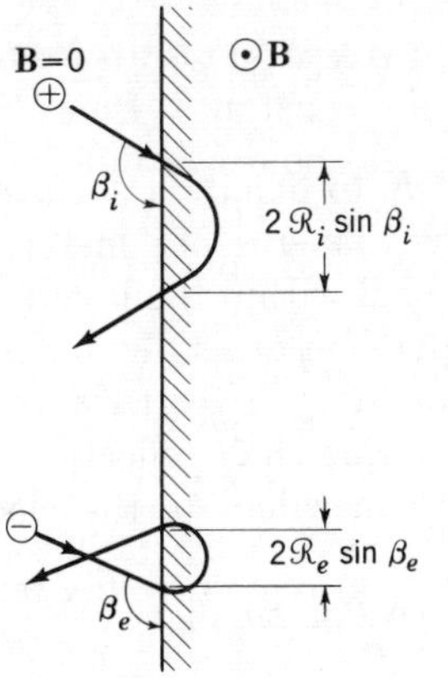

Fig. 3.2 Translation of electrons and ions inside a magnetic wall.

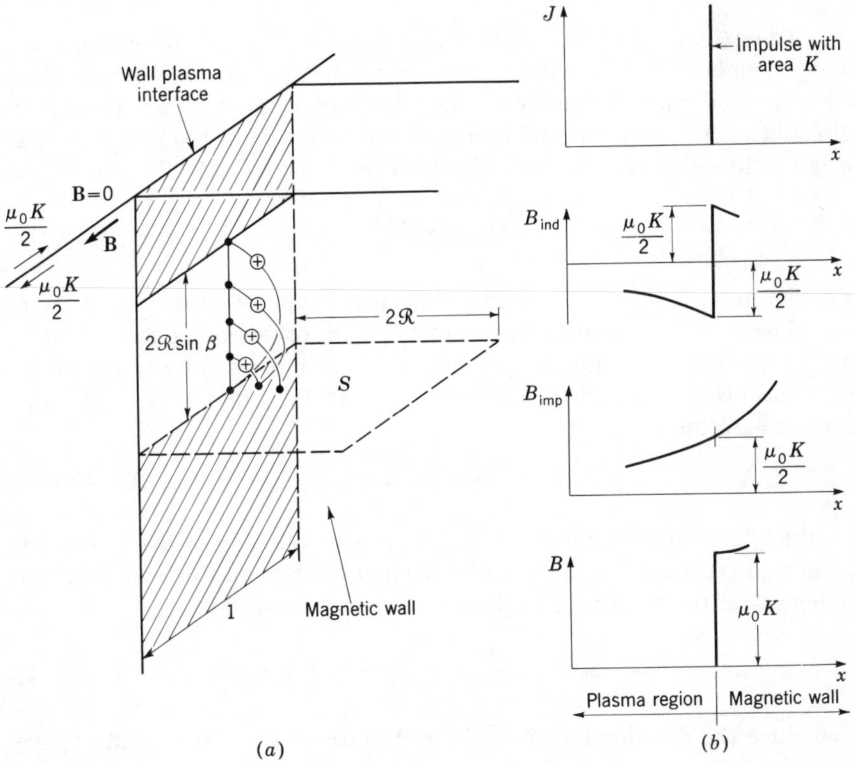

Fig. 3.3 Formation of a magnetic wall as a result of plasma–magnetic field interaction: (*a*) Ion current at the surface of a magnetic wall; (*b*) induced and impressed components of **B**.

and (2.87),

$$K_i = qN_i 2\mathcal{R}_i \sin \beta_i = \frac{2N_i m_i v'_{0,n,i}}{\langle B \rangle} \tag{3.8a}$$

where we use the symbol K to denote a surface current per unit length which has the dimensions amperes per meter, and the symbol $\langle B \rangle$ to denote the average value of **B** within the layer. It is necessary to introduce an average value here because the magnetic flux density varies gradually through the boundary layer as a result of the current contributed by the particles during their reflection.

In a similar way we can calculate the electron surface current as

$$K_e = eN_e 2\mathcal{R}_e \sin \beta_e = \frac{2N_e m_e v'_{0,n,e}}{\langle B \rangle} \tag{3.8b}$$

The total current K is then

$$K = \frac{2}{\langle B \rangle} (N_i m_i v'_{0,n,i} + N_e m_e v'_{0,n,e}) \tag{3.9}$$

To evaluate the component of **B** induced by this surface current we apply Ampère's law, taking note of the symmetry. As indicated in Fig. 3.3*b*, we find that the induced component of magnetic flux density is directed as **B** within the wall and opposite to **B** within the plasma. Its magnitude is the same on both sides and is

$$B_{\text{ind}} = \frac{\mu_0 K}{2} \tag{3.10a}$$

Furthermore, to satisfy the assumed condition that the total **B** is zero in the plasma, it is clear that there must exist another component of magnetic flux density. This component, which is impressed by sources outside the plasma and is therefore denoted by $\mathbf{B}_{\text{imp}}$, must also have the same magnitude, i.e.,

$$B_{\text{imp}} = \frac{\mu_0 K}{2} \tag{3.10b}$$

at the plasma-wall interface. $\mathbf{B}_{\text{imp}}$ is continuous across the boundary layer and is directed as the induced component $\mathbf{B}_{\text{ind}}$ on the wall side. It follows that the total field in the wall has the magnitude

$$B = |\mathbf{B}_{\text{ind}} + \mathbf{B}_{\text{imp}}| = \frac{\mu_0 K}{2} + \frac{\mu_0 K}{2} = \mu_0 K \tag{3.11}$$

and since the flux density varies from 0 to $\mu_0 K$ across the boundary, the average value is

$$\langle B \rangle = \frac{\mu_0 K}{2} \tag{3.12}$$

Therefore, the surface current is, from Eq. (3.9),

$$K = \sqrt{\frac{4(N_i m_i v'_{0,n,i} + N_e m_e v'_{0,n,e})}{\mu_0}} \tag{3.13}$$

Thus we see that although an impressed magnetic field of the proper magnitude must be present, the jump in **B** which causes the magnetic wall is *self-sustained* by its own reaction current. This self-sustenance feature of a jump in **B**, as a result of the interaction between a plasma and an impressed magnetic field, operates to produce a sharp cutoff of the geomagnetic field at the magnetospheric boundary, as we see in the following example.

Example 3.1

From the data of Example 2.3:

(*a*) Determine the current flowing per unit length in the boundary layer at the surface of the magnetosphere.

(*b*) Show that the magnetospheric boundary occurs at 10 earth radii.

Assume that the earth's magnetic field (which at the surface of the earth is $B = 5 \times 10^{-5}$ weber/m²) has a dipole character and consequently falls off inversely as the cube of the distance from the center of the earth.

Solution

(*a*) From Eq. (3.13) we know that

$$K = \sqrt{\frac{4(N_i m_i v'_{0,n,i} + N_e m_e v'_{0,n,e})}{\mu_0}}$$

and from Example 2.3 we know that

$$N_i = \frac{n_i v'_{0,n,i}}{2} \qquad N_e = \frac{n_e v'_{0,n,e}}{2}$$

Thus
$$K = \sqrt{\frac{2(n_i m_i v'^2_{0,n,i} + n_e m_e v'^2_{0,n,e})}{\mu_0}}$$

Using the data of Example 2.3, we obtain

$$K = \sqrt{\frac{2 \times 9.6 \times 10^6 \times 1{,}838 \times 9.11 \times 10^{-31} \times (5 \times 10^5)^2}{4\pi \times 10^{-7}}}$$
$$= 8 \times 10^{-2} \text{ amp/m}$$

Although this is a small current density, the total current which flows is quite large because of the huge dimensions of the magnetosphere.

(*b*) Since
$$B = \mu_0 K$$
$$B = 4\pi \times 10^{-7} \times 8 \times 10^{-2} = 10^{-7} \text{ weber/m}^2$$

To create the wall, the B impressed by the sources of the earth's magnetic field within the earth itself, must be one-half this much. The impressed B at radius r is, however,

$$B(r) = 5 \times 10^{-5} \left(\frac{r_e}{r}\right)^3$$

so that
$$5 \times 10^{-5} \left(\frac{r_e}{r}\right)^3 = \frac{10^{-7}}{2} \qquad \text{or} \qquad \frac{r_e}{r} = 10^{-1}$$

and
$$r = 10r_e \qquad \text{or 10 earth radii}$$

3.6 MACROSCOPIC REPRESENTATION OF COLLISION EFFECTS

(a) Preliminary Remarks

We are now ready to formulate appropriate terms to account for the effects of short-range particle interactions or collisions in the macroscopic description of plasma behavior. For this purpose we shall first discuss the interaction between particles and confining walls and introduce the concept of *pressure gradient* which we apply next to describe the effect of collisions between particles of the same species. To represent the effects of collisions between particles of different species we shall, instead, introduce a "drag" force since these collisions impede the relative flow of one species past the other. It will be useful to begin with a brief review of some facts concerning random particle motion.[1,7]

We have previously noted that collision effects are synonymous with random deviations from the average particle velocities. If we call $\mathbf{u}_i$, $\mathbf{u}_e$ the respective random velocities of a particular ion and a particular electron, and $\mathbf{v}_{it}$, $\mathbf{v}_{et}$ the corresponding total velocities, we have, of course,

$$\mathbf{v}_{it} = \mathbf{u}_i + \mathbf{v}_i \qquad (3.14a)$$
$$\mathbf{v}_{et} = \mathbf{u}_e + \mathbf{v}_e \qquad (3.14b)$$

The useful measures of the variables $\mathbf{v}_{it}$ and $\mathbf{v}_{et}$ are naturally the average value and the mean-square value. Denoting averaging by the symbol $\langle\ \rangle$, and omitting the i, e subscripts, since the results apply in either case, we see that

$$\text{Average of } \mathbf{v}_t = \langle \mathbf{v}_t \rangle = \langle \mathbf{u} + \mathbf{v} \rangle = \langle \mathbf{u} \rangle + \langle \mathbf{v} \rangle = \mathbf{v} \qquad (3.15a)$$
$$\text{Mean-square value of } \mathbf{v}_t = \langle v_t^2 \rangle = \langle u^2 + 2\mathbf{v} \cdot \mathbf{u} + v^2 \rangle$$
$$= \langle u^2 \rangle + \langle v^2 \rangle + 2\mathbf{v} \cdot \langle \mathbf{u} \rangle = \langle u^2 \rangle + v^2 \qquad (3.15b)$$

The mean-square speed of the random motion $\langle u^2 \rangle$, the so-called *variance* of the total motion, is thus itself a useful measure. It is obviously a measure of the average kinetic energy of the random motion U, since

$$U = \tfrac{1}{2} m \langle u^2 \rangle \qquad (3.16)$$

We know from the physics of gases that random particle motion is identifiable as the thermal agitation associated with heat, so that the random motion has an associated temperature T in degrees Kelvin according to the definition

$$U = \frac{\mathfrak{N}}{2} kT \tag{3.17}$$

where k is the Boltzmann constant, 1.38×10^{-23} joule/°K, and $\mathfrak{N}$ is the number of degrees of freedom of the particle, three in a monoatomic gas. Combining Eqs. (3.16) and (3.17), we have

$$\langle u^2 \rangle = \frac{\mathfrak{N} kT}{m} \tag{3.18}$$

A surface subjected to random collision bombardment of the particles of a gas, in effect experiences an average *pressure* which represents the rate of transfer of momentum per unit area in a unit time. This pressure is associated with the thermal agitation, and in an ideal gas is given by $\mathcal{P} = nkT$, where $\mathcal{P}$ is the pressure, n the density or number of particles per unit volume, k the Boltzmann constant, and T the temperature in degrees Kelvin. Combining this expression with Eq. (3.18), we have

$$\mathcal{P} = \frac{nm\langle u^2 \rangle}{\mathfrak{N}} \tag{3.19}$$

(b) Wall-Particle Interactions

The relation between the pressure and the temperature which is a measure of the random motion, is not accidental. We see this if we introduce a perfectly reflecting wall in the path of a stream of particles initially moving with respect to the wall with velocity $\mathbf{v}'$. In front of the wall we then see that after a steady state is reached, for every incoming particle, there is a reflected particle which has the same tangential component of velocity $\mathbf{v}'_t$ but opposite normal component $\mathbf{v}'_n$. As a result, if we now determine the average particle velocity, we find that the only contribution comes from the tangential component. The normal velocity component has zero average value so that it now constitutes a random component. Thus

$$\mathbf{v}'_n = \mathbf{u}_n \tag{3.20}$$

We will now show that the pressure exerted by an ionized gas on a magnetic wall is given by a relation similar to that for an ideal gas. We will also discuss the static and dynamic implications of this pressure with regard to power conversion.

As mentioned in Sec. 2.9*b*, pressure exerted by the charged particles on the wall is the product of the change in momentum of the particle

$|\Delta(mv)| = 2mv'_{0,n}$ and N, the number of particles colliding with the wall per unit surface in a unit time. Note that N can also be interpreted as the frequency with which collisions occur per unit surface of the wall. To evaluate this frequency we generalize the arguments given in Example 2.3. We choose, for convenience, a reference frame fixed to the wall, and we consider a specific group of particles with mass m^g and density n^g, which impinge on the wall at right angles with velocity $\mathbf{v}'^g_n$. The N^g particles of this group which will reach the wall within one second are all contained in a parallelopiped having the unit surface of the wall as one

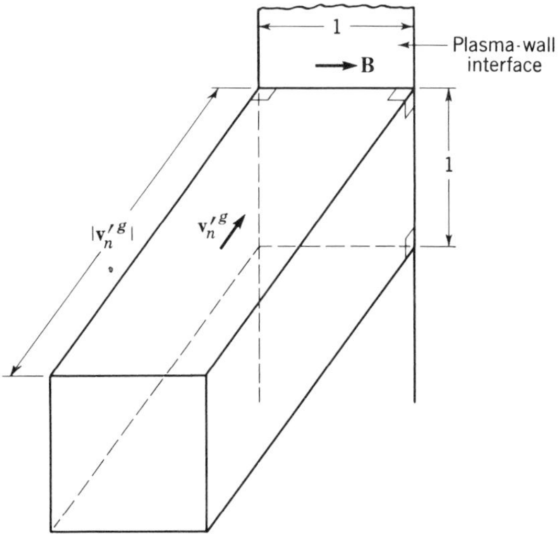

Fig. 3.4 Volume occupied by the N^g particles colliding with a unit surface of the wall in one second.

face and four sides $|\mathbf{v}'^g_n|$ long normal to the wall. Since the volume of this parallelopiped is, as indicated in Fig. 3.4, $(1)(1)(|\mathbf{v}'^g_n|)$, then N^g is

$$N^g = n^g v'^g_n \tag{3.21}$$

From Eq. (2.48) the partial pressure that the g group of particles exerts on the wall is

$$\mathcal{P}^g = N^g \times 2m^g v'^g_n \tag{3.22a}$$

and, from Eq. (3.21),

$$\mathcal{P}^g = 2n^g m^g (v'^g_n)^2 \tag{3.22b}$$

If we recognize that v'^g_n is random, we can write, according to Eq. (3.20),

$$\mathcal{P}^g = 2n^g m^g (u'^g_n)^2 \tag{3.23}$$

Although Eq. (3.23) has been derived for particles impinging normally on the wall, it is valid, in general, for an arbitrary angle of incidence, because the tangential component of velocity does not affect the change in momemtum or the count of particles reflected by the wall per unit time (see Prob. 3.4).

For a particular particle species, many groups are involved. In these groups n and m are constants, but u_n varies randomly. The partial pressure $\mathcal{P}_s$ for the entire s species is found by summing the contributions of all the groups in the species:

$$\mathcal{P}_s = \sum_g \mathcal{P}_g = 2m^g \sum_g n^g(u_n{}^g)^2 = 2m_s(\tfrac{1}{2}n_s\langle u_{ns}{}^2\rangle) = n_s m_s \langle u_{ns}{}^2\rangle \qquad (3.24)$$

where $\langle u_{ns}{}^2\rangle$ is the mean-square speed of the random motion for the s species and $m^g = m_s$. Finally, the total pressure in the gas is found by summing the contributions of all the species,

$$\mathcal{P} = \sum_s \mathcal{P}_s = \sum_s n_s m_s \langle u_{ns}{}^2\rangle \qquad (3.25)$$

The $\frac{1}{2}$ factor enters in Eq. (3.24) because the summation extends only over the impinging particles, which contribute only half the total density of particles in front of the wall. It can be seen from Eqs. (3.19) and (3.24) that the partial pressure due to a single-particle species reduces to that of an ideal gas of identical particles when $\langle u_n{}^2\rangle$ is taken to be $\langle u^2\rangle/\mathfrak{N}$. This comes about because the direction normal to the wall is but one of the $\mathfrak{N}$ degrees of freedom among which the random kinetic energy is equipartitioned.

We have seen that the presence of a wall effectively randomizes the motion of the particles of a gas in front of the wall, and that, conversely, the random motions in the body of a gas are associated with the force exerted on a boundary surface. This effect deserves further investigation. Since the force appears only at the surface of the wall whereas the pressure is now defined according to Eq. (3.25) in terms of the properties of the gas outside the wall, we reach the conclusion that the pressure, although numerically equal to the force per unit area, cannot strictly speaking be identified with it. The force action arises from the fact that the bombardment of particles occurs on one side only of the wall surface. It is therefore the *pressure difference* across the wall which we can identify with this force.

With this in mind we return our attention to Eq. (3.25); making use of Eqs. (3.12), (3.13), and (3.21), and the considerations above, we can show that

$$K\langle B\rangle = \Delta\mathcal{P} \qquad (3.26)$$

where $\Delta\mathcal{P}$ is the pressure difference across the wall from the wall to the plasma. This is the steady-state integrated form of the magnetoplasma-dynamical equation which we shall derive in Sec. 3.7*b*. It states that the force, which the magnetic field exerts on the current according to the Biot-Savart law, is balanced by the pressure difference. Also, if we substitute $-\Delta H$ for K, as given by Ampère's law (ΔH taken from the wall to the plasma), we get

$$-\langle B\rangle\,\Delta H = \Delta\mathcal{P}$$

or since

$$H = \frac{B}{\mu_0}$$

$$-\Delta\mathcal{P} = \frac{\langle B\rangle\,\Delta B}{\mu_0} = \Delta\left(\frac{1}{2}\frac{B^2}{\mu_0}\right) \tag{3.27}$$

The last equation states that in going across the boundary layer, the decrease in the plasma pressure is balanced by an increase in the density of energy stored in the magnetic field. This leads to the concept that the pressure exerted by the material particles is balanced by a "magnetic pressure," a viewpoint that is advantageous in discussing the confinement of hot plasmas in what have become known as "magnetic bottles."

Of greater interest to us are wall-particle interactions in situations in which the wall is seen moving as, for instance, in the pulsed plasma rocket mentioned in Sec. 2.14, and illustrated in Fig. 2.17. The actual physical structure is cylindrical, but the problem is more conveniently studied in the developed view of Fig. 2.17*b* where the normal to the paper represents the tangential direction in the circular cross section of the actual structure. Here we may apply either a current or a voltage source; if these are step functions in time, we shall see that identical results can be achieved with either one. We shall choose the current source as the simpler to follow.

The operation is as follows:

1. Before the application of the current source, the interelectrode region is filled with a finite volume of neutral plasma which is essentially at rest.
2. When the current is impressed, it flows initially at the surface of the plasma facing the source, since a finite time is required for the propagation or diffusion of the electromagnetic field.
3. The current flows, as shown in Fig. 3.5, in a continuous path from the source forward along the upper conductor, through the plasma, and back along the lower conductor. In the developed view, which ideally has an infinite extent normal to the paper, this current flow completely encircles a rectangular channel as shown. Since this is entirely analogous to the flow of current in a long coil of wire, we know that a magnetic field as shown is produced inside the confines of the channel; the magnetic field outside is zero. This means that a magnetic wall forms at the source end. If I is the total current impressed and l is the length of the channel,

the current per unit length is $K = I/l$, and the magnetic flux density is $B = \mu_0 K = \mu_0 I/l$.

4. The interaction of the current sheet K on the surface plasma and the flux density **B** produces a force per unit surface of the wall of magnitude $KB/2 = (\mu_0/2)I^2/l^2$ directed toward the plasma; or, from an alternative viewpoint, there is a magnetic pressure $\frac{1}{2}B^2/\mu_0 = \mu_0 I^2/2l^2$. This pressure propels the "wall," i.e., the charged particles that constitute the interface current, toward the plasma.

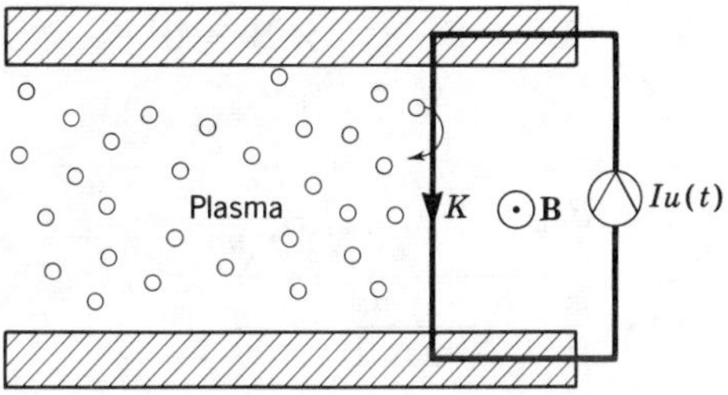

Fig. 3.5 Current path in developed view of plasma rocket.

5. As the wall moves toward the plasma, the particles collide with the wall, exerting pressure on it. An equilibrium condition is established for a wall velocity such that the pressure balances the magnetic pressure found in step 4 above.
6. In this equilibrium condition, the quantities of interest are as follows:

Quantity	Electrode reference frame	Wall reference frame
1. Electric field in wall	**E**	$\mathbf{E}' = 0$
2. Electric field in plasma	0	0
3. Magnetic field in wall	**B**	$\mathbf{B}' = \mathbf{B}$
4. Magnetic field in plasma	0	0
5. Wall velocity	$\mathbf{v}_w$	0
6. Particle velocity entering wall	0	$-\mathbf{v}_w$
7. Particle velocity leaving wall (exhaust velocity)	$2\mathbf{v}_w$	$\mathbf{v}_w$

This information derives from our previous study of wall-particle collision in Sec. 2.14.

We now wish to determine the wall velocity $\mathbf{v}_w$ and the electric field **E**. To determine these quantities, we note from Eqs. (3.20) and (3.25) that the pressure developed by the normally incident ions and electrons is

$$\mathcal{P} = (n_i m_i + n_e m_e) v_w^2 \tag{3.28}$$

Thus we immediately find v_w from

$$\mathcal{P} = \frac{\mu_0}{2} \frac{I^2}{l^2} = (n_i m_i + n_e m_e) v_w^2$$

so that

$$v_w = \frac{I}{l} \sqrt{\frac{\mu_0}{2(n_i m_i + n_e m_e)}} \tag{3.29}$$

The electric field may be found from

$$\mathbf{E}' = \mathbf{E} + \mathbf{v}_w \times \mathbf{B} = 0$$

i.e.,

$$E = B v_w$$

Thus we have

$$E = B v_w = \frac{\mu_0 I}{l} \frac{I}{l} \sqrt{\frac{\mu_0}{2(n_i m_i + n_e m_e)}}$$

$$= \frac{I^2}{l^2} \sqrt{\frac{\mu_0^3}{2(n_i m_i + n_e m_e)}} \tag{3.30}$$

Since according to Eq. (3.29) v_w has the same functional dependence as I, then v_w and B are both step functions in time, so that E is likewise a step function. The plasma rocket is further studied in Prob. 3.5.

(c) Like-particle Interactions

The collision-free model [Eqs. (3.3) and (3.4)] will now be modified by the inclusion of the force terms due to collisions between particles of the same species.

It is plain that these collision effects would be absent if all the ions had an identical velocity $\mathbf{v}_i$ and all the electrons an identical velocity $\mathbf{v}_e$. The like-particle collisions are due to the random component velocities $\mathbf{u}_i$, $\mathbf{u}_e$, respectively. As we have previously noted, random collision bombardment of a surface is manifested macroscopically as *pressure*, and we shall show that like-particle interactions lead to a pressure-gradient term.

To do this, let us consider a small rectangular parallelopiped of volume $\delta\tau$ containing ions, as shown in Fig. 3.6*a*. This volume of ions is subjected to ion pressures on all its faces. We shall assume that the pressure at any one point is isotropic, that is, the same in any direction, and as a result the partial pressure of the ions, $\mathcal{P}_i$, is a pure scalar quantity. If $\mathcal{P}_i$ were the same on all faces of the parallelopiped (e.g., collisionless case), no net force would act on $\delta\tau$; but if the pressure varies from point to point, the pressure gradient represents a net unbalance force. We shall evaluate this force, with reference to the enlarged view of Fig. 3.6*b*. The "origin corner" of $\delta\tau$ is the point (x,y,z), and the side lengths are

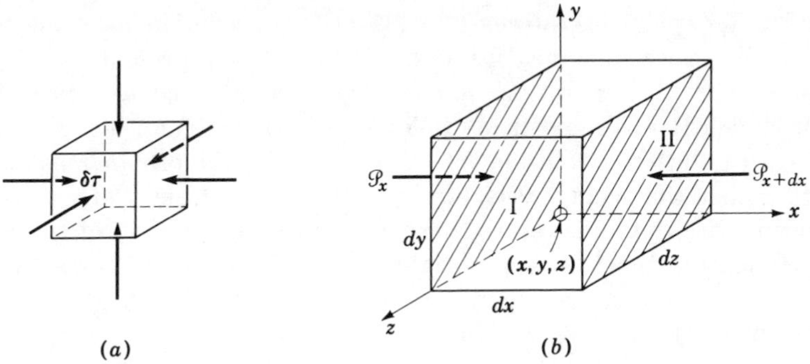

Fig. 3.6 Like-particle collision pressure on a volume $\delta\tau$.

respectively dx, dy, dz. Consider the small forces df_x, df_{x+dx} on the two faces denoted I and II, respectively. The pressure on these faces may vary with x, y, z, but the y and z variations are identical on the two faces and so cancel each other out, leaving only the contribution of the x variation. We see this by approximating the forces as the midpoint pressure times the face area; thus

$$df_x = \left(\mathcal{P}_i + \frac{\partial \mathcal{P}_i}{\partial y}\frac{dy}{2} + \frac{\partial \mathcal{P}_i}{\partial z}\frac{dz}{2}\right) dy\, dz$$

$$df_{x+dx} = \left(\mathcal{P}_i + \frac{\partial \mathcal{P}_i}{\partial x}\, dx + \frac{\partial \mathcal{P}_i}{\partial y}\frac{dy}{2} + \frac{\partial \mathcal{P}_i}{\partial z}\frac{dz}{2}\right) dy\, dz$$

and the *net* force δf_x in the x direction is

$$\delta f_x = df_x - df_{x+dx} = -\frac{\partial \mathcal{P}_i}{\partial x}\, dx\, dy\, dz = -\frac{\partial \mathcal{P}_i}{\partial x}\, \delta\tau$$

In exactly the same way, we write the results for the other faces and combine them vectorially. The result is, for both ions and electrons,

$$\delta\mathbf{f}_{ii} = -\nabla \mathcal{P}_i\, \delta\tau = -(\text{grad } \mathcal{P}_i)\, \delta\tau \tag{3.31a}$$

$$\delta\mathbf{f}_{ee} = -\nabla \mathcal{P}_e\, \delta\tau = -(\text{grad } \mathcal{P}_e)\, \delta\tau \tag{3.31b}$$

Thus the quantities $-\nabla \mathcal{P}_i$, $-\nabla \mathcal{P}_e$, are the per-unit volume forces applied to $\delta\tau$ due to like-particle collisions. As a result, they may be added to the right-hand sides of Eqs. (3.3) and (3.4), respectively.

(d) Unlike-particle Interactions

In the previous section we have seen that like-particle collisions occur only as a consequence of the random or chaotic motion; the orderly motion does not contribute to the like-particle interaction at all. This happens, of course, because the relative velocity of two like particles is due only to random components, the average component dropping out.

With *unlike* particles, however, collisions are predominantly due to the difference in average velocities, since this term is present in the relative velocity of any two unlike particles; as a result collisions can occur independently of the particle random motions. In fact, it is reasonable to expect that the collision effect will be directly proportional to the difference of the average velocities $\mathbf{v}_e - \mathbf{v}_i$. As in the case of the pressure we will write the force terms as the average of the product of the change in momentum times an appropriate collision frequency. It follows that the force affecting the average motion of the ions because of collisions with the electrons takes the form

$$\delta\mathbf{f}_{ie} = n_i\nu_{ie}m(\mathbf{v}_e - \mathbf{v}_i)\ \delta\tau \tag{3.32}$$

where ν_{ie} is the collison frequency, or the average number of collisions that one ion makes with the electrons in a unit time, and m is a mass characteristic for the momentum interchanged in each collision. The force per unit volume is then

$$\mathbf{f}_{ie} = n_i\nu_{ie}m(\mathbf{v}_e - \mathbf{v}_i) \tag{3.33}$$

It is certainly true that Eq. (3.33) has been written on the basis of a plausibility argument, rather than a rigorous detailed development of the basic theory. If, however, we do go through all the details we discover that:

1. The mass m is the so-called *reduced mass* per unit volume

$$m = \frac{m_e m_i}{m_e + m_i} = \frac{m_e}{1 + m_e/m_i} \tag{3.34}$$

   For all practical purposes, it is apparent that m may be approximated by m_e.
2. Equation (3.33) is not exact, but it is an excellent first approximation. It can be shown that $\mathbf{f}_{ie}$ is the first and predominant term of a series in which all higher-order terms vanish when electrons and ions have equal temperatures and symmetrical distributions of velocities.

It is clear that Eq. (3.33) represents a force proportional to the *relative* average velocity between ions and electrons, and so is, in effect, exactly equivalent to a viscous friction or "drag" between the two sets of particles. As we shall see, this microscopic picture of the drag in fact develops into the resistance to the flow of electric current in conductors and yields the resistivity of a conducting material which is described by Ohm's law!

Since $\mathbf{f}_{ie}$ was defined as force per unit volume acting on the *ions* because of collisions with the electrons, the corresponding force $\mathbf{f}_{ei}$ on the electrons must be, by Newton's law of action and reaction,

$$\mathbf{f}_{ei} = n_e\nu_{ei}m(\mathbf{v}_i - \mathbf{v}_e) = -\mathbf{f}_{ie} \tag{3.35}$$

Equation (3.35) requires that $n_e\nu_{ei} = n_i\nu_{ie}$. This is easily shown to be true since ν_{ei}, the number of collisions that one electron makes with the ions, is proportional to the ion density n_i, and likewise ν_{ie}, the number of collisions that one ion makes with the electrons, is in the same way proportional to the electron density n_e.

3.7 MAGNETOPLASMA - DYNAMICAL (MPD) EQUATIONS

(a) Two-fluid Model

We have now described the local or short-range interaction forces by means of Eqs. (3.31) and (3.35). This completes the description of the forces which determine the dynamical behavior of the multiparticle system, and overall equations of motion may now be written, by simply introducing the collision force $\mathbf{f}_{ii} + \mathbf{f}_{ie}$ acting on the ions, and $\mathbf{f}_{ee} + \mathbf{f}_{ei}$ acting on the electrons, into Eqs. (3.3) and (3.4). Thus we obtain

$$m_in_i\frac{\partial \mathbf{v}_i}{\partial t} = -\nabla\mathcal{P}_i + n_i\nu_{ie}m(\mathbf{v}_e - \mathbf{v}_i) + n_iZe(\mathbf{E} + \mathbf{v}_i \times \mathbf{B}) \tag{3.36}$$

$$m_en_e\frac{\partial \mathbf{v}_e}{\partial t} = -\nabla\mathcal{P}_e + n_e\nu_{ei}m(\mathbf{v}_i - \mathbf{v}_e) - n_ee(\mathbf{E} + \mathbf{v}_e \times \mathbf{B}) \tag{3.37}$$

In examining these equations we discover that, unlike Eqs. (3.3) and (3.4) for the ion and electron fluids in a collisionless plasma, Eqs. (3.36) and (3.37) form a set of *coupled* equations in $\mathbf{v}_i$ and $\mathbf{v}_e$. The coupling appears explicitly in the terms representing $\mathbf{f}_{ei}$ and $\mathbf{f}_{ie}$; these are the mathematical formulation of the physical mechanism provided by collisions which prevents free relative motion of the electrons and ions. In addition to this explicit coupling, there exists a coupling that is implicit in **E** and is due to the electric-field component induced by the space charges. The difference between the two mechanisms is that the **E** coupling is essentially static since it is due to charge displacement, whereas the collision coupling is dynamic, appearing only when the electron and ion fluids are in relative motion. Both coupling mechanisms become more effective as the density of particles increases, so that eventually, in dense plasmas, electrons and ions move together and may be considered to form a single fluid. In this case, an alternative set of equations is more convenient, and we shall derive these in the next section.[2]

(b) One-fluid Model

Although the particle equations (3.36) and (3.37) constitute a complete description of our system model within the simplifying assumptions which we have made, they do not convey this description in terms convenient to the observer interested in gross effects or the "terminal power-conversion characteristics." In addition to the average fields **E** and **B**, such an observer would be concerned with the following average or macroscopic quantities:

Electrical	*Mechanical*
(1) Space-charge density ρ	(3) Mass density ξ
(2) Current density $\mathbf{J}$	(4) Mass-center velocity $\mathbf{v}$
	(5) Total pressure $\mathcal{P}$

1. The space-charge density ρ is simply the total charge per unit volume; in terms of the particle-number densities, ρ is plainly given by

$$\rho = e(n_i Z - n_e) \tag{3.38}$$

2. The current density per unit area $\mathbf{J}$ associated with a space charge ρ moving with velocity $\mathbf{v}$ is, of course, $\rho\mathbf{v}$; thus the total current density carried by the particles is

$$\mathbf{J} = \rho_i \mathbf{v}_i + \rho_e \mathbf{v}_e = e(n_i Z \mathbf{v}_i - n_e \mathbf{v}_e) \tag{3.39}$$

3. The mass density ξ is simply the total mass per unit volume,

$$\xi = m_i n_i + m_e n_e \tag{3.40}$$

4. The average velocity of the center of mass $\mathbf{v}$ is by definition

$$\mathbf{v} = \frac{\sum_\alpha n_\alpha m_\alpha \mathbf{v}_\alpha}{\sum_\alpha n_\alpha m_\alpha} = \frac{m_i n_i \mathbf{v}_i + m_e n_e \mathbf{v}_e}{\xi} \tag{3.41}$$

5. The total gas pressure $\mathcal{P}$ is simply the sum of the partial pressures,

$$\mathcal{P} = \mathcal{P}_i + \mathcal{P}_e \tag{3.42}$$

By using these variables in suitable combinations of the particle equations, we achieve some very significant results. First, we evaluate the total force per unit volume by simply adding Eqs. (3.36) and (3.37), and then introduce the five average variables. The unlike-particle collision terms drop out, since internal action-reaction forces must disappear in the overall result, and the result is

$$\xi \frac{\partial \mathbf{v}}{\partial t} + \nabla \mathcal{P} = \rho \mathbf{E} + \mathbf{J} \times \mathbf{B} \tag{3.43}$$

Equation (3.43) is the overall electromechanical equation of motion for a unit-volume element of the fully ionized gas considered as a single fluid. Comparing it with that for a single particle, we see that particle mass goes over into mass per unit volume, particle charge q goes over into the space charge per unit volume, and the $q\mathbf{v} \times \mathbf{B}$ magnetic force on a particle becomes the magnetic force per unit volume $\mathbf{J} \times \mathbf{B}$. The new term which appears is the pressure gradient $\nabla\mathcal{P}$. This is an extremely important term, since it represents the means for external mechanical coupling into the volume element of the fluid.

An immediate conclusion of striking contrast to that in the single-particle case is this: If the gas is electrically neutral, and so constitutes a plasma, then $\rho = 0$, and the term $\rho\mathbf{E}$ vanishes. *Thus the total electric field cannot contribute to power conversion in a neutral medium. The means for power conversion in this case is the total magnetic field.* This is, of course, in diametric opposition to the case of a single charged particle or even of many charged particles of like sign.

To further stress the import of this result we note that, in the absence of a driving field, the slightest departure from neutrality caused by a separation of the electrons from the ions gives rise to restoring forces. Relaxation to the neutral state takes then the form of a damped oscillation whose frequency, in dense plasmas, is quite high because of the combined effect of the large restoring force and the negligible inertia of the electrons. These facts may be established if we consider the induced electric fields caused by the space charge itself, as indicated in Prob. 3.9. For our purpose here it suffices to take notice that these rapid fluctuations in charge density are insignificant provided we limit our interest to phenomena that occur in times much longer than the relaxation time constant, or to frequencies well below this characteristic plasma frequency. Keeping in mind this additional restriction imposed on the validity of our equations we shall henceforth assume that the space charge ρ is essentially zero.

In addition to the overall electromechanical equation, we may derive a second equation which is, in effect, a generalized Ohm's law equation for a volume element of the ionized gas, under the condition that *the gas is electrically neutral and constitutes a plasma.* In this case

$$Zn_i = n_e \qquad \rho = 0 \tag{3.44}$$

and

$$\mathbf{J} = n_e e(\mathbf{v}_i - \mathbf{v}_e) \tag{3.45}$$

If we now multiply the ion equation (3.36) by $Zm_e/en_em_i = m_e/en_im_i$, the electron equation (3.37) by $1/n_ee$, and then subtract the latter from the former, there results

$$\frac{m_e}{n_e e^2}\frac{\partial \mathbf{J}}{\partial t} + \frac{\nu_{ei} m_e}{n_e e^2}\left(1 + \frac{Zm_e}{m_i}\right)\mathbf{J} + \frac{1}{n_e e}\left(\frac{n_e m_e}{n_i m_i}\nabla\mathcal{P}_i - \nabla\mathcal{P}_e\right) = \left(1 + \frac{n_e m_e}{n_i m_i}\right)\mathbf{E} + \left(\frac{n_e m_e}{n_i m_i}\mathbf{v}_i + \mathbf{v}_e\right) \times \mathbf{B} \tag{3.46}$$

By using the definition of mass-center velocity $\mathbf{v}$, by Eq. (3.41) we may write the identity

$$\frac{n_e m_e}{n_i m_i}\mathbf{v}_i + \mathbf{v}_e = \mathbf{v} - \left[\left(\frac{1}{1 + n_e m_e/n_i m_i} - \frac{n_e m_e}{n_i m_i}\right)\mathbf{v}_i - \left(1 - \frac{n_e m_e/n_i m_i}{1 + n_e m_e/n_i m_i}\right)\mathbf{v}_e\right] \tag{3.47}$$

If we now take note of the fact that the ions are much more massive than the electrons, so that

$$\frac{n_e m_e}{n_i m_i} \ll 1 \qquad \frac{m_e}{m_i} \ll 1 \tag{3.48}$$

Eq. (3.47) becomes approximately

$$\frac{n_e m_e}{n_i m_i}\mathbf{v}_i + \mathbf{v}_e \approx \mathbf{v} - (\mathbf{v}_i - \mathbf{v}_e) = \mathbf{v} - \frac{\mathbf{J}}{n_e e} \tag{3.49}$$

Also since $\nabla\mathcal{P}_i$ and $\nabla\mathcal{P}_e$ have, in general, the same order of magnitude, we can neglect $(n_e m_e/n_i m_i)\,\nabla\mathcal{P}_i$ when compared with $\nabla\mathcal{P}_e$. In view of the large mass ratio and introducing Eq. (3.49) into (3.46), we can write

$$\frac{m_e}{n_e e^2}\frac{\partial \mathbf{J}}{\partial t} + \frac{\mathbf{J}}{n_e e^2/\nu_{ei} m_e} + \frac{1}{n_e e}\mathbf{J}\times\mathbf{B} = \mathbf{E} + \mathbf{v}\times\mathbf{B} + \frac{1}{n_e e}\nabla\mathcal{P}_e \tag{3.50}$$

Equation (3.50) obviously expresses the balance of the voltage gradient across the volume element of plasma and is therefore often called the generalized Ohm's law. It is then the "electrical" member of the pair which describe the single-fluid magnetoplasma-dynamic or MPD model. The other member is the "mechanical" member, the equation of motion (3.43). This latter, restated for the case of the plasma, i.e., $\rho = 0$, is

$$\xi\frac{\partial \mathbf{v}}{\partial t} + \nabla\mathcal{P} = \mathbf{J}\times\mathbf{B} \tag{3.43a}$$

The two equations (3.50) and (3.43*a*) constitute the single-fluid MPD equations.

We may usefully consider each equation as predominantly associated with a specific particle species. Thus, since the ions constitute almost the entire fluid mass, the equation of motion (3.43*a*) may be thought of as essentially descriptive of the ionic motion. On the other hand, the generalized Ohm's law (3.50) is essentially a description of the electron motion. In fact it can be obtained directly by viewing the electrons from a reference frame attached to the ions and transforming Eq. (3.37) accordingly, if we neglect the terms arising from the rotation of the ion reference frame and then make the justifiable assumption that $\mathbf{v}$ can be approximated by $\mathbf{v}_i$.

It is of considerable interest to examine the individual terms of Eq. (3.50):

1. The term involving the time derivative of the current density is an inductive term actually associated with the inertia of the electron itself. The presence of such a term predicts, for example, that if a short-circuited coil is rotated steadily in a region free of impressed fields and then suddenly stopped, a momentary current will flow, owing to the electron inertia. This phenomenon, though very small and difficult to measure, has actually been observed.[3]
2. The term involving the current density itself is plainly an ohmic drop effect. We have thus derived Ohm's law starting from microscopic considerations! The denominator of the **J** term then defines the conductivity as

$$\gamma = \frac{n_e e^2}{\nu_{ei} m_e} \tag{3.51}$$

   The presence of the collision frequency in the expression for the conductivity clearly relates this parameter to the rapidly fluctuating microfields which characterize the encounters between electrons and ions. We thus conclude that the dissipation which we associate with the resistive voltage drop is none other than a macroscopic account of the randomizing effect that collisions have on the orderly motion of the electrons as expressed by the current.
3. The term involving $\nabla \mathcal{P}_e$ may be interpreted as follows: Since the gas pressure associated with random motion may be expressed in terms of temperature (Sec. 3.6*a*), the pressure-gradient term is also, in effect, a temperature-gradient term, so that we have in this term a temperature gradient associated with a voltage gradient. This is the *thermoelectric effect.* The thermoelectric effect is currently under intensive investigation as a power-conversion means both for generation of electricity directly from heat power and for refrigeration without moving parts.
4. The term involving $\mathbf{J} \times \mathbf{B}$ indicates the presence of a voltage gradient perpendicular to the plane of **J** and **B** when a current density **J** flows in a magnetic field **B**. This term represents the *Hall effect,* and the coefficient of $\mathbf{J} \times \mathbf{B}$ is the Hall coefficient $R_H = 1/n_e e$. The Hall effect plays an important part in magnetoplasma-dynamic generation schemes designed to utilize the kinetic energy associated with the flow of highly conducting plasmas. These will be discussed in detail in Chap. 5. The Hall effect has also been an important tool in semiconductor research,

since it provides information on the sign and concentration of charge carriers. In addition, the Hall effect is currently being used in control and computational applications.

We next consider two examples which illustrate the relationships of Eq. (3.50). The first deals with thermionic generators, and the second with an experimental procedure which exploits the Hall effect to measure plasma characteristics.

Example 3.2

Thermionic generators are devices presently under development for the direct conversion of thermal energy into electrical form.[4,5] A thermionic generator consists of a diode in which the cathode is maintained at a higher temperature than the anode by means of a suitable heat source, for instance, the exhaust gases of a rocket. If the cathode is hot enough, electrons are boiled off the surface by thermionic emission and

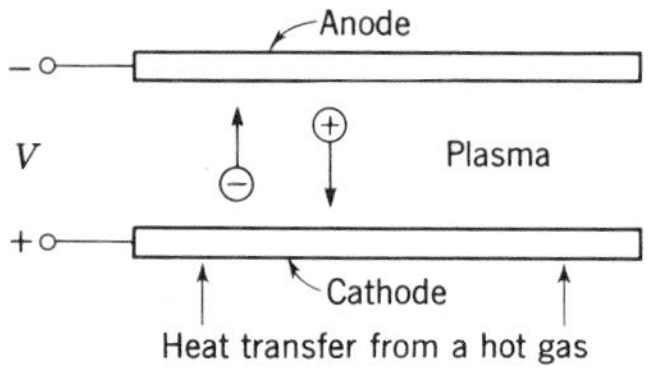

considerable current can be made to flow from the cathode to the anode and through an externally connected electric load, thus providing electric energy. The diode is normally filled with an easily ionizable gas, such as cesium, to avoid space-charge limitation of the current. Suppose the device is short-circuited; as we shall see, this corresponds to the condition $\mathbf{E} = 0$. Also assume

$$|\nabla T_e| = 5 \times 10^6 \text{ °K/m} \qquad \gamma = 100 \text{ mhos/m} \qquad n_e = n_i = n = 10^{18}/\text{m}^3 \qquad \mathbf{v} = 0$$

[With respect to the last two assumptions, note that in thermionic generators there exists a slight departure from electrical neutrality ($n_e \neq n_i$), and also that the velocity of the center of mass of the ionized components is small but not zero ($\mathbf{v} \neq 0$). These deviations can be neglected when evaluating $\mathbf{v}_e$, $\mathbf{v}_i$, and $\mathbf{J}$, but must be taken into account when solving dynamical relations such as Eq. (3.43).]

(*a*) Evaluate the steady-state current density $\mathbf{J}$ if $\mathbf{B} = 0$ (the induced $\mathbf{B}$ is neglected).

(*b*) Determine the electron and ion velocities if $Z = 1$ and the atomic weight of cesium is 132.91.

(*c*) The current in the diode induces a magnetic field perpendicular to $\mathbf{J}$. Unless properly compensated, this magnetic field causes the electrons to gyrate and thus impairs the operation of the device. For what value of induced $\mathbf{B}$ does the Hall effect require compensation?

Solution

(*a*) In the steady state Eq. (3.50) reduces to

$$\frac{\mathbf{J}}{\gamma} + \frac{1}{n_e e}\mathbf{J} \times \mathbf{B} = \mathbf{E} + \mathbf{v} \times \mathbf{B} + \frac{1}{n_e e}\nabla \mathcal{P}_e$$

With **E** and **B** = 0 we have

$$|\mathbf{J}| = \frac{\gamma}{n_e e}|\nabla \mathcal{P}_e| = \frac{\gamma k}{e}|\nabla T_e| = \frac{100 \times 1.38 \times 10^{-23} \times 5 \times 10^6}{1.6 \times 10^{-19}}$$
$$= 4.32 \times 10^4 \text{ amp/m}^2$$

(*b*) For $n_e = n_i = n$, $Z = 1$, we have $\mathbf{J} = ne(\mathbf{v}_i - \mathbf{v}_e)$. We then get another relation between $\mathbf{v}_i$ and $\mathbf{v}_e$ from the condition

$$\mathbf{v} = \frac{m_i\mathbf{v}_i + m_e\mathbf{v}_e}{m_i + m_e} = 0$$

From these two equations we obtain

$$\mathbf{v}_e = -\frac{\mathbf{J}}{en}\frac{m_i}{m_i + m_e} \qquad \mathbf{v}_i = \frac{\mathbf{J}}{en}\frac{m_e}{m_i + m_e}$$

$$v_e = \frac{4.32 \times 10^4}{1.6 \times 10^{-19} \times 10^{18}} = 2.7 \times 10^5 \text{ m/sec}$$

$$v_i = 2.7 \times 10^5 \frac{1}{132.91 \times 1{,}837} = 1.1 \text{ m/sec}$$

(*c*) From inspection of Eq. (3.50) we see that the Hall effect becomes appreciable when

$$|\mathbf{J} \times \mathbf{B}| \approx |\nabla \mathcal{P}_e|$$

or

$$B = \frac{|\nabla \mathcal{P}_e|}{J} = \frac{n_e k|\nabla T_e|}{J}$$

If for a conservative calculation, we assume for **J** the value obtained in part (*a*), then the Hall effect becomes appreciable when

$$B = \frac{10^{18} \times 1.38 \times 10^{-23} \times 5 \times 10^6}{4.32 \times 10^4} = 1.6 \times 10^{-3} \text{ weber/m}^2$$

From this value of B and a given geometry one can find the maximum allowable current by using Ampère's law.

Example 3.3

A magnetoplasma-dynamic generator consists of a channel in which a plasma flows across a magnetic field, as shown schematically in the figure. The motion-induced electric field drives currents through pairs of electrodes connected to one or

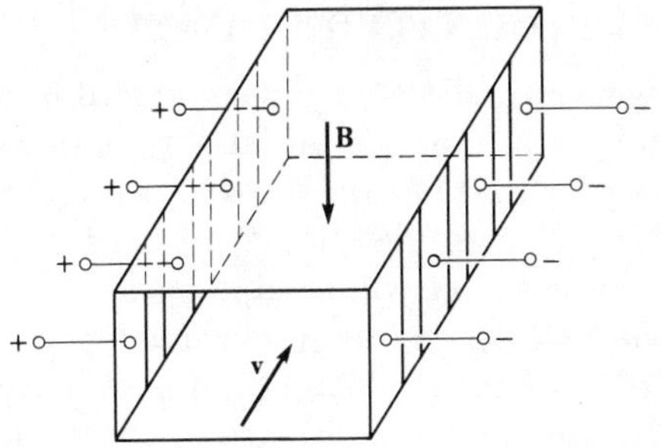

more load resistances. In order to determine the properties of the plasma the following experiment is performed:

(*a*) The electrode pairs facing each other are short-circuited through ammeters, so that (as we shall see) E_y, the component of electric field perpendicular to v and B, vanishes, and J_y can be measured.

(*b*) At the same time, adjacent electrodes are connected to high-impedance voltmeters; since the adjacent electrodes are electrically isolated and there is no other provision for current flow in the direction of $\mathbf{v}$, the component of current density J_x vanishes, and E_x can be measured.

Evaluate the electron density n_e and the collision frequency ν_{ei} if in the steady state:

Short-circuit current density:	$J_y = -10^6$ amp/m^2
Flow velocity:	$v_x = 10^3$ m/sec
Longitudinal electric field:	$E_x = -10^2$ volts/m
Electron pressure gradient:	$\nabla \mathcal{P}_e = 0$
Magnetic flux density:	$B_z = 1$ weber/m^2

Solution

Under the condition of the experiment, with $\partial J/\partial t$, $\nabla \mathcal{P}_e = 0$, the generalized Ohm's law of Eq. (3.50) reads

$$\frac{\mathbf{J}}{n_e e^2/\nu_{ei} m_e} + \frac{1}{n_e e}\mathbf{J} \times \mathbf{B} = \mathbf{E} + \mathbf{v} \times \mathbf{B}$$

Taking into account the orientation of the vectors and the fact that $J_x = 0$, we obtain for the x component

$$\frac{1}{n_e e} J_y B_z = E_x$$

or

$$n_e = \frac{1}{e}\frac{J_y B_z}{E_x} = \frac{1}{1.6 \times 10^{-19}} \frac{10^6 \times 1}{10^2} = 6.25 \times 10^{22} \text{ electrons/m}^3$$

Then taking into account that J_x and $E_y = 0$, we obtain for the y component

$$\frac{J_y}{n_e e^2/\nu_{ei} m_e} = -v_x B_z$$

or

$$\nu_{ei} = \frac{v_x B_z n_e e^2}{J_y m_e} = \frac{10^3 \times 1 \times 6.25 \times 10^{22} \times (1.6 \times 10^{-19})^2}{10^6 \times 9.11 \times 10^{-31}}$$
$$= 1.76 \times 10^{12}/\text{sec}$$

3.8 THE GENERALIZED OHM'S LAW IN COLLISION - DOMINATED PLASMAS

Although the generalized Ohm's law expressed by Eq. (3.50) is only approximately valid because of the initial assumptions in Sec. 3.3*a* and the approximations which exploit the ratio between the mass of the electrons and ions, it is still more detailed than need be in dense plasmas. For our immediate purposes we will be able to simplify this relation even further, since in the case of the dense plasmas which are of interest in most applications of power conversion at low speeds and low frequencies, the terms explicitly containing the electron density in the denominator are negligible and can be dropped.

To show this, we consider first the three terms on the left-hand side of Eq. (3.50) involving the current density $\mathbf{J}$. Pulling out the common factor $m_e/n_e e^2$ and introducing the cyclotron angular velocity for the electrons

$$\boldsymbol{\omega}_c = + \frac{e\mathbf{B}}{m_e}$$

these become

$$\frac{m_e}{n_e e^2}\left(\frac{\partial \mathbf{J}}{\partial t} + \nu_{ei}\mathbf{J} + \mathbf{J} \times \boldsymbol{\omega}_c\right)$$

Suppose now that amplitude of $\mathbf{J}$ varies sinusoidally in time with radian frequency ω. In this case, we may use phasor notation denoted by a dot on top (see Secs. 7.3, 9.4*c*), so that our three terms may be written as

$$\frac{m_e}{n_e e^2}(j\omega\dot{\mathbf{J}} + \nu_{ei}\dot{\mathbf{J}} + \dot{\mathbf{J}} \times \boldsymbol{\omega}_c)$$

In this grouping it is clear that the inductive term can be neglected for $\omega \ll \nu_{ei}$, that is, as long as we confine ourselves to situations in which the current density varies in time with a characteristic frequency ω much smaller than the electron-ion collision frequency ν_{ei}. Likewise the Hall-effect term can be neglected whenever the collision frequency dominates over the cyclotron radian frequency $\boldsymbol{\omega}_c$.

Neglect of these terms can be explained on physical grounds by the fact that a collision effectively randomizes the motion and tends to destroy the orderly or average component of motion of the particles involved. It follows that, when the time between collisions is much smaller than the period of oscillation of the excitation voltage, the current, which represents the average or orderly response, cannot get appreciably out of phase in time, because of the inertia effect of the mass. Likewise when the time between collisions is much smaller than a period of cyclotron gyration, the particles cannot acquire appreciable drift in the direction perpendicular to $\mathbf{E}$, under the effect of the magnetic field.

In the collision-dominated case we can also neglect the thermoelectric term, since $\nabla \mathcal{P}_e$ has the same order of magnitude as $\mathbf{J} \times \mathbf{B}$. We arrive at this conclusion by observing that, in steady state or slow transients ($\partial/\partial t \to 0$) the equation of motion (3.43*a*) reduces to

$$\nabla \mathcal{P} = \nabla \mathcal{P}_i + \nabla \mathcal{P}_e = \mathbf{J} \times \mathbf{B}$$

where as mentioned before $\nabla \mathcal{P}_i$ and $\nabla \mathcal{P}_e$ are practically equal.

With these approximations the generalized Ohm's law reduces to

$$\frac{\mathbf{J}}{\gamma} = \mathbf{E} + \mathbf{v} \times \mathbf{B} \tag{3.52}$$

We now see that in order to establish the range of validity of this equation, we need to estimate the electron-ion collision frequency, at least in order of magnitude. This can be done by defining a collision interaction sphere and finding its volume rate of sweep; the reader is referred to Probs. 3.11 and 3.12 at the end of the chapter for further details. The results are

$$\nu_{ei} = \pi R_0^2 n_i \langle u_e^2 \rangle^{\frac{1}{2}} \tag{3.53}$$

where $\langle u_e^2 \rangle^{\frac{1}{2}}$ is the average magnitude of the random electron velocity, and R_0 is the collision radius approximately given by

$$R_0 = \frac{Ze^2}{4\pi\epsilon_0 U_e} \tag{3.54}$$

where U_e is the average kinetic energy of random motion. For example if we wish to find R_0 at room temperature ($T = 20°\text{C}$) we have, from Eq. (3.17) with $\mathfrak{N} = 3$,

$$\begin{aligned} U_e &= \tfrac{3}{2} \times 1.38 \times 10^{-23} \times 293 = 6.06 \times 10^{-21} \text{ joule} \\ &= 0.038 \text{ ev} \end{aligned}$$

and from Eq. (3.54) with $Z = 1$,

$$R_0 = \frac{9 \times (1.6 \times 10^{-19})^2}{10^{-9} \times 6.06 \times 10^{-21}} = 380 \times 10^{-10} \text{ m}$$

or $R_0 \approx 400$ A or angstrom units (1 A $= 10^{-10}$ m).

The radius of most atoms is of the order of 1 A. This is also the radius of collision for electron-atom encounters. Thus we see that, at room-temperature thermal energies, the *effective* radius of collision for charged particles is roughly 400 times that of neutral particles. An important consequence of this fact is that our equations can now be applied, as mentioned in Sec. 3.3*a*, to highly but not necessarily fully ionized gases, since the probability of collision with neutral particles is much smaller than with charged particles and can be neglected.

For more energetic particles, R_0 decreases as $1/U_e$. It is interesting to note that R_0 reduces to the order of the atomic radius or 1 A when U_e goes up 400 times, so that U_e has the value $400(0.038) = 15$ ev, approximately. This is in fact the very order of magnitude of the first ionization potential for many atoms, and signifies that it is indeed the Coulomb energy that must be supplied to an orbital electron in order to detach it from the nucleus. At room temperature the collision frequency is

$$\begin{aligned} \nu_{ei} &= \pi \times (380 \times 10^{-10})^2 \times (2 \times 1.76 \times 10^{11} \times 0.038)^{\frac{1}{2}} \times n_i \\ &= 5.2 \times 10^{-10} n_i \end{aligned}$$

The density of an ideal gas at normal temperature and pressure is the *Loschmidt number*

$$n = 2.7 \times 10^{25} \text{ particles/m}^3$$

At this temperature the degree of ionization may be quite low. If we assume, for example, $n_i = 10^{-4}n$, we obtain

$$\nu_{ei} = 5.2 \times 10^{-10} \times 10^{-4} \times 2.7 \times 10^{25} = 1.4 \times 10^{12}/\text{sec}$$

This last frequency is so large that we may conclude that in a dense plasma, the electron-ion collision frequency is very likely to be much larger than the frequency of the impressed fields and the cyclotron frequency, so that the approximate Ohm's law as given by Eq. (3.52) is valid.

Finally we observe that the electron-ion collision frequency ν_{ei} is proportional to n_i and, therefore, in a plasma is proportional to n_e. We thus find, by combining Eqs. (3.51) and (3.53) defining the conductivity and collision frequency, respectively, that in a plasma in which the electron-ion collision frequency is predominant, the conductivity is independent of density of the ionized particles. Also, in this case, we can show that the conductivity is proportional to the $\frac{3}{2}$ power of the temperature.

We shall find that the conductivity is a key parameter in the study of electromechanical power converters, and it is consequently important to be familiar with a number of typical values.

Table 3.1 gives the conductivities of various media which are of interest in electromechanical power conversion.

Table 3.1 CONDUCTIVITY VALUES FOR SEVERAL MEDIA

Medium	Temperature, °K	γ, mhos/m
Highly ionized proton plasma	290	10.8
Highly ionized proton plasma	10^3	69.0
Highly ionized proton plasma	10^4	2.19×10^3
Highly ionized proton plasma	10^5	6.95×10^4
Highly ionized proton plasma	10^6	2.19×10^6
Thermonuclear plasma	10^8	2.19×10^9
Mercury	303	1.04×10^6
Liquid sodium	573	5×10^6
Aluminum	348	2.94×10^7
Copper	348	4.84×10^7

3.9 TRANSITION TO LIQUID- AND SOLID-STATE CONDUCTORS

In our approach so far we have gone from consideration of individual particles to consideration of the collection of particles in an infinitesimal volume element, thus gradually introducing the concept of a material medium which is still in the gaseous state. We now wish to extend our equations to encompass liquid and solid state as well. What must we do to accomplish this?

Our first step is to note that the transition of states from gaseous to liquid to solid is marked by increasingly large particle densities. As this occurs, the interactions between the nuclei and between the electron spins modify the nature of the interparticle forces.[6] The critical particle-density level for a given temperature at which these effects become manifest can be readily estimated. Classical theory predicts that the electrons of an atom fall into the nucleus if the electron distance becomes so small that the potential energy of Coulomb interaction becomes predominant over the particle kinetic energy. Since this does not happen, quantum mechanics must be applied at the density level for which the average interparticle distance corresponds to the collision radius of Eq. (3.54). Thus

$$n = \left(\frac{1}{R_0}\right)^3 \doteq \left(\frac{4\pi\epsilon_0 U_e}{Ze^2}\right)^3 \tag{3.55}$$

is the density level above which our macroscopic equations no longer apply in their original form.

When the particle densities do become larger than those of Eq. (3.55), changes occur in the interparticle forces. Without entering into a detailed discussion of quantum mechanics, we can say that with increasing density and decreasing temperature, binding forces develop which at first prevent changes in the relative distance of the ions, but not in their relative orientation; this is the *liquid state.* In the next stage even the freedom of relative orientation between the ions is lost, and the *solid state* is attained. With regard to the electrons, we distinguish among conductors, semiconductors, and dielectrics, depending on the number of electrons that retain freedom of motion.

Under these circumstances changes in the macroscopic equations, of course, occur in the terms representing the microfields or collision effects. Our general approach is still valid, as is the separation into like- and unlike-particle interaction, but some modifications are required.

(a) Like-particle Interactions

Because of the binding forces which limit the relative motion of the ion, their interactions do not take the form of collisions and cannot be expressed as a pressure-gradient term. Consequently, we shall replace $\nabla \mathcal{P}$ in the MPD equation of motion by a general force term applicable to any case. In recognition of the multiple nature of the contributory physical mechanisms for the application of a mechanical force to the unit volume of conducting material, we simply denote it by $-\mathbf{f}_m$. Thus we eliminate the need to focus our attention on these mechanisms and simply think of $\mathbf{f}_m$ as a mechanical force density applied by some mechanical agency.

The electron term, on the other hand, can still be expressed in conductors as a pressure-gradient term, since the electrons continue to move with relative ease through the medium and can still be said to undergo binary collisions. Thus the $\nabla \mathcal{P}_e$ term is retained in the generalized Ohm's law.

(b) Unlike-particle Interactions

In conductors the general formulation as a viscous drag involving a collision frequency ν_{ei} is still correct, but the calculation of ν_{ei} is more complex and the interpretation of Eq. (3.51) slightly different. Thus, the formulation of this effect as the $\mathbf{J}/\gamma$ term in our MPD Ohm's law equation is still valid, except that we shall not attempt to calculate γ, relying instead on experimental information.

Our final single-fluid MPD equations are thus

$$\xi \frac{\partial \mathbf{v}}{\partial t} - \mathbf{f}_m = \mathbf{J} \times \mathbf{B} \tag{3.56}$$

$$\frac{m_e}{n_e e^2} \frac{\partial \mathbf{J}}{\partial t} + \frac{\mathbf{J}}{\gamma} + \frac{1}{n_e e} \mathbf{J} \times \mathbf{B} = \mathbf{E} + \mathbf{v} \times \mathbf{B} + \frac{1}{n_e e} \nabla \mathcal{P}_e \tag{3.57a}$$

We again note that the high-density approximations apply to Eq. (3.57a), so that the terms explicitly containing the electron density in the denominator can be dropped, giving

$$\frac{\mathbf{J}}{\gamma} = \mathbf{E} + \mathbf{v} \times \mathbf{B} \tag{3.57b}$$

To show that this is true, we shall make some calculations for copper, which is still the most important conducting material from the engineering point of view.

At room temperature, the value of γ is experimentally determined to be 0.59×10^8 mhos/m; the value of n_e may be calculated from the known density (8.94 gm/cm^3), molecular weight (63.57), the universal Avogadro number (6.025×10^{23} molecules/mole), and the supposition that copper is fully "ionized," i.e., that each copper atom contributes one valence or free electron to the conduction process. Thus

$$\begin{aligned} n_e &= \frac{6.025 \times 10^{23}}{63.57} \times 8.94 \\ &= 8.49 \times 10^{22} \text{ electrons/cm}^3 \\ &= 8.49 \times 10^{28} \text{ electrons/m}^3 \end{aligned}$$

Now, in mks units we have

$$\frac{1}{n_e e} = \frac{1}{8.49 \times 10^{28} \times 1.60 \times 10^{-19}} = 7.36 \times 10^{-11}$$

$$\frac{1}{\gamma} = \frac{1}{0.59 \times 10^{8}} = 1.7 \times 10^{-8}$$

and
$$\frac{m_e}{n_e e^2} = \frac{1}{n_e e(e/m_e)} = \frac{7.36 \times 10^{-11}}{1.76 \times 10^{11}} = 4.19 \times 10^{-22}$$

We may now once again apply our previous technique (Sec. 3.8) of comparing the magnitudes of the terms on the left-hand side of Eq. (3.57*a*). These three terms then become

$$\frac{m_e}{n_e e^2}\left(j\omega \dot{\mathbf{J}} + \frac{\dot{\mathbf{J}}}{\gamma m_e/n_e e^2} + \dot{\mathbf{J}} \times \omega_c\right)$$

The "equivalent" collision frequency is thus

$$\nu_{\text{eq}} = \frac{1}{\gamma m_e/n_e e^2} = \frac{1.7 \times 10^{-8}}{4.19 \times 10^{-22}} = 0.4 \times 10^{14} \text{ cps}$$

It is clear that even if **B** is quite large, say, $B = 1$, the cyclotron radian frequency is only

$$\omega_c = \frac{eB}{m} = 1.76 \times 10^{11} \text{ rad/sec}$$

so that the Hall-effect term is more than two orders of magnitude less than the $\mathbf{J}/\gamma$ term. Moreover, the inertial term will be negligible when $\omega < 4 \times 10^{12}$. Neglect of the inertial term is, indeed, consistent with the assumption of neutrality made in deriving the MPD equations.

Finally we can show that the thermoelectric term is relatively small in an electromechanical power converter. To do this, we compare the magnitudes of $\nabla \mathcal{P}_e/n_e$ and $\mathbf{v} \times \mathbf{B}$. Since $\mathcal{P}_e = n_e k T_e$ (see Sec. 3.6*a*), $\nabla \mathcal{P}_e/n_e e = k/e \; \nabla T_e$. The Boltzmann constant k has the value 1.38×10^{-23}, so that

$$\frac{k}{e} = \frac{1.38 \times 10^{-23}}{1.60 \times 10^{-19}} = 0.86 \times 10^{-4} \text{ joule/°K-coul}$$

Now the magnitude of ∇T_e is restricted by the limitations of the materials employed. A temperature rise in the order of magnitude of 100°C typifies rotating machinery, and this takes place in distances which are at least centimeters. Let us be generous in the estimate of $|\nabla T_e|$, and take 10^4 °C/m as an upper limit. This makes $|\nabla \mathcal{P}_e/n_e e| \approx 1$. However, $|\mathbf{v} \times \mathbf{B}|$ in a rotating machine can be about 200, with B limited to 1 by saturation, and v limited to 200 by centrifugal stress. As a result, we see that even a generous estimate of the thermoelectric voltage gradient is more than two orders of magnitude less than the electromechanical voltage gradient.

We have thus established that Eqs. (3.56) and (3.57*b*) now constitute the fundamental relations that a volume element of a high-density, electrically neutral material satisfies when moving in an electromagnetic field.

These equations will provide the starting point for the development of the characteristics and geometry of physical electromechanical power converters.

3.10 SUMMARY

This chapter covered the transition from a single particle to the unit-volume element of a dense conducting material. The salient points of this transition are the following:

1. In multiparticle systems the charged particles interact with one another. It is expedient to consider this interaction as consisting of two parts: the long-range interaction which gives rise to an induced component of the average or macroscopic field, and the short-range interaction which results in a randomization of the motion of the particles, similar to the effect of collisions among billiard balls.
2. The equations for the electrons and the ions in a collisionless plasma are formally identical with those of a single particle. The important difference is that the electromagnetic field quantities now include the induced components which represent the reaction of matter to the impressed fields.
3. This reaction of matter manifests itself:

   (*a*) As a collective displacement of charged particles leading to the formation of space and surface charges.
   (*b*) As a collective motion of charged particles leading to the formation of volume and surface currents.

   An example of effect (*a*) is the free motion of a plasmoid in a magnetic field and of effect (*b*) the formation of a magnetic wall.
4. The interaction between each particle and the collective of all the others during their reflection by a magnetic wall can be interpreted in terms of a balance between a magnetic pressure and a particle pressure. The latter, being a quadratic function of the random velocities, is a convenient measure for their effects.
5. The macroscopic equation for collisionless plasma may be extended by including a pressure term representing the effect of

collisions between like particles and a friction term representing the effect of collision between unlike particles.

6. With increasing density of the plasma, long- and short-range interactions cooperate to couple effectively the ions and the electrons which may then be considered to form a single fluid, whose mechanical behavior is governed by a Newtonian force law and electrical behavior by a generalized Ohm's law. These form the magnetoplasma-dynamical (MPD) set.
7. The generalized Ohm's law contains besides the resistive-drop term, an inertia term, a Hall-effect term, and a thermoelectric term. With increasing density and increasing frequency of collisions between electrons and ions these latter terms become negligible.
8. In the transition from gaseous to liquid and solid state, the high-density MPD equations remain valid provided that we account for electron-spin interactions by treating γ as an experimental parameter and replacing $\nabla \mathcal{P}$ by $-\mathbf{f}_m$ to indicate the possibility of physical mechanisms other than pressure gradient that provide the forces of mechanical cohesion between the volume elements of the conductor.

REFERENCES

1. Kennard, E. H.: "Kinetic Theory of Gases," McGraw-Hill Book Company, New York, 1958.
2. Spitzer, L. Jr.: "Physics of Fully Ionized Gases," Interscience Publishers, Inc., New York, 1956.
3. Tolman, R. C., and T. D. Stewart: Electromotive Forces Produced by the Acceleration of Metals, *Phys. Rev.*, vol. 8, p. 9 (1916). The Mass of the Electric Carrier in Copper, Silver and Aluminum, *Phys. Rev.*, vol. 1, p. 164 (1917).
4. Egli, P. H. (ed.): "Advanced Energy Conversion," vol. 2, 1962 Symposium on Thermionic Power Conversion, Pergamon Press, New York.
5. *Proc. IEEE*, Special Issue on New Energy Sources, May, 1963.
6. Ham, J. M., and G. R. Slemon: "Scientific Basis of Electrical Engineering," John Wiley & Sons Inc., New York, 1961.
7. Arzimovich, L. A.: "Elementary Plasma Physics," Blaisdell Publishing Company, New York, 1965.

PROBLEMS

3.1 A collisionless plasma, infinite in extent, is exposed to a static electromagnetic field with the E and B fields perpendicular to each other. Prove that, if the ions move with velocity

$$\mathbf{v}_i = \frac{\mathbf{E} \times \mathbf{B}}{B^2}$$

then the component of the current-density vector perpendicular to **B**

$$\mathbf{J}_\perp = n_e e(\mathbf{v}_{i,\perp} \cdot - \mathbf{v}_{e,\perp})$$

is a vector of constant magnitude rotating with angular velocity $-\omega_{ce}$.

3.2 (*a*) Determine the motion of an electron released with negligible velocity in uniform and time-invariant **E** and **B** fields perpendicular to each other.

(*b*) Repeat part (*a*) for a proton, and compare the two speeds.

(*c*) Assume now that, instead of a single electron and a single proton, a plasma is fed in; the density $n_e = n_i = n$ is sufficiently low so that the particles do not interact with one another, and the induced fields are negligible. Evaluate the kinetic energy associated with one cubic meter of such a plasma (energy density) as a function of time.

(*d*) If part (*c*) describes the mode of operation of a plasma accelerator, where the plasma is fed in at one end and is exhausted at the other end, what is the optimum distance that the protons should travel within the electromagnetic field for maximum energy gain?

3.3 A collisionless electron gas with low density n is fed with negligible velocity into a region with crossed **E** and **B**.

(*a*) If the current density **J** is defined as $\mathbf{J} = -en\mathbf{v}$, and the electric power absorbed by a unit volume of gas, namely, the electric power density is

$$p_{\text{elec}} = \mathbf{E} \cdot \mathbf{J} = \mathbf{E} \cdot (-ne\mathbf{v})$$

determine p_{elec} as a function of time, and compare it with the density of kinetic energy stored $W_{\text{kin}} = \frac{1}{2}nmv^2$.

(*b*) If the dynamical performance of the gas is to be associated with the equivalent circuit shown, what should be the character of the load and the value of its impedance? Note that $\mathbf{J} \cdot \mathbf{E}/|\mathbf{E}|$ is the component of the current density in the direction of **E**.

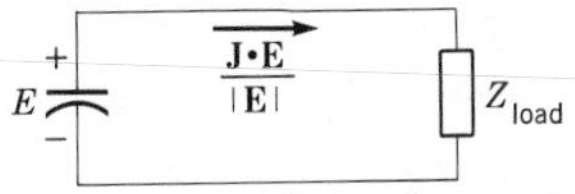

3.4 Derive Eq. (3.23) starting with a group of particles impinging on the wall with an arbitrary angle of incidence. Proceed as in Sec. 3.6*b*: i.e., determine first the change in momentum per particle and then the parallelopiped that initially contains the N^g particles which impinge on the wall in one second.

3.5 Assuming that the fuel in the rocket of Fig. 2.17 is a proton plasma, determine:

(*a*) The pressure $\mathcal{P}$ which the protons exert on the wall if their density in front of the wall is

$$n_p = 10^{22} \text{ protons/m}^3$$

and the exhaust velocity is

$$v_e = 2 \times 10^4 \text{ m/sec}$$

(*b*) The electric field required.

(*c*) The area of the wall if the output power is 1 Mw.

3.6 There is evidence that thermonuclear fusion may occur in solar flares. Assuming this to be the result of the acceleration of deuterons trapped between converging magnetic walls, determine the minimum required magnetic flux density in the walls. In order that the fusion process be self-sustaining, the deuterons must reach an energy of at least 3 Kev with a density of 10^{20} deuterons/m³.

3.7 The insulators of transmission lines are often protected against lightning strokes by means of rod gaps or arcing horns which provide flashover parallel paths for the lightning currents.

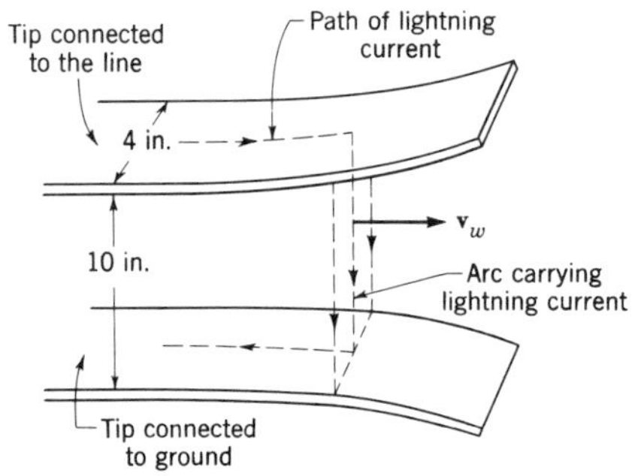

When the lightning strikes, the sudden high-voltage surge ionizes the air between the arcing tips. An arc is ignited at the left side of the picture where the tips are connected to the line and ground, respectively. The voltage across the insulator thus drops to a permissible value while the arc carrying the lightning current progresses to the right. Because of the large currents and powers involved, the air in these gaps can be considered as fully ionized and its resistivity negligible. We can thus assume the arc to form an ideal magnetic wall. Evaluate (*a*) the magnetic pressure, (*b*) the wall velocity, (*c*) the voltage across the gap, if the lightning current is 10^5 amp, the arcing tips are 4 in. wide and are spaced 10 in. apart, and the density of air is 1 kg/m^3.

3.8 The dynamical behavior of a plasma can be described by equivalent circuits as well as by equations.

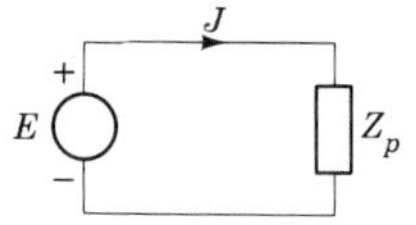

(*a*) Introduce in the circuit shown the proper value of the plasma impedance, according to the two-fluid model, when $B = 0$, $\nabla = 0$ (no spatial variability).

(*b*) Determine the response of the plasma to an impressed step of **E** and its time constant.

3.9 Consider a plasma slab of thickness $d = 10^{-1}$ m and infinite in extent. Assume that at time $t = 0$ the electrons are all displaced to the right by the same amount $\delta = 10^{-8}$ m as shown:

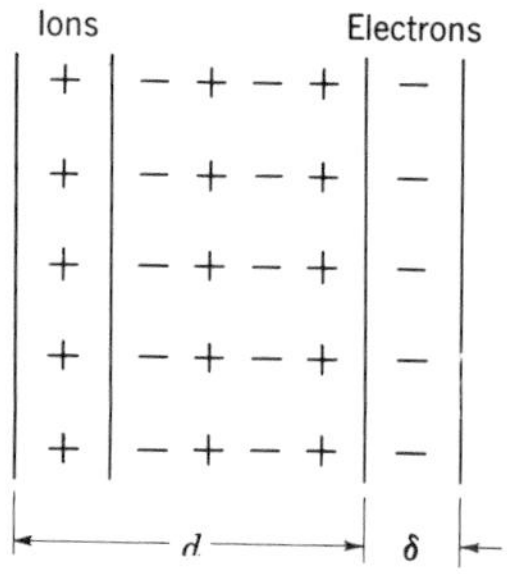

Evaluate:

(*a*) The charge per unit surface of the slab as a function of the displacement of the electrons from the ions if their density is

$$n_e = n_i = n = 10^{22} \text{ particles/m}^3$$

(*b*) The induced electric field in the inner region of the slab as a function of δ.

(*c*) The restoring force, namely, the force of attraction between the ions and the electrons per unit area of the slab at $t = 0$.

(*d*) The motion of the electrons with respect to the ions assumed to be immobile for $t > 0$ if $\nu_{ei} = 10^9$ collisions/sec.

(*e*) The radian frequency of oscillation, ω_p (usually called *plasma frequency*).

(*f*) The time constant for the relaxation to a neutral state.

3.10 In an elastic collision between two charged particles both energy and momentum are conserved. Prove that on the average an electron colliding with stationary ions loses a fraction of energy

$$\frac{\Delta W_{\text{kin}}}{(W_{\text{kin}})_0} = \frac{2m_e m_i}{(m_i + m_e)^2} \doteq 2\frac{m_e}{m_i}$$

3.11 When we deal with charged particles, we consider a collision to have taken place if either of the charged particles is appreciably deflected from its original trajectory. An electron thus undergoes a collision with an ion when the radius of closest approach R_0 is so small that the coulomb energy of interaction is of the same order of magnitude as the kinetic energy of the electron.

(*a*) On this basis derive Eq. (3.54).

(*b*) Determine the collision radius R_0 for an electron temperature of 50,000°K.

3.12 According to our model for collisions between charged particles we can say that an electron-ion collision occurs when an ion comes within an interaction sphere of radius R_0 centered at the electron.

(*a*) On the basis of the volume swept by this interaction sphere in one second, derive Eq. (3.53). Assume for v_e the thermal velocity of the electrons.

(*b*) Determine the conductivity of a highly ionized gas when the electron temperature is 50,000°K.

3.13 Microcosms and macrocosms often display similar behavior. For instance, the probability laws that govern the motion of systems of elementary charged particles were originally investigated by Chandrasekhar for systems of interacting stellar bodies.

(*a*) Substituting gravitational for electrostatic binary interaction, determine the collision radius R_0 of stellar bodies having velocities and mass equal to those of the sun:

$$v = 2 \times 10^4 \text{ m/sec} \qquad M = 1.99 \times 10^{30} \text{ kg}$$

The gravitational force is

$$f_G = -G\, M_1 M_2/r^2$$

with

$$G = 6.668 \times 10^{-11} \text{ newton-m}^2/\text{kg}^2$$

(*b*) How does this collision radius compare with the radius of the sun, $R_s = 6.96 \times 10^8$ m?

(*c*) Assuming that the density of scattering bodies in our galaxy is

$$n_s = 2.77 \times 10^{-51} \text{ stars/m}^3$$

determine the collision frequency.

The result should put you at ease about the likelihood of catastrophic collisions within your lifetime!

3.14 Variations in the overall level of solar activity and some large flares produce modulation effects on the energy of the galactic component of cosmic radiation arriving at the surface of the earth. According to Morrison (1956) and Parker (1961), the energy loss observed in cosmic-ray particles is due to momentum interchange with turbulent clouds of magnetized proton plasma emanating from the sun. As a model for this interaction, assume that the magnetic field in the clouds consists of a random distribution of magnetic dipoles resulting from current vortices.

(*a*) Approximating these dipole fields by bounded magnetic field regions of radius a and uniform magnetic flux density $B = 10^{-6}$ weber/m², determine the minimum

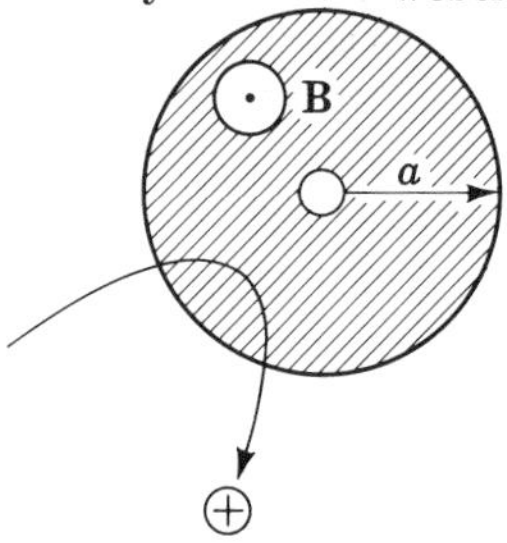

radius a required to cause a deflection larger than 90° when the interacting particle is a nickel nucleus with an initial energy of 2 Bev.

(*b*) Associating with the scattering magnetic dipole a mass equal to the mass of the proton plasma contained in a sphere of minimum radius a, determine the number of elastic collisions that the nickel nucleus has undergone when its energy is reduced by one order of magnitude. Assume that the density of protons in the solar cloud is $n_p = 10^8$ protons/m³, and use the result of Prob. 3.10.

3.15 A gas consisting of electrons with a density n of 10^{12} particles/m³ and a kinetic energy per particle W_{kin} of 0.1 ev is placed in a uniform magnetic field with $B = 1$ weber/m². Would you consider the probability of collision between two particles as appreciable? Justify your conclusion.

3.16 Determine the velocity of the electrons relative to the ions when the current density is 10^6 amp/m²:

(*a*) In a proton plasma with $\xi = 10^{-5}$ kg/m²

(*b*) In copper with $\xi = 8.9 \times 10^3$ kg/m²

chapter 4

THE ACTIVE CONDUCTOR AND ITS DESIGN IN TERMS OF POWER DENSITIES

4.1 INTRODUCTION

In this chapter we study the performance of a volume element of conducting material as determined by the magnetoplasma-dynamical equations. In particular, we focus our attention on the power relations, and we distinguish three modes of operation which we call generating, motoring, and braking. To clarify their physical significance and the conditions for their occurrence, we first proceed to streamline our analytical tools. By taking advantage of the fact that the optimum condition for power conversion corresponds to a perpendicular orientation of the three vectors **J**, **v**, and **B**, we reduce the equations to a scalar form.

We then consider the connections with the external electric and mechanical systems, and, in particular, we concentrate on the following situations: open circuit, voltage-source excitation, and single excitation. These represent limiting cases for the constraints which the circuit connections impose on the electromagnetic variables and correspond to important operating conditions for the entire converter. To gain confidence in the validity of the macroscopic equations, we check our results and interpret them by resorting to the microscopic representation.

We next represent the scalar equations in terms of equivalent circuits and introduce the concept of *slip*, a convenient parameter for quick identification of the operating conditions.

Knowledge of the force or power associated with the unit-volume element is the first step in the synthesis of power converters in that it directly permits determination of the required volume of *active* conductor, the volume of conductor in which power conversion takes place. This volume is dictated by material limitations and by efficiency considerations.

Once the volume of active conductor is determined, we need to establish its geometry. We find that practical engineering requirements stemming from the magnetic circuit dictate the use of a thin sheet or thin strips of conductor in a narrow air gap. We take advantage of this geometry to simplify the analysis further by eliminating variation of all quantities across the thickness of the conductor. For the case in which maximum symmetry prevails, we finally complete the synthesis and determine all the dimensions of the active conductor. This is achieved by simply observing that the heat originating in the Joule losses has to flow across its surface and that the flow rate is directly related to the method of cooling and the temperature rise allowed by the type of insulation used.

4.2 POWER - DENSITY RELATIONS

The fundamental mechanism underlying the operation of electromechanical power converters of the magnetic type is the interaction between current-carrying conductors in relative motion. The building block for these conductors, and therefore for the whole converter is the unit-volume element, whose performance is governed by the magneto-plasma-dynamical equations derived in the previous chapter. Since we are concerned here with power conversion, we have an immediate interest in evaluating this performance in terms of power.

In this respect we note that in the case of a single particle, one equation was sufficient to describe its motion in an electromagnetic field, so that the balance between mechanical and electric power followed directly from this equation. In the case of a volume element of conducting material, the mechanical and electrical behavior are expressed by *two* separate equations, whose coupling is not immediately evident. One may then wonder whether or not such a balance of power exists and if so how it can be demonstrated.

In order to determine the power relations for a volume element of conducting material, we first take the dot product of Eq. (3.56) with $\mathbf{v}$, thus obtaining

$$\xi \mathbf{v} \cdot \frac{\partial \mathbf{v}}{\partial t} = \mathbf{J} \times \mathbf{B} \cdot \mathbf{v} + \mathbf{f}_m \cdot \mathbf{v} \tag{4.1}$$

Since

$$\xi \mathbf{v} \cdot \frac{\partial \mathbf{v}}{\partial t} = \frac{\partial}{\partial t}\left(\frac{\xi v^2}{2}\right)$$

we observe that the term on the left represents the time rate of change of kinetic energy stored in the unit volume of conducting material: this we call *kinetic power density* p_{kin}. The first term on the right-hand side represents the time rate of work done by the force of electromagnetic origin $\mathbf{J} \times \mathbf{B}$ and is therefore called the *converted power density* p_{conv}. The second term on the right-hand side represents the time rate of work done by the external mechanical agency through the force $\mathbf{f}_m$ acting on the volume element of the conductor. This is the *mechanical power density* p_{mech}.

According to the definitions,

$$p_{\text{kin}} = \frac{\partial}{\partial t}\left(\frac{1}{2}\,\xi v^2\right) \tag{4.2a}$$

$$p_{\text{conv}} = \mathbf{J} \times \mathbf{B} \cdot \mathbf{v} \tag{4.2b}$$

$$p_{\text{mech}} = \mathbf{f}_m \cdot \mathbf{v} \tag{4.2c}$$

we can write

$$p_{\text{kin}} = p_{\text{conv}} + p_{\text{mech}} \tag{4.3}$$

Next, taking the dot product of Eq. (3.57*b*) with $\mathbf{J}$, we get

$$\frac{\mathbf{J}^2}{\gamma} = \mathbf{E} \cdot \mathbf{J} + \mathbf{v} \times \mathbf{B} \cdot \mathbf{J} \tag{4.4}$$

We recognize in the term on the left-hand side of Eq. (4.4) the ohmic loss per unit volume or *dissipated power density* p_{diss}. The first term on the right-hand side is evidently the *electric power density* p_{elec}, and since

$$\mathbf{v} \times \mathbf{B} \cdot \mathbf{J} = -\mathbf{J} \times \mathbf{B} \cdot \mathbf{v}$$

the last term is the negative of the converted power density. With the definitions,

$$\frac{\mathbf{J}^2}{\gamma} = p_{\text{diss}} \tag{4.5a}$$

$$\mathbf{E} \cdot \mathbf{J} = p_{\text{elec}} \tag{4.5b}\dagger$$

we can write

$$p_{\text{diss}} = p_{\text{elec}} - p_{\text{conv}} \tag{4.6}$$

and the overall power balance

$$p_{\text{elec}} - p_{\text{diss}} = p_{\text{conv}} = p_{\text{kin}} - p_{\text{mech}} \tag{4.7}$$

The power densities appearing in Eq. (4.7) are, of course, scalar quantities; these may be positive or negative, with the exception of p_{diss}, which is

† This definition of electric power density holds only for materials that are not magnetically polarizable. In magnetically polarizable materials p_{elec} has an additional component due to a magnetic force which is the magnetic counterpart of the Lorentz force.

obviously always positive. The significance of the signs of these densities as defined above is as follows:

1. A positive sign for p_{elec} means that the volume element of conductor is accepting or absorbing electric power; in other words electric energy flows *into* the volume element. Conversely a negative sign means power delivered or an energy flow *out* of the conductor element. The sign of p_{mech} is interpreted in the same way.
2. A positive sign for p_{kin}, of course, means that kinetic energy and speed are increasing.
3. According to Eq. (4.7), p_{conv} conveys information about the direction of the energy flow. When p_{conv} is positive, electric power is absorbed by the volume element. Part of this goes into ohmic losses; the rest is p_{conv}. This then appears as the sum of mechanical power *out* of the element and the rate of *increase* of kinetic energy. Conversely, a negative sign for p_{conv} means that the sum of the mechanical power *in* and the rate of *decrease* of kinetic energy is now positive; the converted power now appears on the electrical side as the sum of the ohmic dissipated power and the electric power *out*. If we view the power-conversion process in the volume element by the fluid-flow analogy depicted in Fig. 4.1, it is clear that the sign of p_{conv} tells us the direction of power "flow" across the "junction" between the electrical and mechanical sides, with a plus sign meaning power going from the electrical side to the mechanical side, and conversely. The dotted arrows on the mechanical sides indicate that all the combinations of p_{mech} and p_{kin} are possible. On the electrical sides instead, the three modes of operation shown in Fig. 4.1 represent the only three possibilities, in view of the one-way nature of p_{diss}. These modes are named in accord with the usual engineering nomenclature employed with power converters whose overall operation corresponds to the direction of conversion shown. Thus in (*a*) a *motor* is a device in which electric power goes in and mechanical or kinetic power is taken out; and conversely in (*b*) for a *generator*.

In these cases p_{diss} is usually relatively small, so that p_{conv} is comparable to p_{elec} in both sign and magnitude. This is not true in mode (*c*), however, in which all the power going in on both sides goes down the dissipative "drain." This form of operation is a purely dissipative regime which did not appear in the discussion of Sec. 2.14 since it arises from charged-particle collisions. In fact p_{diss} vanishes when the collision frequency ν_{ei} approaches zero, as can be seen by introducing Eq. (3.51) into Eq. (4.5*a*). This mode of operation is called *braking* since it is associated with an electromagnetic force opposite to the direction of motion, and for

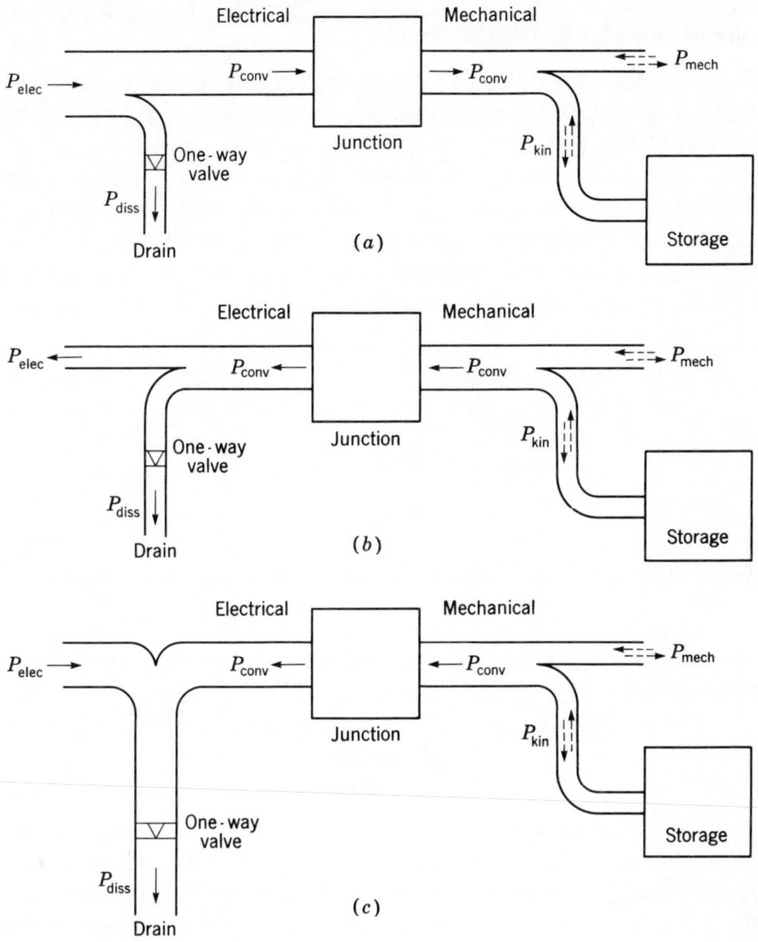

Fig. 4.1 Fluid-flow analogy of power conversion: (*a*) Motoring; (*b*) generating; (*c*) braking.

this reason it sometimes finds use as a deliberate mode for the rapid extraction of the kinetic energy of the moving conductor and coupled masses.

We may summarize the sign criteria for these modes in Table 4.1.

Table 4.1 SIGN CRITERIA FOR THE THREE OPERATING MODES

p_{elec}	p_{conv}	Operating modes
+	+	Motoring
−	−	Generating
+	−	Braking

4.3 THE SCALAR EQUATIONS

Rather than continue with our study in terms of the vector equations, it is convenient to simplify our analysis by considering a particular orientation of the vectors in the power-conversion process.

The orientation which we choose represents not only a practical condition, but one that we strive to attain in order to achieve the greatest possible conversion of power. It is easy to see what this orientation must be. Since p_{conv} is the triple scalar product $\mathbf{J} \cdot \mathbf{B} \times \mathbf{v}$, for given magnitudes of the three vectors, the most power is converted when these vectors form

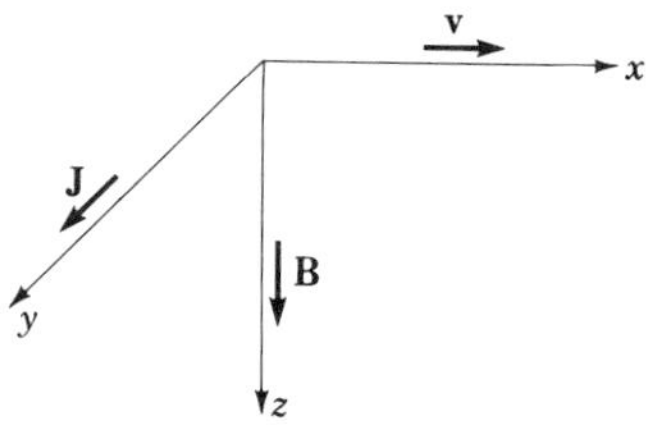

Fig. 4.2 Vector orientation yielding maximum power conversion for given vector magnitudes.

an orthogonal set. Thus we shall assume the orientation of Fig. 4.2, where we define

$$\begin{aligned} \mathbf{v} &= v\mathbf{x}_0 \\ \mathbf{J} &= J\mathbf{y}_0 \\ \mathbf{B} &= B\mathbf{z}_0 \end{aligned} \tag{4.8}$$

It should be noted that Fig. 4.2 and Eq. (4.8) establish a convention for the relative orientation of the vectors. Although the scalar quantities v, J, and B may be either positive or negative, for the directions as shown, p_{conv} is positive, so that we have the *motoring* mode of power conversion; it follows that *positive values of v, J, and B correspond to the motoring condition in our convention.*

It is now easy to see that $\mathbf{E}$ must also be parallel to the y axis in the $\mathbf{y}_0$ direction. We have just noted that we are in the motoring mode; consequently, $\mathbf{E} \cdot \mathbf{J}$ is nonzero and positive, so that $\mathbf{E}$ must have a $\mathbf{y}_0$ component. Furthermore, there cannot be any other component, as may be readily seen from the components of the generalized Ohm's law Eq. (3.57*b*), when we use the definitions of Eq. (4.8). Consequently, we see that

$$\mathbf{E} = E\mathbf{y}_0 \tag{4.9}$$

and substituting back in Eq. (3.57*b*), we find

$$\frac{J}{\gamma} = E - vB \tag{4.10}$$

Similarly, we find that the equation of motion (3.56) has $\mathbf{x}_0$ components exclusively, with

$$\mathbf{f}_m = f_m\mathbf{x}_0 \tag{4.11}$$

and

$$\xi\frac{\partial v}{\partial t} = JB + f_m \tag{4.12}$$

The power densities are given in scalar terms by

$$\begin{aligned} p_{\text{conv}} &= JvB \\ p_{\text{mech}} &= f_m v \\ p_{\text{elec}} &= JE \end{aligned} \tag{4.13}$$

We note from Eq. (4.12) that $f_m = -JB$ in the constant-velocity case; this gives $f_m < 0$ for v, B, J, >0, so that $p_{\text{mech}} < 0$ as is consistent with our motoring convention for positive v, J, and B.

The reader should note the change of sign when the scalar equation (4.10) is compared to its vector original equation (3.57*b*). This is, of course, the consequence of our particular choice of vector orientation.

4.4 ILLUSTRATIVE ELECTRIC - CIRCUIT CONNECTIONS

An early understanding of the modes of operation is very important, since these modes characterize the operation of the entire converter. In order to clarify the significance of these operating regimes, we must first depict to ourselves the situation considered by our equations, that is, a conductor element moving with velocity $\mathbf{v}$ with respect to a reference system in which we measure the electric field $\mathbf{E}$ and the magnetic field $\mathbf{B}$. Next we must specify the connections which this element has with the external electric, magnetic, and mechanical systems. These are the *circuit connections*. In general, they provide three additional relationships which have to be solved simultaneously with Eqs. (4.10) and (4.12) in order to determine the five variables of the electromechanical system: E, J, B, v, and f_m. In many cases, however, our task will be facilitated since some of these quantities are prescribed and can be considered as known.

We consider a conducting element of unit dimensions sliding between two perfectly conducting bars, while maintaining contact with the bars, as shown in Fig. 4.3*a*. The whole arrangement is surrounded by a loop carrying an impressed direct current I to represent schematically the source of an impressed magnetic flux density $\mathbf{B}_{\text{imp}}$. A high-impedance voltmeter such as a vacuum-tube voltmeter is permanently connected between the bars in the immediate vicinity of the conductor; its reading measures the electric field $\mathbf{E}$ prevailing at the location of the unit-volume conductor element, but as seen by the observer with respect to whom the conductor moves with velocity $\mathbf{v}$. The switch S allows for three

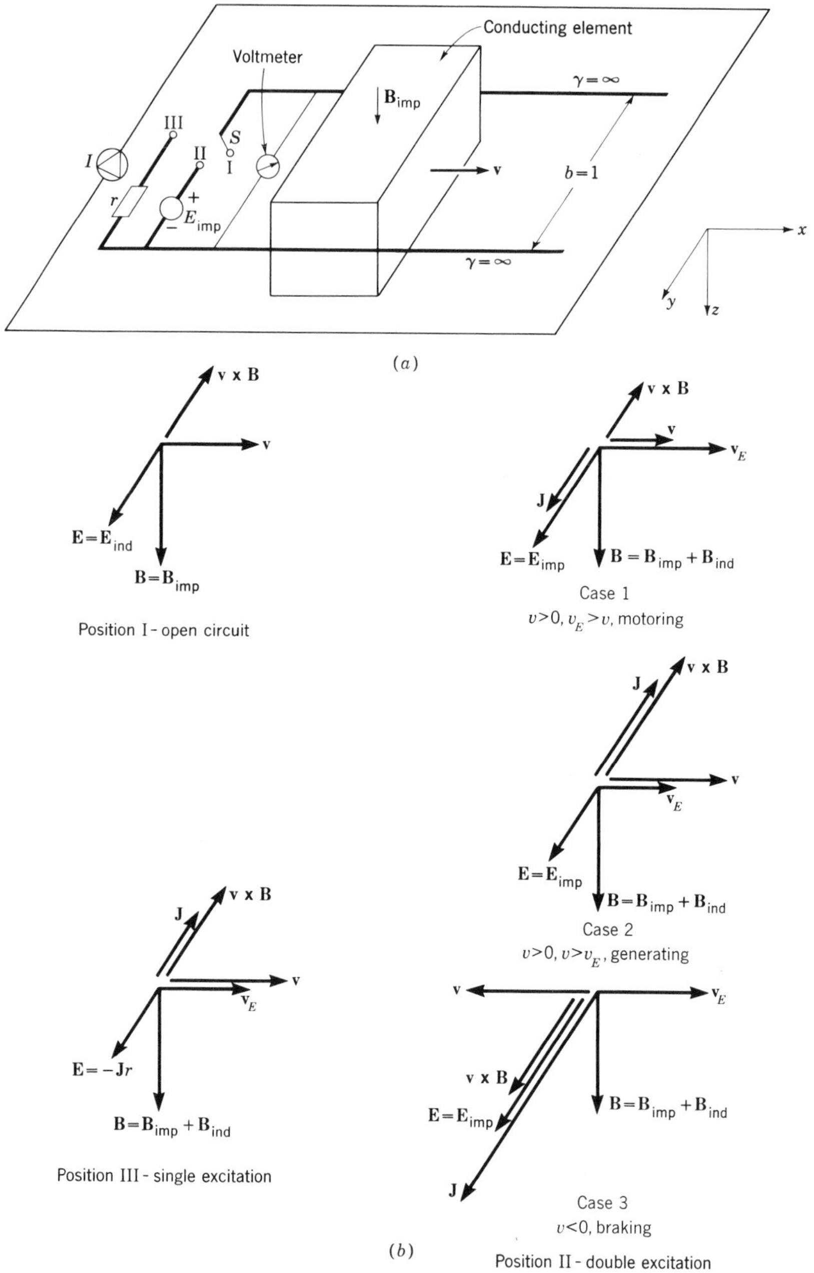

Fig. 4.3 Illustrative circuit connections: (*a*) Arrangement of the conducting element; (*b*) vector orientation.

typical connections of the conducting element: (1) open circuit (position I), (2) voltage source excitation (position II), and (3) resistive load (position III). We shall consider these three cases in turn. The reader will note, incidentally, that the arrangement provides the orthogonal orientation of **J**, **v**, **B** required for most economical power conversion, and our scalar equations apply, with E and $B > 0$.

(a) Open Circuit

First we consider the open-circuit case, when the bars are disconnected from all but the voltmeter. Since the impedance of the electric circuit is practically infinite, no current flows in the conductor ($J = 0$), and the generalized Ohm's law yields in its scalar form

$$0 = E - vB \tag{4.14a}$$

Taking into account the reaction of the charged particles, we write **E** and **B** as a sum of impressed and induced components,

$$\begin{aligned} E &= E_{\text{imp}} + E_{\text{ind}} \\ B &= B_{\text{imp}} + B_{\text{ind}} \end{aligned} \tag{4.15}$$

and since $E_{\text{imp}} = 0$ and $B_{\text{ind}} = 0$ in the open-circuit case, Eq. (4.14a) becomes

$$0 = E_{\text{ind}} - vB_{\text{imp}} \tag{4.14b}$$

From Eq. (4.14b) we see that the voltmeter reads $E = E_{\text{ind}} = vB_{\text{imp}}$. This is the field produced by the surface charge which accumulates at the extremes of the conductor according to the mechanism explained in the example of the plasmoid in Sec. 3.5a. With the vector orientation depicted in Fig. 4.3, positive charge accumulates at the far end of the conductor and negative charge at the near end. Equation (4.14b) now provides a proof that the induced field does indeed neutralize the motional electric field so that the total field vanishes, as seen in the frame of reference of the moving conductor. It is left as an exercise for the reader (Prob. 4.3) to confirm this result by evaluating the surface charge and the associated field.

We also observe that since $J = 0$, the electromagnetic force and the converted power vanish, so that if no mechanical force is applied, the conductor velocity will remain constant. In other words, the electrons and ions drift with velocity v_E.

(b) Voltage-source Excitation

Next we consider the case in which the switch in Fig. 4.3 is moved to position II, and the conducting element is connected to an ideal voltage source or, as we shall call it, in power-networks terminology, an *infinite busbar*. In this case we have two sources impressing respectively a magnetic and an electric field. For this reason the present condition of opertion will also be referred to as *double excitation*. Since the surface-charge accumulation, if any, is now dictated by the source, we denote the electric field by

$$E = E_{\text{imp}} \tag{4.16}$$

The impressed field does not necessarily balance the motion-induced field. As a result, the charged particles within the conductor element are driven by the net field and flow as a current in the path which closes through the external circuit. This current produces an induced component of magnetic flux density B_{ind} which has to be computed by taking into account the geometry of the circuit. The electric current flows in the exact amount required for the microfield due to electron-ion encounters to balance the net electric field according to the generalized Ohm's law. Equation (4.10) thus becomes

$$\frac{J}{\gamma} = E_{\text{imp}} - v(B_{\text{imp}} + B_{\text{ind}}) \tag{4.17}$$

We next proceed to identify the various operating modes. Inasmuch as we have given impressed electric and magnetic fields and given circuit geometry, the current density and hence the operating mode are uniquely defined by the magnitude and sign of the velocity. This is very simply seen when we compare the conductor velocity with the drift velocity v_E. As we recall from Eq. (2.68), $\mathbf{v}_E$ is defined by $\mathbf{E} = -\mathbf{v}_E \times \mathbf{B}$; thus $\mathbf{v}_E$ is in the $\mathbf{x}_0$ direction, and the scalar relationship takes the form $E = v_E B$, with $v_E > 0$ for our conventional orientation. Introducing $E = v_E B$ into Eq. (4.17), we obtain

$$\frac{J}{\gamma} = (v_E - v)(B_{\text{imp}} + B_{\text{ind}}) \tag{4.18}$$

We can now distinguish the following situations:

1. $v > 0$ (in the same direction as v_E), and $v < v_E$. It is clear from Eq. (4.18) that $J > 0$. Thus Eq. (4.13) tells us that p_{conv} and p_{elec} are both positive, so that this is the motoring mode.

   In support of this mathematical derivation we can offer the following physical interpretation. The electrons and ions in the conductor move in crossed E and B fields and therefore, if allowed to move freely, would tend to reach the drift velocity. However, here they move with a lower velocity; this means that they are impeded by an external force, or, in other words, they deliver mechanical work to the agency applying the external force. This is then motoring.

2. $v > 0$, but now $v > v_E$. Equation (4.18) thus tells us that $J < 0$. It follows from Eq. (4.13) that both p_{elec} and p_{conv} are now negative, or that the power flows in the direction opposite to that in the previous case. This defines the generating mode. Physically, if the electrons and ions in the conductor move faster than the drift velocity, they must be driven by an external force, and therefore they must absorb mechanical power.
3. $v < 0$: i.e., v and v_E are in opposite directions. In this case $J > 0$ from Eq. (4.18), and $p_{elec} > 0$, but $p_{conv} < 0$ from Eq. (4.13). This means that both electric and converted powers flow into the conductor and are dissipated as Joule heat. This is then the braking regime.

Physically we may argue as in the previous case that if the electrons and ions move in a direction opposite to that in which they would tend to

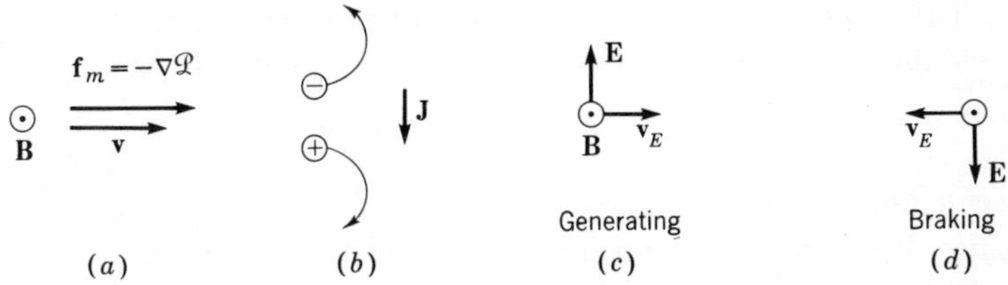

Fig. 4.4 Microscopic description of the generating and braking modes.

drift, they must be driven, and therefore they must absorb mechanical power. However, this criterion alone does not permit distinguishing in the microscopic representation between the braking and the generating regimes. For this purpose we must also consider the electric power. On a microscopic scale, the only mechanism for applying a force to the charged particles is the collision effect implied in the pressure gradient $\nabla\mathcal{P}$. If we assume that the conductor is moving to the right as shown in Fig. 4.4*a*, the pressure is higher on the left side. We then expect a predominance of collisions from the left, so that the initial motion of the elections and ions after a collision has occurred is predominantly to the right, as shown in Fig. 4.4*b*. Soon after the collision, however, the electrons and ions, under the effect of the magnetic field, start to gyrate in opposite directions, thus producing current elements directed downward. In the generating mode the drift velocity $\mathbf{v}_E$ is directed as $\mathbf{v}$, and $\mathbf{E}$ is therefore in the opposite direction to $\mathbf{J}$ as shown in Fig. 4.4*c*. This means that the electric power is negative. In the braking mode $\mathbf{v}$ and

$\mathbf{v}_E$ are in opposite directions. **E** and **J** are in the same direction, and the electric power density is positive, as indicated in Fig. 4.4*d*.

We can also describe the motoring mode in the above manner. In that case suppose **v** and $\mathbf{v}_E$ are to the right. The pressure would be higher on the right, $\mathbf{f}_m$ would reverse, the collisions from the right would predominate, and the current density would be directed upward in the same direction as **E**.

(c) Single Excitation

Finally we consider the case in which the switch of Fig. 4.3 is moved to position III and the electric circuit of the moving conductor closes through a load resistance. In this case the only source is the one that impresses the magnetic field, and this condition of operation will, therefore, be henceforth referred to as *single excitation.* As in the previous case, a current flows in the conductor, and there is therefore an induced component of magnetic field in addition to the impressed component. However, the electric field, as indicated by the voltmeter, is no longer known a priori; it now becomes a function of the resistivity of the load. If we call this resistivity r, then the simple Ohm's law applies, since the load resistance is at rest in our reference frame. Thus we know that

$$E = -Jr \tag{4.19}$$

where the minus sign appears because the direction of **J** reverses in the load. We can now determine E by solving simultaneously with $J/\gamma = E - vB$. This gives

$$E = \frac{vB}{1 + 1/\gamma r} = \frac{v(B_{\text{ind}} + B_{\text{imp}})}{1 + 1/\gamma r} \tag{4.20}$$

By comparing this expression for E with $E = v_E B$, we conclude that

$$v = v_E\left(1 + \frac{1}{\gamma r}\right) \tag{4.21}$$

so that v and v_E have the same sign with v larger than v_E. This means that the only possible operating regime is generating, as we would expect since the load resistance is a passive element and can only absorb power.

A special case of particular interest is the case where r and therefore E vanish. When this so-called short-circuit condition occurs, the totality of the microfields due to electron-ion encounters exactly balances the motion-induced electric field, and all the power converted is dissipated as Joule heat within the conductor.

In the following example, we explore single excitation in greater detail.

Example 4.1

For the case of single excitation in Fig. 4.3:

(a) Find the mechanical force per unit volume in terms of the total magnetic flux density, velocity, conductivity γ, and load resistivity r.

(b) Check the power balance of the system.

Assume steady-state operation ($\partial v/\partial t = 0$).

Solution

(a) In the steady-state case we have, from Eq. (4.12),

$$f_m = -JB$$

We know that $J = -E/r$, and, from Eqs. (4.19) and (4.20),

$$J = -\frac{vB}{r(1 + 1/\gamma r)}$$

Introducing this into the expression for f_m, we get

$$f_m = \frac{vB^2}{r(1 + 1/\gamma r)}$$

(b) Here we find that

$$p_{\text{kin}} = \xi v \frac{\partial v}{\partial t} = 0 \qquad \text{since} \qquad \frac{\partial v}{\partial t} = 0$$

$$p_{\text{mech}} = f_m v = \frac{v^2 B^2}{r(1 + 1/\gamma r)}$$

$$p_{\text{conv}} = JvB = -\frac{v^2 B^2}{r(1 + 1/\gamma r)}$$

$$p_{\text{elec}} = JE = -rJ^2 = -\frac{v^2 B^2}{r(1 + 1/\gamma r)^2}$$

$$p_{\text{diss}} = \frac{J^2}{\gamma} = \frac{v^2 B^2}{\gamma r^2 (1 + 1/\gamma r)^2}$$

From these we can check the overall power balance:

$$p_{\text{elec}} - p_{\text{diss}} = p_{\text{conv}} = p_{\text{kin}} - p_{\text{mech}}$$

4.5 THE EQUIVALENT CIRCUIT

Returning now to the scalar Eqs. (4.10) and (4.12), we next wish to represent these by equivalent circuits. Using the velocity-electric field, force density–current density analog, we immediately obtain the circuits of Fig. 4.5.

We will now illustrate with a few examples how we can use these equivalent circuits and write the solution of electromechanical problems by inspection.

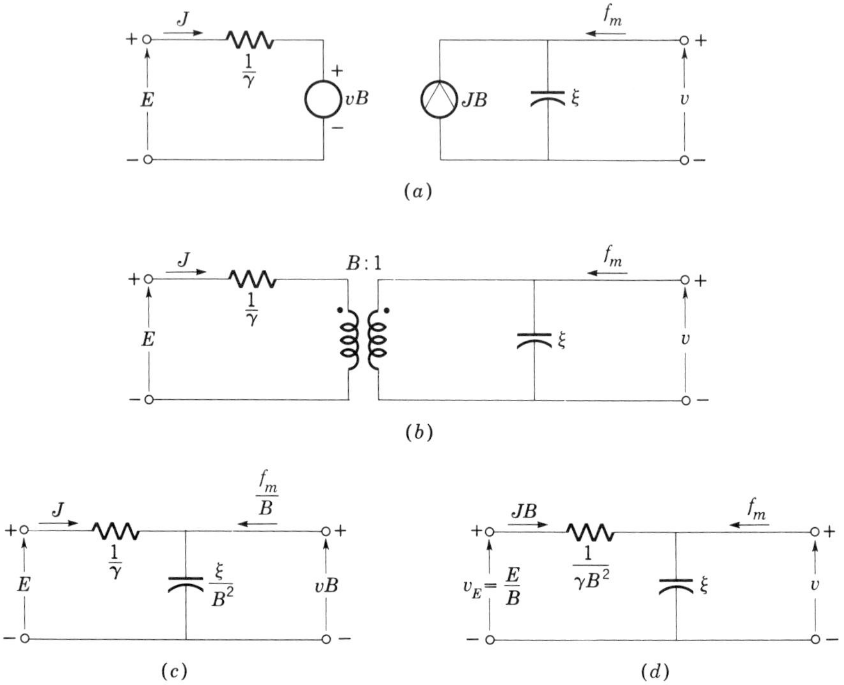

Fig. 4.5 Equivalent circuits for the conducting medium: (*a*) Controlled-source model; (*b*) ideal transformer model; (*c*) mechanical side referred to electrical side; (*d*) electrical side referred to mechanical side.

Example 4.2

Solve Example 4.1*a*, making use of the equivalent circuits.

Solution

We choose to refer to the electrical side, using Fig. 4.5*c* as shown. We note that

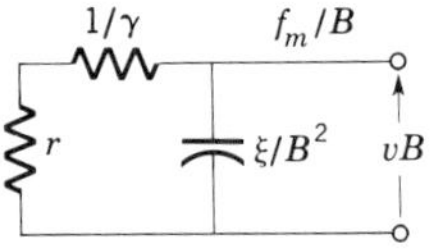

in the steady state the capacitance behaves like an open circuit. Therefore we have

$$\frac{f_m}{B} = \frac{vB}{r + 1/\gamma}$$

and the force is

$$f_m = \frac{vB^2}{(1 + 1/\gamma r)r}$$

which checks our result of Example 4.1.

Example 4.3

Given the mass density ξ, the conductivity γ, and the total magnetic field B, find the velocity v when the conductor is short-circuited and the mechanical force density is the step function

$$f_m u(t) = \begin{cases} 0 & \text{for } t < 0 \\ f_m & \text{for } t > 0 \end{cases}$$

Assume zero initial velocity.

Solution

We refer this time to the mechanical side of Fig. 4.5*d* as shown.

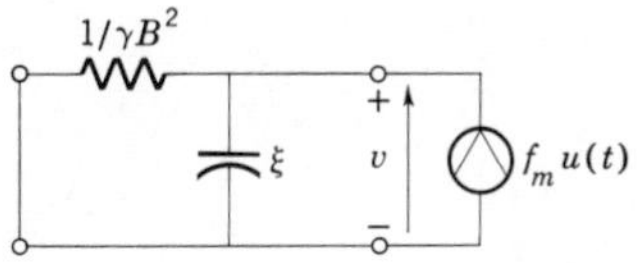

Since this is a simple RC circuit, we know that the solution is a simple exponential of the form

$$v = v_{\text{initial}} e^{-t/\tau} + v_{\text{steady state}} (1 - e^{-t/\tau})$$

where $\quad v_{\text{initial}} = 0 \qquad$ (given)

$$v_{\text{steady state}} = \frac{f_m}{\gamma B^2} \qquad \text{(since } C \text{ is an open circuit as } t \to \infty\text{)}$$

$$\tau = RC = \frac{\xi}{\gamma B^2}$$

Therefore

$$v = \frac{f_m}{\gamma B^2} (1 - e^{-t\gamma B^2/\xi})$$

Example 4.4

Toward the end of World War II the development of faster and higher-flying bombers created the need for better antiaircraft guns. To achieve the required high-projectile velocities, guns based on the principle of electromagnetic acceleration were proposed and became the object of a sizable research effort.

Considering the schematic arrangement shown in the sketch, compare the length

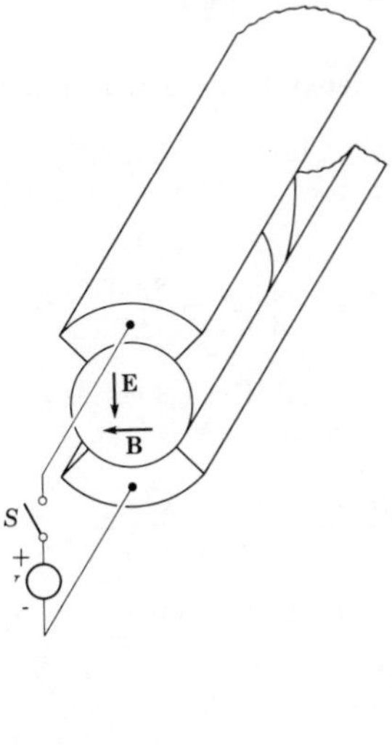

of gun required for a projectile made of copper and a projectile made of aluminum when:

(*a*) The exit velocity is the same.

(*b*) The exit kinetic energy is the same.

Assume equal volume for the projectiles, equal and time-invariant **E** and **B**,

$$\xi_{\text{Cu}} = 8.93 \times 10^3 \text{ kg/m}^3 \qquad \xi_{\text{Al}} = 2.7 \times 10^3 \text{ kg/m}^3$$
$$\gamma_{\text{Cu}} = 5 \times 10^7 \text{ mhos/m} \qquad \gamma_{\text{Al}} = 3.1 \times 10^7 \text{ mhos/m}$$

Solution

Without loss of generality we may consider a unit volume. Using the equivalent circuit in Fig. 4.5*d* as shown, the velocity is

$$v = v_E(1 - e^{-t/\tau})$$

where $\tau = \xi/\gamma B^2$. Integrating this equation once in time, we obtain the distance traveled:

$$x = v_E[t - \tau(1 - e^{-t/\tau})]$$
$$= v_E t - v\tau$$

If we indicate by the index one the values of the variables at the exit of the gun, we have

$$v_1 = v_E(1 - e^{-t_1/\tau})$$
$$x_1 = v_E t_1 - v_1\tau = v_E\left(t_1 - \frac{v_1}{v_E}\tau\right)$$

Solving for t_1, we get

$$t_1 = -\tau \log\left(1 - \frac{v_1}{v_E}\right)$$

and hence for the length of the gun

$$x_1 = -\tau v_E\left[\log\left(1 - \frac{v_1}{v_E}\right) + \frac{v_1}{v_E}\right]$$

We now take the ratio of gun lengths for copper and aluminum:

$$\frac{x_{1,\text{Cu}}}{x_{1,\text{Al}}} = \frac{\xi_{\text{Cu}}}{\xi_{\text{Al}}}\frac{\gamma_{\text{Al}}}{\gamma_{\text{Cu}}}\frac{\log(1 - v_{1,\text{Cu}}/v_E) + v_{1,\text{Cu}}/v_E}{\log(1 - v_{1,\text{Al}}/v_E) + v_{1,\text{Al}}/v_E}$$

When $v_{1,\text{Cu}} = v_{1,\text{Al}}$

$$\frac{x_{1,\text{Cu}}}{x_{1,\text{Al}}} = \frac{\xi_{\text{Cu}}}{\xi_{\text{Al}}}\frac{\gamma_{\text{Al}}}{\gamma_{\text{Cu}}} = \frac{8.93}{2.7}\frac{3.1}{5} = 2.05$$

When the kinetic energies are equal, the velocities are inversely proportional to the square roots of the densities. We then write

$$\frac{x_{1,\text{Cu}}}{x_{1,\text{Al}}} = \frac{\xi_{\text{Cu}}}{\xi_{\text{Al}}}\frac{\gamma_{\text{Al}}}{\gamma_{\text{Cu}}}\frac{\log[1 - (v_{1,\text{Al}}/v_E)\sqrt{\xi_{\text{Al}}/\xi_{\text{Cu}}}] + (v_{1,\text{Al}}/v_E)\sqrt{\xi_{\text{Al}}/\xi_{\text{Cu}}}}{\log(1 - v_{1,\text{Al}}/v_E) + v_{1,\text{Al}}/v_E}$$

A plot of $x_{1,\text{Cu}}/x_{1,\text{Al}}$ vs. $v_{1,\text{Al}}/v_E$ is given below.

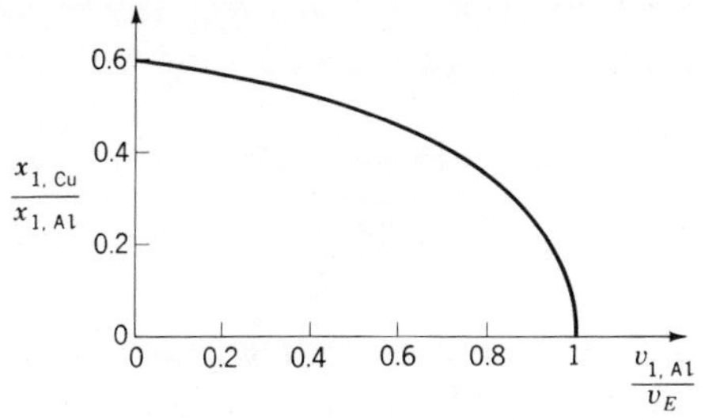

We observe that for equal exit velocity it is advantageous to use aluminum. For equal kinetic energy, instead, it is advantageous to use copper, especially when the exit velocity approaches the drift velocity.

The equivalent circuits are also useful from another point of view. In fact, they clearly put in evidence the analogy with other physical systems. For instance, we may consider the capacitance ξ/B^2 which appears in the electric circuit of Fig. 4.5*c*. Since the circuit is drawn for a volume element of unit dimensions, it describes a parallel-plate capacitor of unit area A and unit spacing d. From the formula for such a capacitor

$$C = \frac{\epsilon A}{d} = \frac{\epsilon \times 1}{1} = \epsilon$$

we deduce that ξ/B^2 can be interpreted as an effective dielectric constant.

This was first pointed out by Alfvén, who recognized the implications of such an analogy with regard to wave propagation. We shall have the opportunity to return to some of these implications in Chaps. 5 and 10, where we will generalize these equivalent circuits to describe the performance of entire converters.

4.6 SLIP, SLIP EQUIVALENT CIRCUIT

We now turn our attention to the circuit of Fig. 4.5*d*, where the electrical side is referred to the mechanical side. Here the across quantity on the right as well as on the left is a velocity. In fact, the "voltage" appearing on the left side is none other than the drift velocity, as we recall from the relationship $E = v_E B$, previously mentioned in Sec. 4.4*b*. The drift velocity is thus a mechanical measure of the electric field E in the presence of the magnetic field B, and this is precisely indicated by the circuit of Fig. 4.5*d*. In this circuit, referral to the mechanical side has transformed E into E/B, which we now recognize as the drift velocity v_E.

The performance of the conducting medium as a power converter can be conveniently studied by analyzing the circuit of Fig. 4.5*d*. It will be particularly useful to use a transfer-ratio approach, and relate all the "voltages" (i.e., velocities) in the circuit to the voltage $v_E = E/B$. To do this, we denote the transfer ratio between v_E and the drop across

$1/\gamma B^2$ by the symbol s, as shown in Fig. 4.6. This is called the *slip*, since it directly measures the *difference* between v and v_E; in fact, by Kirchhoff's law,

$$v = (1 - s)v_E \tag{4.22}$$

$$s = \frac{v_E - v}{v_E} \tag{4.23}$$

The definition of the slip s makes possible a succinct description of the motoring, generating, and braking modes, which follows from the considerations of Sec. 4.4*b*. Looking at Fig. 4.6, we can see that the electric system connected to the terminals on the left delivers electric power, whereas the mechanical system connected to the terminals on the right absorbs power, as long as $v_E > v > 0$, corresponding to $0 < s < 1$. This is the *motoring* mode. When $v < 0$, the electric system still delivers

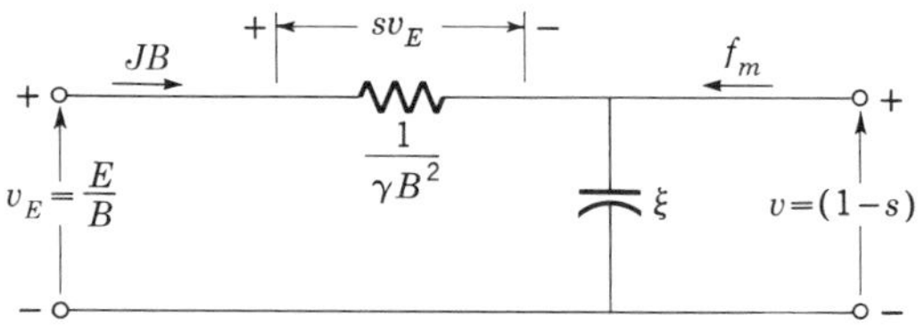

Fig. 4.6 Definition of slip.

power, but now the mechanical system also delivers power. This is the *braking* mode, and here $s > 1$. Finally, if $v > v_E$, the direction of the current JB reverses, the electric system *absorbs* power, and the mechanical system delivers power. Here we have $s < 0$, and this is the *generating* mode. We summarize these results in the tabulation below.

s	*Conversion mode*
$0 > s$	Generating
$0 < s < 1$	Motoring
$1 < s$	Braking

There is another interesting consequence of our definition of the slip. If we write the ohmic drop across the resistor in Fig. 4.6, we obtain

$$JB = \gamma B^2 s v_E \tag{4.24}$$

Thus it appears that for given γ, B, and v_E, the circuit current is proportional to the slip s only. This means that the entire circuit can be reduced to a purely resistive equivalent in which one of the resistors is a function of s. To do this, consider the capacitor ξ and the entire mechanical system in Fig. 4.6, lumped together in a "black box." The current $(\gamma B^2 s)v_E$ flows into this box, and the voltage $(1 - s)v_E$ exists across its terminals. Thus the black box is directly replaceable by a resistance

$$\frac{(1-s)v_E}{\gamma B^2 s v_E} = \frac{1-s}{s}\frac{1}{\gamma B^2}$$

as shown in Fig. 4.7*a*. Furthermore, if we use the impedance scaling technique of multiplying all voltages by B, dividing all currents by B, and multiplying all impedances by B^2, Fig. 4.7*a* converts into the referred-to electrical side result of Fig. 4.7*b*.

The reader may wonder how a circuit that contains a capacitor and an arbitrary system can possibly be converted in a legitimate way into one that is purely resistive. Actually the procedure is perfectly valid. It gives correct results because the slip s, in general, is an *instantaneous*

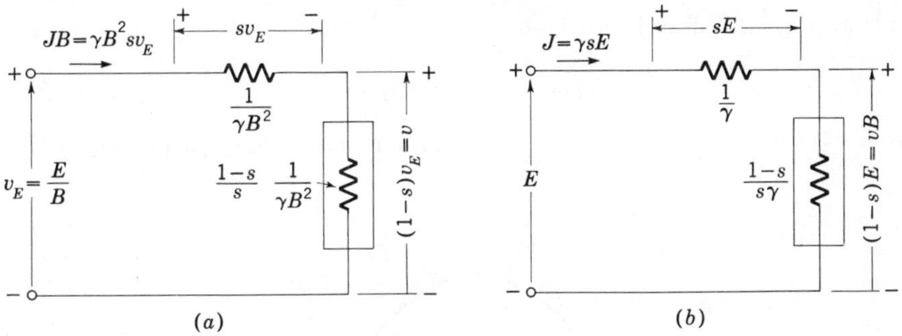

Fig. 4.7 Slip equivalent circuits.

function of time. Thus the resistor $(1 - s)/s\gamma$ is, in general, *time-variable* in the exact manner required to make the circuit current J in Fig. 4.7*b* identical with the value of J.

4.7 POWER - CONVERSION EFFICIENCY, SPECIFIC POWER, AND FORCE DENSITIES

(a) Motoring Mode

In power-conversion applications efficiency of conversion is important, particularly where high power is involved. In the motoring mode $0 < s < 1$, we may define the motoring conversion efficiency as

$$\eta_m = \frac{p_{\text{conv}}}{p_{\text{elec}}} \tag{4.25}$$

From Fig. 4.7*b* it is plain that p_{conv} is the power absorbed by the output resistor $(1 - s)/s\gamma$. Thus η_m is given by the ratio of the output voltage to the source voltage, or

$$\eta_m = 1 - s \tag{4.26}$$

Thus 100 percent efficiency is achieved for $s = 0$, but this corresponds to $v = v_E$ and $J = 0$, and so there is no power converted for this condition. It is clear that the demand for high efficiency must be compromised to meet the dictates of reasonable quantity of converted power. In fact, from Fig. 4.7*b*, the converted power is

$$p_{\text{conv}} = [(1 - s)E]^2 \frac{s\gamma}{1 - s} = (s - s^2)E^2\gamma = (s - s^2)v_E{}^2B^2\gamma$$

$$= \frac{s}{1 - s} v^2B^2\gamma \qquad (4.27)$$

The quantity $E^2\gamma$ is $p_{\text{elec}} = p_{\text{diss}}$ under the *stall* or standstill condition $v = 0$; hence we define

$$p_{\text{st}} = E^2\gamma \qquad (4.28)$$

so that Eq. 4.27 may be written

$$p_{\text{conv}} = (s - s^2)p_{\text{st}} \qquad (4.29)$$

The curve of $p_{\text{conv}}/p_{\text{st}}$ as a function of s, is the parabola shown in Fig. 4.8.

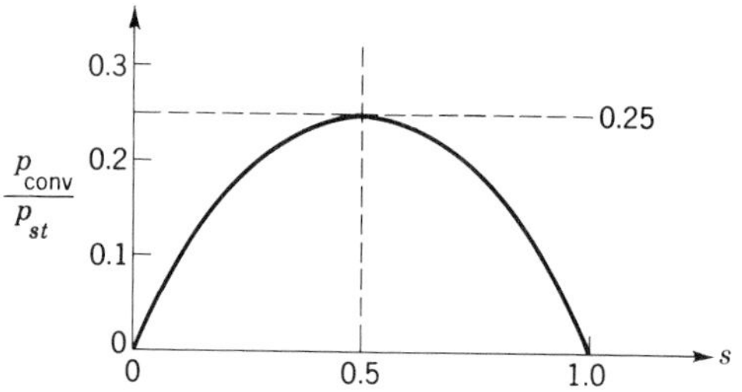

Fig. 4.8 Converted power density as a function of slip in the motoring mode.

This has the maximum value of $\frac{1}{4}$ for $s = \frac{1}{2}$, where the efficiency η_m is $1 - \frac{1}{2}$ or only 50 percent. For high-efficiency operation near $s = 0$, p_{conv} is relatively small.

This incompatibility between efficiency and power output is, when viewed in circuit terms, nothing more than the familiar conflict which arises when power must be obtained from a voltage source E which has a resistive source impedance $1/\gamma$. If the load is exactly matched to the source, we get maximum power output but only 50 percent efficiency, $s = \frac{1}{2}$; and 100 percent efficiency is obtained only when no load current flows under the open-circuit condition, $s = 0$.

(b) Generating Mode

In the generating mode, the electric load absorbs power, and the mechanical source delivers power. We may define the generator efficiency η_g as

$$\eta_g = \frac{p_{\text{elec}}}{p_{\text{conv}}} = \frac{1}{1-s} \qquad s < 0 \tag{4.30}$$

Since p_{elec} and p_{conv} are both negative in the generating mode, the efficiency η_g is positive.

The output power in the generating region is $-p_{\text{elec}}$. From Fig. 4.7*b* we see that

$$-p_{\text{elec}} = -JE = -\gamma s E^2 \tag{4.31}$$

which may be rewritt en as

$$-p_{\text{elec}} = -\gamma s (Bv_E)^2 = -\gamma s \left(\frac{Bv}{1-s}\right)^2 = \frac{-s}{(1-s)^2}\gamma B^2 v^2 \tag{4.32}$$

As is evident from Fig. 4.7, the term $\gamma B^2 v^2$ is the power dissipated in ohmic loss when the electrical side is short-circuited. We define the short-circuit power

$$p_{\text{s.c.}} = \gamma B^2 v^2 \tag{4.33}$$

so that

$$-p_{\text{elec}} = \frac{-s}{(1-s)^2} p_{\text{s.c.}} \tag{4.34}$$

The curve of $-p_{\text{elec}}/p_{\text{s.c.}}$ is shown in Fig. 4.9. There is a maximum at $s = -1$, again corresponding to a matched load condition, with $v_E = v/2$ and $\eta_g = \frac{1}{2}$, only 50 percent efficiency.

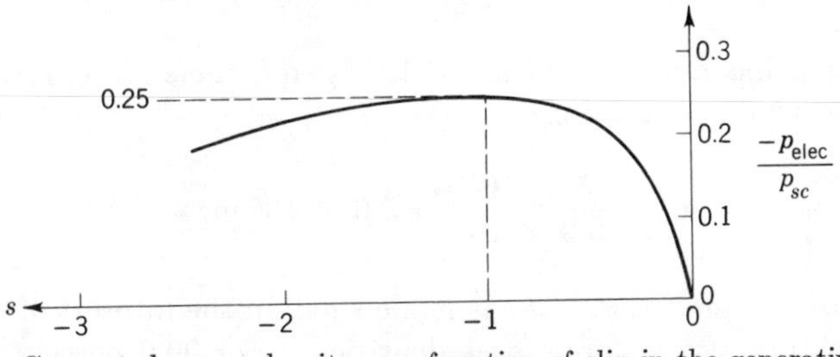

Fig. 4.9 Converted power density as a function of slip in the generating mode.

From the preceding considerations it is clear that the requirements of high efficiency and high power-output density are incompatible, because the former requires operation with v very nearly equal to v_E, and the latter operation with either $v = v_E/2$ or $v = 2v_E$. This means that a high efficiency design will require additional machine size and a larger investment cost, whereas a high-power design will be inefficient and incur larger running costs. The prevailing economics are such that the usual decision is in favor of high efficiency, especially in very large machines. It is interesting to note that it was not until 1878 that these economic considerations became apparent and high-efficiency operation was advocated by E. Thomson, E. J. Houston, and W. Siemens. Earlier machines had been designed for 50 percent efficiency.

(c) Force Volume Density

In the scalar equation (4.12), and in the several circuit models which we have derived for these equations, we have observed that the electromagnetic force per unit volume or force volume density is

$$f = JB = s\gamma EB = s\gamma v_E B^2 \tag{4.35}$$

This specific force-density relation provides a starting point for the synthesis of all electromechanical power converters which employ neutral conducting media, since it directly relates a measure of the application requirement f to the fundamental electrical quantities in the converter. In order to obtain an appreciation of the engineering possibilities let us consider some representative values for γ, B, and v_E. Table 3.1 in Sec. 3.8 lists γ values for different conducting media. In conventional practice at normal temperatures, the saturation of ferromagnetic materials limits B to about 1 weber/m^2, and a conservative estimate of the magnitude of v_E is 100 m/sec, since in rotating devices the speed is limited by centrifugal stress considerations. With these values and $s = 1$ (or $v = 0$), the stall condition, the specific force density at stall for copper is

$$f_{st} = 4.84 \times 10^7 \times 10^2 \approx 5 \times 10^9 \text{ newtons/m}^3$$

Since copper has a density of 8.9×10^3 kg/m^3, the stalling force density produces a stall acceleration

$$a_{st} = \frac{5 \times 10^9}{8.9 \times 10^3} \approx 5.6 \times 10^5 \text{ m/sec}^2$$

or about 57,000 gravities. If s is made small in the interest of efficiency, we still maintain very large force densities. For 99.9 percent efficiency $s = 0.001$, so that

$$f_{\eta = 0.999} = 5 \times 10^6 \text{ newtons/m}^3$$

(d) Power Volume Density

As mentioned before, in large power applications, economic considerations dictate high-efficiency operation. Accordingly, let us consider the efficiency to be 99.9 percent. In the motoring region, this means $s = +0.001$, and in the generating region $s = -0.001001 \approx -0.001$. For such small slip magnitudes, v is essentially equal to v_E, and as may be seen from Eqs. (4.27) and (4.32), both the electric and converted power-density magnitudes are essentially equal for small s. This common magnitude is accurately approximated by

$$p \approx |s|v^2B^2\gamma \tag{4.36}$$

which for $|s| = 0.001$, is of course

$$p \approx \frac{v^2B^2\gamma}{1{,}000} \tag{4.37}$$

We may arrive at representative possible values of the power volume density p by considering a number of alternatives.

Present-day converters employ ferromagnetic cores to enhance the flux density which is economically attainable. As we have already mentioned, saturation effects restrict the use of this technique to flux densities in the order of 1 weber/m². If, however, we make use of superconducting materials maintained at temperatures close to absolute zero, the economical considerations are no longer based on the Joule losses, practically unlimited currents may be achieved, and much larger flux densities are possible without the use of ferromagnetic cores.

In rotating devices employing solid conductors, v is limited by the stress arising from centrifugal forces to about 200 m/sec. However, metal jets having linear velocities of 10^4 m/sec have been obtained by exploding shaped charges, and gaseous plasmas have been accelerated to velocities approaching that of light.

The power densities which correspond to these alternatives are listed in Table 4.2.

Table 4.2 POWER DENSITIES FOR OPERATION WITH 99.9 PERCENT CONVERSION EFFICIENCY

Material	γ, mhos/m	B, webers/m²	v, m/sec	p, Mw/m³
Copper, 75°C.	4.84×10^7	1	200	$\approx 2 \times 10^3$
Copper, 75°C.	4.84×10^7	10	10^4	$\approx 5 \times 10^8$
Plasma, 10^4 °K.	2.2×10^3	1	10^7	$\approx 2 \times 10^8$
Plasma, 10^8 °K.	2.2×10^9	10	10^7	$\approx 2 \times 10^{16}$

Since copper has a density of 8.9×10^3 kg/m³, we see that a pound of copper (roughly $\frac{1}{2}$ kg) can presently convert in the order of 0.1 Mw using conventional practice.

More significant is the power output per unit mass of the overall structure including the iron. A survey of current technology yields the results of Fig. 4.10, which compares the power per unit mass of several converter types. If one considers that the superconducting state eliminates the need for heavy iron structures, and affords economic operation at maximum power output, the enormous potentialities of the newer techniques are readily seen.

The knowledge of the power and force volume densities are the first steps in the synthesis of a power converter, because this knowledge permits the determination of the required volume of conductor actively partaking in power convertion or, as we call it, *active conductor*. The subsequent choice of structure, device type, and actual dimensions follows in logical sequence from the operating specifications, as we shall see in the following sections.

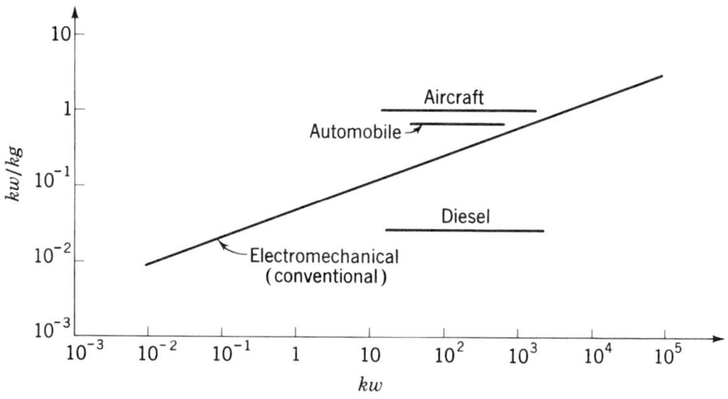

Fig. 4.10 Output power per unit mass as a function of the output power.

The example which follows illustrates how we can use these power densities in finding the volume and weight of the active conductor in an actual generator.

Example 4.5

A turbogenerator delivers 50 Mw at unity power factor with a conversion efficiency of $\eta_g = 0.99925$. Determine the volume and weight of the copper active conductor if its conductivity is $\gamma = 5 \times 10^7$ mhos/m, its density is $\xi = 8.93 \times 10^3$ kg/m³, its velocity is $v = 190$ m/sec, and the effective flux density is $B = 0.5$ weber/m². Note that the conversion efficiency accounts only for the Joule losses in the active conductor itself. The total losses of the converter are normally some five times as much, and accordingly the overall efficiency is lower. In this particular machine it is about 96 percent.

Solution

Since the power delivered is the total electric power of the generator, in order to find the volume of the active conductor we need the density of electric power. This is given, according to Eqs. (4.30) and (4.32) by

$$p_{\text{elec}} = \frac{s}{(1-s)^2}\gamma B^2 v^2 = -\eta_g(1-\eta_g)\gamma B^2 v^2$$

In view of the high efficiency, we may approximate η_g by unity. Thus

$$p_{\text{elec}} = (1 - \eta_g)\gamma B^2 v^2 = -0.00075 \times 5 \times 10^7 \times (0.5)^2 \times (190)^2$$
$$= -3.38 \times 10^8 \text{ watts/m}^3$$

The volume of active conductor is then

$$\text{Vol.} = \frac{-P_{\text{elec}}}{-p_{\text{elec}}} = \frac{5 \times 10^7}{3.38 \times 10^8} = 0.148 \text{ m}^3$$

and the weight is

$$\text{Weight} = 8.93 \times 10^3 \times 0.148 = 1.32 \times 10^3 \text{ kg}$$

4.8 GEOMETRY AND MATERIALS OF POWER CONVERSION

In the preceding section we have seen that the volume density of converted power is essentially determined by the limitations of the materials employed. Once the magnitude of this power density is known, the volume of active conductor to meet a given power requirement is determined. Plainly, the next problem which faces us is to decide upon the configuration and geometry of the power converter.

We have already noted that the three vectors **v**, **B**, and **J** should be mutually orthogonal so as to maximize the magnitude of the converted power

$$p_{\text{conv}} = \mathbf{J} \cdot \mathbf{B} \times \mathbf{v}$$

for given magnitudes of the three vectors **J**, **B**, **v**, and indeed we have derived the scalar equations and the equivalent circuit on this basis. It follows that the magnetic flux is perpendicular to the plane of **J** and **v**, or, in other words, the magnetic flux has to cross the *conducting medium*. If large magnitudes of **B** are to be achieved without the application of extremely large magnetomotive force, then the effective reluctance of the flux path should be kept small. Thus in this respect it is desirable that the conducting medium itself have high permeability, or failing this, have its volume disposed so as to achieve low reluctance.

The class of ferromagnetic materials exemplified by iron, of course, has high relative permeability, but these materials have much lower electric conductivities than good conductors such as copper or high-temperature plasmas. As a result, ferromagnetic materials are generally not suitable for use as the conducting medium, since the higher resistance would increase the ohmic losses.† We therefore seek to use good conductors in low-reluctance configurations.

When using solid conductors, two engineering compromises may be

† In some special applications, conversion efficiency may be sacrificed in favor of other desirable characteristics, by deliberately using high-resistance conductors. See Chap. 10.

directly arrived at, as shown in Fig. 4.11. (In visualizing these arrangements, we have, in fact, not needed to specify the sources of the magnetic flux density **B**, and this problem is left for subsequent study.) These configurations are as follows:

1. The length of the path that the magnetic flux must take across the conductor is reduced by making the conductor a very thin sheet, closely juxtaposed to iron pole pieces. In this arrangement, the conducting sheet moves with respect to the pole structures.
2. The effective permeability of the conductor is increased by intermingling it with iron. This may be done only if the conductor is a solid, typically copper wires, embedded in slots in an iron-alloy

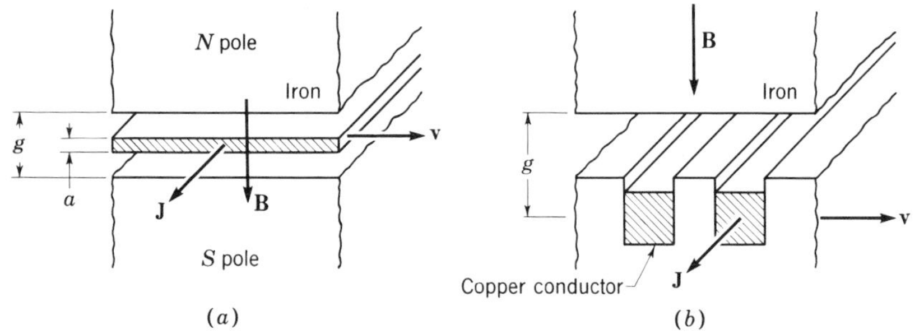

Fig. 4.11 The gap.

structure, formed from punched laminations.† In this case there is relative motion between the upper and lower structures. It will be noted that for a given volume of active conductor these arrangements lead to increased dimensions in the directions of current and velocity, and thereby result in an increase of the linear dimensions of the converter.

Since relative motion must take place for power conversion, some mechanical clearance must be provided between solid moving structures. Thus the gap g in Fig. 4.11a must exceed the copper-conductor thickness a, and there must be clearance between the upper and lower structures of Fig. 4.11b. Since this clearance must be crossed by the magnetic flux, it is generally desirable to make it as small as fabrication techniques will permit.

† When the conductors are embedded in a high-permeability material, the latter carries most of the magnetic flux, and the flux density within the conductor is relatively small. The electromagnetic force thus shifts from the current-carrying conductor to the ferromagnetic material. This local redistribution of force, however, does not affect our power-conversion calculations, as we shall see in Chap. 9.

It is clear from these simple considerations that the region of interest in a large class of electromagnetic power converters is a volume in the form of a thin sheet which comprises a gap in an iron-alloy structure. This gap of length g contains or is adjacent to the active conductors. When the iron structure is slotted, the effective length of the gap is taken as that length between two smooth structures which possesses the same reluctance as the actual slotted structure.

4.9 CURRENT SHEETS AND SURFACE DENSITIES

The fact that the length g of the gap volume is much smaller than its other two dimensions along $\mathbf{J}$ and $\mathbf{v}$ leads to important simplifications in the theory of electromagnetic power converters. These stem principally from the fact that the variation of $\mathbf{J}$ and $\mathbf{v}$ across the length of the gap is

I_1, the current flowing across area la, $= laJ$

I_2, the current flowing across line l, $= Kl$

$$I_1 = I_2, \quad K = aJ$$

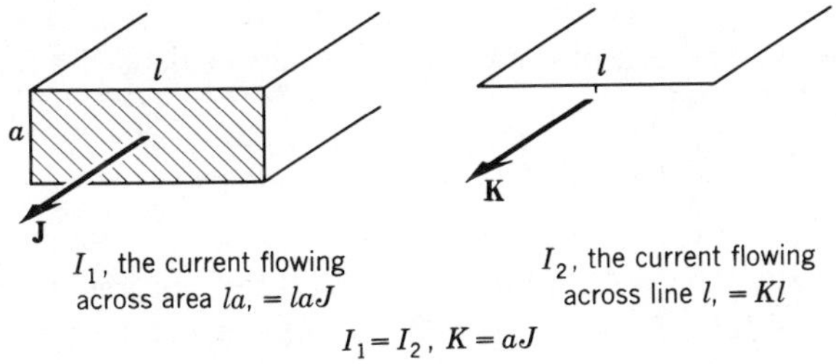

Fig. 4.12 Current sheets.

small, and may be neglected. Also, even though the total $\mathbf{B}$ in the gap may not be perpendicular to its surfaces, the perpendicular component itself does not vary appreciably across the gap. Consequently these variations may be neglected for the purposes of analysis. In doing this, we in effect transform the actual current distributions into equivalent *current sheets* by letting the thickness a of the conductor vanish while the current density $\mathbf{J}$ increases without bound, subject to the condition that the current flowing within any given small length dl along the gap surface in a direction normal to the current flow remains the same as before. In this way we arrive at a surface current density $\mathbf{K}$ amp/m everywhere parallel to the volume current density $\mathbf{J}$; in fact,

$$\mathbf{K} = a\mathbf{J} \tag{4.38}$$

which is plainly the relationship indicated by Fig. 4.12.

By using the surface current density, we may define power and force surface densities analogous to the volume densities we have previously defined. Thus the converted power of Eq. (4.2b) when written in the scalar form assuming mutually orthogonal vectors $\mathbf{v}$, $\mathbf{B}$, and $\mathbf{J}$, becomes,

with the substitution of **K** for **J**,

$$p_{s,\text{conv}} = KvB = ap_{\text{conv}} \tag{4.39}$$

The quantity $p_{s,\text{conv}}$ is actually the power converted in the active conductor per unit area of gap surface measured along the current sheet.

We may also write p_{elec} and p_{diss} as surface densities. To do this most simply we note that p_{elec} is the power supplied by the v_E source in Fig. 4.7*a*, p_{diss} is the power dissipated in the resistor $1/\gamma B^2$, and p_{conv} is the power absorbed in the resistor $(1 - s)/s\gamma B^2$. Since these elements are all in series, the individual powers are all proportional to the respective voltage drops. Thus

$$p_{\text{diss}} = sp_{\text{elec}} = \frac{s}{1 - s}\, p_{\text{conv}} \tag{4.40}$$

These relations hold as well for the surface power densities, so that

$$p_{s,\text{diss}} = sp_{s,\text{elec}} = \frac{s}{1 - s}\, p_{s,\text{conv}} \tag{4.41}$$

which together with Eq. (4.39) determines all the surface power densities. Similarly we obtain from Eq. (4.35) an electromagnetic surface force density

$$f_s = KB \tag{4.42}$$

4.10 ENGINEERING SIGNIFICANCE OF THE SURFACE DENSITIES

The surface densities are more than a mathematical convenience resulting from the approximation of the actual active conductor currents by an equivalent current sheet. In fact, as we shall see in the forthcoming chapters, they are closely associated with the flow of electric power through the gap, and as their maximum attainable values are dictated by the technological limitations of the material used, they are, in fact, the parameters that determine the size of the converter.

The power represented by p_{diss} is actually the conductor Joule loss, and the generated heat must be removed from the converter by means adequate to ensure a temperature rise above the ambient sufficiently low to safeguard the insulating and magnetic properties of the materials used in the construction of the converter. Of the three means by which heat can be transferred,[2] radiation is not very significant because of the relatively low permissible temperature rise, so that conduction or convection by means of gaseous or liquid coolants must be employed.

Since all heat transfer takes place through a surface, the several cooling methods all require adequate surface area to be effective. In general, heat-transfer processes may be characterized by a coefficient of thermal transmission h which is the heat-transfer rate in watts per unit area of surface and per unit degree of temperature rise. The value of h depends on the process, the type of materials, the condition of the surfaces, and the coolant flow rate, if any. However, if we take h to be the heat-transfer coefficient at the surface of one side of the current sheet, we find that it varies over a relatively narrow range of values. This is evidenced in Table 4.3 where we have taken examples of various converters types ranging from very low to very high output powers. A comparison of the tabulated values demonstrates the effectiveness of water when used as the coolant medium.

Table 4.3 THERMAL COEFFICIENTS FOR SEVERAL TYPES OF POWER CONVERTERS

Converter type	Output power	rpm	Cooling method	h, watts/(m²)(°C)
Low-inertia servomotor..	2 watts	1,800	Totally enclosed (radiation)	35
Induction motor.........	15 kw	1,800	Air-cooled	30
Salient-pole synchronous motor................	1 Mw	257	Air-cooled	50
Turbogenerator.........	40 Mw	3,600	Hydrogen-cooled	70
Turbogenerator.........	225 Mw	3,600	Water-cooled	230

The permissible temperature rise ΔT depends on the type of insulating material used and can be deduced by subtracting the ambient temperature, which is normally taken as 40°C, from the limiting temperatures as specified by the IEEE and shown in Table 4.4.

It is plain that under temperature equilibrium conditions the Joule heat must be transferred away from the conductor as fast as it is generated; thus, under equilibrium conditions, and for a certain temperature rise ΔT the surface power density $p_{s,\text{diss}}$ must be equal to $h\,\Delta T$, so that

$$p_{s,\text{diss}} = h\,\Delta T \tag{4.43}$$

Equation (4.43) serves to delineate further the physical dimensions of the power converter. Starting with a desired power level and efficiency, the power-density figures of Table 4.2 determine the order of magnitude of the *volume* of active conductor required. Upon the selection of h and ΔT, Eq. (4.43) determines $p_{s,\text{diss}}$, and the *surface* of the active conducting sheet in the gap follows directly; thus one more step in the ultimate determination of the linear dimensions of the converter has been accomplished.

Table 4.4 LIMITING TEMPERATURES FOR SEVERAL INSULATING MATERIALS

Insulation class	Description of insulating materials	Hot-spot limiting temperature T, °C
O	Untreated fabrics of cotton, silk, linen. Untreated paper, fiber, wood.	90
A	Oil-varnish, wax, or compound-impregnated fabrics or sheets of cotton, silk, linen, paper, wood, fiber; oil varnish, Bakelite; organ ic filler compounds.	105
B	Asbestos, fiber glass, mica tape, oxide films, inorganic fillers, asbestos boards. (A limited amount of organic materials may be used for binding purposes.)	130
H	Mica, asbestos, fiber glass, and similar inorganic materials in buildup form with binding substances composed of silicone compounds or materials with equivalent properties; silicone compounds in rubbery and resinous forms, or materials with equivalent properties in minute proportions. Class *A* material may be used only where essential for structural purposes during manufacture.	180

We may formally write down the equations for the steps outlined just above. If we use capital letters for the *total* power and let

$$\begin{aligned} V &= \text{volume of active conductor} \\ A &= \text{surface of one side of the current sheet in air gap} \end{aligned} \tag{4.44}$$

then

$$V = \frac{P_{\mathrm{conv}}}{p_{\mathrm{conv}}} \tag{4.45}$$

With the efficiency initially assumed, the slip is known from either Eq. (4.26) or Eq. (4.30). Then from Eq. (4.40)

$$P_{\mathrm{diss}} = \frac{s}{1-s} P_{\mathrm{conv}} \tag{4.46}$$

and

$$A = \frac{P_{\mathrm{diss}}}{p_{s,\mathrm{diss}}} = \frac{s}{1-s} \frac{P_{\mathrm{conv}}}{h\,\Delta T} \tag{4.47}$$

In the preceding paragraphs we have seen that the Joule heat surface power density $p_{s,\mathrm{diss}}$ is an important engineering parameter in the design of the power converter. The surface current density K is also related to this surface power density and is, in fact, determined when h and ΔT are specified. To show this, we may use Eqs. (4.39), (4.41), and (4.43) to write

$$K = \frac{p_{s,\mathrm{conv}}}{vB} = \frac{1-s}{s} \frac{h\,\Delta T}{vB} \tag{4.48}$$

and using Eq. (4.27), this may be written as

$$K = \sqrt{\frac{(1-s)\gamma}{s}}\,\frac{h\,\Delta T}{\sqrt{p_{\text{conv}}}} \tag{4.49}$$

so that K is known, once the power density, conductivity, efficiency, heat-transfer coefficient h, and temperature rise ΔT are decided upon. For copper and liquid coolant at room temperature, the surface current density K can reach an order of magnitude of 2×10^5 amp/m.

Example 4.6

If the generator of Example 4.5 rotates at 3,600 rpm, is wound with class B insulation and is cooled with hydrogen, calculate:

(*a*) The area and thickness of the active conductor as sketched.
(*b*) The radius and length of the gap.
(*c*) The surface current density.

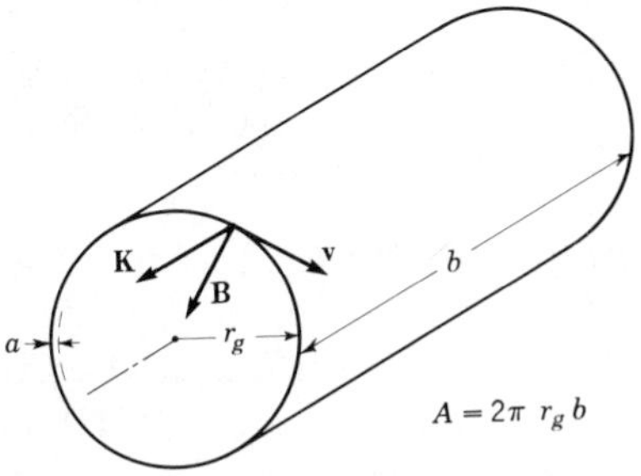

Solution

(*a*) In order to evaluate the area we must know the total power dissipated. This is

$$P_{\text{diss}} = sP_{\text{elec}} = 0.00075 \times 5 \times 10^7 = 3.75 \times 10^4 \text{ watts}$$

The area is then given by Eq. (4.47) as

$$A = \frac{P_{\text{diss}}}{p_{s,\text{diss}}} = \frac{P_{\text{diss}}}{h\,\Delta T}$$

We take for h the value quoted in Table 4.3 for a similar turbogenerator with hydrogen cooling, i.e., $h = 70$ watts/(m²)(°C). For the temperature rise, we take the difference between the hot-spot temperature of 130°C, which Table 4.4 allows for class B insulation, and the ambient temperature of 40°C. We thus obtain

$$A = \frac{3.75 \times 10^4}{70(130 - 40)} = 5.95 \text{ m}^2$$

The thickness of the active conductor is then

$$a = \frac{\text{vol.}}{\text{area}} = \frac{0.148}{5.95} = 2.5 \times 10^{-2} \text{ m} = 2.5 \text{ cm}$$

This represents an average thickness, because the conductors in turbogenerators are placed in slots, as shown in Fig. 4.11*b*. In the actual construction of this machine, the copper conductors occupy only 28 percent of the gap surface, the remainder being taken by the insulation and the iron teeth which separate the slots. The individual conductors then have a depth in the slot of

$$\frac{2.5 \times 10^{-2}}{0.28} = 8.95 \times 10^{-2} \text{ m}$$
$$= 8.95 \text{ cm}$$

(*b*) The radius of the gap is determined by the rpm and the velocity of the conductor. Since $v = 2\pi r_g$ (rpm)/60,

$$r_g = \frac{v \times 60}{2\pi \text{ (rpm)}} = \frac{190 \times 60}{2\pi \times 3{,}600} = 0.505 \text{ m}$$

Since the area of the gap corresponds to the area of the conductor, the length of the gap is

$$b = \frac{A}{2\pi r_g} = \frac{5.95}{2\pi \times 0.505} = 1.87 \text{ m}$$

(*c*) The current surface density is, according to Eq. (4.48),

$$K = \frac{1-s}{s}\frac{h\,\Delta T}{vB} = \frac{1.00075}{-0.00075} \times \frac{70 \times 90}{190 \times 0.5}$$
$$= -8.85 \times 10^4 \text{ amp/m}^2$$

As shown previously, the efficiency and the attainable power density dictate the volume of the active conductor. We have now seen how thermal limitations determine its surface at the gap. There are many other performance specifications to be met by an electromechanical power converter; these will be considered in subsequent chapters, where we shall see how different converters physically realize the fundamental concepts thus far developed and how these converters evolve one from the other in the order of increasing asymmetry of the electromagnetic field configurations.

4.11 SUMMARY

In this chapter we have learned how to determine the dimensions of the active conductor when given a set of specifications for the overall performance of the power converter. We have done this in complete generality without even knowing what features differentiate between the various types of converters. To achieve this result we have concentrated our attention on a unit element of the conductor as follows:

1. The performance of a unit-volume element of conducting material is characterized by these power volume densities: kinetic, mechanical, converted, electric, and dissipated. Their signs define the three operating modes: motoring, generating, and braking. These modes may be identified by comparing the velocity of the conductor $\mathbf{v}$ with the drift velocity $\mathbf{v}_E$. When $\mathbf{v}$ and $\mathbf{v}_E$ are in the

same direction, motoring obtains when $v/v_E < 1$ and generating when $v/v_E > 1$. Braking corresponds to the case when the conductor moves in the direction opposite to $\mathbf{v}_E$.

2. These modes are brought about by the connections between the conducting element and the external electric and mechanical systems. Typical electric connections are (*a*) the limiting case of open circuit, for which no power conversion occurs, (*b*) the voltage-source excitation which allows for all three modes of operation, and (*c*) connection to a passive network which allows for generation only.
3. For economical reasons power converters are built so as to obtain the best possible output from each volume element of conducting material. This leads to a perpendicular orientation of **J**, **v**, and **B**. The choice of such an orientation considerably simplifies the mathematical formulation in that it eliminates the need for vector equations and allows for a more vivid description in terms of equivalent circuits. Further simplification ensues when the drift velocity is taken as a normalization base and the velocity deficit defined as the slip *s*.
4. In terms of the slip, 100 percent conversion efficiency obtains for $s = 0$, when the converted power density vanishes. On the other hand, if the converted power is maximized, while maintaining constant bus voltage in the motor and constant speed in the generator, the slip is $+\frac{1}{2}$ and -1, respectively, and the corresponding efficiency only 50 percent. Choice of the economical operating slip therefore rests on a compromise between the conflicting requirements of high efficiency (low running costs) and high power density (low investment cost). Usually the choice is high efficiency, especially in large machines.
5. The perpendicular orientation of the **J**, **B**, and **v** vectors implies that the magnetic flux has to cross the conducting medium. The geometry of the active conductor is therefore determined by the consideration that the latter must offer the least reluctance. Two alternatives are possible for solid conductors: The conductor may be a thin sheet, or it may consist of separate strips embedded in slots cut through the iron structure. Both result in the linear dimensions parallel to **J** and **v** being much larger than in the direction of **B**. In this way we are led to the concepts of surface current, surface force, and surface power densities.
6. The surface and volume densities of converted power are both dictated by efficiency considerations. Specifically, the requirement is that the power dissipated per-unit surface be equal to the heat that can flow through the surface. The latter can be

expressed as the product of a coefficient of heat transfer which depends essentially on the method of cooling and a permissible temperature rise which depends on the type of insulation used. For specified operating conditions the surface power densities determine the area of the conducting sheet, and the volume densities determine the volume; the geometry of the active conductor is then uniquely defined.

REFERENCES

1. Partridge, W. S., L. D. Harris, R. A. Davidson, J. C. Clegg, D. R. Card, and W. H. Clark: Feasibility of the Electromagnetic Accelerator, *Univ. Utah Tech. Repts.* OSR-14, 1958.
2. McAdams, W. H.: "Heat Transmission", 3d ed., McGraw-Hill Book Company, New York, 1954.

PROBLEMS

4.1 A unit volume of copper conductor is moving in a uniform electromagnetic field with respect to a reference frame in which E, B, and v measure

$$E = 90 \text{ volts/m} \qquad B = 1 \text{ weber/m}^2 \qquad v = 100 \text{ m/sec}$$

and are oriented as shown.

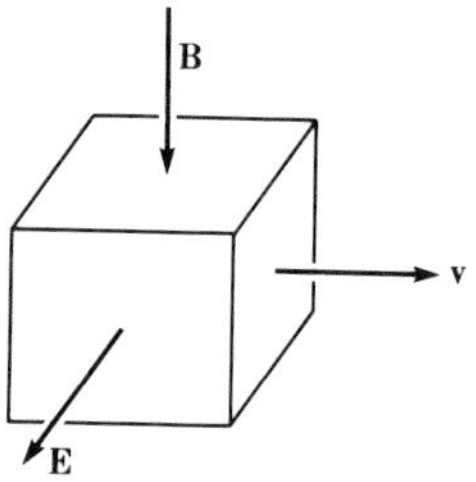

(*a*) Determine the mode of operation (motoring, generating, or braking) and the efficiency of electromechanical power conversion.

(*b*) If the above-mentioned conditions are taken as initial conditions, determine the subsequent motion of the conductor $v = v(t)$ when no external force is applied ($f_m = 0$).

4.2 A dense, fully ionized plasma is moving across uniform E and B fields perpendicular to each other. Determine:

(*a*) The density of kinetic energy if

$$|B| = 1 \text{ weber/m}^2 \qquad |p_{\text{conv}}| = 4 \times 10^8 \text{ watts/m}^3 \qquad s = 2 \qquad \gamma = 200 \text{ mhos/m}$$
$$\xi = 10^{-2} \text{ kg/m}^3$$

(*b*) the two possible values of the initial time rate of change of kinetic energy density p_{kin}, if $|\nabla \mathcal{P}| = 4 \times 10^5$ newtons/m^3 is suddenly applied at $t = 0$.

4.3 Show that when a dense plasmoid is set in motion in a space- and time-invariant magnetic field, the electric field induced by the surface charge exactly neutralizes the motion-induced field. Follow these steps:

(*a*) Find the relative displacement between the electrons and the ions when they drift under the action of the acceleration **a** perpendicularly to **a** and **B** (Eq. 2.77).

(*b*) Evaluate the surface charge σ caused by this displacement.

(*c*) Assume for simplicity that the plasmoid can be approximated by an infinite slab moving parallel to its faces and perpendicularly to **B**, and calculate the electric field within the slab.

(*d*) Introduce for the dielectric constant the expression which accounts for the dynamics of the plasma

$$\epsilon = \epsilon_0 + \frac{\xi}{B^2}$$

(*e*) Show that, when ϵ_0 can be neglected, the induced electric field within the slab reduces to

$$\mathbf{E}_{\text{ind}} = -\mathbf{v} \times \mathbf{B}$$

Note that the condition $\epsilon_0 \ll \xi/B^2$ thus defines a range of validity for the "dense plasma" approximation of Sec. 3.8 and for the ensuing equations.

4.4 In an MPD generator, plasma is forced through a rectangular channel of which two opposite sides are the poles of an electromagnet and the other two are electrodes connected to a load.

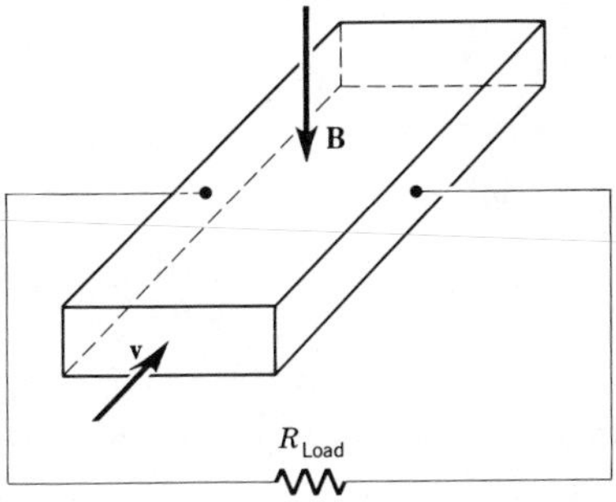

(*a*) In the schematic diagram shown, indicate the direction of **J** and $\nabla\mathcal{P}$ if $\partial v/\partial t = 0$.

(*b*) Evaluate p_{mech} and p_{elec} if

$$\frac{\partial v}{\partial t} = 0 \qquad v = 10^3\ \text{m/sec} \qquad |\nabla\mathcal{P}| = 10^5\ \text{newtons/m}^3 \qquad \gamma = 10^3\ \text{mhos/m}$$

$$B = 3\ \text{webers/m}^2$$

(*c*) What is the efficiency η_g?

4.5 A converter is connected to an infinite bus which maintains across all the volume elements of the active conductor a constant electric field $E = 100$ volts/m.

(*a*) If $B = 1$ weber/m², identify the operating modes as a motor, generator, or brake in terms of the velocity v.

(*b*) Determine the maximum mechanical output when the weight of active copper conductor is 20 lb, the conductivity is $\gamma = 5 \times 10^7$ mhos/m, and the mass density of copper is $\xi = 8.9 \times 10^3$ kg/m³.

4.6 Lunar and solar tides induce currents which flow within and close between the E and F ionospheric layers. The flow of current is accompanied by a change in

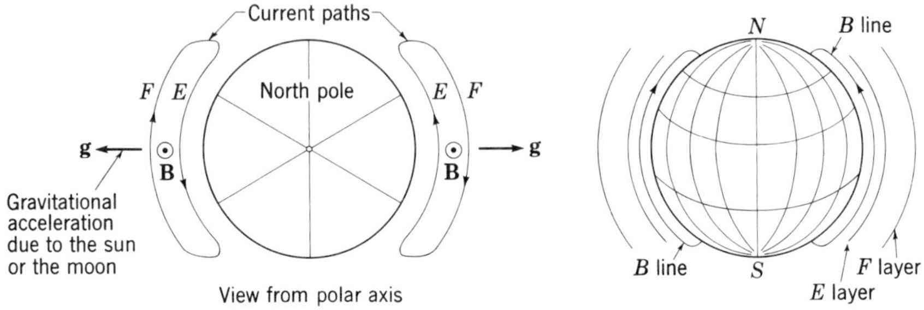

the height of the layers. Prove that the E layer operates in the generating mode and the F layer in the motoring mode.

Hint: Consider the simplified model shown, where the ionospheric layers are

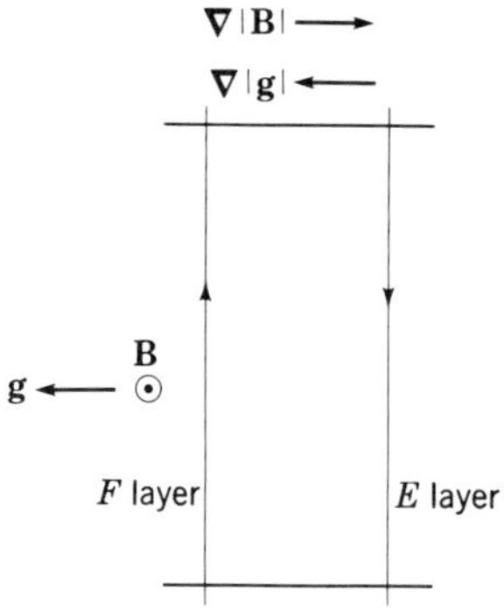

replaced by two identical, perfectly conducting bars, free to slide on perfectly conducting rails. Assume that B and g vary in such a way that

$$\frac{B_E}{B_F} > \frac{g_F}{g_E}$$

4.7 Solar spots are dark regions in the photosphere of the sun characterized by relative low temperature and high magnetic fields. It is believed that the low temperature results from the inhibiting action which the magnetic field exerts on the convection from hotter subphotospheric layers. To obtain a measure of the inhibiting action of B:

(*a*) Indicate in a plot the functional dependence of $v_\perp$ on B with $|\nabla \mathcal{P}|$ constant, and $|\nabla \mathcal{P}|$ on B with $v_\perp$ constant.

(*b*) Evaluate the back pressure $|\nabla \mathcal{P}|$ and the dissipated power density p_{diss} for the following typical conditions:

$$v = 3 \times 10^3 \text{ m/sec} \qquad \gamma = 10^3 \text{ mhos/m} \qquad B = 0.2 \text{ weber/m}^2$$

Assume steady-state and short-circuit conditions.

4.8 Shown in the figure is a cutaway view of a proposed "magnetic flux pump" whereby the magnetic flux produced by the current in the outside coil is concentrated

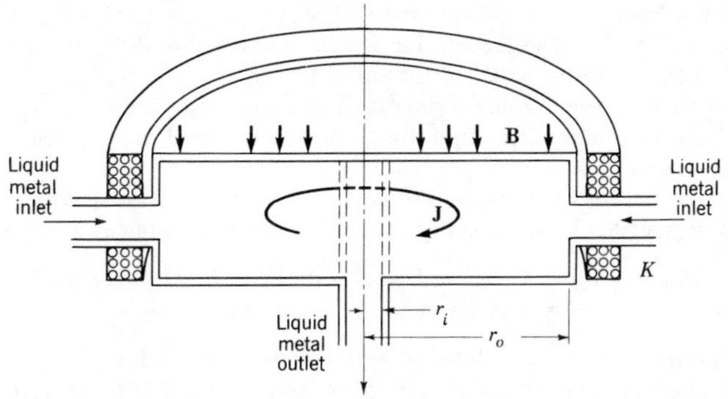

in the inner region by the radial motion of a conducting fluid. Evaluate the magnetic field intensity H as a function of r when the conducting fluid is liquid sodium with a conductivity $\gamma = 5 \times 10^6$ mhos/m, its radial velocity is $v(r) = v_0 r_0/r = 20/r$ m/sec, a surface current density $K = 10^6$ amp/m flows in the outside coil, and the device is enclosed in a material with infinite permeability $\mu = \infty$ so that H has only the axial component.

4.9 In modern measuring instruments, damping of the oscillations is obtained by means of eddy-current dampers consisting, as shown, of a thin aluminum disk

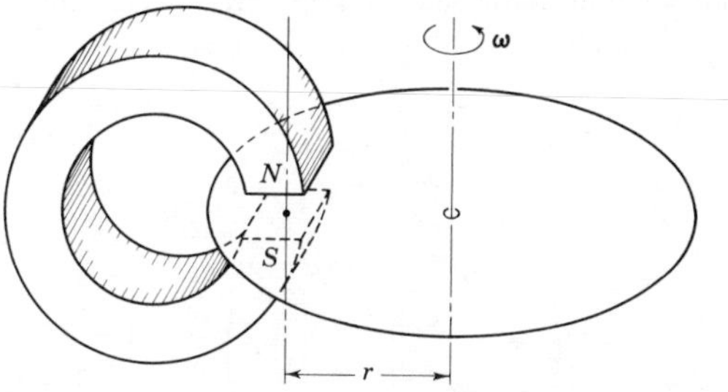

rotating between the pole faces of a permanent magnet. Evaluate the damping torque as a function of the angular velocity ω if the disk's thickness is $d = 10^{-3}$ m, the conductivity is $\gamma = 2.8 \times 10^7$ mhos/m, the slip is $s = -0.8$, the pole faces are situated at a radius $r = 6 \times 10^{-2}$ m, and their area is $A = 10^{-4}$ m^2 and $B = 1$ weber/m^2.

Note that in this case the slip is a purely geometric factor which depends on the shape of the pole face. Its absolute value is the ratio of the resistances of the current paths under and outside the pole face.

4.10 A 250-Mw MPD generator is designed to operate with 70 percent efficiency. Determine the volume of the channel (volume of active conductor) if $B = 3$ webers/m^2, the conductivity of the ionized gas is $\gamma = 10^3$ mhos/m, and its velocity is $v = 10^3$ m/sec.

4.11 An electric locomotive is driven by eight 1,000-hp motors operating with a conversion efficiency of $\eta = 0.997$. Evaluate:

(*a*) The total volume of active copper conductor if $E = 50$ volts/m.

(*b*) The total pull or "tractive effort" of the locomotive at stalling ($v = 0$) if $B = 1$ weber/m² and the overall motor-to-wheel transmission ratio is 1:1.

(*c*) The velocity of the locomotive when, running downhill, it feeds back into the supply system a power equal to the rated power.

Assume that all the volume elements of the conductor are exposed to the same value of electromagnetic field, and that the electric and mechanical connections remain unchanged.

4.12 A power converter is used to hoist or lower a constant-force (gravity) load with steady velocity. In the hoisting mode the converter runs as a motor with

$$P_{\text{mech}} = 3 \text{ kw} \qquad \eta_m = 1 - s = 0.97 \qquad B = 1 \text{ weber/m}^2$$
$$\gamma = 5 \times 10^7 \text{ mhos/m} \qquad v = 30 \text{ m/sec}$$

(*a*) Determine the total volume of active conductor used.

(*b*) The load is to be *lowered* at $v = \frac{1}{4}$ m/sec, with B still 1 weber/m². What is the ratio of the new value of input voltage to that required for hoisting at 30 m/sec? What region of operation is this?

(*c*) Repeat (*b*) if the load is to be lowered at $v = 10$ m/sec, with $B = 1$ weber/m².

4.13 A motor develops a 1,000-joule torque when stalling and a power of 3 kw when running in steady state with an efficiency of $\eta = 99$ percent.

(*a*) What is the torque developed under the specified running conditions?

(*b*) What is the volume of the active copper conductor if

$$B = 1 \text{ weber/m}^2 \qquad \gamma = 5 \times 10^7 \text{ mhos/m} \qquad r_g = 0.1 \text{ m}$$

4.14 It is believed that the earth's magnetic field is maintained by thermal convection motion in the molten conducting core. These motions drag and twist

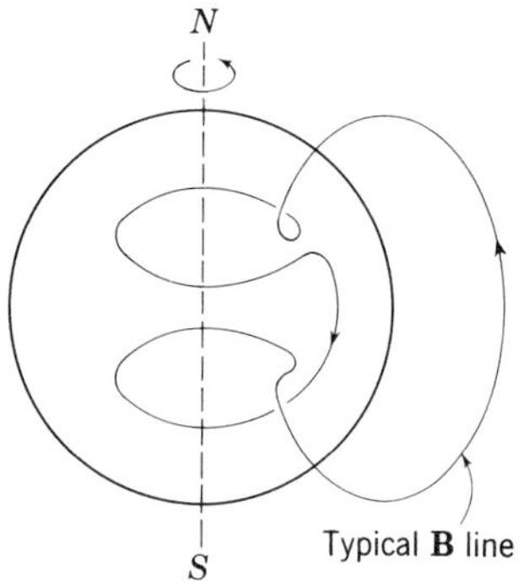

the magnetic flux-density lines in complicated patterns as shown. If

$$\gamma = 10^6 \text{ mhos/m} \qquad v = 10^{-3} \text{ m/sec} \qquad B = 4 \times 10^{-2} \text{ weber/m}^2$$

(*a*) Evaluate p_{diss}.

(*b*) Evaluate the volume of active conductor. Assume that the currents flow in a ring of radius equal to the core radius $r_c = 3.46 \times 10^6$m and that the earth magnetic field has an equivalent dipole strength of 8.1×10^{15} webers/m.

4.15 A 700-hp motor operates with $B = 0.5$ weber/m², $s = 0.005$, and rotates at 1,188 rpm.

(*a*) Find K if $r_g = 0.25$ m, $b = 0.4$ m.

(*b*) Find the Joule loss in the active conductor.

(*c*) Find the heat-transfer coefficient h if the steady-state temperature rise of the conductor is 60°C.

4.16 The design specifications for a liquid-cooled turbogenerator call for output power $P = 300$ Mw (at unity power factor) with a conversion efficiency $\eta = 0.9985$ when it rotates at 3,600 rpm.

Assuming

$$v = 220 \text{ m/sec} \qquad B = 0.58 \text{ weber/m}^2 \qquad \gamma = 5 \times 10^7 \text{ mhos/m}$$

and a maximum temperature rise of 90°C, determine the dimensions of the active conductor.

chapter 5
HOMOPOLAR CONVERTERS

5.1 INTRODUCTION

In the previous chapter we have used the volume elements of conducting material, which are acted upon by an electromagnetic field, as building blocks to synthesize that part of the conductor which contributes to power conversion, the *active* conductor.

In this chapter we continue to build the converter outward by turning our attention to the magnetic field structure, using the guiding principle of providing the largest possible number of conducting elements with the conditions conducive to optimum performance. In this way, we select as our ideal structure, a structure everywhere uniform in **B**; and proceeding to the best practical realization, we evolve the cylindrically symmetric *homopolar converter*.

We next evaluate the performance of the homopolar converter, and find that the electric impedance level of this type of device is inescapably low. Although this rigidity in impedance level prevents the widespread use of homopolar machines, we nevertheless find some interesting and novel applications such as pulse and MPD generators, pumps for liquid metals, and plasma rockets.

Quite aside from its use as a converter, the homopolar structure is interesting from the theoretical point of view, because it represents the simplest one-dimensional model embodying the major features of the electromechanical power-conversion process. It can thus be utilized to gain some insight into and qualitative information about complex natural situations. Furthermore, in considering those applications that employ bounded structures, we begin the study of the effects of nonuniformities in the magnetic field upon the performance of the converter. The detailed analysis of these extremely discontinuous structures, however, is postponed, in the following chapters, in favor of the preliminary study of the heteropolar converter with harmonic variation, which constitutes the smoothest possible nonuniformity.

5.2 UNIFORM STRUCTURES

We are now ready to extend the process of orderly synthesis which has carried us from the elementary particle and the conversion characteristics of an infinitesimal volume of active conductor to the physical structure of an actual converter. In keeping with the logical synthesis procedure which we have been following, we shall begin conceptually with the most symmetrical and uniform structure that we can achieve, in order to permit a direct transition from the infinitestimal model by a process of simple integration.

The most symmetrical electromagnetic power converter is a device infinite in extent in all directions and possessing, as shown in Fig. 5.1, a

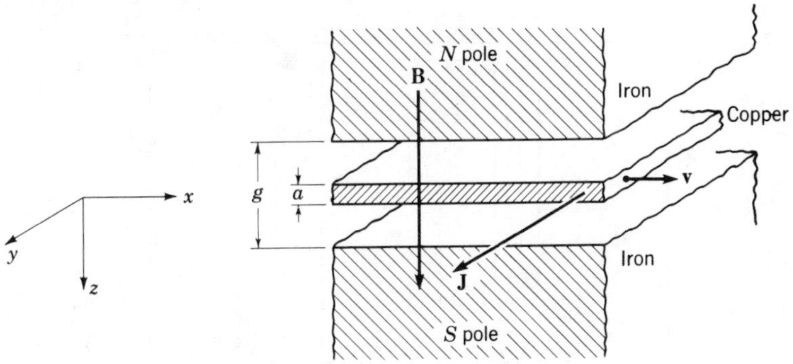

Fig. 5.1 Uniform structure.

uniform air gap, a uniform and time-invariant magnetic field, and a conductor in the form of a sheet moving along the gap. We have, in fact, naturally envisaged such an arrangement in our discussion of the air gap in Sec. 4.8. A device of this type is called *homopolar* or *acyclic* because the conductor everywhere encounters magnetic flux of the same polarity. It is plain that this structure is physically unrealizable, because of its infinite extent. In the next section we shall consider the nearest approximation to this ideal converter which retains the operating characteristics of the infinite uniform structure.

5.3 CONVERTERS WITH CYLINDRICAL SYMMETRY

In order to achieve the best approximation to an infinite structure, at least in one direction, we can render the gap endless by closing it back on itself in a homopolar structure with cylindrical symmetry. An example of such a structure is the axial-type homopolar converter shown in Fig. 5.2. Here the gap takes the form of a cylindrical shell in which the azimuthal, axial, and radial directions correspond respectively to the x, y, and z directions of Fig. 5.1.

It is, of course, necessary to limit the axial length of the converter and so the structure departs from the ideal endless extent in one direction. However, the effects arising from the finite length in the axial direction are not significant, as we later show.

In the particular construction of Fig. 5.2 the inner iron core is stationary, and the conductor takes the form of a cylindrical cup; in other constructions the inner core rotates with the conductor. In both cases the motion of the conductor is a rotation around the central axis with

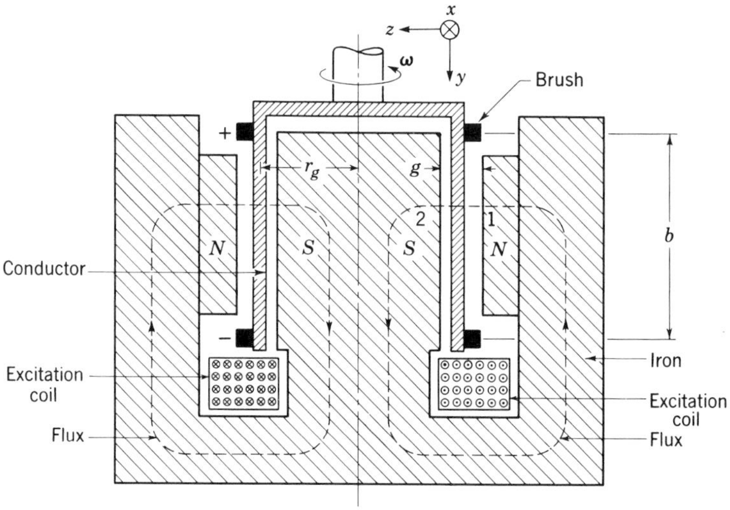

Fig. 5.2 Homopolar converter.

angular velocity ω which gives each active element of the conductor the same azimuthal velocity

$$v = \omega r_g \tag{5.1}$$

with respect to the polar structure.

Although a permanent magnet may be used, the magnetic flux more commonly results from the magnetomotive force set up by the direct current in the excitation coil; it crosses the gap radially with very nearly constant density in the narrow gap, traverses the pole pieces, and closes around the stationary structure as shown.

Since the electric circuit consists of two parts, the active conductor and the external circuit which are in relative motion, the conductor current must pass through a set of sliding contacts, the *brushes*. The necessity for a sliding contact is, of course, an undesirable feature, since it increases maintenance problems. Moreover, as we shall see below, this machine is necessarily a low-voltage, high-current device, which makes the relatively high-resistance sliding contact a serious limitation in high-power applications. In some instances, liquid-metal brushes such as mercury or sodium-potassium eutectic alloy have been used in order to keep the contact resistance as low as possible.

(a) Electrical Performance

The homopolar machine is a low-voltage, high-current converter and hence a low-impedance device. To demonstrate this we shall determine the electrical performance of the axial converter of Fig. 5.2.

In view of the small value of the ratio g/r_g we can neglect, as in Sec. 4.9, the variations of **J**, **v**, and **B** across the gap; likewise, in view of the small value of the ratio g/b, we can neglect the fringing of the magnetic field at the ends in the axial direction. Under these conditions all the volume elements of the active conductor have identical performance, as described by Eqs. (4.10) and (4.12), which are repeated here for convenience:

$$E = \frac{J}{\gamma} + vB \tag{5.2}$$

$$f_m = \xi \frac{\partial v}{\partial t} - JB \tag{5.3}$$

We observe that in Eq. (5.2) E is the field measured in the reference frame for which the conductor moves with velocity **v**, and is therefore the field measured in a reference frame fixed to the brushes and the circuit external to the converter. Moreover, for steady-state conditions, the currents, and consequently the magnetic fields, are time-invariant, so that the voltage between any two points and, in particular, the terminal voltage, is uniquely defined.

In this case we have, from Faraday's law,

$$\oint \mathbf{E} \cdot d\mathbf{l} = -\int_S \frac{\partial \mathbf{B}}{\partial t} \cdot d\mathbf{s} = 0 \tag{5.4a}$$

since the magnetic field is static. Consequently, if we choose a loop fixed to the brush system, as shown in Fig. 5.3, consisting of a mathematical line spanning the distance between the positive and negative brushes outside the active conductor, and closing through the active conductor, we find that the terminal voltage V is

$$V = \int_{+\ \substack{\text{outside}\\\text{conductor}}}^{-} \mathbf{E} \cdot d\mathbf{l} = -\int_{-\ \substack{\text{inside}\\\text{conductor}}}^{+} \mathbf{E} \cdot d\mathbf{l} \tag{5.5}$$

Making use of Eq. (5.2), and observing that, in conformity with the convention established for **E** in Sec. 4.3, **E** and $d\mathbf{l}$ have opposite directions inside the conductor, we obtain

$$V = -\underset{\substack{\text{inside}\\\text{conductor}}}{\int_-^+} \mathbf{E}\cdot d\mathbf{l} = +\int_0^b \left(\frac{J}{\gamma} + vB\right) dy = \left(\frac{J}{\gamma} + vB\right) b \qquad (5.6a)$$

Equation (5.6*a*) gives the terminal voltage in steady state. We now want to see how well this result applies during transient conditions when the currents and therefore the magnetic field vary with time. In this case we cannot so easily dispose of the surface integral of Eq. (5.4*a*), and

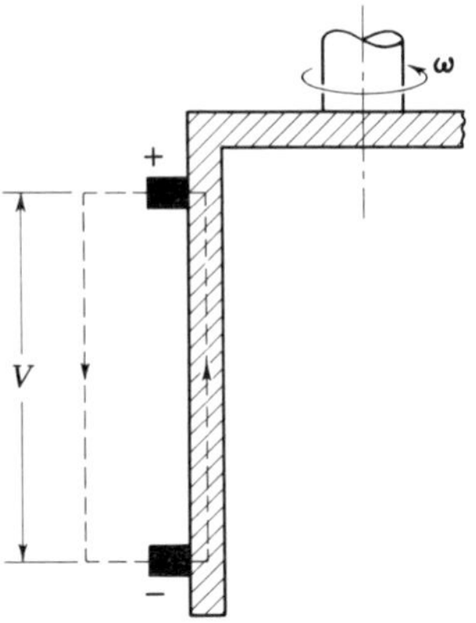

Fig. 5.3 Loop used for the determination of the terminal voltage.

we must carry it along as an additional term which modifies Eq. (5.6*a*). We see this as follows:

Equation (5.4*a*) now becomes

$$\underset{\substack{\text{outside}\\\text{conductor}}}{\int_+^-} \mathbf{E}\cdot d\mathbf{l} + \underset{\substack{\text{inside}\\\text{conductor}}}{\int_-^+} \mathbf{E}\cdot d\mathbf{l} = -\int_S \frac{\partial \mathbf{B}}{\partial t}\cdot d\mathbf{s} \neq 0 \qquad (5.4b)$$

and Eq. (5.6*a*) is therefore

$$V = \underset{\substack{\text{outside}\\\text{conductor}}}{\int_+^-} \mathbf{E}\cdot d\mathbf{l} = -\underset{\substack{\text{inside}\\\text{conductor}}}{\int_-^+} \mathbf{E}\cdot d\mathbf{l} - \int_S \frac{\partial \mathbf{B}}{\partial t}\cdot d\mathbf{s} \qquad (5.6b)$$

or

$$V = \left(\frac{J}{\gamma} + vB\right) b - \int_S \frac{\partial \mathbf{B}}{\partial t}\cdot d\mathbf{s} \qquad (5.6c)$$

The terminal voltage thus becomes a function of the loop bounding the surface of integration S. We observe, however, that our terminals are in effect rings; the cylindrical symmetry of the device thus leads us to choose loops, which, like the one of Fig. 5.3, lie in a plane passing through the axis of rotation. These loops are not cut by the component of flux which crosses the active conductor and is the sole contributor to power conversion. As a result, the arbitrariness in the choice of a loop does not affect the power-conversion process which is of primary interest. The term involving $\partial \mathbf{B}/\partial t$ on the right-hand side of Eq. (5.6*c*) can be interpreted as a voltage arising from the time rate of change of current in an inductance which may be assigned to the circuit external to the converter (see Prob. 5.9). Formally this is achieved by defining our terminal voltage along a path which lies close to the surface of the active conductor, thus making the magnetic flux interlinked with the loop vanishingly small. In any case, as we shall see in Sec. 5.5*b*, homopolar devices are so designed that the flux interlinked with the circuit of the active conductor, and consequently the associated inductance, is very small.

With this in mind we hold Eq. (5.6*a*) to be valid for transient as well as steady-state conditions.

Although Eq. (5.6*a*) gives the terminal voltage, this is not expressed specifically in terms of the total circuit quantities, which are as follows:

I_a = terminal or total current in the active conductor (often called the armature current)
R = resistance of the conductor measured between the brushes (cylindrical brushes are assumed)
Φ = total magnetic flux crossing the gap

In order to relate these to the corresponding quantities, per-unit volume, we note that whereas the elements of the conductor are effectively connected in series in the axial direction, they are connected in parallel along the direction of motion. Consequently, to obtain I_a we evaluate the integral

$$I_a = \int_S \mathbf{J} \cdot d\mathbf{s} \tag{5.7}$$

over the cross-sectional area of the conductor, as shown in Fig. 5.4. Since we have approximated $\mathbf{J}$ as constant in the conductor, this reduces to the multiplication of the constant-current density and the cross-sectional area itself. Since the conductor cross section is an annular ring with inner radius $r_g - a/2$ and outer radius $r_g + a/2$, the total area is $\pi[(r_g + a/2)^2 - (r_g - a/2)^2] = 2\pi r_g a$. Therefore,

$$I_a = J 2\pi r_g a \tag{5.8}$$

Likewise, neglecting the slight end effect, the resistance of the conductor is

$$R = \frac{1}{\gamma} \frac{b}{2\pi r_g a} \tag{5.9}$$

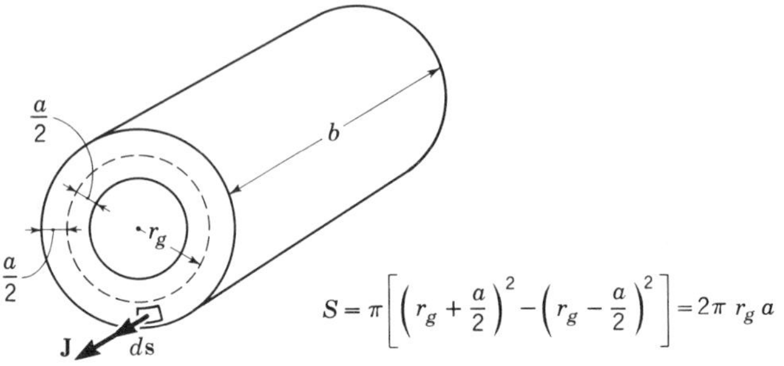

Fig. 5.4 Surface used for the evaluation of the armature current.

Finally, the total magnetic flux is found by evaluating the integral

$$\Phi = \int_S \mathbf{B} \cdot d\mathbf{s} \tag{5.10}$$

over the area of the gap, as indicated in Fig. 5.5; since B is constant and normal to the gap, this reduces to the product

$$\Phi = B2\pi r_g b \tag{5.11}$$

Introducing these integral quantities into Eq. (5.6*a*), and using $v = \omega r_g$, we obtain

$$V = RI_a + \frac{\omega}{2\pi}\Phi \tag{5.12}$$

With the terminal relationship established, we can now evaluate the characteristics of the homopolar machine. As we have previously mentioned, v is limited to about 200 m/sec by centrifugal stress in the rotating conductor, and B is limited to about 1 weber/m^2 by saturation of the iron. In addition, structural considerations limit the length of the rotating conductor to about one meter. As a result, the order of magnitude of the generated voltage vBb in Eq. (5.6*a*) is limited to the relatively low value of 200 volts. This voltage is much too low to afford the economic transmission of power over large distances, which is the major

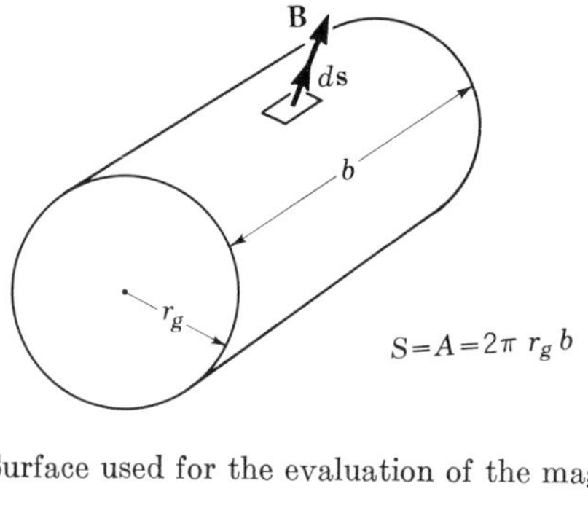

Fig. 5.5 Surface used for the evaluation of the magnetic flux.

asset of electricity. (In order to minimize the Joule losses which are proportional to the square of the current flowing in the line, the voltage levels in use today approach the megavolt range.) Actually, in small structures the generated voltage is quite a bit smaller than the limiting value; if we consider a machine which has a conductor with a 6-in. diameter and a length of 1 ft running at 3,600 rpm with $B = 1$ weber/m^2, the generated voltage is only about 8.8 volts. With such small voltages, high power can only be achieved by operating with large values of current in the conductor. As a result, homopolar machines have usually been used as generators in such applications as resistance welding and electrolytic processes where high currents are required. A typical large generator manufactured by General Electric[1] is rated at 67 volts, 150,000 amp, and 10,000 kw at 3,600 rpm. Its load impedance level is then

$$\frac{67}{150{,}000} \approx 4 \times 10^{-4} \text{ ohm}$$

This machine uses liquid-metal brushes of sodium-potassium eutectic alloy.

We next consider an example illustrating the design of the active conductor.

Example 5.1

A homopolar generator is designed to conform to the following specifications:

Output power:	$-P_{\text{elec}} = 400$ kw
Output voltage:	$V = 50$ volts
Conversion efficiency:	$\eta_g = 0.999$
Speed:	3,600 rpm

Determine the dimensions of the active conductor when the allowable flux density in the gap is $B = 1.8$ weber/m^2, the surface current density is $K = 5{,}000$ amp/m, and the conductor is copper with $\gamma = 5 \times 10^7$ mhos/m. With regard to the relatively low value of the allowable surface current density K, note that in the case of the homopolar converter K may not be determined by thermal considerations but by the sliding contacts. In fact, if J_b is the current density in the brushes, and w is the length of one brush in the axial direction, then $J_b = I_a/2\pi r_g w$. Also $K = I_a/2\pi r_g$, so that $K = J_b w$. K is thus given by the product of J_b, which is relatively small since it represents the current-carrying capacity per unit area of the *sliding contacts*, and w, which is of necessity only a small fraction of the length of the active conductor.

Solution

From Eq. (5.12) and the definition of η_g we have

$$\frac{\omega\Phi}{2\pi} = V - RI_a = \frac{V}{\eta_g}$$

or

$$\Phi = \frac{2\pi}{\omega}\frac{V}{\eta_g} = \frac{2\pi \times 60}{2\pi \times 3{,}600}\left(\frac{50}{0.999}\right) = 0.835 \text{ weber}$$

If A is the surface of the gap, then

$$A = \frac{\Phi}{B} = \frac{0.835}{1.8} = 0.463 \text{ m}^2$$

We can now find v, since

$$v = \frac{p_{s,\text{conv}}}{KB} = \frac{p_{s,\text{elec}}}{\eta_g KB} = \frac{P_e}{\eta_g KBA} = \frac{4 \times 10^5}{0.999 \times 5 \times 10^3 \times 1.8 \times 0.463} = 96 \text{ m/sec}$$

The radius is, then, from Eq. (5.1),

$$r_g = \frac{v}{\omega} = \frac{96 \times 60}{2\pi \times 3{,}600} = 0.254 \text{ m}$$

The length is

$$b = \frac{A}{2\pi r_g} = \frac{0.463}{2\pi \times 0.254} = 0.29 \text{ m}$$

and the thickness

$$a = \frac{1}{\gamma}\frac{b}{2\pi r_g}\frac{1}{R} = \frac{1}{\gamma}\frac{b}{2\pi r_g}\frac{P_e \eta_g}{(1-\eta_g)V^2}$$
$$= \frac{0.29 \times 4 \times 10^5 \times 0.999}{5 \times 10^7 \times 2\pi \times 0.254 \times 0.001(50)^2} = 5.82 \times 10^{-4} \text{ m}$$

(b) Mechanical Performance

We shall now integrate the electromechanical equation of motion [Eq. (5.3)] in order to obtain the dynamical equation in terms of total circuit quantities. First, we multiply through by r_g in order to obtain the elementary torque relation for each conductor element:

$$\ell = f_m r_g = \xi r_g \frac{\partial v}{\partial t} - JBr_g \tag{5.13}$$

Now we recognize that the elementary torques contributed by all the volume elements are all the same and are directed along the converter axis, so that the integration to find the total torque $\mathfrak{L}$ reduces to a simple multiplication of Eq. (5.13) by the total volume of the active conductor. Thus, as indicated in Fig. 5.6, we obtain

$$\mathfrak{L} = f_m r_g (2\pi r_g ab) = \xi 2\pi r_g{}^2 ab \frac{\partial v}{\partial t} - JB2\pi r_g{}^2 ab \tag{5.14}$$

Introducing the moment of inertia Θ, which for the thin cylindrical conducting shell of mass M and radius r_g is

$$\Theta = Mr_g{}^2 = (\xi 2\pi r_g ab) r_g{}^2 = \xi 2\pi ab r_g{}^3 \tag{5.15}$$

and the total magnetic flux Φ, the armature current I_a, and the angular velocity ω as before, we find

$$\mathfrak{L} = \Theta \frac{d\omega}{dt} - I_a \frac{\Phi}{2\pi} \tag{5.16}$$

The overall performance of Eqs. (5.12) and (5.16) can be expressed by equivalent circuits similar to those shown in Fig. 4.5. In particular, referring the mechanical side to the electrical side as in Fig. 4.5c, we may represent the rotating homopolar converter by the equivalent circuit shown in Fig. 5.7. With the aid of Eqs. (5.12) and (5.16) and Fig. 5.7, we

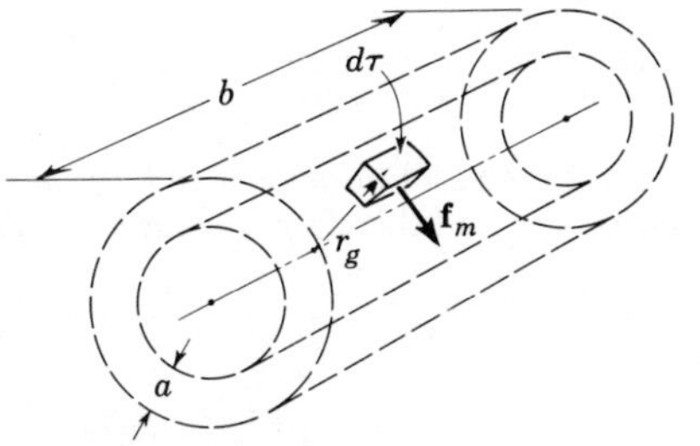

$$\ell = f_m r_g$$

$$\mathfrak{L} = \int_v f_m r_g \, d\tau = f_m r_g \,(2\pi r_g ab)$$

$$\Theta = \int_v r^2 \xi \, d\tau = r_g^2 \xi (2\pi r_g ab)$$

$$\frac{\mathfrak{L}}{\Theta} = \frac{f_m}{r_g \xi}$$

Fig. 5.6 Volume used for the evaluation of the total torque $\mathfrak{L}$, the moment of inertia Θ, and the torque inertia ratio $\mathfrak{L}/\Theta$.

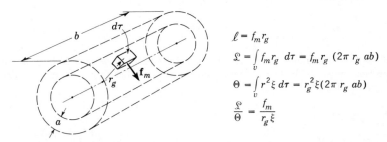

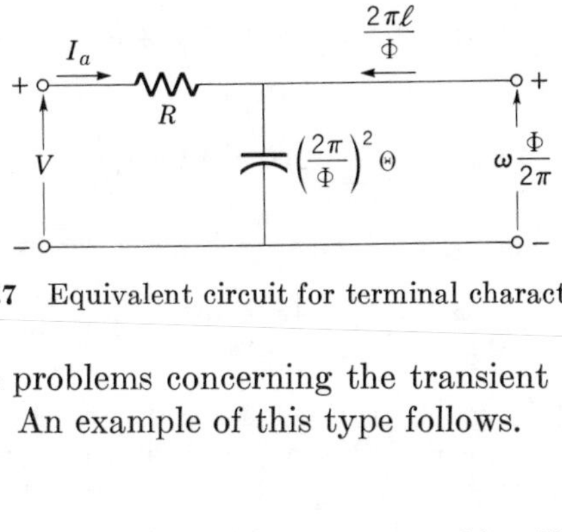

Fig. 5.7 Equivalent circuit for terminal characteristics.

may readily solve problems concerning the transient behavior of homopolar converters. An example of this type follows.

Example 5.2

The active conductor of a homopolar converter with cylindrical symmetry has the parameters:

Total resistance:	$R = 6 \times 10^{-6}$ ohm
Moment of inertia:	$\Theta = 7 \times 10^{-4}$ kg-m²
Total gap flux:	$\Phi = 15 \times 10^{-3}$ weber

A torque $\mathfrak{L}$ of 100 newton-m is applied to the rotor at $t = 0$ with the electric circuit open and the rotor initially at rest. At time $t = 3$ msec the torque is removed by disconnecting the clutch, and a load $R_L = 1.2 \times 10^{-4}$ ohm is simultaneously connected to the brushes.

(*a*) Assuming negligible friction, find the angular velocity $\omega(t)$ and the armature current $I_a(t)$ as functions of time.

(*b*) Find the overall efficiency of energy conversion from the energy delivered by the torque source to the energy absorbed by the load R_L.

Solution

(*a*) For the time from $t = 0$ to $t_0 = 3$ msec, the current $I_a(t)$ is zero, because the electric terminals are open-circuited.

$$I_a(t) = 0 \qquad \text{for } t = 0 \text{ to } t_0 = 3 \text{ msec}$$

From Eq. (5.16) we have, for $I_a = 0$,

$$\mathcal{L} = \Theta \frac{d\omega}{dt}$$

Since the torque is constant for the first 3 msec, we observe a uniform angular acceleration given by the torque/inertia ratio $\mathcal{L}/\Theta$, and therefore a linear variation of the angular velocity

$$\omega = \frac{\mathcal{L}}{\Theta} t$$

or

$$\omega = \frac{100}{7 \times 10^{-4}} t = 1.43 \times 10^5 t \text{ rad/sec} \qquad \text{for } t = 0 \text{ to } t_0 = 3 \text{ msec}$$

The final angular velocity is

$$\omega_0 = 1.43 \times 10^5 \times 3 \times 10^{-3} = 429 \text{ rad/sec}$$

which corresponds to

$$(\text{rpm})_0 = \frac{\omega_0}{2\pi} \times 60 = 4{,}100 \text{ rpm}$$

At $t_0 = 3$ msec the equivalent voltage across the capacitor is

$$V_0 = \omega_0 \frac{\Phi}{2\pi} = 429 \times \frac{15 \times 10^{-3}}{2\pi} = 1.02 \text{ volts}$$

and at this time the load R_L is connected across the electric terminals (Fig. 5.7). Thus the initial value of the current discharging the inertial capacitance through the series resistance $R + R_L$ is

$$I_{a,0} = -\frac{V_0}{R + R_L} = -\frac{1.02}{1.26 \times 10^{-4}} = -8 \times 10^3 \text{ amp}$$

The time constant of the discharge is

$$\tau = (R_L + R)\left(\frac{2\pi}{\Phi}\right)^2 \Theta = 1.26 \times 10^{-4} \times \frac{(2\pi)^2}{225 \times 10^{-6}} \times 7 \times 10^{-4} = 15 \text{ msec}$$

For $t \geq 3$ msec the expressions for ω and I_a are

$$I_a = I_{a,0} \exp[-(t - t_0)/\tau] = -8 \times 10^3 \exp[-(t - 3 \times 10^{-3})/(15 \times 10^{-3})]$$

$$\omega = \omega_0 \exp[-(t - t_0)/\tau] = 429 \exp[-(t - 3 \times 10^{-3})/(15 \times 10^{-3})]$$

The time behavior of ω and I_a are shown in the figure.

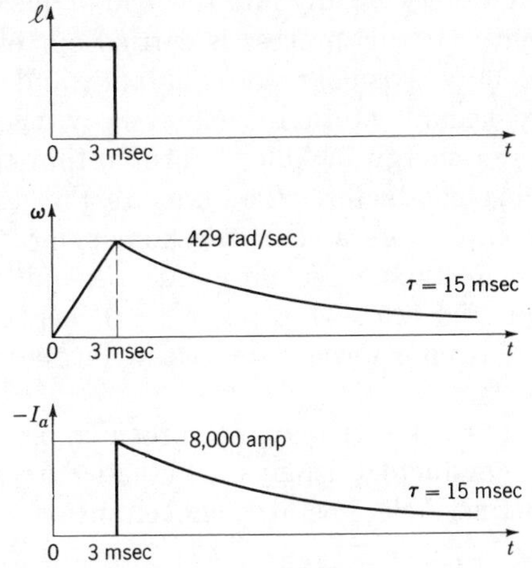

(*b*) The total energy delivered by the torque source is stored as kinetic energy of the rotor at $t_0 = 3$ msec. This energy will be finally delivered to the resistances. Therefore,

$$\text{Total energy} = (R + R_L) \int_{t_0}^{\infty} I_a^2\, dt$$

The energy absorbed by the load R_L is

$$R_L \int_{t_0}^{\infty} I_a^2\, dt$$

Therefore the overall efficiency of energy conversion is

$$\eta = \frac{R_L \int_{t_0}^{\infty} I_a^2\, dt}{(R_L + R) \int_{t_0}^{\infty} I_a^2\, dt} = \frac{R_L}{R_L + R} = \frac{1.2 \times 10^{-4}}{1.26 \times 10^{-4}} = 0.952$$

Since $R \ll R_L$, we could have calculated η approximately by

$$\eta = \frac{R_L}{R_L + R} = \frac{1}{1 + R/R_L} \approx 1 - \frac{R}{R_L}$$

or

$$\eta = 1 - \frac{6 \times 10^{-6}}{120 \times 10^{-6}} = 1 - 0.05 = 0.95$$

5.4 INERTIAL CAPACITORS

(a) Pulse Generators

Certain practical applications, such as welding, radar, and plasma research offer an excellent opportunity to study the dynamical performance of the homopolar converter. In these applications, electric power at extremely high levels is required for very short periods of time. In these situations the appropriate engineering approach is to accummulate the energy required at a relatively low rate, storing it in a suitable device and then discharging it very rapidly into the load by means of a switching or triggering element. If this process is carried out exclusively on the electrical side, the energy is usually stored in bulky and expensive capacitor banks. A more elegant solution is achieved by using the homopolar generator to store the energy in kinetic form within the much smaller volume of its moving conductor. To compare the densities of stored energy in ordinary capacitors and in the homopolar devices it is convenient to refer back to the equivalent circuit per-unit volume of active conductor shown in Fig. 4.5*c*. Letting $f_m = 0$, because if we neglect viscous friction there is no external force acting on the active conductor, we obtain Fig. 5.8.

As mentioned in Sec. 4.5 we may interpret Fig. 5.8 to the effect that the unit volume of conductor displays a "kinetic capacitance" ξ/B^2 in addition to the intrinsic electrostatic capacitance ϵ_0 (of a unit cube

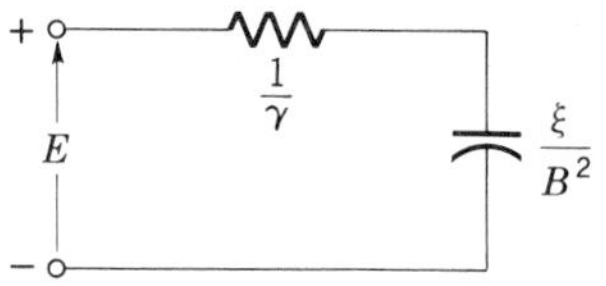

Fig. 5.8 Kinetic capacitance and series resistance per unit volume.

between parallel faces). Thus ξ/B^2 can be considered an equivalent "dielectric permittivity."[2] Since for copper $\xi = 8.9 \times 10^3$ kg/m³, the equivalent relative dielectric constant for the case $B = 1$ is

$$\frac{\xi}{\epsilon_0 B^2} = \frac{8.9 \times 10^3}{10^{-9}/36\pi} \doteq 10^{15}$$

Since the dielectric constant of most capacitor materials is between 1 and 10, it is clear that it is possible to store about 10^{14} times as much energy in the homopolar converter as in an equal volume of electrostatic capacitance.

One of the shortcomings of using a conventional rotating machine with copper conductors as a pulse generator is the relative slowness of the converter in delivering electric energy to the load. Assuming that the load has a constant voltage, the charge would be delivered to the E terminals of Fig. 5.8 with a time constant $(1/\gamma)\xi/B^2$. For copper with $\gamma = 5.9 \times 10^7$, $\xi = 8.9 \times 10^3$, and taking $B = 1$, the resulting intrinsic time constant is 1.5×10^{-4} or 150 μsec. This value, although short enough for some applications, is much too long for others. In order to reduce the intrinsic time constant, it has been proposed to use hot plasma in place of copper, because of the much lower mass density ξ of the plasma. This would also have the useful effect of greatly increasing the output voltage and energy-storage capability of the homopolar generator, since plasmas are readily accelerated to very high velocities. The resulting device has been called the *hydromagnetic capacitor*.[3] The following example demonstrates the potentiality of such a scheme for storage of energy in kinetic form.

EXAMPLE 5.3

A certain hydromagnetic capacitor consists of a cylindrical structure, as shown in a cutaway view. The "dielectric material" between the two coaxial electrodes is

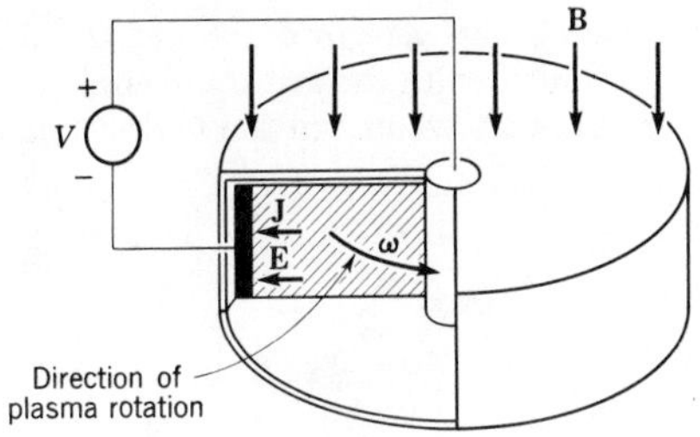

a magnetized plasma, which is set in motion by the impressed electric field and accelerated up to approximately the drift velocity. The device is then disconnected from the supply, and the energy stored in kinetic form is discharged into an electric load while the plasma slows down with a time constant, as discussed above.

(*a*) Assuming that the layers of the plasma can slide freely past each other, and that B is space- and time-invariant, determine E and v_E as a function of the radius r.

(*b*) Assuming

$$B = 1 \text{ weber/m}^2 \qquad \xi_H = 10^{-6} \text{ kg/m}^3 \qquad \gamma = 5 \times 10^6 \text{ mhos/m}$$

determine the intrinsic time constant of such a capacitor.

(*c*) Compare the energy stored per-unit volume and per-unit weight in this hydromagnetic capacitor and in an ordinary capacitor with paper dielectric if the latter has a relative dielectric constant $\epsilon_r = 3.5$ and an average mass density $\xi_P = 2.5 \times 10^3$ kg/m³. Assume equal electric-field intensity.

Solution

In a cylindrical structure with dielectric constant ϵ we have $E = \lambda/2\pi\epsilon r$, where λ, the linear charge density, is found from

$$V = \int_{r_i}^{r_o} E\,dr = \frac{\lambda}{2\pi\epsilon}\int_{r_i}^{r_o}\frac{dr}{r} = \frac{\lambda}{2\pi\epsilon}\ln\frac{r_o}{r_i}$$

Therefore

$$E = \frac{V}{\ln(r_o/r_i)}\frac{1}{r} \qquad \text{and} \qquad v_E = \frac{E}{B} = \frac{V}{B\ln(r_o/r_i)}\frac{1}{r}$$

(*b*) The capacitance per-unit length in the axial direction is

$$C = \frac{\lambda}{V} = \frac{2\pi\epsilon}{\ln(r_o/r_i)}$$

Proceeding as in (*a*) we can find the resistance per-unit length as

$$R = \frac{1}{I_a} \int_{r_i}^{r_o} \frac{J}{\gamma}\, dr = \frac{1}{I_a} \int_{r_i}^{r_o} \frac{I_a\, dr}{2\pi r \gamma} = \frac{1}{2\pi\gamma} \ln \frac{r_o}{r_i}$$

The time constant is then

$$\tau = RC = \frac{\epsilon}{\gamma} = \frac{\xi_H}{\gamma B^2}$$

We thus have

$$\tau = \frac{10^{-6}}{5 \times 10^6 \times 1} = 2 \times 10^{-13}\,\text{sec}$$

Note that this calculation does not take into account the inductive effects arising from the magnetic flux interlinked with the armature circuit.

(*c*) The energy stored per-unit volume in the hydromagnetic capacitor is

$$W_H = \tfrac{1}{2}\xi_H v_E{}^2 = \tfrac{1}{2}\xi_H \frac{E^2}{B^2} = \tfrac{1}{2}\epsilon_H E^2$$

and in the paper capacitor

$$W_P = \tfrac{1}{2}\epsilon_r \epsilon_0 E^2$$

We thus have

$$\frac{W_H}{W_P} = \frac{\epsilon_H}{\epsilon_r \epsilon_o} = \frac{10^{-6} \times 4\pi \times 9 \times 10^9}{3.5} = 2.97 \times 10^4$$

The ratio of the energies stored per-unit weight is

$$\frac{W_H}{W_P}\frac{\xi_P}{\xi_H} = 2.97 \times 10^4 \times \frac{2.5 \times 10^3}{10^{-6}} = 7.42 \times 10^{13}$$

In practice, the ratio of energies stored per unit volume of active materials may turn out to be even higher than that indicated by the previous example, because in dielectrics the breakdown phenomenon limits the allowable field intensity E to values of the order of 10^6 volts/m, whereas no such limitation seems to exist with inertial capacitors. On the other hand, when considering the inertial capacitors one should include the weight of the magnet, which is certainly appreciable, even when superconducting coils are used. Other drawbacks of this energy-storage device are the low efficiency resulting from viscous friction and the operational difficulties associated with the sliding contacts at the electrodes.

(b) Energy-conversion Efficiency

The efficiency of electromechanical energy conversion in the homopolar pulse generator is readily calculated from fundamental relations in capacitive circuits. As an example, we shall calculate the efficiency of the energy conversion under the following circumstances:

1. The conductor is initially at a velocity v_0 and slows down to a velocity v_1 as the electric pulse is delivered.

2. There is no source of mechanical power during the pulse.
3. The load maintains constant E as current is delivered to it.
4. B is constant.

It will be convenient to use Fig. 4.5d for this calculation ($f_m = 0$). The initial energy in the capacitor is $W_0 = \frac{1}{2}\xi v_0^2$; the initial charge is $q_0 = \xi v_0$. Similarly the final energy and charge are $W_1 = \frac{1}{2}\xi v_1^2$, $q_1 = \xi v_1$. The kinetic energy lost is $\Delta W_{\text{kin}} = \frac{1}{2}\xi(v_0^2 - v_1^2)$; the energy delivered to the load is $\Delta W_E = (E/B)(q_0 - q_1) = v_E\xi(v_0 - v_1)$. The energy-conversion efficiency for this discharging process is plainly

$$\eta_{\text{e.d.}} = \frac{\Delta W_E}{\Delta W_{\text{kin}}} = \frac{v_E\xi(v_0 - v_1)}{\frac{1}{2}\xi(v_0^2 - v_1^2)} = \frac{v_E}{v_{\text{av}}} \tag{5.17}$$

where we define v_{av} as $(v_0 + v_1)/2$.

Similarly if the homopolar device is brought up to speed operating as a motor (fed by the electrical port) the energy-conversion efficiency for this charging process is

$$\eta_{\text{e.c.}} = \frac{v_{\text{av}}}{v_E} \tag{5.18}$$

Equations (5.17) and (5.18) indicate that the efficiency of energy conversion decreases as the average velocity departs from the drift velocity. Thus if the charging operation, for example, begins at zero speed and terminates at v_E, then $v_{\text{av}} = v_E/2$, and the efficiency is only 50 percent. The efficiency can be increased by beginning the charging process at higher speeds, and in this case less energy is converted. However, in so doing, relatively little energy conversion is sacrificed because of the quadratic dependence of the kinetic energy on the velocity. We find here a trade-off between efficiency and amount of energy converted, quite analogous to the power-density case of Chap. 4.

The decrease of efficiency as v_{av} departs from v_E is to be expected because all converters operate most efficiently at low values of slip s, i.e., when the conductor velocity nearly equals the drift velocity. Consequently the expressions derived for the efficiency of energy conversion of the homopolar pulse generator apply to a much larger class of converters; in fact, they apply to all converters with constant electromagnetic excitation. It is also clear from the equivalent circuit of Fig. 5.7 that for the purpose of pulse generation an ordinary capacitor bank would be subject to the same efficiency limitations. The electromechanical converter, however, is definitely at an advantage because in many cases it is possible to vary B and therefore adjust v_E to the instantaneous velocity of the conductor. Again referring to Fig. 5.8, this corresponds to a parametric variation of the capacitance ξ/B^2 in such a way as to maintain the voltage across the capacitance at almost the same level as the source voltage.

This technique of regulating B is very important in practice, because high power drives such as those used in steel mills, punch presses, propulsion, traction, etc., have long accelerating and decelerating transients due to high inertia. Under these conditions the efficiency would be low and the operation uneconomical unless B were varied. One way to achieve this regulation of the field is to connect the field coil in series with the armature circuit.

The low efficiency which characterizes acceleration and deceleration at constant electromagnetic excitation has important technical implications. In fact, the energy dissipated into heat is mostly absorbed by the conductor itself, so that its temperature may rise above the allowable limits. This problem, which will be discussed in detail in Chap. 10, is illustrated by the following example:

Example 5.4

Consider the electromagnetic guns of Example 4.4.

(*a*) By evaluating the energy dissipated as a function of the kinetic energy and the normalized exit velocity v_1/v_E, compare the performance of guns with copper and aluminum projectiles.

(*b*) The maximum velocity obtainable with chemical explosives in the form of shaped charges is of the order of 10^4 m/sec. Let us investigate the performance of electromagnetic guns at this exit-velocity level. Assuming that all the energy dissipated heats up the projectile fired by the gun, determine the minimum temperature rise of the aluminum projectile if the specific heat is $c_{\text{Al}} = 2.67 \times 10^6$ joules/(m³)(°C).

Solution

(*a*) We can write

$$W_{\text{diss}} = W_{\text{kin}} + W_{\text{diss}} - W_{\text{kin}} = \left(\frac{W_{\text{kin}} + W_{\text{diss}}}{W_{\text{kin}}} - 1\right) W_{\text{kin}}$$
$$= \left(\frac{1}{\eta_{\text{e.c.}}} - 1\right) W_{\text{kin}}$$

For the conductor starting from rest, Eq. (5.18) gives

$$\eta_{\text{e.c.}} = \frac{v_{\text{av}}}{v_E} = \frac{v_1}{2v_E}$$

so that the dissipated energy may be written

$$W_{\text{diss}} = \left(\frac{2v_E}{v_1} - 1\right) W_{\text{kin}}$$

For a given final kinetic energy, we observe that W_{diss} varies from an infinitely large value, when $v_1/v_E \to 0$ and the gun length is vanishingly small (see Example 4.4), to an asymptotic value equal to W_{kin}, when $v_1/v_E = 1$, and the gun is infinitely long.

We may now compare the copper and aluminum projectiles for the two cases of equal values of (1) v_1/v_E and (2) W_{kin}.

(1) For equal v_1/v_E,

$$\frac{W_{\text{diss,Cu}}}{W_{\text{diss,Al}}} = \frac{W_{\text{kin,Cu}}}{W_{\text{kin,Al}}} = \frac{\xi_{\text{Cu}}}{\xi_{\text{Al}}} = \frac{8.93}{2.7} = 3.3$$

(2) For equal kinetic energy,

$$\frac{W_{\text{diss,Cu}}}{W_{\text{diss,Al}}} = \frac{2v_E/v_{1,\text{Cu}} - 1}{2v_E/v_{1,\text{Al}} - 1} = \frac{2v_E/v_{1,\text{Cu}} - 1}{2[(v_E/v_{1,\text{Cu}})\sqrt{\xi_{\text{Al}}/\xi_{\text{Cu}}}] - 1} > 1$$

because aluminum is lighter than copper.

In both cases, less energy is dissipated with the aluminum projectile. This proves that aluminum, despite its lower conductivity, is a better-suited material for this kind of application.

(*b*) The minimum temperature rise occurs when the dissipated energy is a minimum, that is, for $v_E/v_1 \to 1$. We then have

$$W_{\text{diss}} = \left(2\frac{v_E}{v_1} - 1\right) W_{\text{kin}} = W_{\text{kin}} = \tfrac{1}{2}\xi v_1^2$$

$$\Delta T_{\text{min}} = \frac{W_{\text{diss}}}{c_{\text{Al}}} = \frac{\frac{1}{2}\xi v_1^2}{c_{\text{Al}}} = \frac{2.7 \times 10^3 \times 10^8}{2 \times 2.67 \times 10^6}$$
$$= 5.07 \times 10^4 \text{ °C}$$

Since aluminum melts at 658°C, it is clear that such velocities are not attainable with electromagnetic acceleration when E and B are maintained constant during the acceleration period.

5.5 MAGNETIC CIRCUIT

(a) Field Excitation

In the preceding discussion we have postulated the existence of a known and uniform distribution of magnetic flux within the gap. It is the purpose of this section to find out how we can set up this desired flux distribution and actually determine the required intensity and location of the currents which constitute the sources of the magnetic field. A problem of this kind would be extremely complex in arbitrary configurations, but it is considerably reduced here by the following facts: (1) the symmetry of the structure and (2) the possibility of an important simplifying approximation. This approximation is that the reluctance of the magnetic circuit outside the gap is so low, when compared with the reluctance of the gap itself, that it can be considered in effect an ideal magnetic short circuit.

This is certainly a reasonable assumption, since we can choose a ferromagnetic material of liberal cross section and relative permeability of several thousands for that part of the magnetic circuit outside the gap.

We first consider the *no-load* case when no current flows in the active conductor. Making use of the relation between the magnetic field intensity and its sources expressed by Ampère's circuital law, we have

$$\oint \mathbf{H} \cdot d\mathbf{l} = \int_S \mathbf{J} \cdot d\mathbf{s} \tag{5.19}$$

and performing the integration along the path of a typical flux line as shown in Fig. 5.2, we can then formally write

$$\int_{1\ \text{along gap}}^{2} \mathbf{H}_{\text{gap}} \cdot d\mathbf{l} + \int_{2\ \text{along iron}}^{1} \mathbf{H}_{\text{iron}} \cdot d\mathbf{l} = nI_f \tag{5.20}$$

where n is the number of turns of the field excitation coil, and I_f is its current. This equation becomes considerably simpler when we make the approximation previously mentioned; thus, considering the iron an ideal short circuit, the integral along the path in iron vanishes, the boundaries of the gap become surfaces of constant magnetic potential, and H_{gap} is uniform and perpendicular to the iron surfaces. The desired excitation magnetomotive force is then directly found as

$$nI_f = H_{\text{gap}} l_{\text{gap}} = H_{\text{gap}} g = \frac{B}{\mu_0} g \tag{5.21}$$

Now that we have evaluated the field excitation, we turn to the structural aspects of the magnetic circuit; these, as we shall see, determine the overall dimensions of the converter.

(b) Overall Dimensions

The purpose of the ferromagnetic structure is to channel effectively the flux interlinked with the field-excitation coil into the gap and through the active conductor. To this end the flux density in the iron must be kept everywhere below the value corresponding to saturation. Previously, we have noted that for best utilization of the active conductor we want the flux density B_g in the gap to be as high as possible. It thus follows that (1) B_g should have the maximum level compatible with saturation, and (2) the cross section of the magnetic flux path in the iron should equal or exceed the area of the active conductor.

In homopolar devices, where the specified output voltage and angular velocity suffice to determine the length and the radius of the active conductor, as illustrated in Example 5.1, these requirements have important consequences on the design of the converter.

To appreciate the restrictions imposed by the magnetic circuit, we refer to Fig. 5.9, which shows in cross section the magnetic circuit of the homopolar converter of Fig. 5.2. We see that there are four parts to the magnetic circuit; these are in order, the inner axial path in the iron, the radial path in the gap, the outer axial path in the iron, and the radial return path in the iron (we neglect leakage of flux outside these paths). Designating the flux densities as $B_{e,1}$, B_g, $B_{e,2}$, $B_{e,3}$, respectively, in the order stated above, we have from the constancy of the total flux Φ:

$$\begin{aligned} \Phi &= B_{e,1}(\pi r_g^2) = B_g(2\pi r_g b) = B_{e,2}(\pi r_o^2 - \pi r_g^2) \\ &= B_{e,3}(2\pi r_g b_o - 2\pi r_g b) \end{aligned} \tag{5.22}$$

Now if the flux densities are at all unequal, we desire B_g to be the largest; thus we have

$$\frac{B_{e,n}}{B_g} \leq 1 \qquad n = 1, 2, 3 \tag{5.23}$$

Using the $B_{e,1}$, B_g relationship, for example, this means that

$$\frac{b}{r_g} = \frac{1}{2}\frac{B_{e,1}}{B_g} \leq \frac{1}{2} \tag{5.24}$$

Whenever, as in Example 5.1, this inequality is not satisfied, we must build several units and connect them in series so as to increase the effective

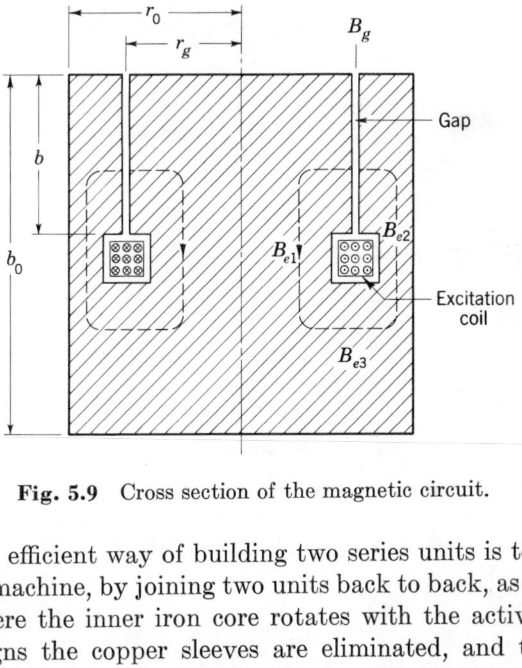

Fig. 5.9 Cross section of the magnetic circuit.

overall b. An efficient way of building two series units is to construct a twin uniaxial machine, by joining two units back to back, as illustrated in Fig. 5.10. Here the inner iron core rotates with the active conductor. In some designs the copper sleeves are eliminated, and the armature current simply flows on the surface of the steel conductors in the rotor and in the stator.

As we see from Eqs. (5.22) and (5.23), for a given Φ the cross sections of the various parts of the magnetic circuit in iron, and consequently the weight and cost of the unit, are minimized when

$$B_{e,1} = B_{e,2} = B_{e,3} = B_g$$

This also has the generally beneficial result of making b/r_g take on its upper bound in Eq. (5.24), thus reducing the number of series-connected units required. For this condition of overall uniformity in B, we find

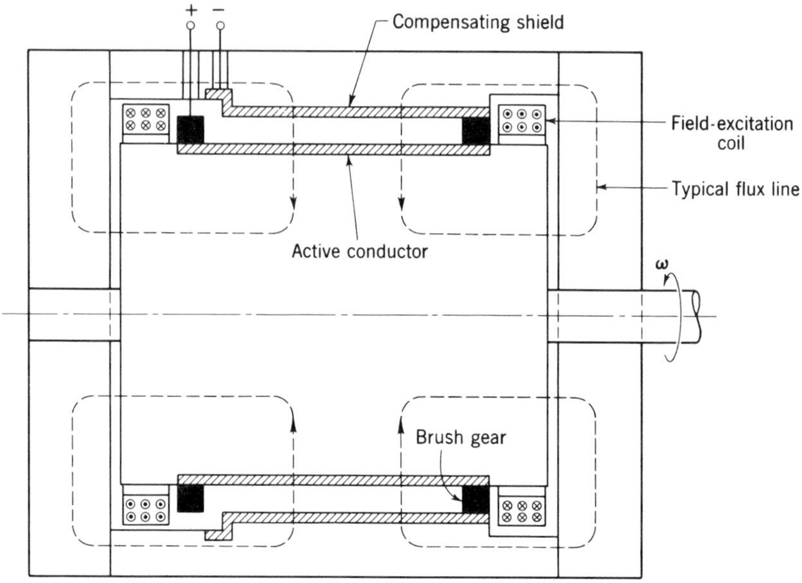

Fig. 5.10 Twin homopolar converter (with split magnetic flux path).

from Eq. (5.22) that

$$\frac{b}{r_g} = \frac{1}{2} \tag{5.25a}$$

$$r_o = \sqrt{2}\, r_g \tag{5.25b}$$

$$b_o = 2b \tag{5.25c}$$

This means that the overall cross-sectional area A_o is

$$A_o = \pi r_o^2 = 2\pi r_g^2 = 4\pi r_g b = 2A \tag{5.26a}$$

and the overall length b_o is

$$b_o = 2b = \sqrt{\frac{A}{\pi}} \tag{5.26b}$$

so that the overall volume of the converter is

$$\text{Overall volume} = A_o b_o = \sqrt{\frac{4A^3}{\pi}} = \sqrt{\frac{4}{\pi}\left(\frac{P}{p_s}\right)^3} \tag{5.26c}$$

(c) Armature Reaction

So far we have considered the magnetic excitation at no load. We next consider the more interesting case in which the converter is loaded and current flows in the active conductor. As we have repeatedly emphasized in Secs. 3.3*b*, and 3.5, the sources arising from the dynamical response of the active conductor must be included when evaluating the electromagnetic field to which the conductor is exposed. Fortunately, in this instance the evaluation of the induced or armature reaction field is straightforward because of the cylindrical symmetry of the endless homopolar conductor. As shown in Fig. 5.11, the armature current, which, according to Eq. (5.8), is uniformly distributed within the conductor with a density

$$J = J_y = \frac{I_a}{2\pi r_g a} \tag{5.27}$$

sets up a magnetic field whose flux lines are concentric circles about the axis of the converter; there is no radial or axial component of field due to

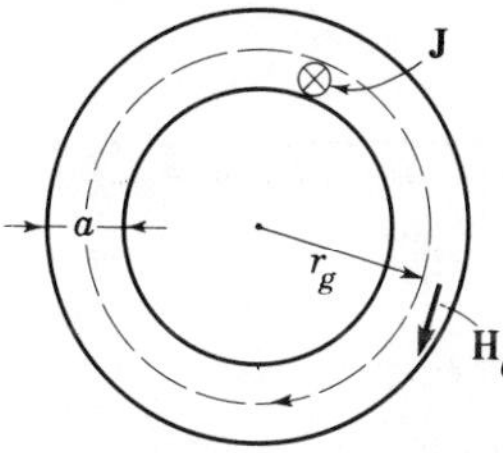

Fig. 5.11 Cross section of the active conductor.

the armature current. Introducing Eq. (5.27) into Eq. (5.19), we find that the field due to I_a in the region occupied by the conductor is

$$H = H_\theta = \frac{1}{2\pi r} \int_{r_g - a/2}^{r} \frac{I_a}{2\pi r_g a} 2\pi r \, dr = \frac{I_a}{2\pi r} \frac{r^2 - (r_g - a/2)^2}{2 r_g a} \tag{5.28}$$

If the iron remains unsaturated, we can find the total B by superposition of the components separately due to the field excitation and the armature reaction. In this case an important fact to note is that the induced B field does not generate any motional electric field because it has no component perpendicular to the velocity of the conductor. This is a property peculiar to the endless homopolar structure which is not shared by any other structure. Thus, we might conclude that the generated voltage equals the no-load voltage under all load conditions. However, unless adequate means are taken to compensate for the "armature reaction," the induced azimuthal field would soon saturate the outer iron structure as the armature current is increased, thus indirectly affecting the active or radial component due to the excitation current. In this respect as well, the homopolar is at an advantage when compared with other types because the saturation can be easily avoided by screening the outer iron structure with a current sheet carrying a current equal in magnitude and opposite in direction to the armature current. In fact, we can place both terminals of the machine of Fig. 5.2 at the upper end, connecting one to upper brushes directly and the other to the lower brushes by means of a stationary cylindrical shell which lines the outer surface of the gap. As shown in Fig. 5.12, the armature current then flows in opposite directions in the moving conductor and in the stationary shell, so that the azimuthal field vanishes in the region outside the stationary shell and in the iron. The same scheme has also been illustrated in the twin converter of Fig. 5.10.

Compensation of the armature reaction is instrumental in extending the validity of Eq. (5.6*a*) to physical terminals placed outside the gap. In fact, by confining the induced magnetic field to the narrow region consisting of the gap, the stationary compensating shell reduces the amount

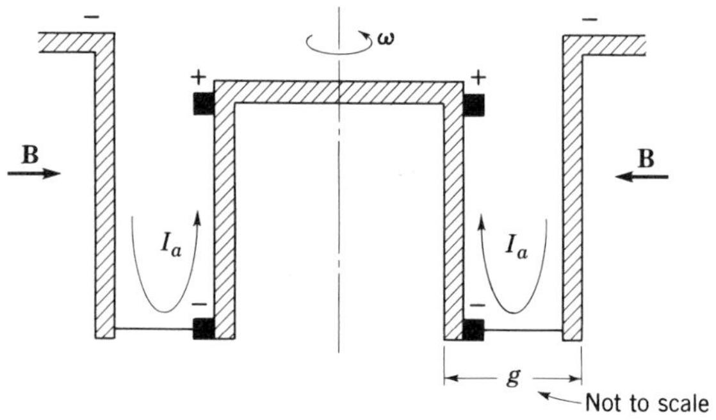

Fig. 5.12 Compensation of armature reaction.

of magnetic flux interlinked with the armature circuit, so that inductive effects become truly negligible when compared with inertia effects (see Prob. 5.9).

*5.6 POYNTING VECTOR

We return now to Eq. (5.28). By letting $r = r_g + a/2$, the tangential component of the magnetic field intensity at the surface of the active conductor is

$$H_\theta = \frac{I_a}{2\pi(r_g + a/2)} \tag{5.29}$$

The quantity $I_a/2\pi(r_g + a/2)$ is the current per unit length of developed gap, a quantity which we have previously called the surface current density K; thus

$$H_\theta \Big|_{r=r_g+a/2} = K \tag{5.30}$$

This leads to further substantiation of the statement made in Sec. 4.10 that the surface power densities are associated with the power flow through the gap. In fact, according to electromagnetic theory, the total electric power flowing out of a closed surface is given by the flux of the Poynting vector

$$\mathbf{N} = \mathbf{E} \times \mathbf{H}$$

which passes through this surface. Thus we find P_{out} as

$$P_{out} = \int_S \mathbf{N} \cdot d\mathbf{s} = \int_S \mathbf{E} \times \mathbf{H} \cdot d\mathbf{s} \tag{5.31}$$

We now choose the surface of the active conductor as the surface of integration S. We then notice that, because of the triple scalar product which appears on the right-hand side of Eq. (5.31), only the components of $\mathbf{E}$ and $\mathbf{H}$ which are normal to $d\mathbf{s}$ and are therefore tangential to the surface of the active conductor, contribute to the integral. It then follows that the integration over the inner cylindrical surface and the lateral planar surfaces gives no contribution, because the tangential component of $\mathbf{H}$ vanishes on the first of these surfaces, and the tangential component of $\mathbf{E}$ vanishes on the second. Consequently, we are concerned only with the outer cylindrical surface.

Moreover we notice that since we are dealing with power, we expect to obtain different results depending on the reference frame we choose for our evaluation. We first choose a frame of reference (primed) fixed to the active conductor. There the electric field is

$$E' = E'_y = \frac{J'}{\gamma} = \frac{K'}{a\gamma} \tag{5.32}†$$

and the azimuthal component of the magnetic field is

$$H'_\theta = K' = H_\theta \tag{5.33}$$

so that

$$N'_n = -E'_y H'_\theta = -\frac{K'^2}{a\gamma} = -p_{s,\mathrm{diss}} \tag{5.34}$$

Since N'_n is constant over the surface of integration, then

$$P'_{out} = \int_S \mathbf{N}' \cdot d\mathbf{s}' = -(p_{s,\mathrm{diss}})2\pi r_g b = -P_{\mathrm{diss}} \tag{5.35}$$

This means that the outflowing electric power equals the negative of the dissipated power or that the inflowing electric power covers as expected the Joule losses.

We next choose a reference frame fixed to the brushes and the

† Note that, as shown in Appendix A, for $v \ll c$ and $\rho = 0$, the current densities J and K are invariant to a transformation of frames in relative motion: $J = J'$; $K = K'$.

external circuit. In this frame we have

$$E = E_y = \frac{K}{a\gamma} + vB \tag{5.36}$$

and

$$H_\theta = K \tag{5.30}$$

so that

$$N_n = -E_y H_\theta = -\frac{K^2}{a\gamma} - KvB = -p_{s,\text{diss}} - p_{s,\text{conv}} \tag{5.37}$$

and the total outward flowing electric power is

$$P_{\text{out}} = \int_S \mathbf{N} \cdot d\mathbf{s} = -(p_{s,\text{diss}} + p_{s,\text{conv}})2\pi r_g b = -P_{\text{diss}} - P_{\text{conv}} \tag{5.38}$$

This means that the electric power flowing into the conductor now provides the power converted in mechanical form as well as the Joule losses.

From Eqs. (5.34), (5.37), and (4.6), we now observe that

$$\begin{aligned} N'_n &= -E'_y K = -p'_{s,\text{elec}} \\ N_n &= -E_y K = -p_{s,\text{elec}} \end{aligned} \tag{5.39}$$

In other words the normal component of the Poynting vector evaluated at the surface of the active conductor equals, except for the sign, the surface density of electric power measured in that frame. The change in sign results from the convention established in Sec. 4.2 whereby positive electric power is defined to be power flowing into rather than out of the conductor. We finally note that the total inward flowing electric power is given by

$$P_{\text{elec}} = -\int_S \mathbf{N} \cdot d\mathbf{s} = 2\pi r_g b p_{s,\text{elec}} = A p_{s,\text{elec}} \tag{5.40}$$

This equation provides the formal justification for the procedure established in Sec. 4.10.

*5.7 BOUNDED STRUCTURES

The preceding survey of homopolar devices so far has been limited to structures with cylindrical symmetry; to complete the picture we next turn to homopolar devices with bounded structures. Several devices which have aroused much technical interest in recent years fall into this category, so that the bounded structure does have practical application. These devices also introduce the opportunity to study the effects of nonuniformity in the field distribution. As we shall see, this nonuniformity greatly influences the performance of the converter.

(a) Circulating Pumps for Liquid Metals

A very interesting homopolar device in use today is a pump with no moving parts used for circulating liquid-metal coolants in nuclear reactors. In this application the converter operates in the motoring region, the conductor is a liquid metal, and the gap is finite in both directions. Schematically the device might take the form shown in Fig. 5.13. Voltage is impressed across the electrodes to create an electric field E in the liquid metal which fills the tubing, and the resulting current flow interacts with the impressed magnetic field to create a volume force density that accelerates the liquid metal to velocities approaching the drift velocity

$$v_E = \frac{E}{B}$$

The performance characteristics of such a pump are derived in the following example.

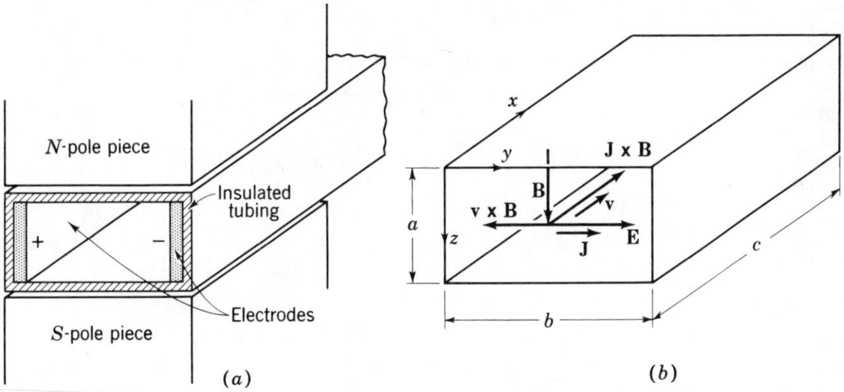

Fig. 5.13 Homopolar pump for liquid metal: (*a*) Cutaway view; (*b*) dimensions and vector orientation.

Example 5.5

A "fast breeder" nuclear reactor uses a sodium-potassium alloy as a coolant. Assuming that the circulating pump is of the type shown in Fig. 5.13:

(*a*) Calculate the dimensions of the channel and the required voltage V if the pump delivers a volume of coolant $Q = 0.25\ \text{m}^3/\text{sec}$ against a pressure difference P.D. $= 10^7$ newtons/m² at maximum power output.

(*b*) Plot the delivery vs. pressure-difference (P.D.) characteristic of the pump. Given:

$$\gamma = 7 \times 10^6\ \text{mhos/m} \qquad B = 1\ \text{weber/m}^2 \qquad v_E = 5\ \text{m/sec} \qquad \frac{a}{b} = \frac{1}{4}$$

where a is the dimension of the channel along **B**, and b the dimension along **E**.

Solution

(*a*) For maximum power $s = \frac{1}{2}$, and $v = v_E/2 = 2.5$ m/sec. Since the delivery or flow rate is

$$Q = abv = \frac{b^2}{4} v$$

we obtain

$$b = \sqrt{\frac{4Q}{v}} = \sqrt{\frac{4 \times 0.25}{2.5}} = 0.635 \text{ m}$$

If c is the dimension of the channel along $\mathbf{v}$,

$$c = \frac{\text{P.D.}}{(\nabla \mathcal{P})_x} = \frac{\text{P.D.}}{-f_m} = \frac{\text{P.D.}}{s\gamma B^2 v_E} = \frac{10^7}{\frac{1}{2} \times 7 \times 10^6 \times 1 \times 5} = 0.57 \text{ m}$$

The voltage is

$$V = v_E B b = 5 \times 1 \times 0.635 = 3.16 \text{ volts}$$

(*b*) To find the Q vs. P.D. characteristic, we eliminate v from the relations

$$Q = \frac{b^2}{4} v = 0.1v$$

and

$$\text{P.D.} = -f_m c = JBc$$
$$= s\gamma v_E B^2 c = \gamma B^2 c(v_E - v)$$

to obtain

$$Q = 0.1 \times \left(v_E - \frac{\text{P.D.}}{\gamma B^2 c}\right) = 0.5 - 2.5 \times 10^{-8} \text{ P.D.}$$

This is the straight line shown.

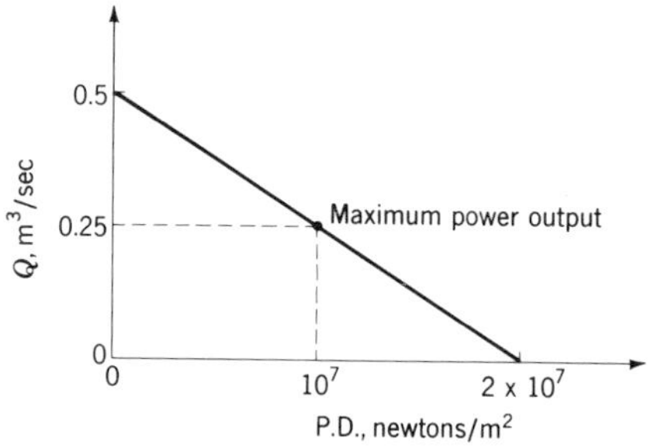

(b) Flowmeters

Of course, homopolar devices with liquid conductors can also operate as generators. An interesting application of this sort is the hydromagnetic flowmeter. This device is designed to measure the flow of a conducting liquid in a channel and has been used for measuring the flow of blood in the arteries. It is based on the fact that in a given channel, the rate of flow is proportional to the velocity. If the channel is placed between the poles of a magnet and the motion-induced field is detected by means of two electrodes, as shown in Fig. 5.14, the reading of the galvanometer will be proportional to the velocity and therefore to the rate of flow. This is illustrated in the following example.

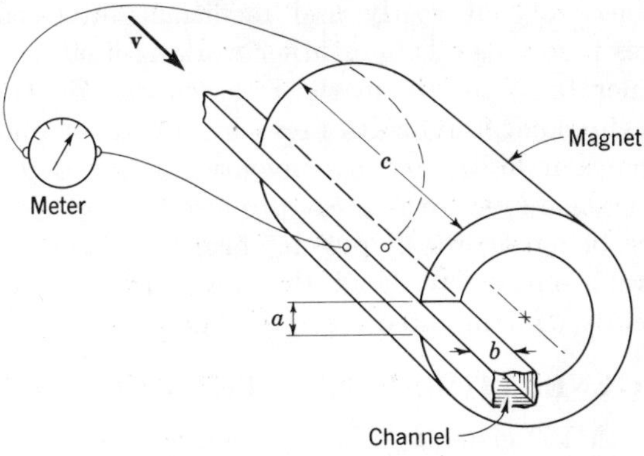

Fig. 5.14 Hydromagnetic flowmeter.

Example 5.6

An artery carries 10^{-5} m³ of blood per second. The artery is placed in the gap of a permanent magnet where $B = 0.8$ weber/m². Determine:

(*a*) The voltage measured by a D'Arsonval meter whose resistance is matched to the resistance of the source for maximum output if the dimensions of the hydromagnetic channel are $a = 2$ mm, $b = 4$ mm, $c = 5$ mm, and the conductivity of the blood is $\gamma = 1.5$ mhos/m

(*b*) The resistance R_m of the meter

Solution

(*a*) The blood velocity is

$$v = \frac{Q}{ab} = \frac{10^{-5}}{2 \times 4 \times 10^{-6}} = 1.25 \text{ m/sec}$$

When the load is matched, $s = -1$, and $v_E = v/2$.

$$V = v_E B b = \frac{1.25 \times 0.8 \times 4 \times 10^{-3}}{2} = 2 \times 10^{-3} \text{ volt}$$

(*b*)
$$R_m = \frac{b}{\gamma a c} = \frac{4 \times 10^{-3}}{1.5 \times 2 \times 5 \times 10^{-6}} = 2.67 \text{ ohms}$$

(c) Plasma Rockets and MPD Generators

The linear structures of Figs. 5.13 and 5.14 can also be used when the conductor is a gaseous plasma. In the motoring application the homopolar device becomes a plasma "gun" which is capable of accelerating the low-mass-density plasma to high exhaust velocities. Such rockets may eventually be used in interplanetary flight. In the generating applications the kinetic energy of a flame or other highly ionized gas is directly converted into electric power. Such devices are the object of intensive studies since their practical development would make it possible to go directly from a combustion reaction to the generation of electric power without the necessity of costly and inefficient intermediate thermodynamic stages involving steam or other working fluids.

MPD generators are still in the research and development stage, and several technological difficulties remain to be overcome before these devices become competitive with conventional power-generation technology. Nevertheless, there is great promise in this approach, and its development is being vigorously pursued because of the truly revolutionary possibilities it offers. We shall, therefore, briefly review some of the schemes presently contemplated for MPD generation.

*5.8 MPD GENERATORS WITH SEGMENTED ELECTRODES

At present MPD generators fall into four main categories. Besides the generator with continuous electrodes, whose structure is schemat-

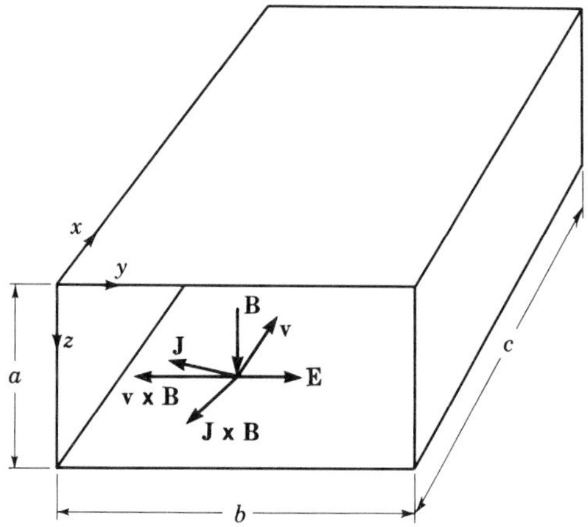

Fig. 5.15 Orientation of the main vectors in a MPD generator with continuous electrodes.

ically shown in Fig. 5.15, there exist *three* other schemes designed to operate with conducting media in which the Hall effect is appreciable. The desire to operate at large magnetic flux densities in order to maximize the converted power density, along with the necessity of operating with moderately low gas densities in order to restrict heat transfer to the electrodes, leads to the choice of operating conditions in which the electron cyclotron radian frequency is comparable in magnitude with the electron collision frequency. In this case, as we recall from the discussion in Chap. 3, the Hall-effect term $(1/n_e e)\mathbf{J} \times \mathbf{B}$ in Eq. (3.50) must be retained.

The effect of this term is to produce a current response which is not in the same direction as the electric-field excitation. Such a property of the medium, which we call *anisotropy,* strongly affects the performance characteristics of MPD generators and results in special electrode structures designed to circumvent and exploit the Hall effect.

To see how this comes about consider the structure of Fig. 5.15. The presence of continuous electrodes in the direction of motion constitutes an effective short circuit for the component of electric field in this direction, so that $E_x = 0$. Thus, when the Hall effect is appreciable, there must exist in the plasma an x-directed component of current density J_x. To evaluate J_x we write the x and y components of Eq. (3.50), neglecting the inertial and the thermoelectric terms:

$$\frac{\nu_e m_e}{n_e e^2} J_x + \frac{1}{n_e e} J_y B_z = E_x \tag{5.41a}$$

$$\frac{\nu_e m_e}{n_e e^2} J_y - \frac{1}{n_e e} J_x B_z = E_y - v_x B_z \tag{5.41b}$$

Note that we have here replaced ν_{ei} by ν_e, since in these applications the plasmas are often partially ionized and the electrons collide with the neutral particles as well as with the ions.

Letting $E_x = 0$, we obtain from Eq. (5.41a)

$$J_x = -\frac{e}{\nu_e m_e} J_y B_z = -\beta_e J_y \tag{5.42}$$

where we have introduced

$$\beta_e = \frac{eB_z}{\nu_e m_e} = \frac{\omega_{ce}}{\nu_e} \tag{5.43}$$

as a measure of the Hall effect.

This equation shows that, when the cyclotron radian frequency is comparable with the collision frequency, there exists an appreciable component of current density J_x which does not contribute to the power-conversion process but results in circulating currents which reduce the overall efficiency of the device. Moreover, if we introduce Eq. (5.42) into Eq. (5.41b) and solve for J_y, we have

$$J_y = \frac{E_y - v_x B_z}{(\nu_e m_e / n_e e^2)(1 + e^2 B_z^2 / \nu_e^2 m_e^2)} = \frac{\gamma(E_y - v_x B_z)}{1 + \beta_e^2} \tag{5.44}$$

We now see that the Hall effect also strongly limits the amount of current flowing in the direction of the electric field and thus also the amount of power converted. To eliminate these adverse effects, a proposed solution is the replacement of the continuous electrodes with two arrays of segments electrically insulated from each other so as to suppress the current density J_x. By letting $J_x = 0$ in Eq. (5.41b) we see that this arrangement restores the y component of current density to the level that J_y would attain when $\beta_e = 0$; i.e.,

$$J_y = \gamma(E_y - v_x B_z) \tag{5.45}$$

Suppression of J_x causes the buildup of an x-directed component of electric field which, according to Eq. (5.41a), is

$$E_x = \frac{1}{n_e e} J_y B_z \tag{5.46}$$

Such an arrangement of segmented electrodes has already been mentioned and sketched in connection with Example 3.3 and appears again in Fig. 5.16.

In addition to the possibility of suppressing the current-density component in the direction of motion, the segmentation of the electrodes

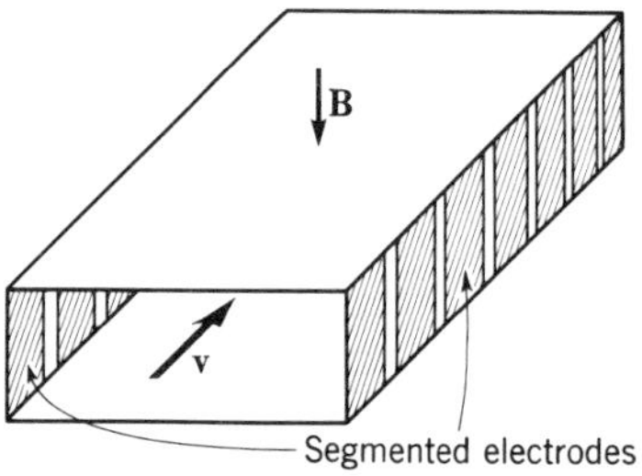

Fig. 5.16 MPD generator with segmented electrodes.

provides some flexibility for achieving other conditions, by proper choice of the circuit connections. This actually makes possible the exploitation of the Hall effect as a useful mechanism in MPD converters, as we shall see.

(a) Faraday, Hall, and de Montardy Generators

We have already noted that the generator with segmented electrodes offers the possibility of eliminating J_x, with the consequent buildup of an E_x given by Eq. (5.46). This is accomplished in the arrangement of Fig. 5.17a by connecting each pair of facing segments to separate load circuits which are electrically insulated from each other. This type of MPD generator is named after Faraday, who developed the theory and attempted to prove the feasibility of these devices by using the streaming water of the Thames river as the active conductor, the geomagnetic field as the field excitation, and dangling wires as the electrodes.

Although the supply of separate load circuits from a single generating unit is, as we shall see, standard practice in large a-c systems (polyphase supply), it is objectionable for certain applications.

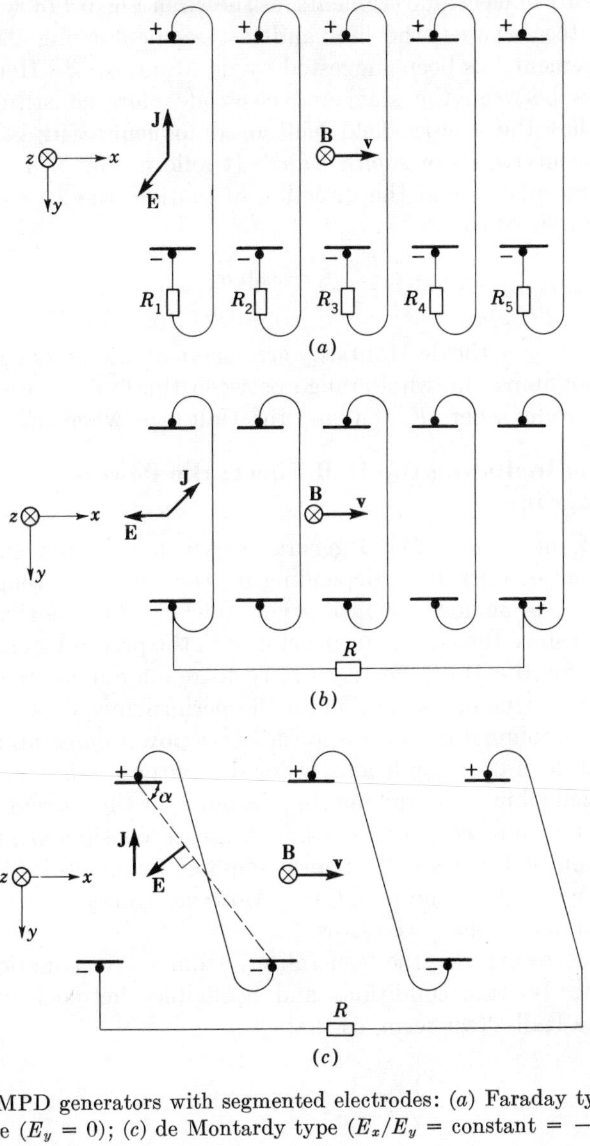

Fig. 5.17 MPD generators with segmented electrodes: (*a*) Faraday type ($J_x = 0$); (*b*) Hall type ($E_y = 0$); (*c*) de Montardy type (E_x/E_y = constant = $-\tan \alpha$).

With the segmented electrodes now available, other possibilities present themselves. For example we might short-circuit all facing pairs of electrode segments and connect a single load between the first and last pair, as shown in Fig. 5-17*b*. This type of generator is called the *Hall generator*. In this case $E_y = 0$, but both J_x and J_y are present.

A final possibility consists of a progressive series connection between staggered pairs of electrode segments, as shown in Fig. 5.17*c*, with a single load connected between the first and last segment along the channel. This arrangement has been suggested by de Montardy.[4] Here the connecting bars between the staggered electrode pairs constitute a short circuit so that the electric field has no component lying in the plane joining the center lines of such a pair. It follows that if α is the angle between these planes and the direction of motion, the E_x and E_y components are related by

$$\frac{E_x}{E_y} = -\tan\alpha \tag{5.47}$$

By adjusting α, the de Montardy arrangement allows for considerable flexibility, spanning the whole range between the limiting cases of continuous electrodes where $E_x = 0$ and the Hall type where $E_y = 0$.

(b) Analysis Including the Hall Effect; the Power-density Diagram

Each of the various MPD generation schemes is best suited for a specific regime of operation, depending on the relative strength of the Hall effect. To achieve quantitative understanding, an analysis is required, and since the technique developed in the preceding chapter does not account for the Hall effect, we have to refine our approach here.

Again, we focus our attention on the performance of a volume element of active conductor, and we consider the power densities attainable under various operating conditions. For this purpose, we shall first solve the generalized Ohm's law and obtain a formula for the current density **J**. This is a little more complicated than the case considered in Chap. 4 since retention of the Hall-effect term imposes further consideration of the vector character of the equation. However, the analysis is readily accomplished, as we shall see below.

We now return to the generalized Ohm's law equation (3.50). Assuming steady-state conditions and negligible thermoelectric effect, we retain the Hall-effect term, so that

$$\frac{\mathbf{J}}{\gamma} + \frac{1}{n_e e}\mathbf{J}\times\mathbf{B} = \mathbf{E}' \tag{5.48}$$

where $\mathbf{E}' = \mathbf{E} + \mathbf{v}\times\mathbf{B}$ is the electric field as sensed by the moving conductor, and $\gamma = n_e e^2/\nu_e m_e$ is the conductivity.

In order to solve for **J** we first multiply Eq. (5.48) by γ and get

$$\mathbf{J} + \frac{\gamma}{n_e e}\mathbf{J}\times\mathbf{B} = \gamma\mathbf{E}' \tag{5.49}$$

Then we cross-multiply Eq. (5.49) by $(\gamma/n_e e)\mathbf{B}$ to obtain

$$\frac{\gamma}{n_e e}\mathbf{J}\times\mathbf{B} + \frac{\gamma^2}{(n_e e)^2}(\mathbf{J}\times\mathbf{B})\times\mathbf{B} = \frac{\gamma^2}{n_e e}\mathbf{E}'\times\mathbf{B} \tag{5.50}$$

Since in the case of interest $\mathbf{J}$ and $\mathbf{B}$ are perpendicular to each other, we obtain by expanding the triple product

$$\frac{\gamma}{n_e e}\mathbf{J}\times\mathbf{B} - \frac{\gamma^2 B^2}{(n_e e)^2}\mathbf{J} = \frac{\gamma^2}{n_e e}\mathbf{E}'\times\mathbf{B} \tag{5.51}$$

Finally we eliminate the $\mathbf{J}\times\mathbf{B}$ term by subtracting Eq. (5.51) from Eq. (5.49), and find

$$\mathbf{J}\left[1 + \frac{\gamma^2 B^2}{(n_e e)^2}\right] = \gamma\left(\mathbf{E}' - \frac{\gamma}{n_e e}\mathbf{E}'\times\mathbf{B}\right) \tag{5.52}$$

or

$$\mathbf{J} = \frac{\gamma}{1+\beta_e^2}\left(\mathbf{E}' - \frac{\beta_e}{B}\mathbf{E}'\times\mathbf{B}\right) \tag{5.53}$$

where we have introduced, as in Eq. (5.43),

$$\beta_e = \frac{\gamma B}{n_e e} = \frac{n_e e^2}{\nu_e m_e}\frac{B}{n_e e} = \frac{\omega_{ce}}{\nu_e} \tag{5.43}$$

The electric, converted, and dissipated power densities can now be obtained by dot-multiplying Eq. (5.53) by $\mathbf{E}$, $\mathbf{B}\times\mathbf{v}$, and $\mathbf{J}/\gamma$, respectively. These power densities lead to the determination of the optimum regimes of operation and provide guidelines for the design of MPD generators. We shall proceed to this by using an elegant method first suggested by Bürgel[5] and later perfected by Kowbasiuk et al.,[6] which displays the performance of the various generators in graphical form.

The first step is to dot-multiply Eq. (5.53) by $\mathbf{E}$ and find the electric power density:

$$p_{\text{elec}} = \mathbf{E}\cdot\mathbf{J} = \frac{\gamma}{1+\beta_e^2}\left[E^2 + \mathbf{E}\cdot\mathbf{v}\times\mathbf{B} - \frac{\beta_e}{B}\mathbf{E}\cdot(\mathbf{v}\times\mathbf{B})\times\mathbf{B}\right] \tag{5.54}$$

In terms of the components

$$\mathbf{v} = v\mathbf{x}_0 \qquad \mathbf{B} = B\mathbf{z}_0 \qquad \mathbf{E} = E_x\mathbf{x}_0 + E_y\mathbf{y}_0$$

Eq. (5.54) becomes

$$p_{\text{elec}} = \frac{\gamma}{1+\beta_e^2}(E_x^2 + E_y^2 - vBE_y + \beta_e E_x vB) \tag{5.55}$$

It will be convenient to normalize the electric power by referring it to its maximum value. As we recall from Sec. 4.7*b*, the maximum value is

$$p_{\text{elec, max}} = -\tfrac{1}{4}\gamma v^2 B^2 \tag{5.56}$$

we then express Eq. (5.55) in terms of the following dimensionless variables:

$$p^n_{\text{elec}} = \frac{p_{\text{elec}}}{p_{\text{elec, max}}} \qquad X = -\frac{E_x}{vB\sqrt{1+\beta_e^2}} \qquad Y = \frac{E_y}{vB\sqrt{1+\beta_e^2}} \tag{5.57}$$

and so obtain

$$-\tfrac{1}{4}p^n_{\text{elec}} = X^2 + Y^2 - \beta_e \frac{X}{\sqrt{1+\beta_e^2}} - \frac{Y}{\sqrt{1+\beta_e^2}} \tag{5.58}$$

This equation can be rewritten as

$$\tfrac{1}{4}(1 - p^n_{\text{elec}}) = (X - X_e)^2 + (Y - Y_e)^2 \tag{5.59}$$

where

$$X_e = \frac{\beta_e}{2}\frac{1}{\sqrt{1+\beta_e^2}} \tag{5.60a}$$

$$Y_e = \frac{1}{2\sqrt{1+\beta_e^2}} \tag{5.60b}$$

Thus the loci of constant power density p^n_{elec} in the XY plane are concentric circles having a radius $\frac{1}{2}\sqrt{1 - p^n_{\text{elec}}}$ and a center at the point (X_e, Y_e).

In a similar way one can show that the ratio of the dissipated power to the magnitude of the converted power

$$p^n_{\text{diss}} = \frac{p_{\text{diss}}}{|p_{\text{conv}}|} = 1 - \eta_g \tag{5.61}$$

satisfies the equation

$$\tfrac{1}{4}(p^n_{\text{diss}})^2 = (X - X_d)^2 + (Y - Y_d)^2 \tag{5.62}$$

where

$$X_d = p^n_{\text{diss}} \frac{\beta_e}{2}\frac{1}{\sqrt{1+\beta_e^2}} = p^n_{\text{diss}} X_e \tag{5.63a}$$

$$Y_d = \left(1 - \frac{p^n_{\text{diss}}}{2}\right)\frac{1}{\sqrt{1+\beta_e^2}} = (2 - p^n_{\text{diss}})Y_e \tag{5.63b}$$

so that the loci of constant dissipated power in the XY plane are circles of radius $\frac{1}{2}p^n_{\text{diss}}$ centered at (X_d, Y_d).

Plots of these loci in a fixed XY plane would be very awkward indeed. In order to simplify the task of plotting, it is useful first to investigate the geometric relationships implicit in Eqs. (5.59) and (5.62).

The straight line which joins the centers (X_e, Y_e) and (X_d, Y_d) of the two families of circles is given by

$$\frac{Y - Y_e}{X - X_e} = \frac{Y_e - Y_d}{X_e - X_d} \tag{5.64}$$

introducing X_d and Y_d from Eqs. (5.63*a*) and (5.63*b*), we find that

$$\frac{Y - Y_e}{X - X_e} = \frac{-Y_e}{X_e} \tag{5.65}$$

or

$$Y = -\frac{Y_e}{X_e}X + 2Y_e \tag{5.66}$$

This is a straight line with slope

$$-\frac{Y_e}{X_e} = -\frac{1}{\beta_e} \tag{5.67}$$

as we see from Eq. (5.66). It intersects the Y axis at $(O,2Y_e)$, and the X axis at $(2X_e,O)$. The segment of this line lying in the first quadrant

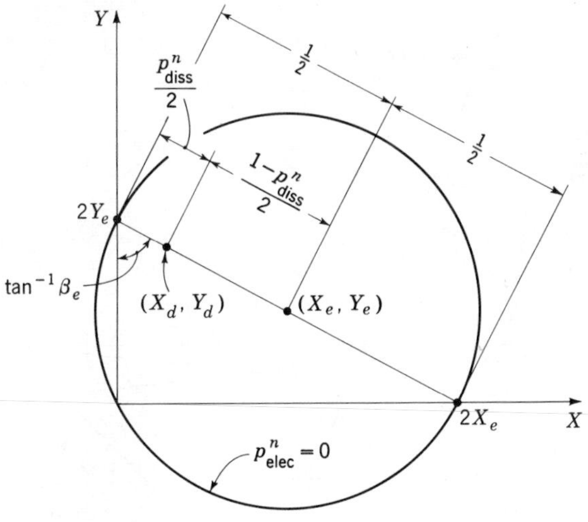

Fig. 5.18 Geometry of the power-density loci.

of the XY plane thus has a length $2\sqrt{X_e^2 + Y_e^2}$ which, from Eqs. (5.60*a*) and (5.60*b*), is independent of β_e and equal to unity. Furthermore, the ends of this segment lie on the circumference of the $p^n_{\text{elec}} = 0$ circle, as we see from Eq. (5.59). These facts are illustrated in Fig. 5.18.

We also know that the distance between the centers of the two families of circles is $[(X_e - X_d)^2 + (Y_e - Y_d)^2]^{\frac{1}{2}}$. Using Eqs. (5.63*a*) and (5.63*b*), we find that this distance is $(1 - p^n_{\text{diss}})/2$. Since the radius of the dissipated power-density circles is $p^n_{\text{diss}}/2$, it follows that *all* the dissipated power-density circles pass through the Y-axis extreme of the line-of-centers segment.

From the facts we have elicited above, it is clear that a universal set of loci can be constructed as follows:

1. Draw a line segment of unit length, taken horizontal for convenience. (This is the first quadrant line-of-centers segment.) The midpoint of this segment is the common center of all the p^n_{elec} circles, with radii $\frac{1}{2}\sqrt{(1 - p^n_{\text{elec}})}$. The p^n_{diss} circles are drawn with radii $\frac{1}{2}p^n_{\text{diss}}$, the centers chosen on the line so that the circles all pass through the left end of the line.

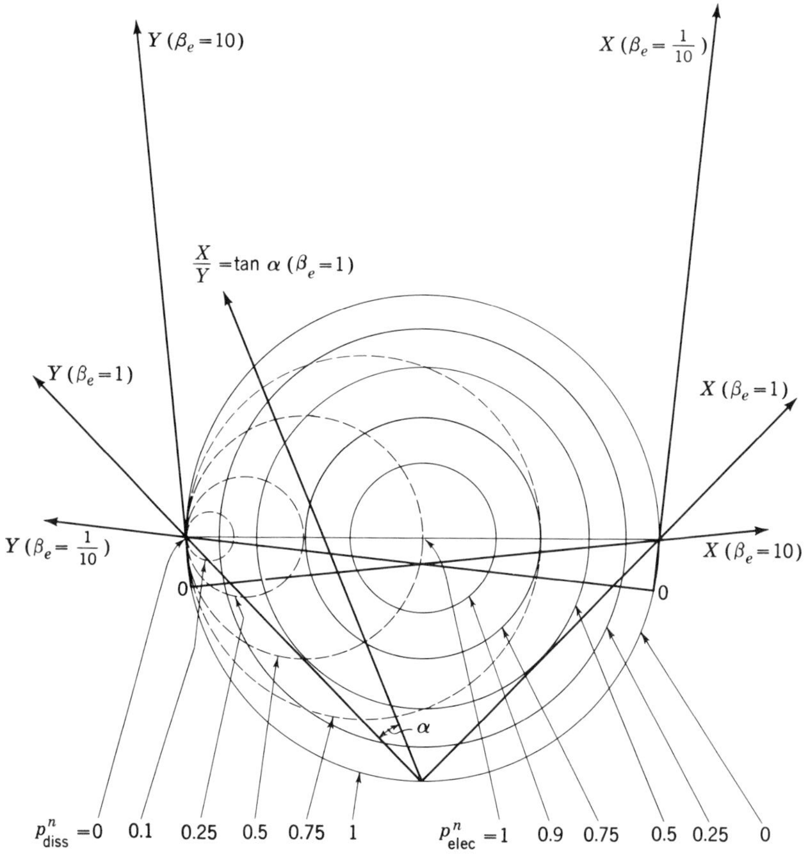

Fig. 5.19 Power-density diagram.

2. To locate the X and Y axes for a particular β_e, first draw a circle of radius $\frac{1}{2}$ circumscribing the line segment. Starting from the left end of the line, draw a straight line making a clockwise angle of $\tan^{-1}\beta_e$. This is the Y axis. Extend the Y axis to its intersection with the circumscribing circle; this is the origin. The X axis is, of course, drawn through this point perpendicular to the Y axis. By proceeding in this way the loci of Fig. 5.19 have been obtained, as well as the axes, for the β_e values of $\frac{1}{10}$, 1, 10.

(c) Comparative Evaluation

The power-density diagram of Fig. 5.19 now provides the means for a quick evaluation of the performance of the various generator types. In fact, for each of these types the locus described by the operating point is a straight line on the diagram.

First, the generator with continuous electrodes, which is characterized by the condition $E_x = 0$ is constrained to operate along the lines $X = 0$. At the other extreme, the Hall-type generator characterized by $E_y = 0$ operates along the $Y = 0$. An intermediate situation is represented by the de Montardy generator where the condition

$$-\frac{E_y}{E_x} = \frac{Y}{X} = \cot \alpha \tag{5.68}$$

implies that its operating points describe lines passing through the origin with slope $\cot \alpha$ relative to the X and Y axes.

Finally, to identify the line of operation of the Faraday-type generator characterized by the condition $J_x = 0$, we equate to zero the x component of Eq. (5.53),

$$J_x = \frac{\gamma}{1 + \beta_e^2} [E_x - \beta(E_y - vB)] = 0 \tag{5.69}$$

or

$$E_x - \beta_e(E_y - vB) = 0 \tag{5.70}$$

We then introduce the variables X and Y from Eq. (5.57) to find

$$Y = -\frac{X}{\beta_e} + \frac{1}{\sqrt{1 + \beta_e^2}} \tag{5.71}$$

But this equation is identical with Eq. (5.66), which is that of the line of centers. We thus conclude that the line of operation of the Faraday generator is none other than the line passing through the centers of the circles.

We are now in a position to make comparative evaluation of the several types. First we see that for a given output power, *the point of least dissipated power lies on the line of centers.* This means that under all conditions of operation, the Faraday generator provides the most efficient performance. It follows that if we turn our attention to the other types, the nearer their operating line lies to this optimum line, the better is their performance. For instance, a generator with continuous electrodes ($X = 0$) operates with reasonable efficiency for $\beta_e = \frac{1}{10}$ but yields negligible output for $\beta_e = 10$. The opposite is true for the Hall-type generator ($Y = 0$), which, as the name indicates, operates satisfactorily when the Hall effect is appreciable, i.e., for large values of β_e, but poorly for small β_e.

From the power-density diagram we also see that in the intermediate range where $\beta_e \approx 1$, neither the generator with continuous electrodes nor the Hall type provides more than half the maximum output. However, the continuous-electrode type operates with higher efficiency. As for the de Montardy generator, it will always outperform the other two limiting types, if the angle α is properly chosen. However, with small β_e, this angle would have to be small, thus causing poor utilization of the generator length.

Following is an example which illustrates the use of the power-density diagram in designing an MPD generator.

Example 5.7

An MPD generator is designed to develop a rated power of 1,000 Mw with a conversion efficiency of $\eta = 0.75$. Compare a Hall-type and a de Montardy-type generator on the basis of:

(*a*) The volume of channel required
(*b*) The angle α
(*c*) The efficiency at half-rated power

Assume

$$\beta_e = 10 \qquad \gamma = 5 \times 10^3 \text{ mhos/m} \qquad v = 1.5 \times 10^3 \text{ m/sec} \qquad B = 3 \text{ webers/m}^2$$

Solution

(*a*) From Eqs. (5.60*a*) and (5.60*b*) we have $X_e = 0.4975$, $Y_e = 0.04975$. Thus we may construct the power-density diagram as shown, with the line of the centers

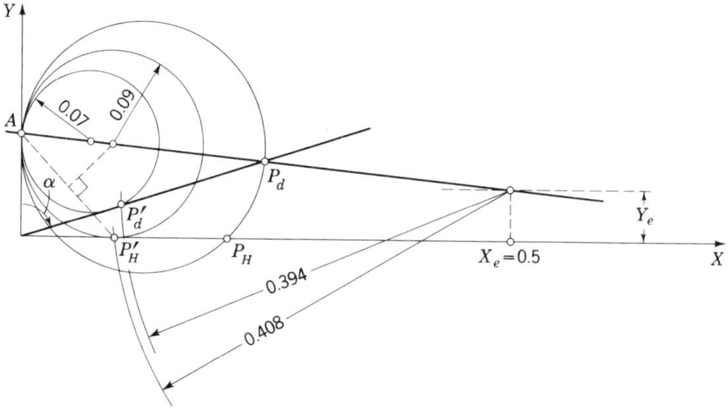

intersecting $2Y_e = 0.0995$ on the Y axis and $2X_e = 0.995$ on the X axis. The loss circle which corresponds to the efficiency 0.75 has a radius of

$$\frac{1}{2} p^n_{\text{diss}} = \frac{1}{2} \frac{p_{\text{diss}}}{|p_{\text{conv}}|} = \frac{1}{2}(1 - \eta) = 0.125$$

The intersection of this circle with the line $Y = 0$ determines the operating point P_H for the Hall generator. The distance between P_H and the point (X_e, Y_e) measures

0.29. This corresponds to a normalized electric power density

$$p^n_{\text{elec}} = 1 - (2 \times 0.29)^2 = 0.673$$

The maximum power density is

$$\begin{aligned} p_{\max} &= -\tfrac{1}{4}\gamma v^2 B^2 = -\tfrac{1}{4} \times 5 \times 10^3 \times (1.5 \times 10^3 \times 3)^2 \\ &= -2.52 \times 10^{10} \text{ watts/m}^3 \end{aligned}$$

and the actual volume density

$$p_{\text{elec}} = -2.52 \times 10^{10} \times 0.673 = -1.7 \times 10^{10} \text{ watts/m}^3$$

The volume of the channel for the Hall generator is then

$$\text{Vol.} = \frac{10^9}{0.673 \times 2.52 \times 10^{10}} = 0.58 \text{ m}^3$$

For the de Montardy generator we choose the point of maximum power output P_d that lies on the line of centers, and we draw the operating line OP_d.

The distance between the points P_d and (X_e, Y_e) measures 0.25. This corresponds to a normalized electric power density

$$p^n_{\text{elec}} = 1 - (2 \times 0.25)^2 = 0.75$$

The volume of the channel for the de Montardy generator is therefore

$$\text{Vol.} = \frac{10^9}{0.75 \times 2.52 \times 10^{10}} = 0.53 \text{ m}^3$$

(*b*) The angle α for the de Montardy generator measures 73°. For the Hall generator α is, of course, 90°.

(*c*) Half-rated power for the Hall generator corresponds to

$$p^n_{\text{elec}} = \tfrac{1}{2} \times 0.673 = 0.336$$

and a radius for the power circle

$$\tfrac{1}{2}\sqrt{1 - 0.336} = 0.408$$

This circle intersects the operating line $Y = 0$ at P'_H. The center of the loss circle is then obtained as the intersection of the perpendicular bisector of the line AP'_H and the line of centers. Drawing the loss circle thus obtained through A and P'_H, we find that its radius is 0.09. This corresponds to an efficiency

$$\eta = 1 - 2 \times 0.09 = 0.82$$

For the de Montardy generator the half-rated power corresponds to a

$$p^n_{\text{elec}} = \tfrac{1}{2} \times 0.75 = 0.375$$

and a radius for the power circle

$$\tfrac{1}{2}\sqrt{1 - 0.375} = 0.394$$

This circle intersects the operating line OP_d at the point P'_d. We find the loss circle passing through P'_d as before. Its radius is 0.07 and corresponds to an efficiency

$$\eta = 1 - 2 \times 0.07 = 0.86$$

It follows, that the de Montardy generator has smaller volume, smaller α which means greater length, and higher efficiency at half load.

As this book is being written, practical MPD generators are not yet in operation, but their use appears to be imminent. On the basis of our study just concluded, however, we are in a position to compare the merits of the several types of generators with respect to their operation in relation to the overall power plant. The major advantage of the Hall and de Montardy types is that they feed into single loads, whereas the Faraday type requires a number of load circuits equal to the number of segment pairs. In addition, the Hall and de Montardy types both provide a higher voltage across the load than the Faraday type.

The presence of the axial component of electric field creates difficult insulation problems in large generating units. In fact, large MPD generators are expected to be integrated as an additional stage (called *topping* stage) in conventional steam-turbine plants. Since such plants rely for their operation on a thermodynamic cycle, their efficiency increases as the upper temperature in the cycle increases. This upper temperature is the temperature of the combustion gases. With the present price of the steels used in the boilers it is not economical to operate at higher temperatures than 1200°F. However, the refractory materials envisaged for MPD generators can withstand much higher temperatures. It will therefore be economical to "top" the conventional steam stage with an MPD stage. In this scheme the combustion gases will be heated in the furnace at a higher temperature than can be tolerated in the steam boiler and will cool down, by releasing part of their energy in an MPD stage, before entering the boiler. Unfortunately the hot gases, if they serve as active conductor in the MPD generator, must be endowed with good electric conductivity. It follows that the hot gases provide effective electric connections, so that the furnace must be maintained at the same potential as the entrance to the generator, and the boiler at the same potential as the exit. In other words, with the Hall and de Montardy generators, the output voltage is applied in full between the furnace and the boiler.

5.9 INDUCED OR REACTION FIELDS IN BOUNDED STRUCTURES

In the previous sections we have reached an understanding of the mode of operation of the linear homopolar devices on the basis of the performance of a unit volume of conducting material. We cannot, however, generalize these results and obtain an accurate evaluation of the performance of the whole device with the simple integration technique that was used for homopolar converters with cylindrical symmetry. The reason is that linear devices are of necessity bounded in the direction of motion of the conductor, and end effects in that direction are much more important than along the direction of the generated field.

In fact, as was pointed out in Sec. 5.3*a*, the terminal voltage is obtained by integrating or summing up the contributions of all the volume elements in the direction of E. Because these elements are then effectively connected in *series*, it is immaterial if their individual contributions are unequal; there are no adverse effects except that the utmost performance is not being abstracted from all the elements of the active conductor. On the other hand, all elements lined up in the direction of motion are connected in *parallel* so that any variations in v, B, or γ in that direction eventually result in circulating or eddy currents within the active conductor. In the usual engineering practice we can achieve adequate uniformity in v and γ; however, we cannot avoid variations in B. These occur because of the nonuniformity of both the impressed and the induced fields. In fact, not only does the impressed field decay at both ends, where the polar structure terminates, but the reaction field as well has a component perpendicular to the direction of motion which varies in intensity along that direction. The existence of a component of the reaction field normal to the conductor can be shown in the following way: Consider the active conductor of Fig. 5.20 which carries a current density normal to the paper, constant in magnitude but bounded within a certain region. The current distribution can be considered to consist of elementary current filaments, each one of which sets up a purely azimuthal magnetic field. For every point P on the center plane of the current distribution, and in particular for points on the conductor itself, the field component normal to the conductor vanishes because the contribution of every current filament on one side is exactly balanced by the contribution of a symmetrically located filament on the other side, as shown in Fig. 5.20. However, for every point Q off the center plane the current filaments on the short side compensate only the contribution of the symmetrically located portion of the long side; the remainder of the current filaments on the long side produces a net normal component of the magnetic field. In an infinite structure, of course, one can always find symmetrically canceling filaments so that the normal field component vanishes everywhere and the field has only a tangential component.

The fact that the induced field crosses the conductor itself affects the generated voltage and, consequently, the current distribution. It appears then, that in a *linear* homopolar device, as well as in all converters other than the cylindrically symmetric uniform homopolar structure, the performance can be determined only if the voltage gradient equation (5.2) is solved simultaneously with the magnetic circuit equation (5.19), taking into account the armature reaction. For the linear homopolar device this problem is rather complicated, and no attempt will be made to solve it. Instead we shall first undertake, in the following chapters, the study of periodic structures which possess a higher degree

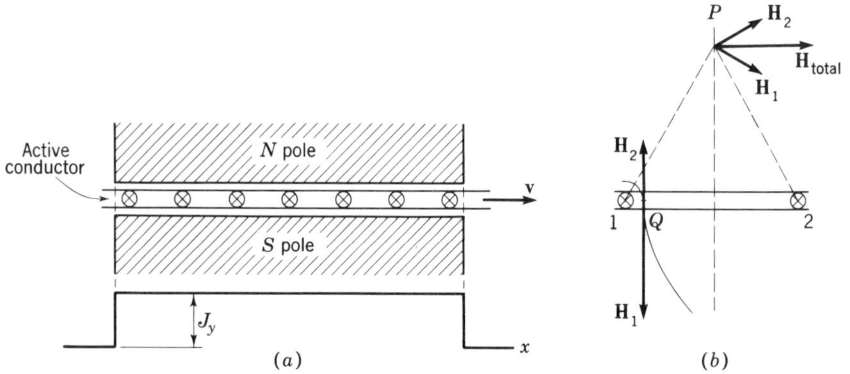

Fig. 5.20 Magnetic field in a bounded current distribution.

of symmetry and which are therefore more amenable to a mathematical analysis.

5.10 SUMMARY

In this chapter we have studied the converter type which has the greatest symmetry and uniformity: the homopolar converter. The following are the most important results:

1. The electrical and mechanical performance of the converter as a whole essentially parallels that of a single volume element.
2. Electromechanical power conversion can be used with advantage to store energy at extremely large densities in rotating masses. Efficiency considerations limit this application to velocity intervals in the neighborhood of the drift velocity.
3. Continuity of the magnetic flux path is the major factor in the determination of the overall geometry and dimensions of the converter.

4. When saturation effects are negligible, the armature reaction in endless structures does not affect the terminal voltage. It does, however, provide the agency for the flow of power in terms of the Poynting vector.
5. Bounded structures with linear motion find novel applications in such devices as pumps for liquid metals, flowmeters, plasma rockets, and MPD generators.
6. In the plasma regimes presently contemplated for MPD generators, the Hall effect cannot be neglected. As a consequence, the electrodes must be segmented. Of the three types of possible electrode connections, the Faraday type provides the best performance, but requires a number of load circuits equal to the number of segment pairs. The Hall type is indicated only for large values of β_e, and the de Montardy type provides the highest degree of flexibility.
7. The armature reaction in bounded structures does affect the terminal voltage. This is a characteristic of all converter types in which the conductor in its motion is exposed to a varying intensity of magnetic flux density.

REFERENCES

1. Acyclic Generator *Electromech. Design*, September, 1964.
2. Alfvén, H.: "Cosmical Electrodynamics," Oxford University Press, London, 1950.
3. Anderson, O. A., W. R. Baker, A. Bratenahl, H. P. Furth, J. Isa, Jr., W. B. Kunkel, and J. M. Stone: Hydromagnetic Capacitor, *J. Appl. Phys.*, vol. 30, no. 2, pp. 188–196 (February, 1959).
4. de Montardy, A.: MHD Generator with Series Connected Electrodes, Symposium on Magneto-Plasma-Dynamic Electric Power Generation, Newcastle upon Tyne, Sept. 6–8, 1962.
5. Bürgel, B.: An Investigation of MHD Generators by a Simplified Graphical Method, Symposium on Magneto-Plasma-Dynamic Electric Power Generation, Newcastle upon Tyne, Sept. 6–8, 1962.
6. Kowbasiuk, V. I., S. A. Medin, V. A. Prokudin, and S. A. Stepanov: Some Aspects of Noble Gases MHD-Generator Operation, *Proc. International Symposium on Magnetohydrodynamic Electrical Power Generation*, vol. 2, p. 703, Paris, July, 1964.

PROBLEMS

5.1 A certain homopolar converter is rated at 9,000 rpm and 24 open-circuit volts; it has a gap radius $r_g = 0.1$ m.

(*a*) How much flux crosses the gap?

(*b*) If $B = 1.2$ webers/m^2, what is the length of the active conductor, what is the number of required units, and what are the approximate overall dimensions of each unit if B is constant along the flux path in the iron?

(*c*) If, under full load as a generator, the gap-surface dissipation is 1.8 kw/m^2 and the efficiency is 99 percent, find (1) full-load current, (2) total armature resistance, (3) full-load surface current density, (4) full-load driving torque required.

5.2 Study the feasibility of using a homopolar device as a starter for a car engine.

Specified are:

$$V = 12 \text{ volt} \qquad P = 3{,}000 \text{ watts} \qquad \text{rpm} = 6{,}000 \qquad \eta = 0.999 \qquad v = 30 \text{ m/sec}$$

(*a*) Assuming $B = 1.6$ webers/m^2, determine the dimension of the active copper conductor, r_g, b, a, and the surface current density K.

(*b*) Neglecting mechanical friction and assuming that the load consists of an inertia equal to 10^4 times the inertia of the active conductor, evaluate the dynamical time constant τ and the energy dissipated during acceleration from stall to full speed, W_{diss}.

(*c*) Determine the temperature rise of the active conductor during acceleration if transfer of heat is neglected.

(*d*) Draw your conclusions.

For copper, the specific heat is $c = 390$ joules/(kg)(°C), $\gamma = 5 \times 10^7$ mhos/m, and $\xi = 8.9 \times 10^3$ kg/m^3.

5.3 When storage of energy in kinetic form is a desirable feature in a converter, the radial structure, which is endowed with higher inertia, is preferred. In the radial structure shown and assuming uniform **B**, evaluate:

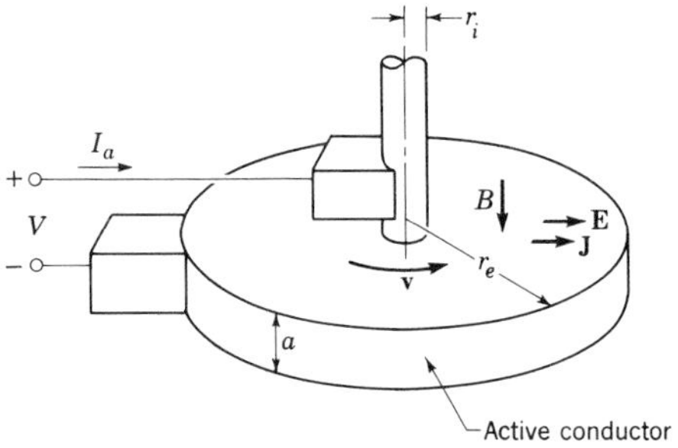

(*a*) The no-load voltage V_0.

(*b*) The magnetic field due to the armature current I_a.

(*c*) The electrical and dynamical performance of the converter under load.

Note that **v**, **E**, and **J** are functions of the radius r. The functional dependence differs from that of Example 5.3 since the conductor is now a solid.

5.4 A homopolar machine is set up on a test stand and coupled to a dynamometer which provides a constant unidirectional torque of 100 newton-m under all operating conditions. The machine operates with a total gap flux of 1 weber, and the armature resistance is 0.05 ohm.

(*a*) Find the terminal voltage as a function of rotor angular velocity over all possible values.

(*b*) Determine the boundary values of terminal voltage which delineate the motoring, generating, and braking regions.

5.5 A homopolar pulse generator operates with the following duty cycle:

(1) It is connected to a source of constant voltage $\mathbf{E}_s$ and accelerated from one-quarter full speed to full speed as a motor with pure inertia load.

(2) It is then switched to an electric load which develops a constant voltage drop $\mathbf{E}_e$, and is permitted to decelerate to one-fourth its full speed before "recharging."

Evaluate the ratio of the energy utilized in the load to the energy absorbed from the source per cycle if $\mathbf{E}_e = 0.1\mathbf{E}_s$ and $\mathbf{B}$ is maintained constant during the whole cycle.

5.6 An inertia storage bus drive employs a flywheel coupled to a rotating power converter. At regular stops the converter is used as a motor to bring the flywheel up to speed; in between stops the converter runs as a generator, taking energy from the flywheel and supplying the wheel-drive motors. The stops are arranged so that the flywheel is down to three-quarters speed before recharging.

Assume that:

(*a*) On charging, the power converter is connected to constant-voltage electric mains.

(*b*) On discharging, the average load presented by the wheel-drive motors has the character of a constant emf corresponding to a slip of -1 with respect to the maximum flywheel speed.

(*c*) The air-gap flux density B_g is constant.

Find the overall efficiency of energy conversion from the electric mains to the input of the wheel-drive motors.

5.7 A 5-watt homopolar motor drives a flywheel with negligible friction. The active conductor is copper with:

Conductivity:	$\gamma = 5 \times 10^7$ mhos/m
Mass density:	$\xi = 8.9 \times 10^3$ kg/m^3
Conversion efficiency:	$\eta = 0.99$
Magnetic flux density:	$B = 1$ weber/m^2

The inertia of the flywheel corresponds to 10^3 times the inertia of the active conductor. The direction of the rotation while operating in steady state is reversed by suddenly changing the polarity of the voltage impressed on the armature. (Flux density B is unchanged.) Determine:

(*a*) The energy dissipated in the armature conductor from the instant the polarity is reversed until a new steady state is reached.

(*b*) The time that elapses from the instant the polarity is reversed until the motor velocity vanishes.

5.8 In the generator of Example 5.1, determine:

(*a*) The number of units required.

(*b*) The approximate overall dimensions of each unit, assuming that B remains constant along the flux path in the iron.

(*c*) The required magnetomotive force nI if the gap length is $g = 10^{-4}$ m and the reluctance of the magnetic flux path in iron is negligible.

5.9 The tangential component of H sets up a flux Φ in the gap interlinked with the armature current. This flux can be associated with an inductance L_a. In the generator of Example 5.1:

(*a*) Determine the flux interlinked with the armature current in the gap and the associated inductance L_a where $L_a = \Phi/I_a$.

(*b*) Compare the L_a/R time constant of the armature circuit with the RC time constant under rated field excitation.

Assume that the armature reaction is compensated by means of a stationary shell and the gap length is $g = 10^{-4}$ m.

5.10 Consider a system of two homopolar converters connected by means of a coaxial line as shown. (The gap length g has been grossly exaggerated, in order to be able to sketch a few lines of force of the Poynting vector $\mathbf{N}$).

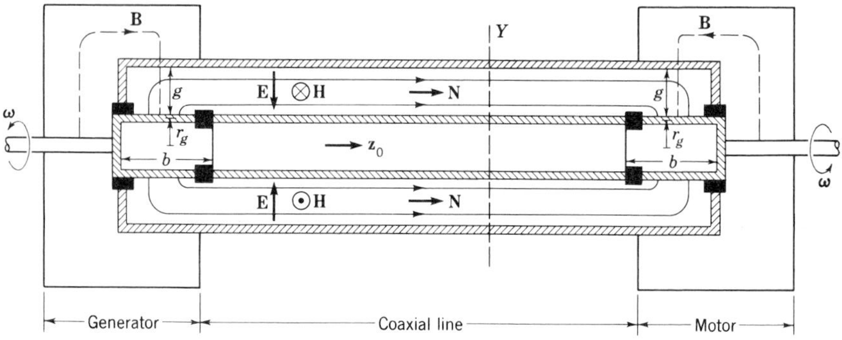

(*a*) Show that the flux of the Poynting vector passing through the control surface Y is VI_a.

(*b*) By evaluating the flux of the Poynting vector over the surface of the active conductor in the motor, show that the power absorbed equals $P_{\text{diss}} + P_{\text{conv}}$.

Assume that the coaxial transmission line is lossless.

5.11 When the rotation of a celestial body in its own magnetic field is observed from an inertial frame (which does not take part in the rotation), an electric field is detected.

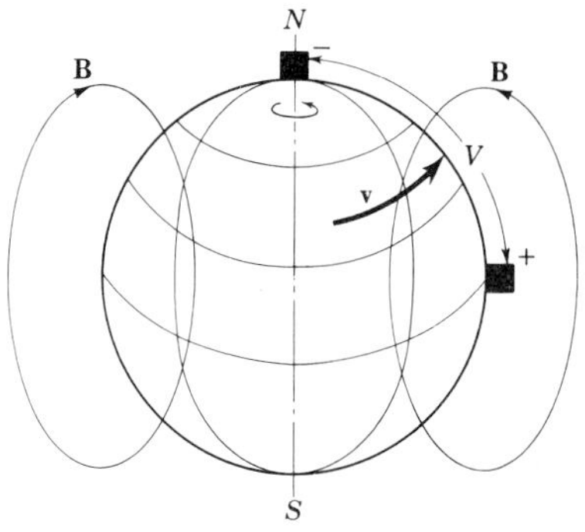

(*a*) Show that the voltage so detected in the inertial frame between the pole and the equator of the earth is $V_e \doteq 10^5$ volts.

Assume

$$v = 5 \times 10^2 \cos \varphi \text{ m/sec} \qquad \text{(along a line of latitude)}$$

$$B_r = 6 \times 10^{-5} \sin \varphi \text{ weber/sec} \qquad r_e = \frac{4}{2\pi} \times 10^7 \text{ m}$$

where φ is the latitude.

(*b*) Assuming that such a celestial body becomes enshrouded by a conducting gas cloud initially at rest in the inertial frame, sketch the initial current distribution in the meridian plane. What is the final velocity of the cloud with respect to the celestial body?

5.12 It has been observed that the large satellites, such as Echo 1, are subject to an appreciable drag force of electromagnetic origin when moving across the geomagnetic field in the ionospheric plasma. This is a case of homopolar generation with the conductive coating of the satellite representing the active conductor, the geomagnetic field supplying the magnetic excitation, and the surrounding plasma providing a load through which currents can flow, as indicated in the sketch. The same effect when utilized in reverse could provide means for propulsion.

Consider an interplanetary vehicle of the type shown and determine:

(*a*) Its thrust-speed characteristic (i.e., plot T vs. v) when the voltage of the power source is $V = 1$ volt, the magnetic flux density is $B = 10^{-9}$ weber/m², the

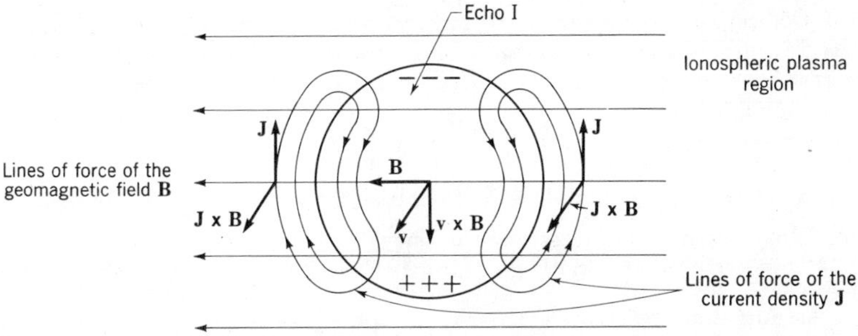

effective length of the active conductor is $b = 100$ m, the effective resistance of the armature circuit is $R_a = 10^{-5}$ ohm.

(*b*) The time and energy required to reach nine-tenths of the steady-state velocity when the mechanical load is negligible and the mass of the vehicle is $M = 10^4$ kg.

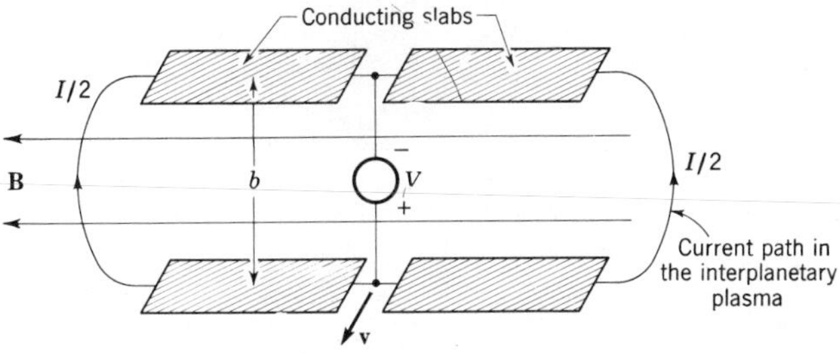

5.13 An MPD generator is designed to operate under the following conditions:

Output power: $P = 10$ Mw
Output voltage: $V = 600$ volts
Conversion efficiency: $\eta = 0.5$
Pressure difference (head): P.D. $= 2.5 \times 10^5$ newtons/m²
Magnetic flux density: $B = 2.5$ webers/m²
Fluid conductivity: $\gamma = 10^3$ mhos/m $\quad \beta_e \ll 1$

(*a*) Find the velocity v, the flow rate of the active fluid Q in cubic meters per second, and the dimensions of the rectangular channel if $a/b = \frac{1}{2}$.

(*b*) If the voltage V, B and, of course, the dimensions of the channel are kept constant, find the new velocity v, efficiency η, and pressure difference P.D., when the load resistance is twice the rated value.

5.14 A proposed scheme for a d-c transformer envisages the following homopolar motor-generator set. A liquid conductor circulates in a closed loop passing through two electromechanical power-conversion stages, one promoting and the other impeding the flow. Assuming that B is maintained in both stages at the maximum value allowed by economic considerations, the voltage level can be changed by changing b or v.

(*a*) If Joule and friction losses limit both the aspect ratio (the ratio of broad to narrow side in a rectangular channel) and the velocity differential to one order of magnitude, what is the maximum voltage step-up that can be achieved by stepping up both b and v in the high-voltage stage?

(*b*) Determine the dimensions of the ducts for the pump and the generator in such a 5-Mw d-c transformer having a voltage ratio of 3.5 to 35 volts. Assume that both ducts have equal cross section with aspect ratio of 10:1 and that the conductor is liquid sodium with

$$\gamma = 7 \times 10^6 \text{ mhos/m} \qquad B = 2.5 \text{ webers/m}^2 \qquad v = 15 \text{ m/sec}$$
$$J = 2 \times 10^6 \text{ amp/m}^2$$

(*c*) What is the overall electrical efficiency?

5.15 An experimental MPD generator is designed for 1 Mw rated output with an efficiency $\eta_g = 0.5$.

(*a*) If $B = 2.5$ webers/m² and $\nu_e = 5 \times 10^9$/sec, which generator type would you use?

(*b*) Assuming $v = 10^3$ m/sec and $\gamma = 5 \times 10^2$ mhos/m, determine the volume of the channel.

(*c*) If B and v are maintained at the same level, what is the efficiency at 50 and 25 percent rated load?

chapter 6
POWER CONVERSION IN HETEROPOLAR STRUCTURES; SYNCHRONOUS CONVERTERS WITH UNIFORM AIR GAP

6.1 INTRODUCTION

In this chapter we turn from the chosen extreme of simplicity and uniformity in the homopolar converters of Chap. 5 to structures having periodic variations and zero average value of the magnetic field in the gap. Such structures are called *heteropolar*, in view of the alternations which occur in the polarity of the flux density along the periphery of the gap.

We begin by seeking means to overcome the rigid relation between voltage and physical dimensions in the homopolar converter, and trace the source of this inflexibility in impedance level to the uniformity of the field distribution, a condition which we had initially imposed in Chap. 5 in order to achieve the most effective performance in each and every volume element of the active conductor. By relaxing this constraint and permitting a heteropolar distribution in the gap, we find that we are enabled to form *coils* by making series connections of individual insulated conductors which are displaced along the gap in the direction of motion. The large range of possibilities in choosing alternative series-parallel connections of these coils then provides great flexibility in the selection of the terminal characteristics of the converter, although, as we emphasize, the specific groupings of the individual conductors are actually extrinsic to the process of power conversion, which is fundamentally dependent only on the values of the field vectors prevailing in the gap. Another consequence of the heteropolar field distribution is the establishment of alternating electrical quantities on the armature side of the converter, a condition which is by far the most common in power-conversion technology today.

We next turn specifically to the synchronous converter with uniform gap, the heteropolar machine which most nearly resembles the homopolar device in its mode of field excitation, that is, by direct current. We acquaint ourselves with the structural characteristics of such machines and with the means for impressing a sinusoidal magnetic flux distribution in the gap. It is then seen that such a distribution, when viewed from the armature conductors which are in motion relative to the field conductors, varies in both space and time and takes the form of a traveling wave. This space-time duality which stems directly from the spatial variability and the Galilean coordinate transformation between the coordinate reference frames also appears in the form of a fixed ratio between rotor speed and electric frequency, known as the *synchronous tie*. The synchronous tie is a key relationship in determining the performance characteristics of the converter.

It is then seen that the current flow in the axially oriented armature conductors produces an induced or reaction magnetic field which has a component perpendicular to the direction of motion and so contributes to the power conversion. We are thus faced with two new problems: that of dealing with alternating quantities, and that of accounting for the armature reaction. At this point, however, we again exploit the orderly logical synthesis which has proceeded from the motion of single particles to the field-vector transformations and the MPD equations, utilizing field configurations increasing in complexity and asymmetry. Thus, we defer the question of the determination of **B** to Chap. 7, and presuming a known magnetic flux density, apply our knowledge of the basics of the power-conversion process to a study of the interaction between the conductor elements and the prevailing magnetic field in this heteropolar case. In this way we find that:

1. In general, portions of the armature conductor operate in all power-conversion modes, motoring, generating, and braking at any one instant; the three modes appear in distinct bands along the periphery of the gap. As time progresses, each element of the armature conductor passes through all three modes. This multimodal distribution of the armature conductor means that power circulates within the converter from one region of the gap surface to another and thence back through the external networks. Consequently, we do not have maximum utilization of the gap surface for power conversion, as compared with the homopolar case, and this is the price paid for the advantages of heteropolarity.
2. The overall or average mode of operation of doubly excited con-

verters does not depend, as with homopolar devices, on the shaft speed, but rather on the relative displacement of the magnetic flux-density wave which is impressed on the stator and the electric-field-intensity wave which is impressed on the rotor. This displacement is, in fact, the only variable through which the mechanical drive can exercise control of the operation of the converter, since the speed of the doubly excited synchronous converter is dictated by the electric line frequency and the synchronous tie.

Finally, we compute the average values of the surface and volume power densities. These allow us to design the armature conductor in much the same way as was previously done with uniform structures. Moreover, we note that a necessary condition for net power conversion over the whole gap periphery and over a whole cycle is that the current- and flux-density waves have the same periodicity and be at a relative standstill.

Examination of the condition for power conversion in terms of waves is an indication of things to come. The present chapter, in fact, serves as a transition from the viewpoint which considers electromechanical power conversion as the interaction between electromagnetic fields and ionized matter, to the more abstract concept of such power conversion as a consequence of coupling between waves. This latter viewpoint will be developed in the subsequent chapters.

6.2 IMPEDANCE - LEVEL CONTROL; HETEROPOLAR STRUCTURES

In Sec. 5.3*a* it has been shown that the homopolar converter is a device with low electric impedance. However, since this was demonstrated only for a particular type of conductor, the general applicability of the statement is left open to question. To investigate the matter further, suppose we assume a skeptical view of this statement and make an attempt to synthesize a high-impedance axial homopolar converter in which the individual elements that form the active conductor are not joined one to another to form a continuous solid as in our example of Chap. 5, but rather are separated by insulation so as to form individual conductors parallel to the axis but displaced in the direction of motion.

Using the idea that the series connection of these elements will result in higher terminal voltages, we might try to place several of the individually insulated conductors in the gap, connected in series as shown in Fig. 6.1. Thus we would hope to achieve an induced voltage of $3vBb$ for the three conductors illustrated.

Since this scheme is, in fact, the only way we might conceivably build up the voltage output of the homopolar converter, its failure would indeed verify the low-impedance character of this device. And fail it does; the induced voltage at the brushes is not $3vBb$, but remains at the single-conductor value of vBb. This happens because the *connectors* themselves have to move across the magnetic field, and thereby develop induced voltages vBb that buck out all but one of the conductor voltages. Consequently, it is plain that we can usefully connect the conductors in parallel only, which is in effect the way they are connected in the devices of the previous chapter; thus the low electric impedance is unavoidable.

Although the attempt of Fig. 6.1 fails, it does furnish a clue for determining the manner in which the successful series connection of conductors in the gap may be achieved. Either we must (1) arrange for the

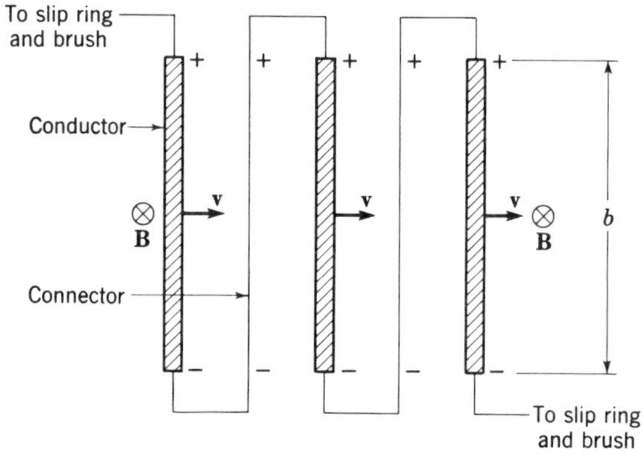

Fig. 6.1 Attempt at series connection in a homopolar converter.

two conductors which are to be connected in series to experience motional electric fields of *opposite* polarity, so as to avoid the use of a connector oriented parallel to the conductors, or (2) devise an arrangement whereby the connector between conductors of like polarity can be placed in a field-free region. In case 1, it is necessary that the flux density **B** reverse polarity along the gap from one conductor to the other, as shown in Fig. 6.2*a*, since both conductors are presumed to be traveling in the same direction with the same speed. Consequently, we must now have alternations in the polarity of the magnetic flux density. In this case, the converter is called *heteropolar*, in contrast with the designation *homopolar* for the uniform field case. A simple two-pole cylindrical realization of this configuration is shown in Fig. 6.2*b*.

Although the means for accomplishing case 2 may not be at all obvious at the outset, it is readily found if we again turn to the heteropolar structure. This technique, shown in Fig. 6.3 and known as the *Gramme ring winding*, after M. Gramme who developed it commercially in 1870,

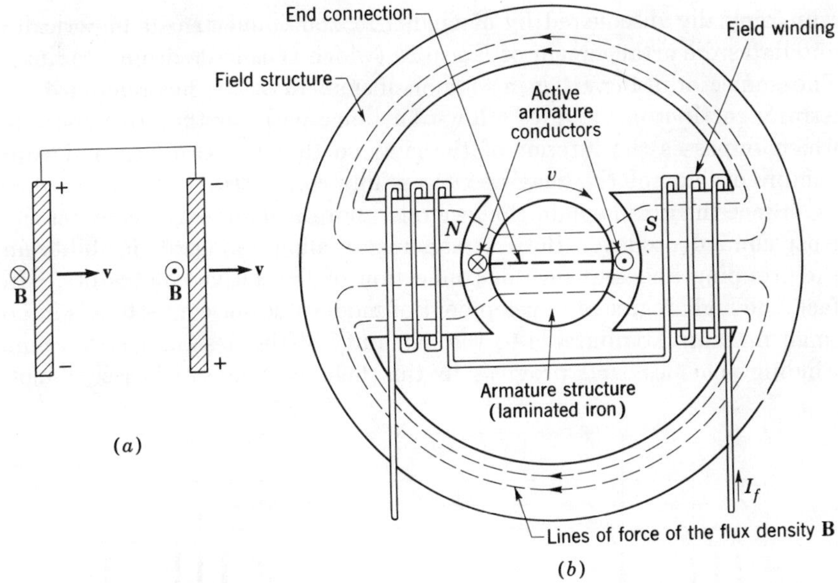

Fig. 6.2 Diagrammatic sketch of heteropolar converter: (*a*) Successful series connection of conductors in gap; (*b*) cylindrical structure for heteropolar converter (drum winding).

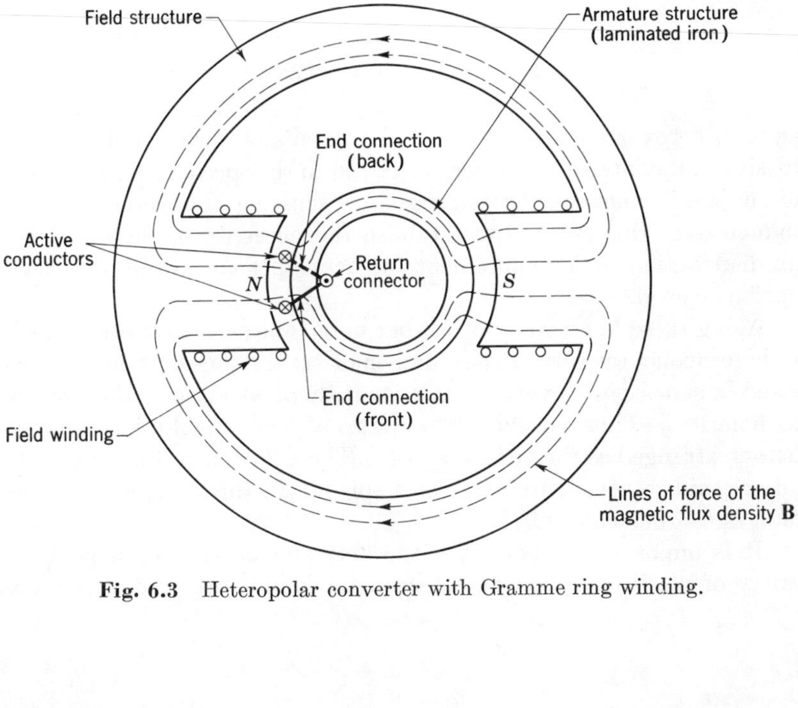

Fig. 6.3 Heteropolar converter with Gramme ring winding.

was originally discovered by Pacinotti in 1860, and in fact historically antedates the arrangement of Fig. 6.2*b* (which is called a drum winding). The connector in Fig. 6.3 is in a region of small magnetic field, because the ferromagnetic ring provides a low-reluctance path for the magnetic flux which bypasses the interior of the ring, so that the two adjacent conductors of like polarity may be successfully connected.

Since the drum winding is generally more economical, it is by far the most common today. Both arrangements allow for great flexibility in the grouping and sequence of connection of the active conductors. In fact, the high degree of development of modern power converters is in no small measure attributable to the ingenuity of the designers in devising winding schemes, and progress in this field continues. We shall not,

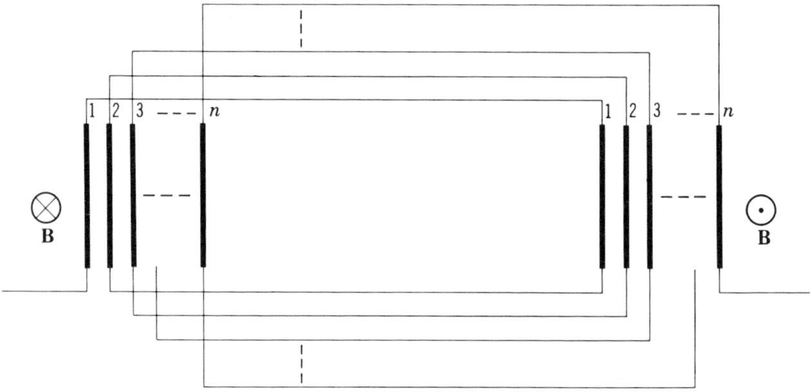

Fig. 6.4 $2n$ conductors in series.

however, be overly concerned with the details of such windings in this exposition; the interested reader is referred to the specialized literature on the subject.[1] Our specific purpose in discussing connections between conductors at this point is to establish the necessity of the heteropolar flux distribution as a requirement for achieving control of the electric impedance level.

Along these lines, we may further note that once we have turned to the heteropolar converter, the number of conductors that may be connected in series can be very large, even if there is only one alternation in flux polarity. Thus, consider two groups of n electrically insulated conductors, arranged as shown in Fig. 6.4. These $2n$ conductors are in series and are said to constitute a *coil* of n turns. In this way, high terminal voltages can be achieved.

It is important to note that the heteropolar scheme offers a great variety of possible end connections of the conductors, and thus a great flexibility in the impedance-matching capability of the converter. This is achieved without in any way affecting the electromechanical performance, since the significant quantities **J** and **E** are not dependent on the end connections of the conductors. Thus the individual conductors of each *group* in Fig. 6.4 could just as well be connected all in parallel, if desired, rather than in series as depicted. Other intermediate series-parallel arrangements are also possible. Table 6.1 compares the terminal properties of the all-series connection with those of the all-parallel connection.

Table 6.1 TERMINAL PROPERTIES OF ALL-SERIES AND ALL-PARALLEL CONNECTIONS

All series	*All parallel*
$I_{\text{terminal}} = I_{\text{conductor}}$	$I_{\text{terminal}} = nI_{\text{conductor}}$
$V_{\text{terminal}} = 2nV_{\text{conductor}}$	$V_{\text{terminal}} = 2V_{\text{conductor}}$
$Z_{\text{terminal}} = \dfrac{V_{\text{terminal}}}{I_{\text{terminal}}} = 2nZ_{\text{conductor}}$	$Z_{\text{terminal}} = \dfrac{2}{n} Z_{\text{conductor}}$
$P_{\text{terminal}} = V_{\text{terminal}} I_{\text{terminal}} = 2nP_{\text{conductor}}$	$P_{\text{terminal}} = 2nP_{\text{conductor}}$

If the gap conditions are identical in the two cases, we may use this table to relate the terminal quantities:

$$\frac{I_{\text{series}}}{I_{\text{parallel}}} = \frac{1}{n} \qquad \frac{V_{\text{series}}}{V_{\text{parallel}}} = n$$

$$\frac{Z_{\text{series}}}{Z_{\text{parallel}}} = n^2 \qquad \frac{P_{\text{series}}}{P_{\text{parallel}}} = 1$$

It is plain from the above that the impedance-matching capability of the converter can be varied over a range from unity to n^2, by various dispositions of the conductors. Thus, the conductors may be all in series to constitute one multiturn coil with maximum impedance; or they may be disposed into several coils, which are in turn parallel-connected, to give medium impedance; or each group of n conductors may be all in parallel, to constitute a single-turn coil with minimum impedance. Of course, for given gap geometry and field conditions, these alternative connections have nothing to do with the fundamental power-conversion process in the gap, as emphasized by the constancy of the terminal power seen above.

Example 6.1

Heteropolar motors are often built so that they may be adapted to different supply voltages, simply by changing coil connections. To illustrate the ideas discussed above, we consider the following problem:

(*a*) If a motor must operate from standard 110/220/440-volt a-c supplies, what is the minimum number of identical parallel branches required in the 110-volt connection?

(*b*) If the nominal output of the motor at 110 volts is 1 kw, what is the power developed when it is properly connected to 220- and 440-volt supplies?

(*c*) Can the same motor be connected to a 330-volt supply? If so, what fraction of the nominal armature-surface current density can be allowed?

Solution

(*a*) If we use the all-series connection for 440 volts and the all-parallel connection for 110 volts, it is clear that four branches are required. These may be connected in two parallel groups of two series branches per group for 220 volts, as shown in the figure, where each winding is represented by a resistance symbol. In each case V_B = 110 volts.

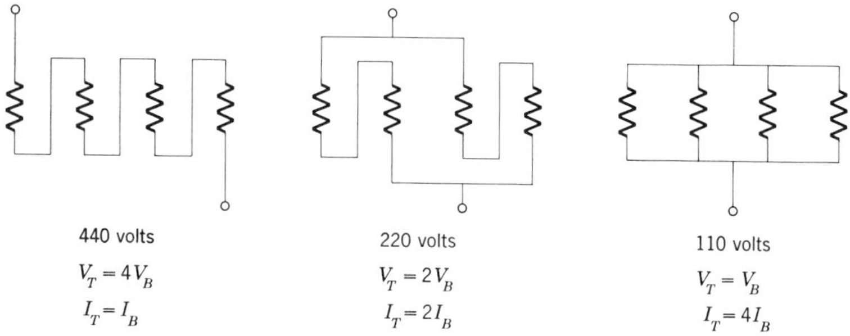

(*b*) The power is unchanged when the gap quantities are the same, as we have seen before: 1 kw for each of the illustrated connections.

(*c*) Here we may plainly consider two alternatives:

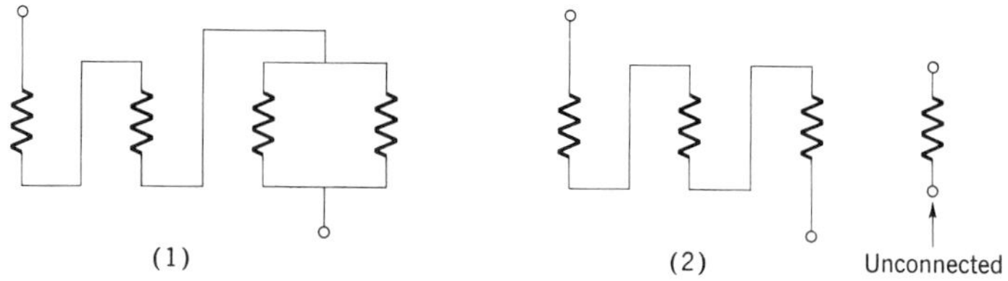

Arrangement 1 above is undesirable since it is unbalanced; i.e., all the branches used do not contribute equally to the electromagnetic gap quantities. Moreover, the terminal current is still limited to the nominal I_T in order not to exceed the allowable heat dissipation in the branch conductors. Consequently, there is little, if any, advantage to this connection, and we turn to arrangement 2.

In arrangement 2, V_T = 330 volts, V_B = 110 volts, and the nominal I_T is allowable. However, since only three branches are used (instead of four), the armature-surface current density will be three-fourths of its nominal value. In many cases, this will mean that the allowable output power is less (although in some instances in synchronous machines the output power can be maintained; see Prob. 7.7).

6.3 STRUCTURAL AND PERFORMANCE CHARACTERISTICS

(a) Periodic Alternations and Flux Waveforms

One of the consequences of the use of the heteropolar structure is that the periodic variation of the magnetic flux density along the gap leads to periodic alternations in the electric field experienced by the active conductors, as indicated in Fig. 6.5. In general, this means that the electrical side of the converter either delivers alternating voltage and current in the generating case, or is driven by alternating voltage and current in the motoring case. This may be a disadvantage in those applications that require direct current on the electrical side, since an auxiliary rectifier is then necessary. Such loads, however, are relatively rare, and consequently electric-power systems are predominantly a-c.

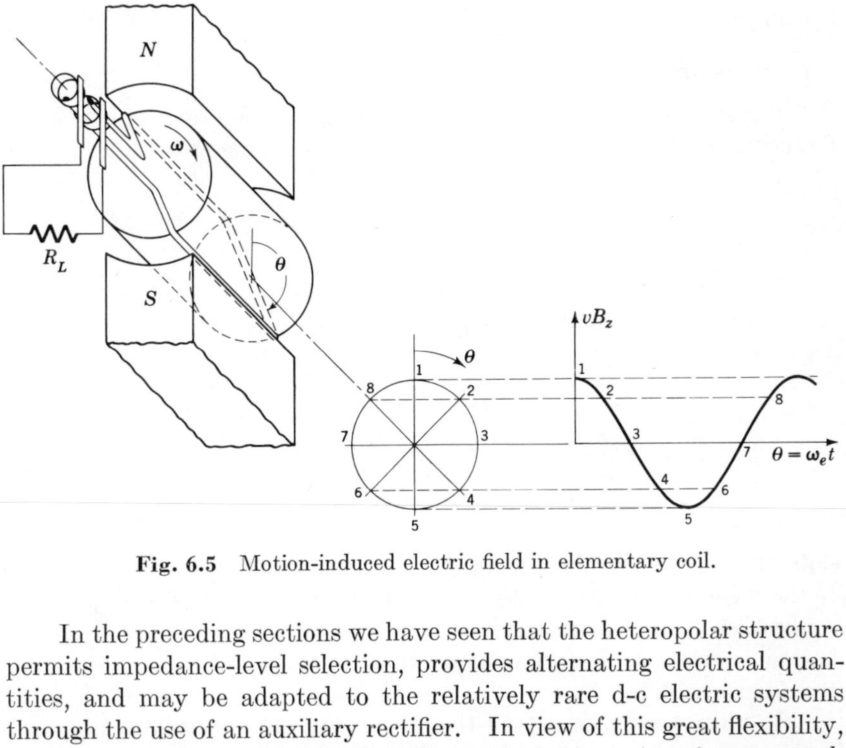

Fig. 6.5 Motion-induced electric field in elementary coil.

In the preceding sections we have seen that the heteropolar structure permits impedance-level selection, provides alternating electrical quantities, and may be adapted to the relatively rare d-c electric systems through the use of an auxiliary rectifier. In view of this great flexibility, the use of the heteropolar configuration is the basic engineering approach to power conversion in rotating machinery, and, consequently, this structure is overwhelmingly predominant, if not quite universal, in conventional power technology.

Having established the reasons for the requirement of a periodic alternation in the magnetic flux density, we next turn to the question of the choice of the flux-density distribution in the gap. If this could be made a square wave, and if it were possible to match this distribution everywhere with a corresponding square-wave distribution in **J**, we would then achieve the greatest possible power output for a given volume of active conductor. However, in a-c heteropolar converters we cannot simultaneously obtain a square-wave distribution in both **B** and **J** because these two quantities, as explained in Sec. 7.2, are related by an integration in space according to Ampère's law. Moreover, it is desirable to generate and distribute electric power without harmonics in order to avoid the generally deleterious effects of such harmonics in frequency-sensitive electric loads. For these reasons, we shall first devote our attention to heteropolar converters with sinusoidal space distribution of flux density. The techniques which we shall develop may then be used in the case of nonsinusoidal distributions by simply applying them to the successive harmonics in turn.

(b) Iron Cores

We shall now begin a detailed study of the heteropolar converter. In such a machine, the field and armature conductors are placed in axial

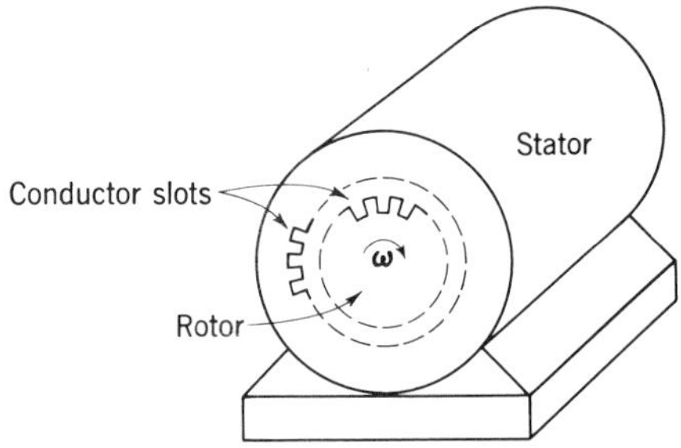

Fig. 6.6 Heteropolar structure with uniform air gap.

slots on opposite sides of the air gap (Fig. 6.6); thus we are now turning to the second of the two engineering compromises of Sec. 4.8 (Fig. 4.11*b*). At first we shall confine our attention to structures in which the air gap is symmetrical and uniform, except for the presence of the slots, as illustrated in Fig. 6.6.

Uniform gap structures of the above type are very commonly used, particularly in high-power machines such as turbogenerators and polyphase induction motors. They differ from the type illustrated in Fig. 6.2*b*, which is called a *salient*-pole structure, in that their heteropolar character depends on the distribution of current in the conductors rather than the presence of structural asymmetries which establish a preferred path for the magnetic flux. A uniform structure of the type we shall consider may then be said to have a *magnetically isotropic gap*.

Another characteristic of the iron structures in heteropolar converters is that, in general, they are not machined out of solid material, as in the case of the homopolar converter; they consist instead of stacks of thin electrically insulated laminations of the type shown in Fig. 6.7. The purpose of this construction is to prevent the circulation of currents in the iron structure which would result in Joule losses and impair the performance of the converter. As we shall see, in heteropolar devices at least one of the structures carries a flux which varies with time; the time rate of change of this flux induces a voltage according to Faraday's law. This, in turn, tends to drive eddy currents which would flow unimpeded in a massive structure.

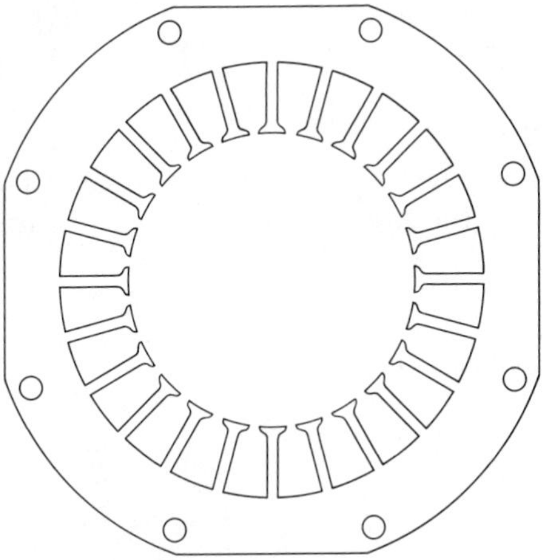

Fig. 6.7 Stator lamination for a small motor with semiopen slots.

(c) Windings

The conductors of a heteropolar converter usually lie side by side and, for best utilization of the converter, fill the entire periphery of the gap. The totality of the active conductors on one side of the gap forms what we shall call a *winding*. In most machines the winding terminates in external networks; in such cases the winding consists of a number of coils lying in separate slots and connected to form *phase groups*, one for each phase of the polyphase system. In order to approximate the sinusoidal field distribution mentioned in the previous section, it would be desirable to retain the maximum symmetry in the winding and have a large number of phases. Practical considerations, however, limit the number of phases to two in control systems and three in power systems. Figures 6.8 and 6.9 show typical arrangement of the coils, and Fig. 6.10 gives a schematic diagram of the winding layout.

When the winding is *not* connected to external networks, there is no need for matching the impedance level or keeping the number of phases low. In this case each conductor is simply short-circuited at

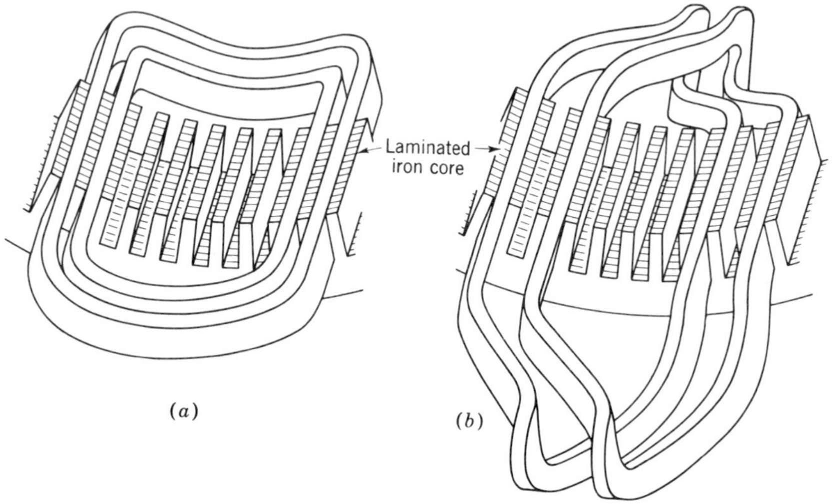

Fig. 6.8 Typical single-layer stator windings (coil ends omitted for greater clarity): (*a*) Chain winding; (*b*) diamond coils.

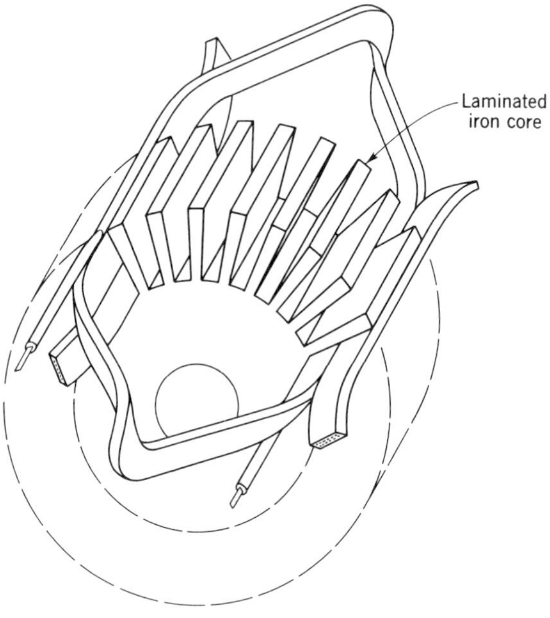

Fig. 6.9 Typical two-layer arrangement of multiturn coils on the rotor of a heteropolar converter.

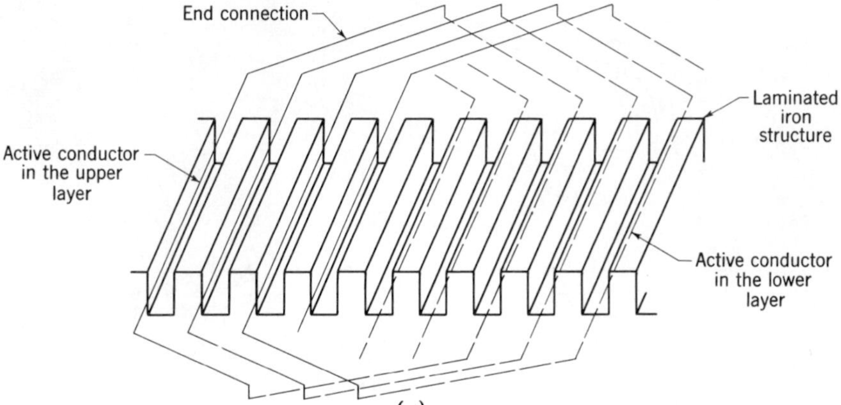

(a)

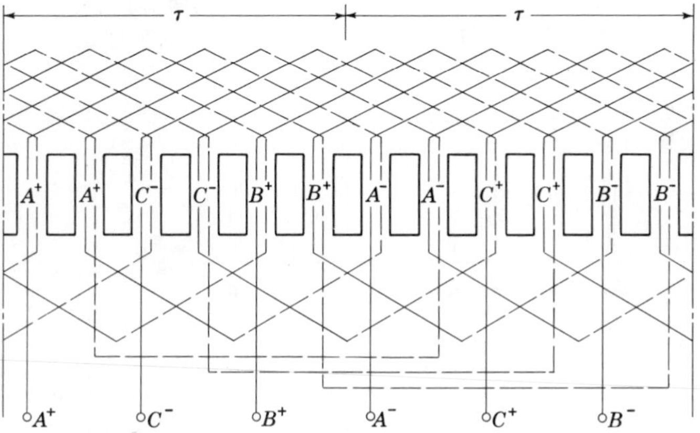

(b)

Fig. 6.10 Typical two-layer winding layout: (a) Developed view of a two-layer winding; (b) schematic diagram of a three-phase two-layer winding with two slots per phase and pole.

both ends by connecting rings, and the winding takes the shape of a *squirrel cage*, as shown in Fig. 6.11.

(d) Approach

Heteropolar structures are used in a great variety of converter types. Our first task is then to choose an approach for our study which will make the understanding of their operation easy and present the various types in a logical sequence. In performing this task we shall be guided by the following considerations.

We know that by virtue of the generality of our derivation, when we deal with low-velocity, low-frequency converters of the magnetic type,

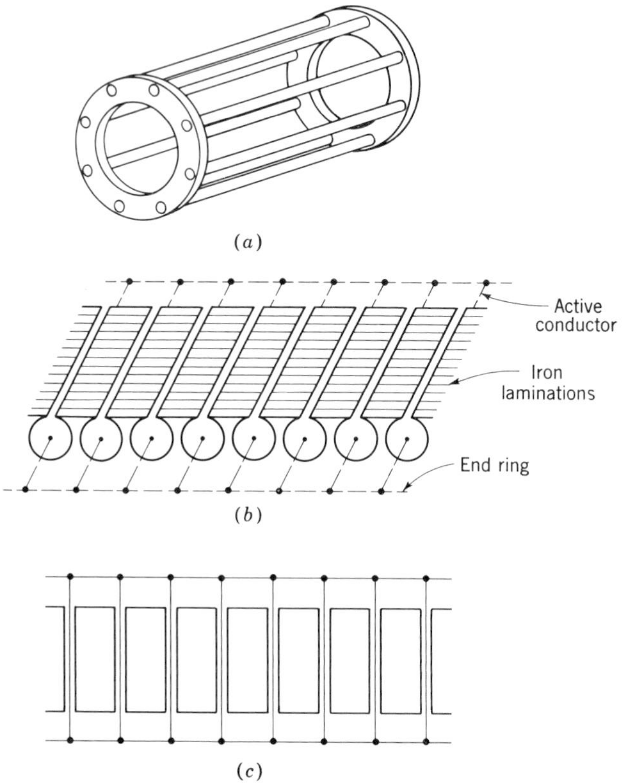

Fig. 6.11 Squirrel-cage winding: (*a*) Geometrical configuration of the winding; (*b*) developed view of laminated-iron structure and conductor arrangement in slots; (*c*) schematic diagram.

each of the volume elements of its active conductor must satisfy the fundamental MPD equations,

$$\xi \frac{\partial \mathbf{v}}{\partial t} - \mathbf{f}_m = \mathbf{J} \times \mathbf{B} \tag{3.56}$$

$$\frac{\mathbf{J}}{\gamma} = \mathbf{E} + \mathbf{v} \times \mathbf{B} \tag{3.57b}$$

no matter how complex the converter might be. We observe that these equations, as well as the associated power relations [Eqs. (4.1) and (4.4)], do not contain derivatives operating on the electromagnetic field vectors **E** and **B**. As a consequence, insofar as the volume elements are concerned, their dynamical behavior will not be affected if the field distribution is space- or time-variant, rather than uniform and constant. However, since the field equations and, in particular, the circuital laws of Faraday and Ampère [Eqs. (1.3*a*) and (1.3*b*)] involve such derivatives, we can expect marked differences between the performances of the heteropolar and the homopolar converters to result from the cooperative interaction of these volume elements. In other words, we expect particular features arising from the space and time variability of the electromagnetic field to show up in the circuit properties or terminal characteristics of the converter.

In view of this identity of the power-conversion process at the volume-element level, we shall at first set aside consideration of the circuit aspects and concentrate on the performance of the active conductors in the gap. We thus resort to a conceptual scheme in which the actual setup of the physical terminals is replaced by an idealized arrangement which is simpler and more symmetrical, but otherwise completely equivalent in terms of the overall performance characteristics of the converter.

For a clue on how these terminal characteristics will differ from those of the homopolar converter we may go back to the situations considered in Chaps. 2 and 3 dealing with microscopic models. Indeed the main operational feature of the homopolar type, the tendency of the active conductor to approach the drift velocity, is directly inferable from the dynamics of its elementary charged constituents in uniform crossed **E** and **B** fields. Similarly in the case of the heteropolar converter we may derive some insight from the behavior of charged particles in the limiting case studied, that of a rapidly varying magnetic field, i.e., a magnetic wall or wavefront. We find there that the particles are reflected and, in the absence of collisions, have no average motion normal to the wavefront. We thus deduce that in a heteropolar converter the active conductor will likewise tend to attain a condition of standstill with respect to the electromagnetic wave or, in other words, will tend to move with the phase velocity of the wave.

This indicates that the phase velocity of the magnetic field wave plays a role very similar to that of the drift velocity. We shall, therefore, place great emphasis on this wave and its motion. Moreover, we recall from the treatment of moving magnetic walls that great simplification in the calculations accrues from choosing a frame attached to the wavefront as the frame of reference. We shall continue to use this frame, henceforth called the *wave frame*, as the basis for our analysis. Since new concepts are better visualized when they do not merely represent mathematical abstractions but also have physical significance, it is apparent that our understanding of the heteropolar power-conversion process will be facilitated if we start with the converter type in which the wave frame is attached to one of its structures. Furthermore, in order to gain even better insight, at first we let the wave frame coincide with the laboratory frame; in other words, we begin by considering the case where the magnetic field wave is at standstill with respect to the stator.

Finally, consideration of the electric currents and associated electromagnetic forces in the microscopic models brings to light another important difference between the homogeneous and inhomogeneous fields, and therefore between the homopolar and heteropolar converters. In the homogeneous field no steady current can flow through the conductor, and therefore no steady electromagnetic force can act upon it, unless there exists an electric field impressed from the outside of the conductor and its velocity differs from the drift velocity. This is evidenced, for instance, by the free motion of a plasma blob across a homogeneous magnetic field, as discussed in Sec. 3.5*a*.

In an inhomogeneous field, instead, the reflection undergone by the particles gives rise to currents and corresponding electromagnetic forces, even in the absence of external electrical sources, and even when the current-carrying conductor moves with the wavefront, as demonstrated by the situation prevailing at the magnetospheric boundary discussed in Examples 2.3 and 3.1.

This leads us to the conclusion that, when we will take a comprehensive look at the heteropolar converter and investigate the active conductors in relation to their physical terminals and external circuits, we shall find that relative motion between the active conductors and the external networks will not represent an essential condition for the operation of the converter.

6.4 SYNCHRONOUS MACHINES

Our homopolar converter of the previous chapter, of course, used d-c excitation of its magnetic field. The heteropolar converter of Fig. 6.6 can be used with a-c excitation for both field and armature conductors or, in common with the homopolar converter, with direct current in the field (and alternating current in the armature only). When the field excitation is d-c, the heteropolar converter is called a *synchronous machine;* the reason for this name will be given shortly. Synchronous machines span the whole range of power from a fraction of a watt in clock motors to about a kilomegawatt in the largest generating units. They are chosen because of their efficiency and reliability and low maintainance and cost whenever operation at constant speed is called for. This and the next two chapters will concern themselves with converters of this type; all a-c operation of heteropolar converters will be treated in Chaps. 9 and 10.

(a) Field Conductors

The field coil of the homopolar machine was placed on the stator. In conformity with this precedent, as well as the conceptual structure of Fig. 6.2*b*, we shall likewise place the field conductors of the synchronous converter on the stator and the armature conductors on the rotor. We shall, however, see subsequently in Chap. 9 that the electromagnetic character of the heteropolar converter is such that the locations of field and armature (with respect to stator and rotor) may indeed be interchanged. This fact is exploited in high-power machines, where it is desirable to utilize the rotor and its attendant sliding contacts for the lower-power conductor, which is the field.

We also assume that the d-c-carrying field conductors are disposed so as to produce in the gap a flux density whose radial component varies sinusoidally with displacement along the stator, as shown in Fig. 6.12. In a later section, we shall prove that such a flux density results when the currents in the field conductors are so distributed as to create an axially directed surface current density $\mathbf{K}_f$ which itself varies sinusoidally with

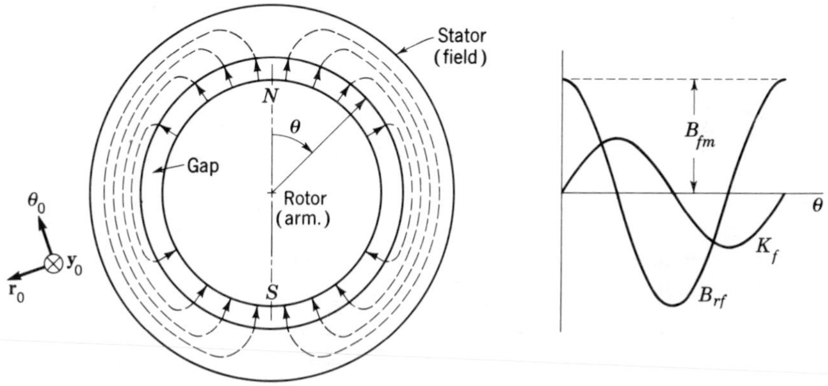

Fig. 6.12 Two-pole sinusoidal distribution of radial flux density.

displacement along the stator and is 90° out of phase with the **B** distribution (Fig. 6.12). This $\mathbf{K}_f$ may be realized, as indicated in Fig. 6.13, by appropriately controlling the three factors: (1) amount of current per conductor, (2) number of conductors per slot, and (3) slot spacing. For example, if the slots are equally spaced and each slot has the same number of conductors, then the current per conductor must vary sinusoidally along the stator. Alternatively, we can keep the current magnitude per conductor constant and space the slots equally, but vary the number of conductors per slot in an almost sinusoidal manner; or again, we can keep the current magnitude per conductor and the number of conductors per slot constant, but vary the slot spacing. For further details in this connection the reader is referred to Prob. 6.8 at the end of the chapter.

For simplicity in Fig. 6.12 we have chosen to illustrate a two-pole converter, or a converter in which there is only one alternation in the flux density along the periphery of the gap. More generally, there may

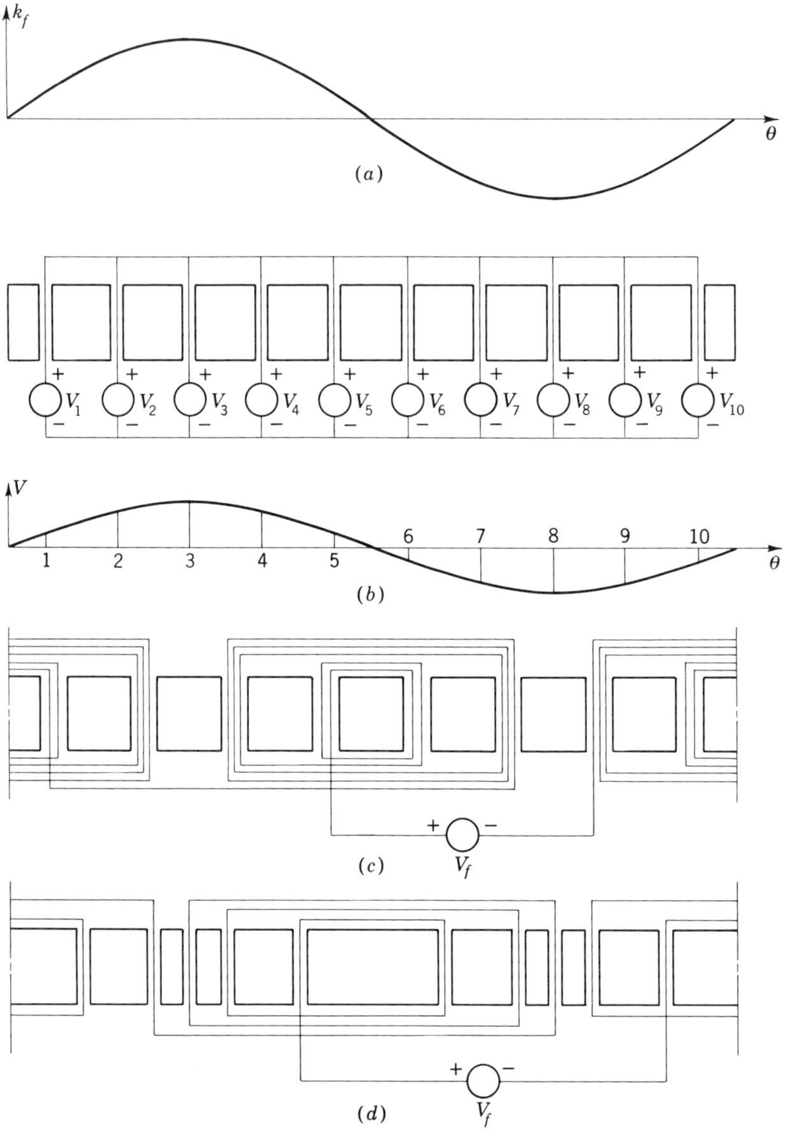

Fig. 6.13 Approximate realizations of a sinusoidal field current distribution, schematic diagrams of the developed windings: (a) Desired current distribution; (b) alternative 1—conductors connected to form a star and supplied by an array of sources; (c) alternative 2—equidistant slots, variable conductor density; (d) alternative 3—variable slot spacing.

be p such alternations, where p is an integer. The number p is then the number of *pole pairs*. The reader may wonder why p should ever be anything but unity, in view of the fact (pointed out in Sec. 6.2) that impedance-level control is possible with only a single alternation in flux polarity. As we shall later see, the reason is that for a given electric frequency the *speed* of the synchronous converter is inversely proportional to the number of pole pairs p, so that we may often build a machine for the desired speed without the use of gear speed changers, simply by properly selecting the value of p. Multipole-pair machines are mostly built with salient poles, as shown in Fig. 6.14.

If we use the quantity θ to denote the angle measured with respect to one of the p points on the stator at which the flux density is an outward maximum, and assume the positive unit-vector triad shown in Fig. 6.12, then the radial flux density in the field pattern illustrated in Fig. 6.12 is given by

$$\mathbf{B}_f = \mathbf{r}_0 B_{rf} = \mathbf{r}_0 B_{fm} \cos (p\theta) \tag{6.1a}$$

$$B_{rf} = B_{fm} \cos (p\theta) \tag{6.1b}$$

These equations indicate that the flux density varies in space as the number of pole pairs times the geometrical angle; in other words, p is the multiplier that transforms the mechanical variable θ into the variable on which the electromagnetic quantities depend.

It would be possible to carry on with the cylindrical coordinates established in Fig. 6.12, but it is much more convenient to develop the gap in the rectilinear form of Chap. 4, and this is a close approximation since the gap spacing g is in all practical cases much less than the radius r_g. In developed form Fig. 6.12 becomes Fig. 6.15. Here the unit vectors $\mathbf{x}_0$ and $\mathbf{z}_0$ replace $\boldsymbol{\theta}_0$ and $\mathbf{r}_0$, respectively; and the natural parameters are the linear displacements x along the stator and the half interval τ. This is the distance along the gap between a successive north and south (or south and north) pole and clearly represents the arc subtending, at the gap, a mechanical angle of π/p rad. The half interval τ is therefore often called the *pole pitch*. If r_g is the radius of the converter at the gap, the linear variables are related to their cylindrical counterparts by

$$x = r_g\theta \tag{6.2a}$$

$$\tau = \frac{\pi}{p} r_g \tag{6.2b}$$

$$\frac{\pi x}{\tau} = p\theta \tag{6.2c}$$

so that Eq. 6.1 goes over to

$$\mathbf{B}_f = \mathbf{z}_0 B_{zf} = \mathbf{z}_0 B_{fm} \cos \frac{\pi}{\tau} x \tag{6.3a}$$

$$B_{zf} = B_{fm} \cos \frac{\pi}{\tau} x \tag{6.3b}$$

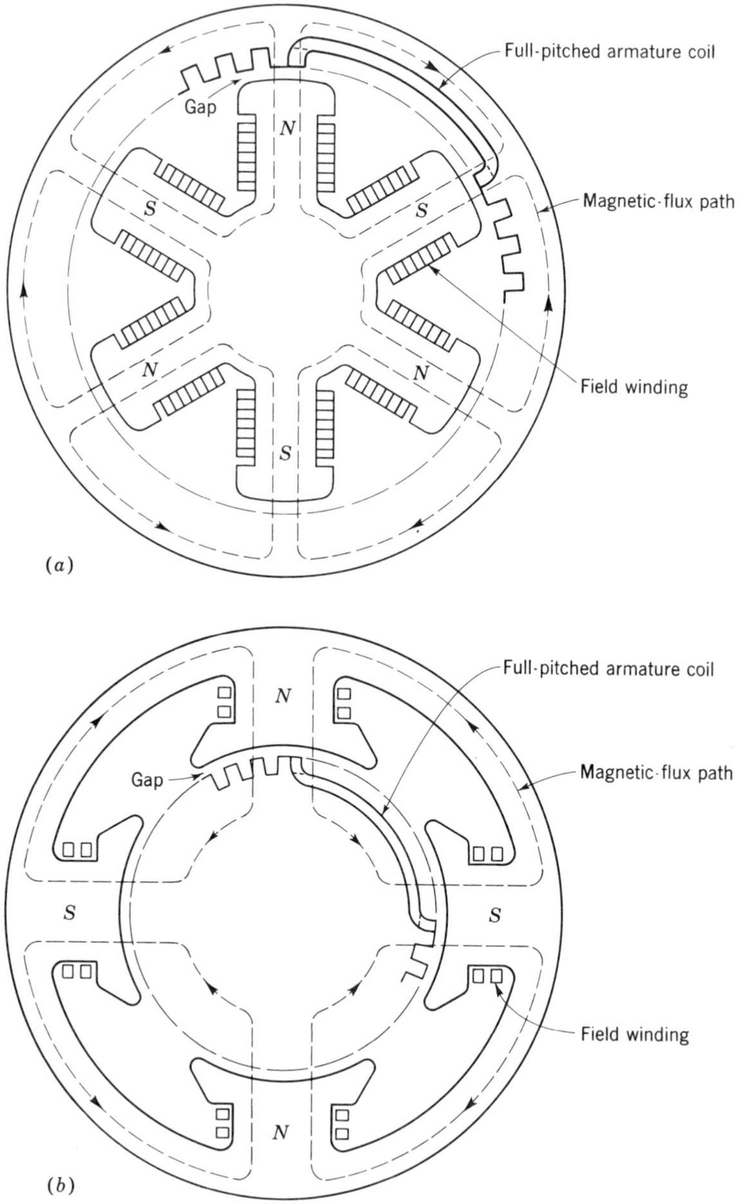

(a)

(b)

Fig. 6.14 Synchronous converters with salient poles: (*a*) Six-pole synchronous converter with field winding on the rotor; (*b*) four-pole synchronous converter with field winding on the stator.

The introduction of the pole pitch τ carries through our philosophy of concentrating on the local gap conditions. Thus, having noted that the number of pole pairs p controls the speed characteristics of the machine, we now prefer to express the variation of the electromagnetic quantities in terms of the local gap periodicity rather than retain the dependence on the speed range and its parameter p. This closely parallels our treatment of the impedance-matching feature which we have also discussed, but subsequently set aside as extrinsic to the power-conversion process.

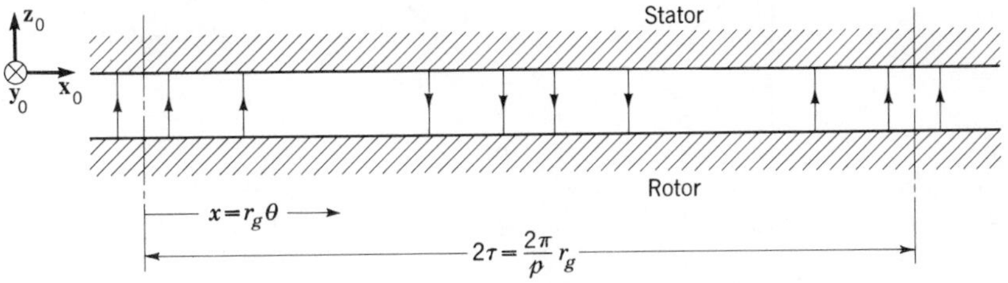

Fig. 6.15 *B* distribution in developed gap.

(b) Armature Conductors

Having had our initial look at the field and its flux pattern, let us look at the armature. First, we shall assume that the armature conductors are uniformly distributed on the rotor periphery. In addition, since we assume a sinusoidal field distribution, these conductors are subjected to continuously differing values of **B** instead of the square wave that might be inferred from our impedance-matching discussion of Sec. 6.2. The impedance-matching facility is in no way impaired by this continuous distribution in **B**, since it depends on polarity *alternation*, not on waveform. In actual practice, the armature conductors will be interconnected so as to form coils, and these coils further connected so as to form a small number of phases, as mentioned in the previous section. The details of the coil connections need not concern us at this time, as they are not material to the basic principles, although they are certainly important in the overall engineering design of the converter. Instead we shall consider an idealized winding scheme of the type shown in Fig. 6.16*c* where each conductor constitutes a separate phase.

As in the homopolar case, we shall assume sufficient axial length so that end effects may be neglected; thus we have no variation of the field quantities in the axial or y direction $\left[\frac{\partial}{\partial y}(\ \ ) = 0\right]$. Under these same circumstances, we concluded in the homopolar case that the terminal voltage was simply the product of the electric-field intensity and the

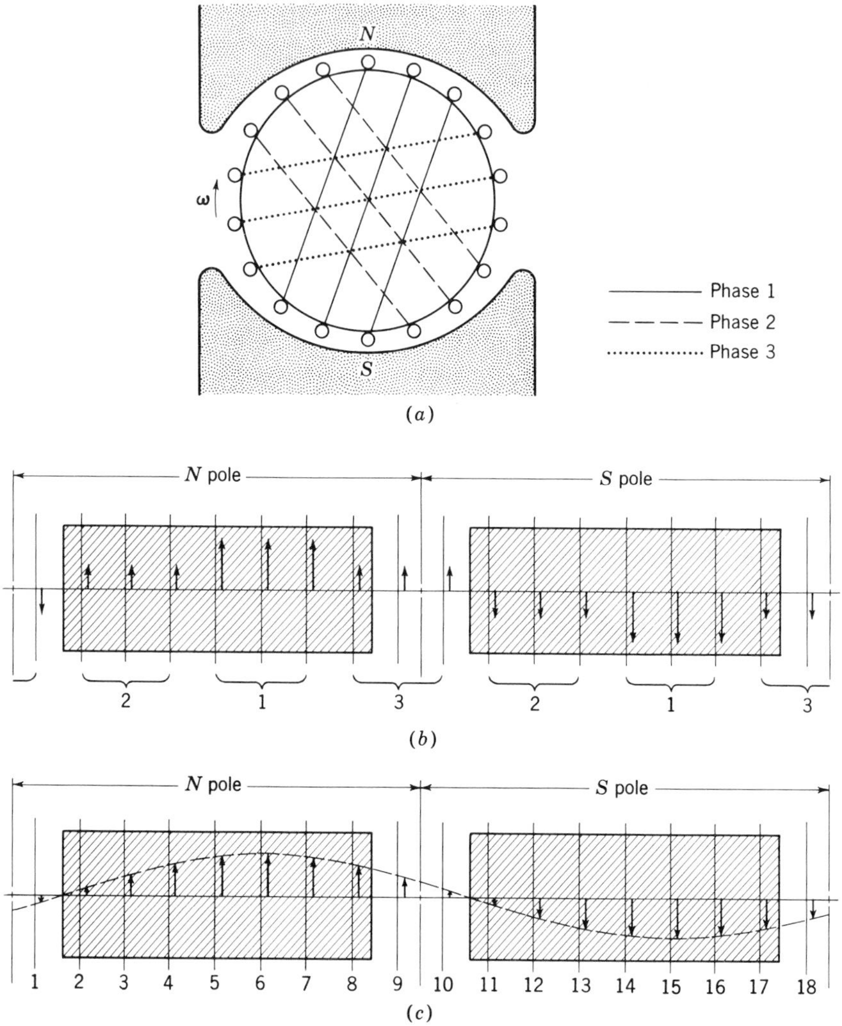

Fig. 6.16 Transition from a practical three-phase winding to an idealized multiphase winding: (*a*) Actual three-phase winding; (*b*) developed view of three-phase winding, showing instantaneous distribution of currents in the conductors; (*c*) idealized equivalent multiphase winding with sinusoidal current distribution.

conductor axial length; in the present case we shall again see that the same result obtains, since the electromagnetic quantities observed in the stator reference frame, although varying in space along the gap periphery, are time-invariant just as in the homopolar converter. Consequently, we may conveniently consider a *unit* axial length of the converter, with the knowledge that it is a simple step to modify our analysis to account for the actual axial dimension.

Conceptually, then, the ends of each unit length of armature conductor are brought out to a corresponding pair of slip rings, which in turn connect to stator terminals by means of brushes. These terminals connect to balanced external circuits which may be either passive or active. In the passive case, each pair of slip rings connects to identical impedances; in the active case, the slip rings are considered to be connected to a set of a-c sources equal in number to the number of armature conductors. These sources have identical internal impedance and active elements which are identical except for a symmetrical progression in phase. We shall call such an array a *balanced polyphase excitation system.* If in addition the sources have constant voltage magnitude (i.e., zero impedance) we shall call the array an *infinite busbar system* or, in short, just an *infinite bus*, as mentioned in Sec. 4.4*b*.

6.5 THE SYNCHRONOUS TIE

In the previous section we called the heteropolar converter with d-c field excitation a synchronous converter. This name is derived from the fact that under d-c field excitation there is a *synchronous tie* or direct proportionality between the a-c frequency in the armature and speed of rotation of the rotor. In this section we shall examine this phenomenon and the concomitant existence of traveling waves.

(a) Coordinate Transformations

Let the rotor angular velocity be ω rad/sec with respect to the stator, clockwise as viewed in Fig. 6.12. This gives the rotor gap surface a linear speed

$$v = \omega r_g \tag{6.4}$$

in the $+x$ direction as viewed for the developed gap of Fig. 6.15.

It is clear that, as seen from a fixed point on the *rotor* surface, the magnetic flux density set up by the field currents will now be time-variable, since such a point experiences a B_{zf} which continuously changes from a maximum to zero, and reverses its polarity as time progresses. To express this fact formally we need the transformation between coordinates measured along axes fixed to stator and rotor, respectively. Thus, we use rectangular coordinates as follows:

1. *Stator:* Here the coordinates are x, y, z, as previously described (Fig. 6.15).
2. *Rotor:* We choose an origin on the rotor surface with coordinate axes parallel to those used on the stator. Since the rotor is completely symmetrical, there is no reason for any but a completely

arbitrary choice of origin point on the rotor surface, except that it is convenient to have the z and z' axes aligned at $t = 0$. We choose such a point, and use the coordinates x', y', z' parallel to x, y, z, respectively.

3. *Coordinate transformation:* Consider a point fixed to the rotor surface; its position, when described in terms of the primed coordinates x', y', z' is time-invariant. The same point viewed from the stator origin will have constant y, z coordinates and an

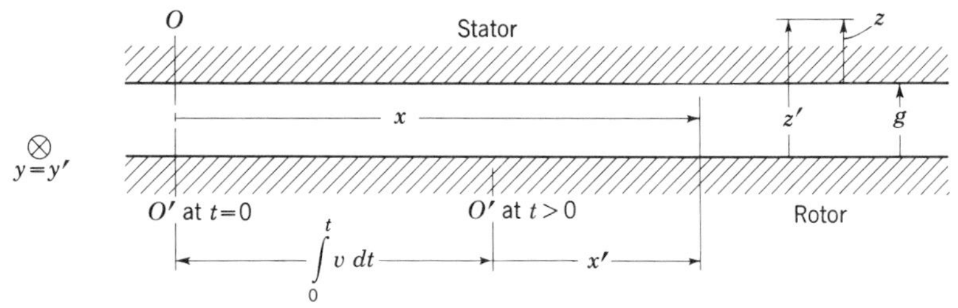

Fig. 6.17 Coordinate transformation.

x coordinate which is time-variable. The relationship at any time t is shown in Fig. 6.17. We see that

$$x = x' + \int_0^t v\,d\tau \tag{6.5a}$$
$$y = y' \tag{6.5b}$$
$$z = z' - g \tag{6.5c}$$

When the rotor velocity is constant, Eq. (6.5*a*) becomes

$$x = x' + vt \tag{6.6a}$$

Equations (6.5*a*) and (6.6*a*) are the Galilean transformation of coordinates resulting from rectilinear motion between the origins of the respective reference frames. The constant-velocity case is of great practical interest, and since it is obviously simpler, we shall consider it first. Thus our coordinate transformation equations are, for the time being,

$$x = x' + vt \tag{6.6a}$$
$$y = y' \tag{6.6b}$$
$$z = z' - g \tag{6.6c}$$

With the coordinate transformations established, we shall now express the magnetic field at the gap in terms of rotor coordinates. To begin with, we note that the vectors **B**, as measured in the stator reference frame, and **B′**, as measured in the rotor reference frame at the same point in time and space, are essentially identical vectors for the low velocities of interest here, as we have discussed in some detail in Chap. 2. Despite this identity of the **B** vectors, the Galilean coordinate transformation together with the spatial variation inherent in the heteropolar configuration, lead to significant differences in the *time behavior* observed at a fixed point on the rotor and a fixed point on the stator. This happens because these points *separate as time progresses.* To see this, we introduce Eq. (6.6*a*) into Eq. (6.3*b*) and get

$$B_{zf} = B_{fm} \cos \frac{\pi}{\tau} (x' + vt) \tag{6.7}$$

Now consider the implications of Eq. (6.7). If we are at a fixed point x' on the rotor, we plainly experience a sinusoidal time variation in B (and, consequently, in all electromagnetic quantities) with frequency ω_e given by

$$\omega_e = \frac{\pi}{\tau} v \tag{6.8a}$$

Using Eqs. (6.4) and (6.2*b*), this may be alternatively written as

$$\omega_e = \frac{\pi}{\tau} \omega r_g = p\omega \tag{6.8b}$$

Equation (6.8*b*) is also the formal expression of the synchronous tie. It tells us that the relative motion between rotor and stator changes a purely spatial variation in the stator frame into a time-varying one in the rotor frame. This is obviously a fundamental phenomenon, which we now encounter for the first time because we have heretofore considered only uniform field distributions.

As we have mentioned before, the synchronous tie represented by Eq. (6.8*b*) also illustrates the motivation for using nonunity values of p. If we rewrite Eq. (6.8*b*) in terms of frequency f_e in cycles per second (cps) and speed n in revolutions per second (rps), then

$$f_e = \frac{\omega_e}{2\pi} \tag{6.9a}$$

$$n = \frac{\omega}{2\pi} \tag{6.9b}$$

and

$$f_e = pn \tag{6.10}$$

From Eq. (6.10) we may take note of some representative values, as given in Table 6.2. It is clear from the equations and this table how the number of pole pairs relates to the desired electric frequency and the mechanical speed of the machine. Example 6.2 following illustrates this relationship.

Table 6.2 REPRESENTATIVE VALUES OF FREQUENCY f_e AND SPEED n

Frequency f_e, cycles per second	No. of pole pairs p	Mechanical speed	
		n, rps	$60n$, rpm
60	1	60	3600
60	2	30	1800
60	6	10	600
60	36	$1\frac{2}{3}$	100
400	1	400	24,000
400	2	200	12,000
400	6	$66\frac{2}{3}$	4000

Example 6.2

Determine the number of pole pairs in a synchronous waterwheel generator if the armature frequency is 60 cycles, the blades of the waterwheel are located at a radius of 2.7 m, and the blade peripheral velocity is approximately equal to the velocity of the water stream, i.e., 30 m/sec.

Solution

The angular velocity is

$$\omega = \frac{30}{2.7}\text{ rad/sec} \qquad \text{or } 1.77 \text{ cps}$$

The number of pole pairs is therefore

$$p = \frac{60}{1.77}$$

or to the nearest integer

$$p = 34$$

At the nominal 60-cycle frequency the blade velocity is

$$v_{\text{blade}} = r_g\omega = 2.7 \times 2\pi \times \frac{60}{34} = 29.8 \text{ m/sec}$$

(b) Traveling Waves

If, from the rotor reference frame, we now view the *totality* of the rotor conductors, rather than focus our attention on an individual one, we observe variations in *both* time and space. The spatial variability is manifested in the form of the continuous phase shift in the flux density experienced by neighboring conductors, as indicated in Fig. 6.18. Thus, if we consider two rotor conductors 1 and 2, the values of B_z observed at the location of these conductors are, from Eq. (6.7) and (6.8*a*),

$$B_{zf,1} = B_{fm} \cos\left(\omega_e t + \frac{\pi}{\tau} x_1'\right) \tag{6.11a}$$

$$B_{zf,2} = B_{fm} \cos\left(\omega_e t + \frac{\pi}{\tau} x_2'\right) \tag{6.11b}$$

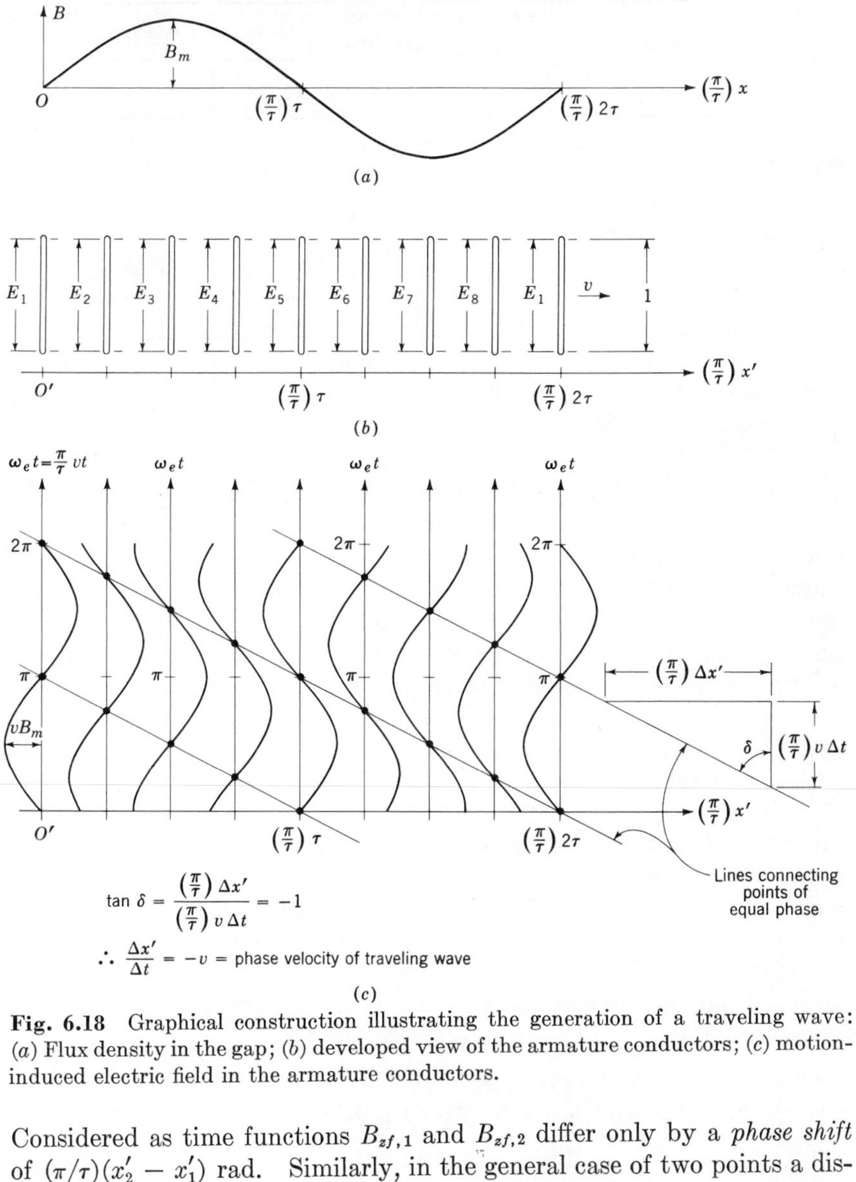

Fig. 6.18 Graphical construction illustrating the generation of a traveling wave: (*a*) Flux density in the gap; (*b*) developed view of the armature conductors; (*c*) motion-induced electric field in the armature conductors.

Considered as time functions $B_{zf,1}$ and $B_{zf,2}$ differ only by a *phase shift* of $(\pi/\tau)(x_2' - x_1')$ rad. Similarly, in the general case of two points a distance $\Delta x'$ apart, there is then an electrical phase shift $\Delta\theta_e$ rad, such that

$$\Delta\theta_e = \frac{\pi}{\tau}\,\Delta x' = p\,\Delta\theta' \tag{6.12}$$

where $\Delta\theta'$ is the mechanical angular displacement along the rotor corresponding to the linear displacement $\Delta x'$.

Now suppose that it were possible to record the flux density experienced by the totality of the rotor conductors at one fixed instant of time. In this case, the uniform phase progression $(\pi/\tau)x'$ makes B_{zf} vary sinusoidally with x', with a periodicity 2τ; or, in other words, a "still photograph" of B_{zf} shows a sinusoidal "wave" of wavelength 2τ. A second photograph of the rotor taken a short time Δt later would reveal that the wave has moved, the crest (or maximum value) having been displaced because of the phase shift $\omega_e \Delta t$. This is readily recognizable as the classical picture of a *traveling wave*. To determine the velocity of the wavefront or the phase velocity, we need only ride a point of constant instantaneous value. According to Fig. 6.18 and Eq. (6.7), such a point is given by

$$x' + vt = \text{constant}$$

or

$$\Delta x' + v\,\Delta t = 0$$

or

$$\frac{\Delta x'}{\Delta t} = -v$$

Thus the wave is seen to travel to the left with a velocity v, from the viewpoint of the rotor. This is entirely consistent, for it will be recalled that the rotor was assumed to be moving to the right as seen from the stator. From the viewpoint of the rotor, then, the stator is seen to move to the left. It is clear that the wave experienced by the rotor is precisely the sinusoidal distribution B_z fixed to the stator, now traveling by virtue of the motion of the rotor with respect to the stator. The time and phase variation in terms of rotor coordinates, and the purely spatial variation in terms of stator coordinates, are then merely dual aspects of the same wave, which is seen as moving in the one frame, and fixed in space in the other. We have, of course, previously encountered a related example in the moving magnetic walls of Chap. 2, where the transformation between reference frames in relative motion alters a stationary wall and zero electric field to a moving wall and nonzero electric field. In fact, the power conversion observed in that case, between a particle stream and the moving magnetic wall, confirms that we shall obtain power conversion from the interaction of the traveling flux-density wave and the charged particles of the rotor conductors.

6.6 CHARACTERISTIC FEATURES OF SYNCHRONOUS CONVERTERS

In this section we begin our study of the synchronous machine by straightforward application of the generalized Ohm's law, just as we have done in the case of the homopolar device. Since the derivation of the MPD equations does not presume the field vectors to be time- or space-invariant, the traveling waves which we now encounter may be directly introduced into our equations. In this way, we can study the performance of the individual volume elements of the active conductors and derive the local operating conditions. Later we shall streamline our analysis by resorting to a phasor approach which compactly describes the wave interrelations and the overall performance of the whole converter.

Our first step will be to reduce the vector form of the generalized Ohm's law to a single scalar equation, taking advantage of symmetry and orthogonality, as we have already done in previous chapters. Referring to Figs. 6.17 and 6.19, our conductor velocity is in the x direction, and all conductors extend in the axial or y direction. As seen from Ampère's law, currents flowing in these conductors can set up a magnetic

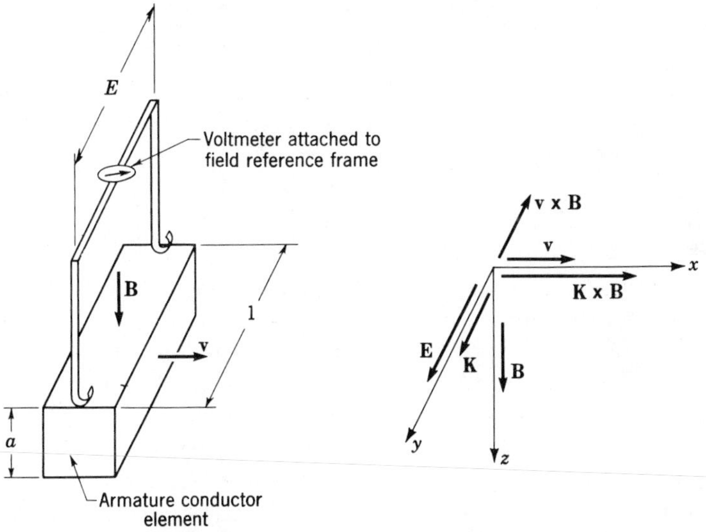

Fig. 6.19 Element of armature conductor and orientation of fundamental vectors.

flux density only in a plane normal to the axis, i.e., in the x or z directions. A component B_x, however, does not contribute to the $\mathbf{v} \times \mathbf{B}$ product since v is also in the x direction. It follows that there is only an axial or y component in the generalized Ohm's law equation. Thus the equation for the armature conductors as seen in the stator reference frame is

$$E_{ay} - v_x B_z = \frac{K_{ay}}{a_a \gamma_a} \tag{6.13a}$$

With the understanding that velocity is along the gap periphery, electric field and current density are parallel to the axis, and the magnetic flux density is the component normal to the gap, unless otherwise specified, we may drop the orientational subscripts and simplify the equation to

$$E_a - vB = \frac{K_a}{a_a \gamma_a} \tag{6.13b}$$

(a) Open-circuit Case

In the open-circuit case, no armature current flows, $K_a = 0$, and Eq. (6.13*b*) reduces to

$$E_a = vB \tag{6.14a}$$

In the absence of armature currents, B is established by the field currents alone, so that $B = B_f$. Thus, introducing the spatial description of B_f given by Eq. (6.3*b*) into Eq. (6.14*a*), we can write

$$E_a = vB_{fm} \cos \frac{\pi x}{\tau} \tag{6.14b}$$

and using the constant-velocity Galilean coordinate transformation equation (6.6*a*),

$$E_a = vB_{fm} \cos \frac{\pi}{\tau} (x' + vt) \tag{6.14c}$$

or

$$E_a = vB_{fm} \cos \left(\omega_e t + \frac{\pi x'}{\tau} \right) \tag{6.14d}$$

Let us give a physical interpretation to the information conveyed by these equations. If we concentrate our attention on a *single* armature conductor identified by a constant value of x', the resulting E_a, as picked up in the stator reference frame via the corresponding slip rings and brushes, is given by Eq. (6.14*d*). Obviously E_a oscillates in time with a radian frequency ω_e and has a phase angle proportional to the location x'. What happens here is that the armature conductor sees a traveling wave B_f (as discussed in the previous section); under the action of this wave, the electrons in the conductor displace themselves in the axial direction. In the open-circuit case, these electrons can only collect on the conductor surface, thus creating a surface charge alternating with time which neutralizes the motional field within the conductor (i.e., $E_a' = 0$). It is this surface charge which then gives rise to E_a, in this case a purely induced or reaction field.

If, on the other hand, we look at the *totality* of armature conductors, we must conclude from Eq. (6.14*b*) that, in stator coordinates, E_a has a sinusoidal distribution in space *without time variation*. Consequently, the overall E_a is a wave synchronized with the B_f wave, stationary with respect to the stator, and traveling to the left with respect to the rotor. In fact, we might argue this a fortiori from Eq. (6.14*a*), where we see the direct proportionality of E_a and B_f without the irrelevancies of the functional dependence. Thus, if B_f is a wave, then E_a is a wave of identical character.

The situation described above is illustrated in Fig. 6.20. The E_a and B_f waves are fixed to the x reference frame; in this frame we see the arma-

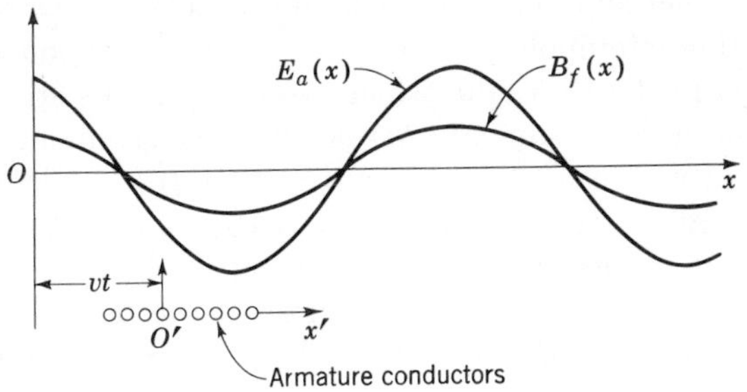

Fig. 6.20 E_a and B_f waves, open-circuit case.

ture conductors slide uniformly past the E_a waves. In this way, each individual armature conductor picks up its sinusoidal time variation.

(b) Armature Reaction

At this point we naturally wish to consider cases in which armature current *does* flow. In doing this, however, we encounter an obstacle. In the heteropolar converter, the armature and field conductors are both axial, lying side by side on either side of the gap; consequently, the armature currents contribute with equal weight to the establishment of the actual B. This means that as soon as we close the armature circuits, B will no longer be equal to B_f and the armature reaction affects the power conversion. As illustrated in Fig. 6.21, this situation is very different from the homopolar case, where $B = B_f$ because the reaction component of B is parallel to $\mathbf{v}$, so that the armature reaction does not affect the power conversion.

It is clear then that we shall have to make a detailed computation of

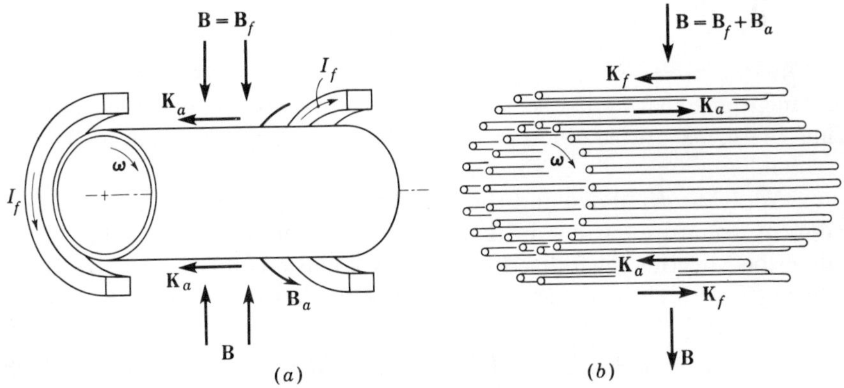

Fig. 6.21 Relative orientation of the field and armature currents in homopolar and heteropolar converters: (*a*) Homopolar converter; (*b*) heteropolar converter.

the armature reaction in order to evaluate completely the terminal characteristic of the heteropolar converter. We shall not, however, do this now. The useful basic results which we seek at this stage are readily derivable if we simply assume the actual B to be a given quantity. Thus, anticipating future results a little, we now state that in the structure under consideration, the component of B contributed by the armature currents, and therefore the total B, turn out to be sinusoidal waves of wavelength and velocity identical to those of the impressed component B_f. The flux densities B_f and B then differ, in general, only by having different amplitudes and a constant phase displacement. We may therefore write

$$B = B_m \cos\left(\frac{\pi x}{\tau} - \delta\right) \tag{6.15}$$

where $B_m \neq B_{fm}$, and δ is an unspecified phase angle which may take on different values under different operating circumstances. With this modest look into the future, we are equipped to proceed with our study.

(c) Operation with Double Excitation: Impressed B_f and E_a

We are now ready to consider a case in which current flows in the armature conductor, in particular the one in which E_a is completely determined by impressed sources. Now both armature and field are fed from active sources, and so we naturally call this the *doubly excited* case.

We postulate that E_a is a sinusoidal distribution which, as in the open-circuit case, and as shown in Fig. 6.22, does not vary with time in the stator reference frame, and therefore represents a wave of the form

$$E_a = E_m \cos\left(\frac{\pi}{\tau} x - \beta\right) \tag{6.16a}$$

$$= E_m \cos\left(\omega_e t + \frac{\pi x'}{\tau} - \beta\right) \tag{6.16b}$$

As mentioned earlier in Sec. 6.4, such an E_a wave is impressed by connecting the armature conductors to a balanced polyphase "infinite busbar system."

With the E_a above and the B of Eq. (6.15) there will generally be a flow of armature current in the axial or y direction. This is, of course, described by the generalized Ohm's law equation (6.13*b*). Thus, introducing Eq. (6.15) and (6.16*a*) into Eq. (6.13*b*), we determine K_a:

$$K_a = a_a\gamma_a \left[E_m \cos\left(\frac{\pi}{\tau} x - \beta\right) - vB_m \cos\left(\frac{\pi}{\tau} x - \delta\right)\right] \tag{6.17}$$

When we expand and regroup the trigonometric functions, and make use of the identity

$$A \sin \theta + B \cos \theta = \sqrt{A^2 + B^2} \cos \left(\theta - \tan^{-1} \frac{A}{B} \right) \tag{6.18}$$

we find that

$$K_a = K_{am} \cos \left(\frac{\pi}{\tau} x - \lambda \right) \tag{6.19a}$$

where

$$K_{am} = a_a \gamma_a \sqrt{E_m{}^2 + v^2 B_m{}^2 - 2vE_m B_m \cos (\delta - \beta)} \tag{6.19b}$$

$$\tan \lambda = \frac{E_m \sin \beta - vB_m \sin \delta}{E_m \cos \beta - vB_m \cos \delta} \tag{6.19c}$$

It is clear that K_a (and likewise J_a) again has the periodicity and distribution of E and B and consequently is a traveling wave synchronized with

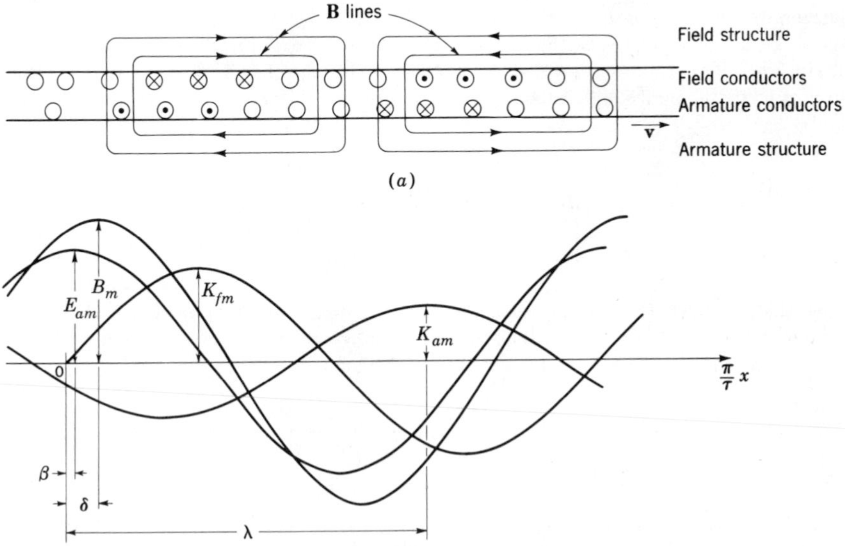

Fig. 6.22 Schematic representation of the electromagnetic field prevailing in the gap of a synchronous generator under load conditions: (*a*) Current and flux distribution; (*b*) relative position of the E_a, B, and K waves in the gap.

the E and B waves, differing only in amplitude and phase. In stator coordinates, then, all electromagnetic quantities are time-invariant.

Example 6.3

A 60-cps synchronous machine having two pole pairs operates with a peak radial component of magnetic flux density $B_m = 1$ weber/m² and a peripheral velocity $v = 50$ m/sec. The converter is connected to an "infinite bus," which impresses a sinusoidal electric-field wave with peak intensity $E_m = 50.5$ volts/m. In a certain operating condition, the electric-field-intensity wave E_a leads the armature-surface current-density wave K_a by a mechanical angle of 30° along the stator, while the radial component of the magnetic flux-density wave B is only slightly out of phase with the E_a wave. For this operating condition, find:

(*a*) The phase displacement of the B wave with respect to the E_a wave.

(*b*) The peak value of the current-density wave K_{am} if the armature conductors are made of copper with a conductivity $\gamma = 5 \times 10^7$ mhos/m and their effective thickness is $a_a = 2 \times 10^{-3}$ m.

Solution

The solution of this problem is more convenient if phasor notation is used, but it is still readily accomplished in trigonometric form.

(*a*) To determine the phase of the wave B, we may work with the expressions for B, E_a, and K_a [Eqs. (6.15), (6.16*a*), and (6.19*a*), respectively], and the phase relationship [Eq. (6.19*c*)]. In terms of quantities used therein, we are given the phase angle $\lambda - \beta$ between E_a and K_a, and we seek the phase angle $\delta - \beta$ between B and E_a. It is therefore desirable to shift our origin of stator coordinates, so that the quantities $\delta - \beta$ and $\lambda - \beta$ occur explicitly, in order to reduce the labor of solution. To do this, we pick as the x origin the point on the stator where E_a is a positive maximum. This represents a shift of angle β with respect to the origin used in the text, so that the angles β, δ, λ have become respectively 0, $\delta - \beta$, $\lambda - \beta$, and

$$E_a = E_m \cos \frac{\pi x}{\tau}$$

$$B_z = B_m \cos \left(\frac{\pi x}{\tau} - \delta + \beta\right)$$

$$K_a = K_{am} \cos \left(\frac{\pi x}{\tau} - \lambda + \beta\right)$$

Since the phase relationship between the waves is unaffected by the choice of origin, it follows that Eq. (6.19*c*) still holds in the new reference frame, provided only we replace the original angles by the new angles. Thus

$$\tan (\lambda - \beta) = \frac{E_m \sin 0 - vB_m \sin (\delta - \beta)}{E_m \cos 0 - vB_m \cos (\delta - \beta)}$$

or

$$\tan (\lambda - \beta) = \frac{-vB_m \sin (\delta - \beta)}{E_m - vB_m \cos (\delta - \beta)}$$

From the given data we know that K_a lags E_a by 30 mechanical degrees; since $p = 2$, this is equivalent to an electrical angle of 60°. Thus

$$\lambda - \beta = 60° \qquad \tan (\lambda - \beta) = \sqrt{3}$$

Using mks units, $vB_m = 50$ and $E_m = 50.5$, so that

$$\tan 60° = \frac{-50 \sin (\delta - \beta)}{50.5 - 50 \cos (\delta - \beta)} = \frac{-\sin (\delta - \beta)}{1.01 - \cos (\delta - \beta)}$$

this last equation may be rewritten as

$$-1.01 \times \sin 60° = \sin (\delta - \beta) \cos 60° - \cos (\delta - \beta) \sin 60° = \sin (\delta - \beta - 60°)$$

or

$$\sin (\delta - \beta - 60°) = -\frac{\sqrt{3}}{2} - \frac{\sqrt{3}}{200}$$

Thus

$$\delta - \beta = 60° - \sin^{-1} \left(\frac{\sqrt{3}}{2} + \frac{\sqrt{3}}{200}\right)$$

It is clear that we can evaluate $\delta - \beta$ by using tables. However, since the result will be small, it is neater and more accurate to use an incremental method. Thus the expansion of $\sin^{-1}(\alpha_0 + \alpha)$ in a power series for small α has for the first two terms

$$\sin^{-1}(\alpha_0 + \alpha) = \sin^{-1}\alpha_0 + \frac{\alpha}{\sqrt{1 - \alpha_0^2}}$$

so that
$$\sin^{-1}\left(\frac{\sqrt{3}}{2} + \frac{\sqrt{3}}{200}\right) = \sin^{-1}\frac{\sqrt{3}}{2} + \frac{\frac{\sqrt{3}}{200}}{\sqrt{1 - \frac{3}{4}}}$$
$$= \frac{\pi}{3} + \frac{\sqrt{3}}{100} \quad \text{or} \quad \frac{2\pi}{3} + \frac{\sqrt{3}}{100}$$

Therefore
$$\delta - \beta = -\frac{\sqrt{3}}{100} \text{ or } -\frac{\pi}{3} \qquad \text{approximately}$$
$$= -0.992° \text{ or } -60°$$

We discard the second possibility since the problem statement tells us that $\delta - \beta$ is small. Consequently,

$$\delta - \beta = -0.99°$$

i.e., the B wave *leads* the E_a wave by 0.99°.

(*b*) From Eq. (6.19*b*) the peak current density is

$$K_{am} = 2 \times 10^{-3} \times 5 \times 10^7 \sqrt{(50.5)^2 + (50)^2 - 2(50)(50.5)\cos(0.992°)}$$

Here it is convenient to use the expansion

$$\cos\alpha = 1 - \frac{\alpha^2}{2} + \cdots$$

so that
$$\cos 0.992° = \cos\frac{\sqrt{3}}{100} = 1 - \frac{3}{2 \times 10^4}$$

and
$$-2(50)(50.5)\cos 0.992° = -2(50)(50.5) + 3(\tfrac{1}{2})(\tfrac{1}{2} + \tfrac{1}{200})$$

Therefore the quantity under the radical becomes

$$(50.5 - 50)^2 + \tfrac{3}{4} + \tfrac{3}{400} = 1 + \tfrac{3}{400}$$

and
$$K_{am} = 10^5\sqrt{1 + \tfrac{3}{400}} = 10^5(1 + \tfrac{3}{800}) = 1.004 \times 10^5 \text{ amp/m}$$

(d) Local Operating Conditions: Motoring, Generating, and Braking Regions

It is now possible to consider the local operating conditions in each element of the armature conductor as power conversion takes place. First, let us find the slip s_a for any point on the armature. It will be recalled (Chap. 4) that in the presence of the orthogonal vectors $E_a\mathbf{y}_0$ and $B\mathbf{z}_0$ there is a drift velocity $\mathbf{v}_E = v_E\mathbf{x}_0$ such that

$$E_a\mathbf{y}_0 + v_E\mathbf{x}_0 \times B\mathbf{z}_0 = 0 \tag{6.20a}$$

or
$$v_E = \frac{E_a}{B} \tag{6.20b}$$

Also, since the armature conductors all have the velocity $v\mathbf{x}_0$ in the stator reference frame, the slip s_a for any armature conductor is, from Eq. (4.23),

$$s_a = 1 - \frac{v}{v_E} = 1 - \frac{vB}{E_a} \tag{6.21a}$$

Using (6.13*b*), this may also be written as

$$s_a = \frac{1}{a_a\gamma_a}\frac{K_a}{E_a} \tag{6.21b}$$

and, using Eqs. (6.16*a*) and (16.19*a*), as

$$s_a = \frac{1}{a_a\gamma_a}\frac{K_{am}\cos\left(\frac{\pi}{\tau}x - \lambda\right)}{E_m\cos\left(\frac{\pi}{\tau}x - \beta\right)} \tag{6.22a}$$

$$= \frac{1}{a_a\gamma_a}\frac{K_{am}}{E_m}\frac{\cos\left(\omega_e t + \frac{\pi}{\tau}x' - \lambda\right)}{\cos\left(\omega_e t + \frac{\pi}{\tau}x' - \beta\right)} \tag{6.22b}$$

It is clear that s_a is now a function of x, or correspondingly a function of x' and t when we follow a specific individual armature conductor.

Suppose we now follow an individual armature conductor in the general case when the E_a and K_a waves are not in phase ($\lambda \neq \beta$). The numerator and denominator of the right-hand side of Eq. (6.22*b*) will then vanish for different values of t, and, as a consequence, the slip s_a for a given conductor will assume all the values from $-\infty$ to $+\infty$ during one electric cycle. It follows that each armature conductor, in general, operates in *all* the three conversion modes of generating, motoring, and braking during a single cycle. Also, when we view the totality of armature conductors in the stator reference frame, we see that the numerator and denominator of the right-hand side of Eq. (6.22*a*) vanish for different values of x when $\lambda \neq \beta$, leading in the same way to the conclusion that all three modes of conversion are present in separate regions in each spatial cycle along the gap; moreover, these regions are fixed to the stator for all of the time. Thus, an individual armature conductor moving through these regions experiences the time succession of the three modes.

The most convenient way to define the several regions of power conversion involves a simple comparison of the local values of E_a and vB. This follows from Eq. (6.21*a*) and the boundaries on s for the three modes as given in Chap. 4. Thus,

$$\frac{vB}{E_a} = 1 - s_a \left\} \begin{array}{ll} > 1 & \text{for generating} \\ > 0, \ < 1 & \text{for motoring} \\ < 0 & \text{for braking} \end{array} \right. \tag{6.23}$$

We see therefore that braking occurs whenever vB and E_a have unlike signs; when the signs are alike, we have motoring if $E_a > vB$ or generating if $E_a < vB$.

Using this simple comparison approach, we find the three regions of power conversion for three different operating conditions as illustrated in Fig. 6.23. In Fig. 6.23*a* we have chosen $E_m > vB_m$, and B leading E_a, i.e., $\beta > \delta$. Here we see finite braking, generating, and motoring regions in each half-cycle along the stator. It is clear that the motoring region is by far the largest, and so we would naturally expect the overall or average operation to be motoring. We shall see that this is indeed the case. In Fig. 6.23*b* we have chosen $E_m < vB_m$, and B again leading E_a, i.e., $\beta > \delta$. Here we again see the finite braking, generating, and motoring regions, this time with the generating region the largest, and the

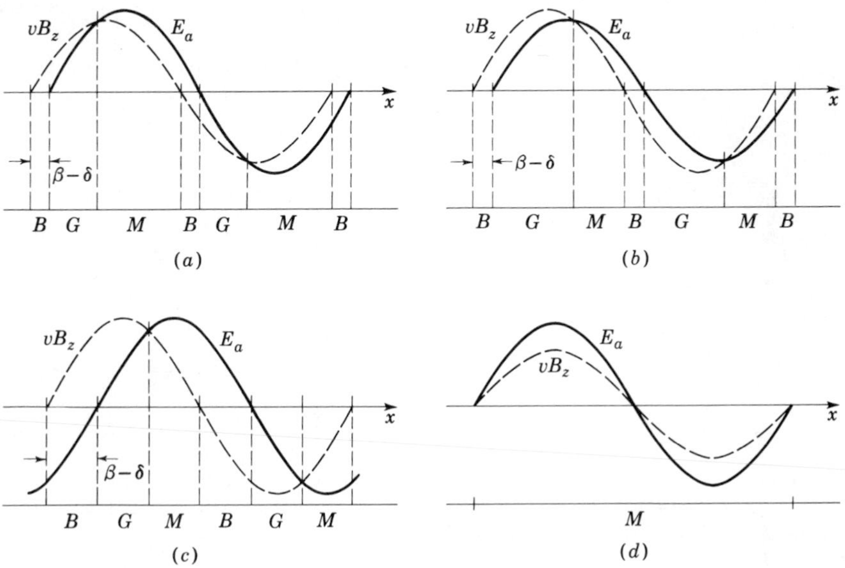

Fig. 6.23 Local regions of power conversion: (*a*) Overall motoring; (*b*) overall generating; (*c*) overall braking; (*d*) motoring everywhere.

overall operation one of generating. Figure 6.23*c* shows a condition where $E_m = vB_m$ and B once again leads E_a, this time by exactly 60°. In this case the braking, generating, and motoring regions are all exactly the same size; it follows that the overall operation is one of braking since the motoring and generating regions exactly cancel each other's contributions to the overall power conversion.

The following examples illustrate the general situation of finding all the modes of power conversion in any steady-state operating condition.

There exist, however, special conditions where only one mode of conversion occurs. Thus, if $\beta = \delta$, so that B, E_a, and consequently K_a are all exactly in phase, then the power conversion must be motoring everywhere if $E_m > vB_m$, or generating everywhere if $E_m < vB_m$. This is very much like the operating condition found in the homopolar converter, where phase plays no part. Figure 6.23*d* illustrates this for motoring everywhere, i.e., $E_m > vB_m$, $\beta = \delta = \lambda$.

The example below illustrates the determination of the regions of power conversion.

Example 6.4

In the machine of Example 6.3 find:

(*a*) The extent of gap periphery over which motoring, generating, and braking takes place.

(*b*) The overall mode of operation of the machine.

Solution

(*a*) To facilitate finding the different regions of power conversion, we sketch the E_a and vB waves. It is clear that θ_{12} is a braking region, θ_{23} is generating, θ_{34} is

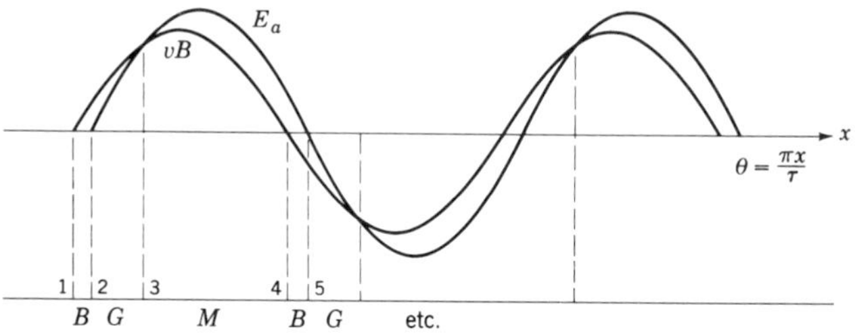

motoring, etc. From the results obtained in the previous example we know that $\theta_{12} = 0.992°$. To find θ_{23}, we use the fact that $E_a = vB$ at point 3, so *that* K_a *must be zero here.* Since the K_a wave lags the E_a wave by 60°, it follows that $\theta_{23} = 60°$. Now $\theta_{45} = \theta_{12} = 0.992°$ by symmetry, so that $\theta_{34} = 120° - 0.992° = 119.01°$ by subtraction. The entire gap periphery is

$$2\pi r_g = 2\pi \frac{v}{\omega} = \frac{2\pi p v}{\omega_e} = \frac{pv}{f_e}$$

in length; consequently the gap is $(2 \times 50)/60 = \frac{5}{3}$ m long. Since the electrical pattern repeats symmetrically every half-cycle, it follows that the lengths of the different regions are:

Braking: $\frac{0.992}{180} \times \frac{500}{3} = 0.9$ cm

Generating: $\frac{60}{180} \times \frac{500}{3} = 55.6$ cm

Motoring: $\frac{119.01}{180} \times \frac{500}{3} = 110.2$ cm

Total: 166.7 cm

(*b*) Of the three regions of operation the largest in extent is the motoring region: 110.2 cm. We therefore conclude that under the conditions specified in the problem the converter as a whole is operating as a motor.

6.7 POWER DENSITIES AND DESIGN

(a) Surface Power Densities

In investigating the operating conditions of the armature conductor we next turn to an examination of the surface power densities defined in Chap. 4, as seen in the stator reference frame. Beginning with the electric surface power density, we have

$$p_{s,\text{elec}} = \mathbf{K}_a \cdot \mathbf{E}_a = K_a E_a \tag{6.24a}$$

and introducing Eqs. (6.16*a*) and (6.19*a*) we have

$$p_{s,\text{elec}} = K_{am} E_m \cos\left(\frac{\pi x}{\tau} - \lambda\right) \cos\left(\frac{\pi x}{\tau} - \beta\right) \tag{6.24b}$$

which may be reduced by trigonometric identity to

$$p_{s,\text{elec}} = \frac{K_{am} E_m}{2}\left[\cos(\lambda - \beta) + \cos\left(\frac{2\pi x}{\tau} - \lambda - \beta\right)\right] \tag{6.24c}$$

It will be useful to define the phase angle φ as the angle by which the E_a wave leads the K_a wave. This angle, in terms of λ and β as given by Eqs. (6.16*a*) and (6.19*a*), is then

$$\varphi = \lambda - \beta \tag{6.25}$$

and introducing φ into Eq. (6.24*c*), we have

$$p_{s,\text{elec}} = \frac{K_{am} E_m}{2}\left[\cos\varphi + \cos\left(\frac{2\pi x}{\tau} - 2\lambda + \varphi\right)\right] \tag{6.26}$$

The electric surface power density is thus a double-frequency sinusoidal distribution with a period of τ instead of 2τ. The average value is $(K_{am}E_m/2)\cos\varphi$, and the oscillating component is $(K_{am}E_m/2)\cos(2\pi x/\tau - 2\lambda + \varphi)$. The value of $\cos(2\pi x/\tau - 2\lambda + \varphi)$ varies between $+1$ and -1 because of the continuous variation of the argument of the cosine function with x, whereas $|\cos\varphi|$ is equal to or less than unity; it follows that the sign of $p_{s,\text{elec}}$ generally alternates along the gap. This, of course, means that electric power flows into the armature conductor in part of the gap and flows out in another part, corresponding exactly to the alternation of motoring, braking, and generating regions that we have already seen. These special cases are worth noting:

1. If $\lambda = \beta$ so that $\varphi = 0$, $\cos\varphi = 1$, then $p_{s,\text{elec}}$ pulsates without any negative values, and this is the case of motoring only, which we have previously illustrated in Fig. (6.23*d*).

2. Similarly, if $\lambda - \beta = \pi$ so that $\varphi = \pi$, $\cos \varphi = -1$, then $p_{s,\text{elec}}$ pulsates without any positive values, and the converter is operating everywhere in the generating region.
3. If $\lambda - \beta = \pm\pi/2$, so that $\varphi = \pm\pi/2$, the average power is zero, signifying that equal portions of the gap absorb and deliver power.

Suppose we now follow a specific armature conductor located at some fixed value of rotor coordinate x'. The K_a, E_a, and $p_{s,\text{elec}}$ for this conductor are then time functions which follow from Eqs. (6.16*a*), (6.19*a*), (6.6*a*), and (6.26); thus

$$K_a = K_{am} \cos \left(\omega_e t + \frac{\pi x'}{\tau} - \lambda \right) \tag{6.27}$$

$$E_a = E_m \cos \left(\omega_e t + \frac{\pi x'}{\tau} - \lambda + \varphi \right) \tag{6.28}$$

$$p_{s,\text{elec}} = \frac{K_{am} E_m}{2} \left[\cos \varphi + \cos \left(2\omega_e t + \frac{2\pi x'}{\tau} - 2\lambda + \varphi \right) \right] \tag{6.29}$$

The above group of equations is undoubtedly familiar to students who recall their a-c circuit theory. Apart from the presence of the given x' and the trivial dimensional differences, these equations plainly depict an alternating "voltage" source with peak value E_m and radian frequency ω_e, delivering like-frequency "current" and "power." The current, which has a peak value K_{am}, lags behind the voltage by a time phase angle φ; as a consequence, the average power is one-half the product of the peak amplitudes and the cosine of this phase angle.

The lesson we learn from these facts is as follows: Whenever there is a *space* displacement between the E_a and K_a waves in the air gap, we find an identical *time phase angle* (in electrical measure) between the corresponding voltage and current in the external circuit. Plainly, this is due to the relationship imposed by the Galilean transformation of coordinates: $x' = x + vt$.

There is a considerable economic import to this space-time phase correspondence. The surface power density is the design parameter which determines the extent of the gap surface, and thus ultimately the size and cost, of the converter. This surface power density is, moreover, directly proportional to the cosine of the phase angle between terminal voltage and current, a number which we recognize to be the familiar *power factor* of the external electric circuit. It follows, then, that for a given power rating as a motor or generator, size and cost of the heteropolar converter go up as the rated power factor goes down. This is, of course, a consequence of the increase in the extent of the opposing mode of power conversion as the K_a and E_a waves shift more and more out of phase, as we have already noted. Thus, as the power factor decreases, increasingly larger portions of the armature conductor are called upon to convert, in addition to the average or active power, a reactive component which circulates from one region of the gap to another through the external circuits; and a larger machine is the result. The problems which arise from a low power factor, and the means for its correction, will be further discussed in the next chapter.

We next turn to the converted surface power density. This is given by

$$p_{s,\text{conv}} = \mathbf{K}_a \cdot \mathbf{B} \times \mathbf{v} = K_a v B \tag{6.30a}$$

and proceeding as before, we find

$$p_{s,\text{conv}} = K_{am} v B_m \cos\left(\frac{\pi x}{\tau} - \lambda\right) \cos\left(\frac{\pi x}{\tau} - \delta\right) \tag{6.30b}$$

or

$$p_{s,\text{conv}} = \frac{K_{am} v B_m}{2}\left[\cos(\lambda - \delta) + \cos\left(\frac{2\pi x}{\tau} - \lambda - \delta\right)\right] \tag{6.30c}$$

and in terms of rotor coordinates,

$$p_{s,\text{conv}} = \frac{K_{am} v B_m}{2}\left[\cos(\lambda - \delta) + \cos\left(2\omega_e t + \frac{2\pi x'}{\tau} - \lambda - \delta\right)\right] \tag{6.30d}$$

We shall find it useful to define a phase angle α as the angle by which the B wave leads the K_a wave. This angle is then

$$\alpha = \lambda - \delta \tag{6.31}$$

and introducing α into Eq. (6.30a), we have

$$p_{s,\text{conv}} = \frac{K_{am} v B_m}{2}\left[\cos\alpha + \cos\left(2\omega_e t + \frac{2\pi x'}{\tau} - 2\lambda + \alpha\right)\right] \tag{6.32}$$

It is clear that $p_{s,\text{conv}}$, in general, also alternates in sign along the gap, in a manner consistent with the succession of the regions characterized by the three different modes of power conversion. The signs of $p_{s,\text{conv}}$ and $p_{s,\text{elec}}$ in fact determine the particular mode of conversion, as we have previously noted.

Aside from its relation to power conversion per se, there is another noteworthy consequence of this sign alternation of $p_{s,\text{conv}}$ along the gap. The surface tangential force density on the armature conductors is

$$f_{sx} = \mathbf{x}_0 \cdot \mathbf{K}_a \times \mathbf{B} = K_a B \tag{6.33}$$

so that

$$f_{sx} = \frac{1}{v} p_{s,\text{conv}} \tag{6.34}$$

Thus the surface force density is directly proportional to $p_{s,\text{conv}}$, and varies in exactly the same way. It follows that any armature conductor on the rotor surface experiences a surface force density which pulsates *in time* at a radian frequency of $2\omega_e$. In view of the inevitable departure of the rotor structure from ideal rigidity, this means that vibration will be set up and noise will occur; a 60-cps machine then will produce noise at 120 cps. It is therefore important for the designer to see to it that none of the natural mechanical modes† of vibration are in the vicinity of $2\omega_e$ rad/sec, if resonance and excessive vibration are to be avoided.

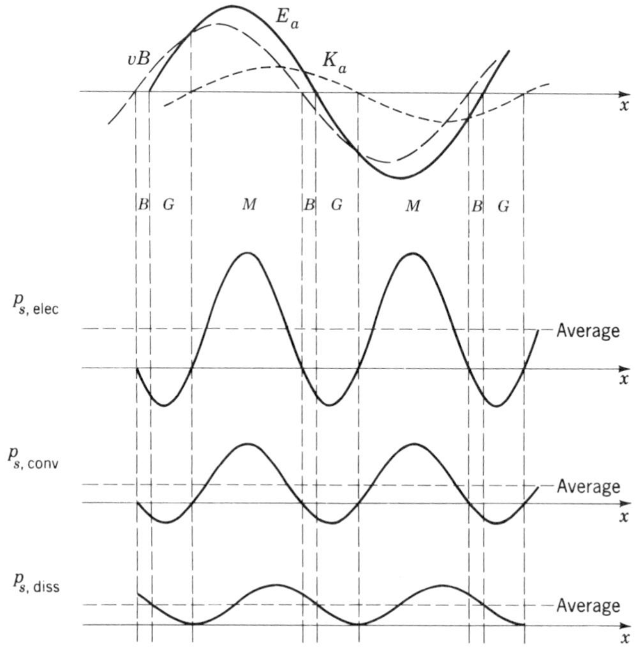

Fig. 6.24 Local power conditions, overall motoring.

The dissipated surface power density may be written in like manner. Thus

$$p_{s,\text{diss}} = \frac{K_a^2}{a_a\gamma_a} \tag{6.35a}$$

$$p_{s,\text{diss}} = \frac{K_{am}^2}{a_a\gamma_a}\cos^2\left(\frac{\pi x}{\tau} - \lambda\right) \tag{6.35b}$$

$$p_{s,\text{diss}} = \frac{K_{am}^2}{2a_a\gamma_a}\left[1 + \cos\left(\frac{2\pi x}{\tau} - 2\lambda\right)\right] \tag{6.35c}$$

$$p_{s,\text{diss}} = \frac{K_{am}^2}{2a_a\gamma_a}\left[1 + \cos\left(2\omega_e t + \frac{2\pi x'}{\tau} - 2\lambda\right)\right] \tag{6.35d}$$

It is clear that $p_{s,\text{diss}}$ is always greater than zero, as we expect.

In Fig. 6.24 we illustrate the relation of the surface power densities

† In a simple mechanical system the natural mode is given by the square root of the ratio: spring constant over inertia.

and the regions of power conversion by showing the several quantities E_a, vB, K_a, $p_{s,\text{elec}}$, $p_{s,\text{conv}}$, $p_{s,\text{diss}}$ for the overall motoring case previously illustrated in Fig. 6.23*a*. Here we see that both $p_{s,\text{elec}}$ and $p_{s,\text{conv}}$ alternate in sign; the larger motoring region dominates to give positive average powers and consequently overall motoring. Note also how the local variations in the signs of $p_{s,\text{elec}}$ and $p_{s,\text{conv}}$ are consistent with the regions of the three modes of power conversion.

We next consider two examples which illustrate the discussion of this section to this point.

Example 6.5

For the machine treated in Example 6.3. determine:

(*a*) The locations along the stator where the electric, converted, and dissipated surface power densities attain their maxima, with respect to the position where the E_a wave has a positive maximum.

(*b*) The value of these maxima.

(*c*) The peak value of the tangential force density.

Solution

(*a*) The power densities attain their extreme values when the argument of the oscillating component is 0 or π, depending on whether the average value is positive or negative. In the case under consideration $\delta - \beta = -0.992°$ and $\varphi = \lambda - \beta = 60°$, so that all average values are positive, as may be seen from Eqs. (6.24*c*) and (6.30*d*). Using these equations, as well as Eq. (6.35*c*), we thus find that the respective peaks occur for:

$p_{s,\text{elec}}$:

$$x = \frac{(\lambda + \beta)\tau}{2\pi} = \frac{(\lambda - \beta)\tau}{2\pi} + \frac{\beta\tau}{\pi} = 0.167\tau \qquad \text{to the right of an } E_a \text{ maximum}$$

$p_{s,\text{conv}}$:

$$x = \frac{(\lambda + \delta)\tau}{2\pi} = \frac{(\lambda - \beta)\tau}{2\pi} + \frac{(\delta - \beta)\tau}{2\pi} + \frac{\beta\tau}{\pi} = 0.149\tau$$

to the right of an E_a maximum

$p_{s,\text{diss}}$:

$$x = \frac{\lambda\tau}{\pi} = \frac{(\lambda - \beta)\tau}{\pi} + \frac{\beta\tau}{\pi} = 0.333\tau \qquad \text{to the right of an } E_a \text{ maximum}$$

We observe that all the maxima occur in the motoring region as we would expect, since the machine is operating as a motor.

(*b*) The corresponding peak values are:

$$(p_{s,\text{elec}})_{\max} = \frac{E_m K_{am}}{2}[1 + \cos(\lambda - \beta)] = \frac{50.5 \times 1.0 \times 10^5}{2} \times 1.5$$
$$= 3.79 \times 10^6 \text{ watts/m}^2$$

$$(p_{s,\text{conv}})_{\max} = \frac{vB_m K_{am}}{2}[1 + \cos(\lambda - \delta)] = \frac{50 \times 1.0 \times 10^5}{2}(1.485)$$
$$= 3.72 \times 10^6 \text{ watts/m}^2$$

$$(p_{s,\text{diss}})_{\max} = \frac{K_{am}^2}{a_a \gamma_a} = \frac{1.0 \times 10^5}{2 \times 10^{-3} \times 5 \times 10^7} = 10^5 \text{ watts/m}^2$$

(*c*) The peak value of the tangential force density is

$$f_{sx} = \frac{1}{v} p_{s,\text{conv}} = \frac{3.72 \times 10^6}{50} = 7.44 \times 10^4 \text{ newtons/m}^2$$

Example 6.6

A synchronous converter operates with the K_a wave leading the E_a wave by 90° and with the peak ohmic drop $K_{am}/a_a\gamma_a = 0.1E_m$.

(a) Determine vB_m and the average values of the surface power densities (in terms of E_m and K_{am}).

(b) Sketch the E_a, vB, and K_a waves, and indicate the local motoring, generating, and braking regions. What is the nature of the overall operation?

Solution

(a) Using a reference point at the peak of the E_a wave as in Example 6.3, we may write

$$E_a = E_m \cos \frac{\pi x}{\tau}$$

$$\frac{K_a}{a_a\gamma_a} = \frac{E_m}{10} \cos \left(\frac{\pi x}{\tau} - \lambda + \beta\right) = \frac{E_m}{10} \cos \left(\frac{\pi x}{\tau} + 90°\right) = \frac{-E_m}{10} \sin \frac{\pi x}{\tau}$$

so that

$$vB = E_a - \frac{K_a}{a_a\gamma_a} = E_m \left(\cos \frac{\pi x}{\tau} + \tfrac{1}{10} \sin \frac{\pi x}{\tau}\right)$$

Using the trigonometric identity

$$A \sin \theta + C \cos \theta = \sqrt{A^2 + C^2} \cos \left(\theta - \tan^{-1} \frac{A}{C}\right)$$

we find

$$vB = E_m \sqrt{1.01} \cos \left(\frac{\pi x}{\tau} - \tan^{-1} \tfrac{1}{10}\right)$$

so that

$$vB_m = E_m \sqrt{1.01}$$

Now

$$p_{s,\text{elec}} = K_a E_a = -K_{am}E_m \sin \frac{\pi x}{\tau} \cos \frac{\pi x}{\tau} = \frac{-K_{am}E_m}{2} \sin \frac{2\pi x}{\tau}$$

and this has an average value of zero, as we would naturally expect. Next,

$$p_{s,\text{conv}} = K_a vB = -\sqrt{1.01}\, K_{am}E_m \sin \frac{\pi x}{\tau} \cos \left(\frac{\pi x}{\tau} - \tan^{-1} \tfrac{1}{10}\right)$$

or

$$p_{s,\text{conv}} = -\frac{\sqrt{1.01}}{2} K_{am}E_m \left[\sin \left(\tan^{-1} \tfrac{1}{10}\right) + \sin \left(\frac{2\pi x}{\tau} - \tan^{-1} \tfrac{1}{10}\right)\right]$$

Here the average is

$$-\frac{\sqrt{1.01}}{2} \sin \left(\tan^{-1} \tfrac{1}{10}\right) K_{am}E_m = -\frac{\sqrt{1.01}}{2} \frac{1}{\sqrt{101}} K_{am}E_m = -\tfrac{1}{20} K_{am}E_m$$

and finally

$$p_{s,\text{diss}} = \frac{K_a^2}{a_a\gamma_a} = +K_a \frac{K_a}{a_a\gamma_a} = -\frac{K_a E_m}{10} \sin \frac{\pi x}{\tau}$$

$$= +\frac{K_{am}E_m}{10} \sin^2 \frac{\pi x}{\tau} = +\frac{K_{am}E_m}{20} \left(1 - \cos \frac{2\pi x}{\tau}\right)$$

This, of course, has an average value of $+K_{am}E_m/20$, as required for conservation of power. We thus have

$$vB_m = E_m \sqrt{1.01}$$

$$\text{Average} \begin{cases} p_{s,\text{elec}} = 0 \\ p_{s,\text{conv}} = -\tfrac{1}{20} E_m K_{am} \\ p_{s,\text{diss}} = +\tfrac{1}{20} E_m K_{am} \end{cases}$$

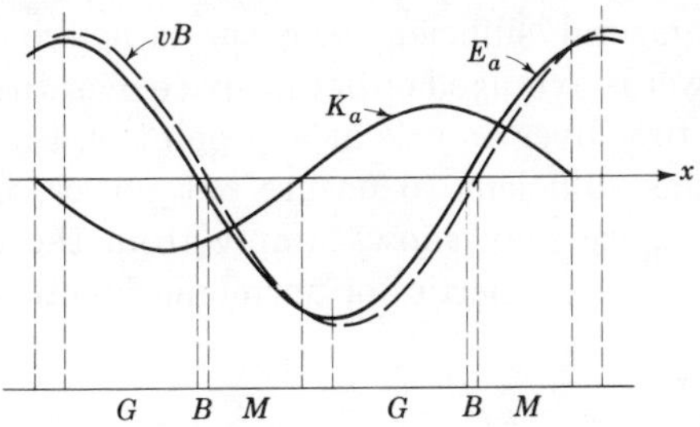

The generating region is exactly a quarter-cycle per electric cycle, and the motoring region is about one degree smaller. Since the generating region predominates, the overall operation cannot be motoring; and since the average $p_{s,\text{elec}} = 0$, we conclude that the *overall* operation *is on the borderline between generating and braking* with the mechanical input covering the power dissipated in the armature conductor.

(b) Average Power Densities

If we determine the average surface power density along the gap by integrating with respect to x, i.e.,

$$\langle p \rangle = \frac{1}{2p\tau} \int_0^{2p\tau} p \, dx$$

(where the symbol $\langle\ \rangle$ means "average of"), it is clear that the double-frequency sinusoidal variations contribute nothing to $\langle p \rangle$, which is determined solely by the constant terms. Thus we find from Eqs. (6.29), (6.32), and (6.35d) that

$$\langle p_{s,\text{elec}} \rangle = \frac{K_{am}}{2} E_m \cos \varphi \qquad (6.36a)$$

$$\langle p_{s,\text{conv}} \rangle = \frac{vK_{am}B_m}{2} \cos \alpha \qquad (6.36b)$$

$$\langle p_{s,\text{diss}} \rangle = \frac{K_{am}^2}{2a_a\gamma_a} \qquad (6.36c)$$

The meaning of the first two of these equations is clear: The signs of $\langle p_{s,\text{elec}} \rangle$ and $\langle p_{s,\text{conv}} \rangle$ depend only on the phase angles φ and α, respectively. *These angles are, of course, the relative angular displacement between the respective waves*; thus $\langle p_{s,\text{elec}} \rangle$ is positive (motoring or braking operation) when the phase displacement between the E_a and the K_a waves is less than 90°, and is negative when the phase displacement exceeds 90°; similarly for $p_{s,\text{conv}}$. The *overall* mode of power conversion can then be determined from a knowledge of the two angles φ and α.

In an earlier section we postulated that the total B wave and, hence, all the electromagnetic waves, have the same periodicity and velocity as the impressed B_f wave. Now, Eqs. (6.36) show that these postulated conditions are, in general, sufficient to ensure a net conversion of power, when the local power is averaged either in space over the gap periphery at any instant, or in time over a cycle at any point on the rotor. Not only are these conditions sufficient to ensure net power, but they are also necessary. In fact, we may show, simply from the definitions of the power densities and the properties of harmonic functions, that these two rules follow:

1. In steady operation, two harmonic waves of the same wavelength interact to produce nonvanishing power only if they *are not in relative motion.* If the two waves were to slide steadily past each other, their relative angular displacement would be proportional to time, so that the cosine of this angular displacement would have no longtime average.
2. Two harmonic waves at relative standstill interact to produce nonvanishing power only if they *have the same wavelength.* If the wavelengths were different, the integral of the wave product would contain sum and difference wavelengths, and would not yield an average term.

These rules are then so fundamentally based that they apply not only to synchronous converters but also to heteropolar converters in general. They are, in fact, the basis for our statement in Sec. 6.3 that the harmonics of a nonsinusoidal field distribution may be treated separately, since by rule 2 these harmonics cannot interact with the fundamental to produce net power.

It should be apparent to the reader that in this section we have merely applied the space-time correspondence which characterizes a traveling wave in order to generalize well-known principles of a-c circuit theory.

(c) Determination of the Dimensions of the Armature Conductor

The average surface power densities derived in the previous section constitute important design parameters. In Chap. 4 we developed formulations giving the specific power densities for the unit volume and surface of the active conductor. These were immediately applicable to the determination of the dimensions of the active conductor in homopolar converters, because of the complete uniformity of the structure. In heteropolar devices, however, we have local variations which must be taken into account. This is automatically accomplished by use of the *average* power density. Thus the ratios of the total power to the average and surface power densities in turn yield the surface and volume of the active conductor shown in Fig. 6.25, i.e.,

$$A = \frac{P}{\langle p_s \rangle} \qquad V = \frac{P}{\langle p \rangle} \tag{6.37}$$

In addition to knowing the total power level, we begin the usual design with the knowledge of the required efficiency and power factor. It is consequently desirable to write the power densities in terms of these latter quantities, as well as those that typify the technological capabilities

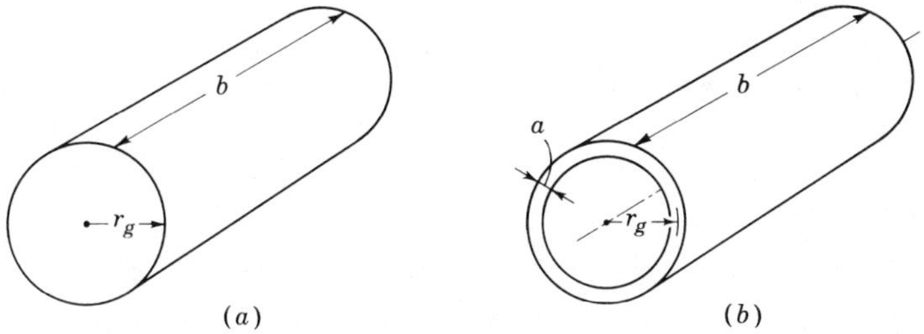

Fig. 6.25 Dimensions of the active conductor in a cylindrical structure: (a) Area $A = 2\pi r_g b = 2p\tau b$; (b) volume $V = 2\pi r_g ba = 2p\tau ba$.

of materials and fabrication, such as B_m and v. We shall do this as follows: First, we repeat Eq. (6.17):

$$K_a = a_a\gamma_a \left[E_m \cos\left(\frac{\pi x}{\tau} - \beta\right) - vB_m \cos\left(\frac{\pi x}{\tau} - \delta\right) \right] \tag{6.17}$$

Next, we note from Eq. (6.19a) that K_a is at its maximum value of K_{am} when $\pi x/\tau = \lambda$. Putting this value into Eq. (6.17) above, we obtain

$$K_{am} = a_a\gamma_a[E_m \cos(\lambda - \beta) - vB_m \cos(\lambda - \delta)] \tag{6.38a}$$

and using the angles φ, α we have

$$K_{am} = a_a\gamma_a(E_m \cos\varphi - vB_m \cos\alpha) \tag{6.38b}$$

or

$$K_{am} = a_a\gamma_a E_m \cos\varphi \left(1 - \frac{vB_m \cos\alpha}{E_m \cos\varphi}\right) \tag{6.38c}$$

To introduce the efficiencies, we recall that

$$\eta_m = \frac{P_{\text{conv}}}{P_{\text{elec}}} = \frac{1}{n_g} \tag{6.39}$$

Furthermore, from Eq. (6.37) this may be written as

$$\eta_m = \frac{P_{\text{conv}}/A}{P_{\text{elec}}/A} = \frac{\langle p_{s,\text{conv}} \rangle}{\langle p_{s,\text{elec}} \rangle} = \frac{1}{\eta_g} \tag{6.40a}$$

and, using Eqs. (6.36), we may write

$$\eta_m = \frac{vB_m \cos \alpha}{E_m \cos \varphi} = \frac{1}{\eta_g} \tag{6.40b}$$

Thus Eq. (6.38*c*) can be put into the form

$$K_{am} = a_a \gamma_a E_m (1 - \eta_m) \cos \varphi \tag{6.41a}$$

or

$$K_{am} = a_a \gamma_a E_m \left(1 - \frac{1}{\eta_g}\right) \cos \varphi \tag{6.41b}$$

Next we combine Eqs. (6.41) and (6.40*b*) with the expressions for the power densities [Eqs. (6.36)] to obtain

$$\langle p_{s,\text{elec}} \rangle = a_a \gamma_a \frac{E_m^2}{2} (1 - \eta_m) \cos^2 \varphi \tag{6.42a}$$

$$\langle p_{s,\text{conv}} \rangle = a_a \gamma_a \frac{E_m^2}{2} \eta_m (1 - \eta_m) \cos^2 \varphi \tag{6.42b}$$

$$\langle p_{s,\text{diss}} \rangle = a_a \gamma_a \frac{E_m^2}{2} (1 - \eta_m)^2 \cos^2 \varphi \tag{6.42c}$$

These expressions, as well as all subsequent ones where η_m appears, apply equally well to generators, with $1/\eta_g$ replacing η_m.

Equations (6.41) and (6.42) are almost in the form we have set out to obtain, except that they are written in terms of E_m rather than vB_m. To overcome this drawback we rewrite Eq. (6.19*c*) as

$$\sin \lambda (E_m \cos \beta - vB_m \cos \delta) = \cos \lambda (E_m \sin \beta - vB_m \sin \delta) \tag{6.19d}$$

Regrouping the terms and introducing the angles φ and δ defined by Eqs. (6.25) and (6.31), respectively, this equation becomes

$$E_m \sin \varphi = vB_m \sin \alpha \tag{6.19e}$$

$$E_m^2 (1 - \cos^2 \varphi) = v^2 B_m^2 (1 - \cos^2 \alpha) \tag{6.19f}$$

If we now use Eq. (6.40*b*) to eliminate $\cos \alpha$, we obtain

$$E_m^2 = \frac{v^2 B_m^2}{1 - (1 - \eta_m^2) \cos^2 \varphi} \tag{6.43}$$

Thus Eq. (6.42) becomes

$$\langle p_{s,\text{elec}} \rangle = a_a \gamma_a \frac{v^2 B_m^2}{2} \frac{(1 - \eta_m) \cos^2 \varphi}{1 - (1 - \eta_m^2) \cos^2 \varphi} \tag{6.44a}$$

$$\langle p_{s,\text{conv}} \rangle = a_a \gamma_a \frac{v^2 B_m^2}{2} \frac{\eta_m (1 - \eta_m) \cos^2 \varphi}{1 - (1 - \eta_m^2) \cos^2 \varphi} \tag{6.44b}$$

$$\langle p_{s,\text{diss}} \rangle = a_a \gamma_a \frac{v^2 B_m^2}{2} \frac{(1 - \eta_m)^2 \cos^2 \varphi}{1 - (1 - \eta_m^2) \cos^2 \varphi} \tag{6.44c}$$

In most cases of practical interest the efficiency η very nearly approaches 1. It is then quite adequate to approximate Eq. (6.44) as follows:

$$\langle p_s \rangle = \langle p_{s,\mathrm{elec}} \rangle \doteq \langle p_{s,\mathrm{conv}} \rangle = a_a \gamma_a \frac{(vB_m)^2}{2} (1 - \eta_m) \cos^2 \varphi \qquad (6.45a)$$

$$\langle p_{s,\mathrm{diss}} \rangle \doteq a_a \gamma_a \frac{(vB_m)^2}{2} (1 - \eta_m)^2 \cos^2 \varphi \qquad (6.45b)$$

In addition to the above equation for the surface densities of current and power, we will also require analogous expressions for the corresponding *volume* densities. By recalling our earlier discussion of this topic in Chap. 4, we see that the respective volume densities (J_a for K_a, p_{elec} for $p_{s,\mathrm{elec}}$, etc.) are obtained by merely *omitting the effective conductor thickness* a_a in Eqs. (6.41), (6.42), (6.44), and (6.45).

The expressions thus obtained for the average power densities in heteropolar structures show that the average density is always less than half the density calculated on the basis of the peak values of the field quantities because of the sinusoidal distributions and the presence of phase shift. This means that if the material is stressed to the maximum, the active conductor in a heteropolar converter always has more than twice the size of the conductor in an homopolar converter of equal power. This is the price one must pay for the advantages resulting from the flexibility in impedance matching.

To illustrate the use of the power densities in synchronous converters we consider the following example.

Example 6.7

The design specifications for a 60-cycle turbogenerator call for an output power of 225 Mw at P.F. (power factor) 0.85, with a conversion efficiency $\eta_g = 0.9985$. The armature conductor is to be copper with $\gamma_a = 5 \times 10^7$ mhos/m.

Considering as limiting factors:

Maximum peak armature current density (on the basis of cooling considerations):	$K_{am} = 1.81 \times 10^5$ amp/m
Maximum conductor velocity:	$v = 220$ m/sec
Maximum peak flux density:	$B_m = 0.815$ weber/m^2

(*a*) Determine for a two-pole machine:

V = volume of armature conductor
r_g = gap radius
b = length of armature conductor
a_a = thickness of armature conductor

(*b*) Repeat part (*a*) for a four-pole machine.

(*c*) Taking $\pi r_g^2 b$ as indicative of the weight and cost of the machine, what conclusion can you come to from a comparison of the results (*a*) and (*b*)?

Solution

(*a*) In view of the high efficiency we calculate the volume of armature conductor, making use of Eq. (6.45*a*) in the volume-density version:

$$\begin{aligned}
\langle p_{\text{elec}}\rangle &= \frac{\gamma_a}{2}(vB_m \cos\varphi)^2\left(1 - \frac{1}{\eta_g}\right)\\
&= \frac{5 \times 10^7}{2}(220 \times 0.815 \times 0.85)^2\left(1 - \frac{1}{0.9985}\right)\\
&= -8.70 \times 10^8 \text{ watts/m}^3\\
V &= \frac{P_{\text{elec}}}{\langle p_{\text{elec}}\rangle} = \frac{-225 \times 10^6}{-8.70 \times 10^8} = 0.259 \text{ m}^3
\end{aligned}$$

For a two-pole machine, $\omega = \omega_e$,

$$r_g = \frac{v}{\omega} = \frac{220}{2\pi \times 60} = 0.583 \text{ m}$$

In order to determine the axial length b, we need the surface of the gap; thus, using Eq. (6.36*a*) with $vB_m \doteq E_m$,

$$\begin{aligned}
\langle p_{s,\text{elec}}\rangle &\doteq \frac{K_{am}vB_m \cos\varphi}{2} = -\frac{1.81}{2} \times 10^5 \times 220 \times 0.815 \times 0.85\\
&\doteq -1.38 \times 10^7 \text{ watts/m}^2
\end{aligned}$$

and

$$2\pi r_g b = \frac{-225 \times 10^6}{-1.38 \times 10^7} = 16.3 \text{ m}^2$$

so that

$$b = \frac{16.3}{2\pi \times 0.583} = 4.45 \text{ m}$$

We find a by dividing the conductor volume by the conductor surface:

$$a = \frac{0.259}{16.3} = 0.0159 \text{ m} = 1.59 \text{ cm}$$

(*b*)

$$V = 0.259 \text{ m}^3 \text{ as before}$$

For a four-pole machine, $\omega = \omega_e/2$, $r_g = 2v/\omega_e = 1.166$ m, and r_g is doubled.

$$2\pi r_g b = 16.3 \text{ m}^2 \text{ as before}$$

$$b = \frac{16.3}{2\pi \times 1.166} = 2.23 \text{ m} \qquad \text{thus } b \text{ is halved}$$

$$a = 0.0159 \text{ m as before}$$

(*c*) For the two-pole machine,

$$\pi r_g^2 b = \pi \times (0.583)^2 \times 4.45 = 4.75 \text{ m}^3$$

For the four-pole machine,

$$\pi r_g^2 b = \pi \times (1.166)^2 \times 2.23 = 9.50 \text{ m}^2$$

The four-pole machine has twice the volume (since r_g is doubled, and b is halved) and, consequently, will be much more expensive.

6.8 SUMMARY

Having reached the end of this chapter, we now pause to look back and review the essential features of what we have learned:

1. The low electric impedance of the homopolar converter is inescapable. This drawback has to be overcome by resorting to polarity alternation in the gap B, so as to permit increased voltage by series connection of individual armature conductors. An immediate consequence of this heteropolarity is the establishment of a-c quantities in the external circuit.
2. The field and armature conductors in the heteropolar converter with uniform air gap are located in axial slots on either side of the gap; we take the field on the stator and the armature on the rotor, although it will be shown in Chap. 9 that these locations may be interchanged. When the field conductors are excited with direct current, the converter is called *synchronous*, because of the synchronous tie or direct proportionality between rotor speed and electric frequency.
3. The magnetic field excitation in the synchronous converter is a sinusoidal wave at rest with respect to the field conductors. Since the armature is moving with respect to the field structure, the B and vB waves, when viewed from the armature, take the form of traveling waves.
4. The component of the total B normal to the gap is contributed to with equal weight by the armature and field conductors since they are located side by side. Therefore, the armature reaction has to be accounted for when evaluating the motion-induced electric field.
5. Under balanced conditions in the external circuit, the induced B field is a wave of equal wavelength and at standstill with respect to the impressed wave. This enables us to proceed with the investigation of power conversion under the assumption that the total B wave is known.
6. We find that all electromagnetic quantities in the gap are sinusoidal waves at standstill with respect to the field structure. The time variation experienced by a given armature conductor results from its motion with respect to this set of waves and is formally expressed by the Galilean coordinate transformation. A space displacement between waves along the gap results in an equal time-phase displacement between the corresponding electrical quantities as measured in the armature conductors and external circuits.

7. By retaining explicit reference to the functional dependence of the electromagnetic quantities in space and time, we put in evidence the detailed configuration of the electromagnetic field in the gap. We thus find that, in general, all three modes of power conversion are present along the gap. As a consequence, part of the power circulates from one region of the gap to another through the external circuits, and the average or net power per-unit surface cannot reach the same ultimate levels as in homopolar converters.
8. The conditions for average power conversion require synchronized waves, all having the same velocity and the same wavelength.
9. Design of the armature-conductor geometry is readily accomplished through the average power densities. The approach is much the same as in the homopolar case, except for the presence of the power factor which measures the displacement between the K_a and E_a waves. The size and cost of an heteropolar converter increase as the power factor decreases.

REFERENCES:

1. Liwschitz-Garik, M.: and C. Gentilini: "Winding Alternating-current Machines,' D. Van Nostrand Company, Inc., Princeton, N.J., 1950.

PROBLEMS

6.1 A coil of a heteropolar converter consists of 24 individual conductors and is placed in two slots with 12 conductors in each slot. All the conductors in each slot are exposed to the same magnetic field and the magnetic field has opposite

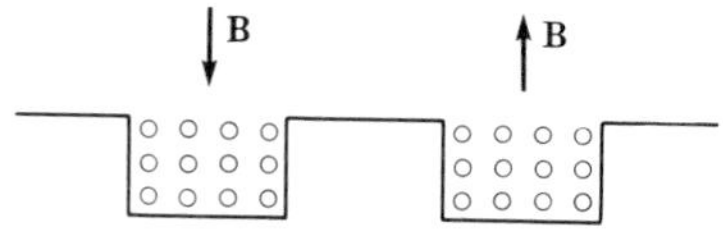

polarity in the two slots as shown. Determine all the possible balanced series-parallel arrangements which permit maximum power output from the coil, and calculate in each case the terminal current, voltage, impedance, and power in terms of the corresponding quantities for one conductor.

6.2 A heteropolar converter has p identical pole pairs. Under each pole there is a slot containing c_s individual conductors. All the conductors in each slot are exposed to the same magnetic field. Determine the possible balanced series-parallel arrangements which permit maximum output power.

6.3 When starting a motor the inrush current (if it is not controlled) is much larger than the nominal current. The control method often used with large induction motors is called "part-winding starting." In this method, some of the parallel branches of the primary winding are disconnected during the starting period.

(*a*) By what percentage is the inrush of current reduced when using the scheme shown, if $Z_1 = Z_2$?

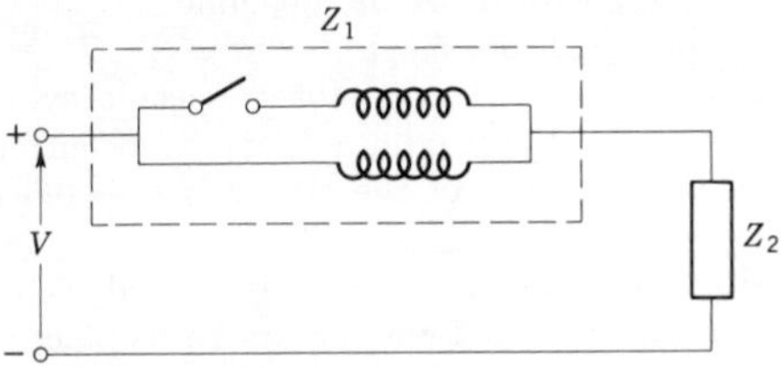

(*b*) By what percentage are the volume and surface current densities J and K changed?

(*c*) By what percentage is the starting torque reduced if B remains practically constant?

Note: Z_1 is the *total* impedance of the primary winding shown in the figure.

6.4 The supply voltage for a synchronous motor has a frequency of 60 cps. The machine has 12 pole pairs. The magnetic field is assumed sinusoidal. Under these conditions:

(*a*) Calculate the angular velocity of the motor, the rpm, and the peripheral speed if $r_g = 1.5$ m.

(*b*) Consider a point on the rotor where $B = B_m$ at $t = 0$. Calculate the time when the magnetic field at the same point on the rotor is $B_m/\sqrt{2}$, 0, $-B_m/\sqrt{2}$, $-B_m$.

(*c*) Give the dependence of B on the time t.

6.5 A sinusoidal wave is moving with phase velocity $v_{\mathrm{ph}}^{(1)}$ with respect to an x-coordinate axis, as shown.

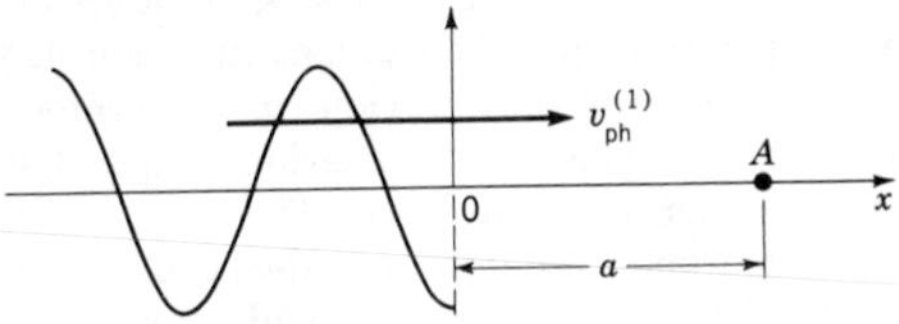

(*a*) Give the analytical and graphical description of the time dependence of the wave, as it is seen from a point A.

(*b*) An observer, initially at A, starts moving *toward* the wave at time $t = 0$ with velocity v_A. Repeat (*a*) for this observer.

(*c*) Repeat (*b*) for the case $v_{\mathrm{ph}}^{(2)} = 0$.

(*d*) Repeat (*b*) for the case $v_A = -v_{\mathrm{ph}}^{(1)}$. Compare the results in (*a*) and (*d*).

6.6 A 60-cps synchronous machine having four pole pairs operates with a peak radial component of magnetic flux density $B = 1$ weber/m², and a velocity $v =$ 40 m/sec. In a certain operating condition the electric surface current density wave K leads the electric-field-intensity wave E by a mechanical angle of 15°. The magnetic flux-density wave B lags the electric-field-intensity wave E by a mechanical angle of 30′.

For this operating condition find:

(*a*) The peak value of the electric-field intensity.

(*b*) The peak value of the surface current density if we use copper ($\gamma = 5 \times 10^7$ mhos/m) and $a = 1.5 \times 10^{-3}$ m.

6.7 In the machine of the previous problem find:

(*a*) The extent of the gap periphery over which motoring, generating, and braking take place.

(*b*) The overall mode of operation of the machine.

(Use the results obtained in Prob. 6.6.)

6.8 The field surface current density for a specific synchronous machine is $K_f = 25 \times 10^3 \cos(p\theta)$ amp/m. the maximum permitted current through each conductor is $I_{\max} = 5$ amp, the diameter of the stator is $r_g = 0.5$ m, and the machine has four poles ($p = 2$).

(*a*) We use seven slots per pole symmetrically placed on the stator. Find the appropriate number of series-connected conductors to be placed in each slot in order to obtain a stepwise approximation to the given K_f.

(*b*) If we place the same number of series-connected conductors in each slot, find the proper position of the slots in order to obtain a stepwise approximation to the given K_f.

(*c*) Finally we use the same number of conductors in each slot, and we place the slots symmetrically on the stator. Find the current through the conductors of each slot in order to obtain a stepwise approximation to the given K_f.

Hint: Use the formula $K_f = n_c n_s I_c$, where n_c = number of conductors per slot, n_s = number of slots per-unit length, I_c = current through each conductor.

6.9 For the machine treated in Probs. 6.6 and 6.7 calculate:

(*a*) The surface electric, dissipated, and converted power densities in terms of the coordinates of the stator.

(*b*) Repeat (*a*) in terms of time t and the coordinates of the rotor.

(*c*) Sketch the results obtained in (*a*). Give the places where maximum and minimum values occur for each power density.

(*d*) Calculate the average power densities.

6.10 Repeat the calculations of Example 6.7 for

P.F. = 0.95 $\quad B_m = 1$ weber/m² $\quad K_{am} = 2 \times 10^5$ amp/m $\quad v = 200$ m/sec

The remaining design specifications are the same as in Example 6.7.

6.11 The lowest natural mode of vibration in the armature of a 12-pole synchronous machine is 800 cps. What is the maximum speed in rpm at which the machine can operate without danger of resonance?

6.12 An airborne synchronous generator is designed for a rated power output of 50 kw at 400 cps when driven at 24,000 rpm and connected to an inductive load characterized by a power factor of 0.8.

Assuming that:

Conductor speed:	$v = 200$ m/sec
Peak flux density:	$B_m = 0.8$ weber/m²
Peak armature current density:	$K_{am} = 3 \times 10^4$ amp/m
Conversion efficiency:	$\eta = 0.995$
Conductor conductivity:	$\gamma = 5 \times 10^7$ mhos/m

determine the gap radius r_g and the armature conductor's active length b and effective thickness a.

6.13 A synchronous generator is to be designed for 300 kw output at 0.85 power factor and 0.998 efficiency. The generator is to be driven at 1,800 rpm and provide 60 cps power. Determine the dimensions of the active conductor, a, b, r_g if

$$b = \tau \qquad K_{am} = 5 \times 10^4 \text{ amp/m} \qquad B_m = 0.8 \text{ weber/m}$$

6.14 A 60-cycle, 2-pole, synchronous generator is rated 500 kw at 0.8 power factor and 0.999 conversion efficiency. It is desired to rewind this machine, so that it can be operated as a 50-cycle, 4-pole synchronous motor with 0.9 power factor. Find the power output and the efficiency of the motor if the cooling and insulation are upgraded, thus allowing for a 10 percent increase in the flux density and a 50 percent increase in the armature-surface current density.

chapter 7
STEADY-STATE PERFORMANCE OF SYNCHRONOUS CONVERTERS

7.1 INTRODUCTION

In the previous chapter we have learned that an arrangement such as that used in synchronous converters satisfies the necessary and sufficient conditions for the net conversion of power. In order to arrive at a quantitative evaluation of the performance of these converters, we now need to solve two problems: (1) to develop a concise representation for the electromagnetic field distributions, and (2) to account for the armature reaction.

We solve the first problem by extending the meaning of the phasor notation ordinarily used with sinusoidal functions of time to include sinusoidal distribution in space and traveling waves.

The problem of armature reaction readily reduces to the simultaneous solution of two coupled equations describing respectively the field and armature circuits, once we determine the linear relation that associates a current-density with a flux-density wave. It turns out that this coupling between field and armature is not bilateral in that the armature reaction affects only the armature voltage, but does not feed back into the field-excitation circuit.

The performance of the synchronous converter is then studied, using circuit models and an equivalent phasor diagram which provides great insight into the force and power relations corresponding to the various steady-state operating conditions. We learn that in the doubly excited case, where the frequency and therefore the velocity are dictated by the infinite bus, changes in the power handled by the converter stem from changes in the relative position of the field structure with respect to the waves impressed on the armature structure. As a consequence, we find that the torque coupling between the $\bar{K}$ armature wave and the $\bar{K}_f$ field wave is analogous to the elastic coupling between two links centered at the shaft.

There are then two typical ways of varying the operating point, control of the torque with constant field current and control of the field current with constant torque; we determine the appropriate loci and find that in the first case there exists a maximum output power, and in the second a minimum excitation current. Beyond these limiting values, steady-state operation is not possible. We learn that, besides power conversion, the synchronous machine has another important application, the supply of reactive volt-amperes (var) to inductive loads.

Finally we investigate the capability of the converter to carry overloads when doubly excited, and to maintain the output voltage within reasonable bounds when operating singly excited with varying load and constant field current. We find that in both cases machines with larger gap and consequently larger size and cost yield better performance.

7.2 QUANTITATIVE EVALUATION OF THE ARMATURE REACTION; RELATION BETWEEN FLUX DENSITY AND SINUSOIDALLY DISTRIBUTED CURRENT SHEETS

In Chap. 6 we examined the basic elements of power conversion in synchronous heteropolar converters. The only step we still need to take in order to accomplish a full analysis of the steady-state performance of this converter is to give a complete quantitative description of the armature reaction.

This is accomplished by the solution of a simple field problem: the determination of the magnetic flux density, in the air gap, which is associated with a sinusoidally distributed surface current sheet. When this is done, we shall be able to describe the performance of the synchronous converter in terms of an overall circuit model and phasor diagram.

We begin by assuming a field surface current density $\mathbf{K}_f$ axially directed and sinusoidally distributed with a period of 2τ as given by

$$\mathbf{K}_f = K_f \mathbf{y}_0 \tag{7.1a}$$

$$K_f = K_{fm} \cos\left[\frac{\pi}{\tau}(x - x_0)\right] \tag{7.1b}$$

where x_0 is the position corresponding to K_{fm}, the maximum value of K_f. This distribution is shown in Fig. 7.1.

We may proceed to determine the resulting magnetic field in an exact and formal way by solving Maxwell's equations in the gap. For reference purposes, this has been done in Appendix B. It is possible, however, to obtain a very good approximation to the exact solution by simply applying Ampère's law, if we assume that B does not itself vary *across* the gap. (As Appendix B shows, this is quite accurate in the practical narrow-gap case $g \ll r_g$ or correspondingly $g \ll \tau$.) Making this assumption, consider the planar rectangular probe loop in Fig. 7.1. This loop is in the xz plane and has two sides normal to the gap in the z direction, side 1 at x_0 and side 3 at an arbitrary point x. The other two sides, 2 and 4, are parallel to the gap in the iron, which is assumed to have infinite permeability ($\mu \to \infty$).

We now apply Ampère's law [Eq. (5.19)] by equating the line integral of **H** along the loop to the total current interlinked with the loop. As the two sides of the loop parallel to the gap are located in the idealized iron,

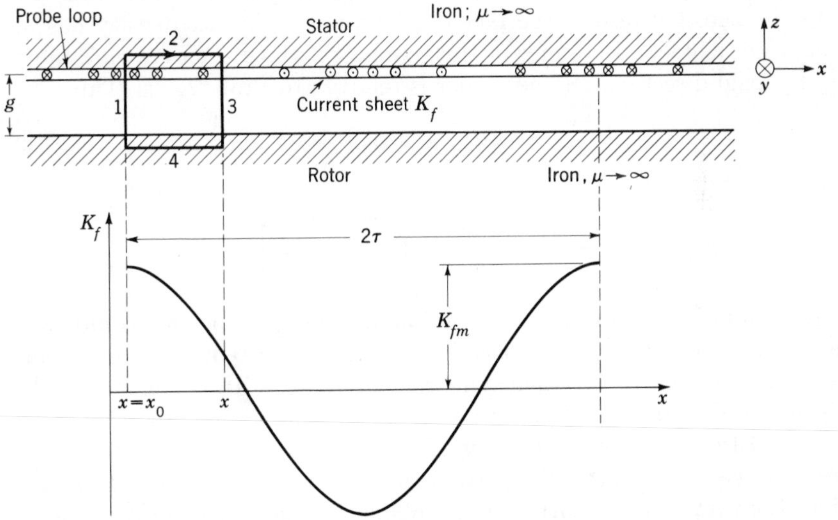

Fig. 7.1 Sinusoidal current sheet and probe loop.

they contribute nothing to $\oint \mathbf{H}_f \cdot d\mathbf{l}$, since **H** is zero in a medium of infinite permeability. Consequently, the only contribution to the line integral comes from the two sides normal to the gap; and since H_{zf} has been assumed not to vary with z, we find

$$\oint \mathbf{H}_f \cdot d\mathbf{l} = g(H_{zf}|_{x_0} - H_{zf}|_x) \tag{7.2}$$

Next, to obtain the total current normal to the loop as a function of the width in the x direction, we integrate the surface current density of Eq. (7.1*b*).

$$I = \int_{x_0}^{x} K_f\,dx = K_{fm} \int_{x_0}^{x} \cos\left[\frac{\pi}{\tau}(x - x_0)\right] dx \tag{7.3}$$

$$= K_{fm}\frac{\tau}{\pi} \sin\left[\frac{\pi}{\tau}(x - x_0)\right] \tag{7.4}$$

Equating (7.2) and (7.4), we obtain

$$H_{zf}|_x = H_{zf}|_{x_0} - \frac{K_{fm}\tau}{\pi g} \sin\left[\frac{\pi}{\tau}(x - x_0)\right] \tag{7.5a}$$

and multiplying by μ_0,

$$B_{zf}|_x = B_{zf}|_{x_0} - \mu_0 \frac{K_{fm}\tau}{\pi g} \sin\left[\frac{\pi}{\tau}(x - x_0)\right] \tag{7.5b}$$

Equation (7.5*b*) shows that B_{zf} varies sinusoidally with the same periodicity as the K_f distribution which produces the field. There also seems to be a constant or average component $B_{zf}|_{x_0}$, whose value is not given by the above development. However, it is easily proved that this constant must be zero because of the fact that the magnetic flux density has no sources or sinks and because of the symmetry which removes variability in the axial direction. (The reader is referred to Prob. 7.1.) Thus

$$B_{zf}|_{x_0} = 0 \tag{7.6}$$

so that Eq. (7.5*b*) becomes

$$B_{zf} = -\mu_0 \frac{K_{fm}\tau}{\pi g} \sin\left[\frac{\pi}{\tau}(x - x_0)\right] \tag{7.7}$$

Equation (7.7) is the result we have sought giving the normal component of magnetic flux density produced by a sinusoidal current sheet on the gap surface. B_{zf} and K_f are then synchronous waves, with B_{zf} leading K_f by 90 electrical degrees. It may be recalled that we anticipated this result in Sec. 6.4*b*, and illustrated it in Fig. 6.12. Note that the same result would have occurred had the current sheet been on the other gap surface, since the total current cutting the probe loop is not affected by the location of the current sheet along the z coordinate. Thus, as far as the normal component of B is concerned, the *particular side of the gap on which the current sheet is located is immaterial.*

We can now very easily verify that the tangential component of B is indeed negligible when compared with the radial component B_z. All that we have to do is take side 4 of the probe loop of Fig. 7.1 just below the stator current sheet, rather than within the rotor. We thus form a loop which is vanishingly small in the z direction, so that the only contribution to the Ampère integral comes from the side right below the current sheet. We find as in Sec. 5.6 that $H_x = K$ and

$$\frac{|B_{xf}|}{|B_{zf}|} = \frac{1}{\tau/\pi g} \ll 1 \tag{7.8}$$

since the gap length g is much smaller than the pole pitch τ.

7.3 PHASOR REPRESENTATION OF HARMONIC WAVES

With the armature reaction disposed of, we next face the task of simplifying our analytical procedures, motivated by the realization that the utility of any theoretical study increases in direct proportion to the convenience and conciseness of the notation employed. It was with this in mind, for example, that we dispensed with the need to take into account repeatedly the vector character of our equations, and introduced the simplified scalar version at the beginning of Sec. 6.6. This was done by taking cognizance, once and for all, of the relative orientation of the field vectors. In the same spirit we may now, having duly learned the details of the variation of the electromagnetic quantities in the previous chapter, forsake the explicit reference to the spatial and temporal dependence. Thus, recalling that all our electromagnetic variables are sinusoidal waves of identical periodicity at relative standstill, we realize that any one of these waves can be distinguished by only two numbers, the amplitude and phase. This means that we can portray such a wave as a complex number or "phasor," and write the laws of power conversion as equations relating phasor quantities. This procedure reduces labor by cutting away repetitive detail when such detail is not required, and has the salutary effect of making possible the derivation of a circuit model and phasor diagram which depict the overall electromagnetic relationships in the converter.

The technique which we use is essentially the one already familiar to the reader from his knowledge of a-c circuit theory. We recall that any electromagnetic quantity in stator coordinates has the spatially distributed form

$$Q = Q_m \cos \frac{\pi}{\tau} (x - x_1) \tag{7.9}$$

which may be rewritten as the real part of a complex exponential function

$$Q = Q_m \operatorname{Re} [e^{j\pi x/\tau} e^{-j\pi x_1/\tau}] = \operatorname{Re} [(Q_m e^{-j\pi x_1/\tau}) e^{j\pi x/\tau}] \tag{7.10}$$

When we write an equation, such as the generalized Ohm's law for the entire gap, using the form indicated in Eq. (7.10), the factor $e^{j\pi x/\tau}$ is common to all terms. The resulting equation may then be rearranged as

$$\operatorname{Re} \left[e^{j\pi x/\tau} \begin{pmatrix} \text{summation of factors} \\ \text{of the form } Q_m e^{-j\pi x_1/\tau} \end{pmatrix} \right] = 0 \tag{7.11}$$

Since this must be true for all x, the quantity inside the parentheses must itself be zero. Thus, the factor $e^{j\pi x/\tau}$ is in effect canceled, and we are left with an algebraic equation involving complex numbers of the form $Q_m e^{-j\pi \pi_1/\tau}$. Such a number is then the *phasor residue* or simply the *phasor* which represents the quantity Q. Specifically, we shall define the rms or effective-value phasor $\bar{Q}$ representing the quantity Q as

$$\bar{Q} = \frac{Q_m}{\sqrt{2}} e^{-j\pi x_1/\tau} \tag{7.12}$$

In using the phasor approach to solve a specific problem, we first determine the phasor $\bar{Q}$ as that particular complex number which satisfies the pertinent equations. Then, from this phasor we can obtain the actual value of the quantity Q, as we see from Eqs. (7.10) and (7.12), by restoring the common factor $e^{j\pi x/\tau}$ and taking the real part,

$$Q = \text{Re}\,[\sqrt{2}\,\bar{Q}\,e^{j\pi x/\tau}] \tag{7.13}$$

The three equations (7.10), (7.12), and (7.13) are then the formal statement of our phasor notation in connection with stationary waves, i.e., sinusoidal distributions in space. The phasor $\bar{Q}$ also serves for the most part to represent the same quantity Q in rotor coordinates, where it appears as a true traveling wave. In rotor coordinates Q is given by

$$Q = Q_m \cos\left[\frac{\pi}{\tau}(x' - x_1) + \omega_e t\right] \tag{7.14a}$$

or

$$Q = \text{Re}\,[Q_m e^{-j\pi x_1/\tau} e^{j\pi x'/\tau} e^{j\omega_e t}] \tag{7.14b}$$

or

$$Q = \text{Re}\,[\sqrt{2}\,\bar{Q} e^{j\pi x'/\tau} e^{j\omega_e t}] \tag{7.14c}$$

If we now write the generalized Ohm's law for the overall gap quantities in rotor coordinates, we find that the factors $e^{j\pi x'/\tau}e^{j\omega_e t}$ cancel just as $e^{j\pi x/\tau}$ canceled before, leaving us with the same phasor residue. Consequently, the phasor $\bar{Q}$ now serves for rotor coordinates as well, as defined by (7.12) and (7.14). In fact, it serves just as well to distinguish the time phase shift between any two quantities at a given location x' in the primed coordinate system as it serves to distinguish the spatial phase displacement along a wave in the unprimed coordinate system x. Thus the single phasor, in connection with the Galilean coordinate transformation, suffices to represent the same quantity in either stator (space) or rotor (traveling wave) coordinates. Here again, as in the case of the average power densities of Sec. 6.7*b*, we have expanded well-known concepts, which in a-c theory apply to time dependence, to include space dependence as well. The phasors thus defined turn out to be useful in describing all kinds of wave-propagation phenomena such as are encountered in acoustic, fluid-dynamic, and electromagnetic theory.

With this phasor convention established, we may now apply it to the scalar version of the equation expressing the generalized Ohm's law. Thus, in accordance with our previous discussion and Eq. (7.11), Eq.

(6.13*b*) becomes in phasor form

$$\bar{E}_a = \frac{\bar{K}_a}{a_a \gamma_a} + v\bar{B} \tag{7.15}$$

where each of these phasors is the complex or phasor factor which establishes the actual quantity according to Eq. (7.13). The phasor equation (7.15) is free of space and time coordinates, and so provides a neat notation for the overall steady-state performance analysis of the converter. As a preliminary illustration of the use of the phasor approach we shall apply this method to the problem previously solved in Example 6.3.

Example 7.1

Solve the problem of Example 6.3 by using phasor methods.

Solution

(*a*) Let us choose the E_a wave as our reference wave, and so represent it as a phasor with zero degrees phase:

$$\bar{E}_a = \frac{50.5}{\sqrt{2}} e^{j0} = \frac{50.5}{\sqrt{2}}$$

From the given information we know that the K_a wave lags the E_a wave by $30p$ or 60 electrical degrees, so that

$$\bar{K}_a = \frac{K_{am}}{\sqrt{2}} e^{-j60^\circ}$$

Moreover the peak amplitude of the vB wave is 50×1 so that

$$v\bar{B} = \frac{50}{\sqrt{2}} e^{-j(\delta-\beta)}$$

where $\delta - \beta$ is to be found.

We now substitute these phasors in Eq. (7.15), obtaining

$$\frac{50.5}{\sqrt{2}} = \frac{K_{am}}{\sqrt{2}\, a_a \gamma_a} e^{-j60^\circ} + \frac{50}{\sqrt{2}} e^{-j(\delta-\beta)}$$

or

$$50.5 = \frac{K_{am}}{a_a \gamma_a} e^{-j60^\circ} + 50 e^{-j(\delta-\beta)}$$

This last equation can be solved analytically, but a more useful procedure is to resort to the *phasor diagram* as shown.

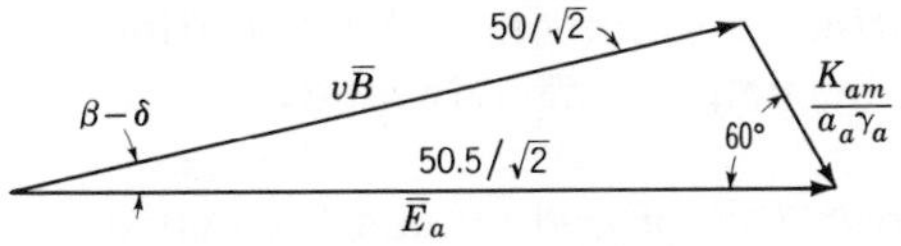

Here it is clear that the simplest procedure in finding $\beta - \delta$ is to use the law of sines in the triangle of phasors, i.e.,

$$\frac{\sin(\pi - \pi/3 - \beta + \delta)}{50.5} = \frac{\sin(\pi/3)}{50}$$

or
$$-\sin\left(\delta - \beta - \frac{\pi}{3}\right) = \frac{50.5}{50}\sin\frac{\pi}{3} = \frac{\sqrt{3}}{2} + \frac{\sqrt{3}}{200}$$

or
$$\sin\left(\delta - \beta - \frac{\pi}{3}\right) = -\left(\frac{\sqrt{3}}{2} + \frac{\sqrt{3}}{200}\right)$$

From this point on, the solution duplicates that of Example 6.3.

(*b*) Determination of K_{am}: If we inspect the phasor diagram, we note that Eq. (6.19*b*) is, in fact, the expression of the law of cosines in the triangle of phasors above, and the amplitude of K_a can therefore be obtained just as in Example 6.3. Alternatively, we could write Eq. (7.15) as

$$\bar{K}_a = a_a\gamma_a(\bar{E}_a - v\bar{B}) = 2 \times 10^{-8} \times 5 \times 10^7 \left(\frac{50.5}{\sqrt{2}} - \frac{50}{\sqrt{2}}e^{j0.992^\circ}\right)$$

and compute $\bar{K}_a$ from this expansion; this, of course, exactly parallels the use of the law of cosines. The quickest method, however, is again to apply the law of sines in the triangle of phasors, giving

$$\frac{K_{am}/a_a\gamma_a}{\sin\,(\beta - \delta)} = \frac{50}{\sin 60^\circ}$$

or
$$K_{am} = a_a\gamma_a 50\frac{\sin 0.992^\circ}{\sin 60^\circ} = 2 \times 10^{-8} \times 5 \times 10^7 \times 1$$
$$= 10^5 \text{ amp/m}$$

which agrees with the value found in Example 6.3.

7.4 GAP REACTANCE; EQUIVALENT CIRCUIT OF A SYNCHRONOUS CONVERTER

We are now ready to undertake the complete analysis of the steady-state performance of the synchronous converter. All the necessary relationships are at hand, in the form of the MPD equation of motion, the

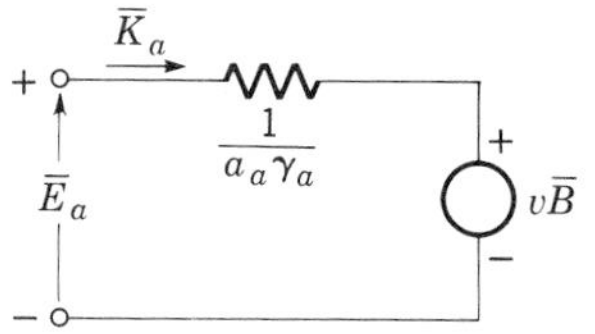

Fig. 7.2 First step circuit model.

generalized Ohm's law, and the armature reaction relationship, i.e., the magnetic link between flux density and current. As we have done before, we shall attempt to integrate these relationships into an overall equivalent-circuit model, taking advantage of the convenient phasor representation.

The first step in this procedure is a familiar one, namely, the portrayal in a series circuit of the relation governing the electrical performance of the armature conductor, as given by Eq. 7.15. We have done this before in Fig. 4.5*a*, and we now repeat it in Fig. 7.2, with K_a replacing J_a.

To complete the electrical side of our circuit model, we next need to introduce the relationship between $\bar{B}$ and the two current sheets in phasor form. We found in Sec. 7.2 that the K_f–B_f relationship is contained in the two equations

$$K_f = K_{fm} \cos\left[\frac{\pi}{\tau}(x - x_0)\right] \tag{7.1b}$$

$$B_f = -\mu_0 K_{fm} \frac{\tau}{\pi g} \sin\left[\frac{\pi}{\tau}(x - x_0)\right] \tag{7.7}$$

Let us now restate this relationship in phasor form. If we start with a phasor $\bar{K}_f$, the phase and amplitude relationship contained in the above pair of equations is satisfied by the phasor $\bar{B}_f$ such that

$$\bar{B}_f = j\mu_0 \frac{\tau}{\pi g} \bar{K}_f \tag{7.16}$$

where j is the unit imaginary number defined by $e^{(\pi/2)j} = j$.

Now the total B consists of components due to both K_f and K_a. Since we are idealizing the ferromagnetic materials in the converter, our system model is linear, so that we can find B by superposing the two components resulting individually from field and armature currents. Consequently, we know that

$$\bar{B} = \bar{B}_f + \bar{B}_a = j\mu_0 \frac{\tau}{\pi g} (\bar{K}_f + \bar{K}_a) \tag{7.17}$$

Thus the total normal component of gap flux density is due to a total or resultant surface current density which is the sum of K_f and K_a. It is useful then to define the total surface current density or as it is sometimes called, the *magnetizing current density*

$$K = K_f + K_a \tag{7.18a}$$

or phasorwise

$$\bar{K} = \bar{K}_f + \bar{K}_a \tag{7.18b}$$

Since we want to relate the motional electric field vB to the currents, let us multiply Eq. (7.17) by v:

$$v\bar{B} = j\mu_0 \frac{\tau v}{\pi g} (\bar{K}_f + \bar{K}_a) = j\mu_0 \frac{\tau v}{\pi g} \bar{K} \tag{7.19a}$$

In Eq. (7.19*a*) we note that the quantity $\mu_0(\tau v/\pi g)$ must be dimensionally an impedance in ohms, since the dimensions of $v\bar{B}$ are volts per meter and those of $\bar{K}$ are amperes per meter. We shall represent this impedance by $\mathfrak{X}_m$, i.e.,

$$\mathfrak{X}_m = \mu_0 \frac{\tau v}{\pi g} \tag{7.20}$$

so that

$$v\bar{B} = j\mathfrak{X}_m \bar{K} \tag{7.19b}$$

Despite the fact that in this equation we use $\mathfrak{X}_m$ to relate two local field quantities, we must remember that $\mathfrak{X}_m$ results from an integration over a loop (Ampère's law). $\mathfrak{X}_m$ therefore truly represents a circuital parameter, as evidenced by the appearance of τ in its definition [Eq. (7.20)]. Since v is proportional to ω, we may rewrite $\mathfrak{X}_m$ in alternative forms, using Eqs. (6.2*b*), (6.4), and (6.8):

$$\mathfrak{X}_m = \frac{\mu_0 \tau v}{\pi g} = \frac{\mu_0 \tau^2}{\pi^2 g}\,\omega_e = \frac{\mu_0 r_g{}^2}{p^2 g}\,\omega_e \qquad (7.21)$$

We see that $\mathfrak{X}_m$ is directly proportional to electrical angular frequency, and this identifies it as an *inductive reactance.* This is hardly surprising, since the parameter $\mathfrak{X}_m$ arises from the analytic description of the magnetic circuit of the air gap. Consequently, we shall call $\mathfrak{X}_m$ the *gap reactance* or *magnetizing reactance.* The corresponding *gap inductance* L_m is then given by

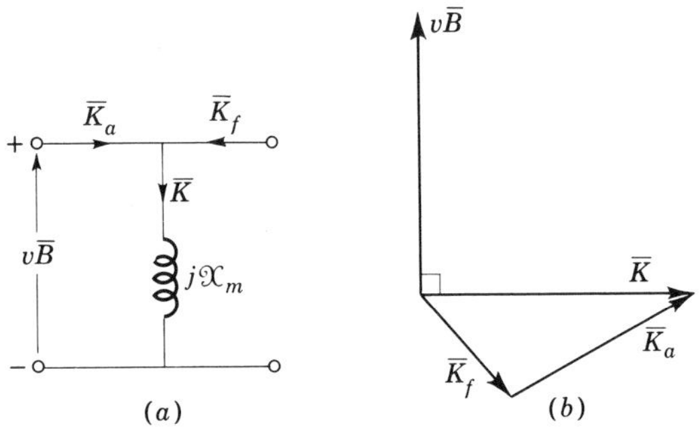

Fig. 7.3 Equivalent gap circuit: (*a*) Circuit; (*b*) phasor diagram.

$$L_m = \frac{\mathfrak{X}_m}{\omega_e} = \frac{\mu_0 r_g{}^2}{p^2 g} \qquad (7.22)$$

In view of these facts, we may portray Eq. (7.19) as shown in Fig. 7.3. Example 7.2 illustrates the computation of gap reactance and inductance.

Example 7.2

A synchronous converter operating at 60 cps has a peak motional electric field of 100 volts/m when operating with no armature current and a peak field surface current density of 1.67×10^4 amp/m. Find the magnetizing reactance and the gap inductance. What is the gap radius of this machine if it runs at 3,600 rpm and has a 2-mm gap?

Solution

Since $\bar{K}_a = 0$, $\bar{K} = \bar{K}_f$ from (7.18), then from (7.19*b*),

$$|v\bar{B}| = \mathfrak{X}_m|\bar{K}_f|$$
$$100 = \mathfrak{X}_m(1.67 \times 10^4)$$
$$\mathfrak{X}_m = 6 \times 10^{-3} \text{ ohms}$$

From (7.22),

$$L_m = \frac{\mathfrak{X}_m}{\omega_e} = \frac{6 \times 10^{-3}}{2\pi \times 60} = \frac{10^{-4}}{2\pi} \text{ henrys}$$
$$= 15.9 \text{ microhenrys}$$

Since $\qquad \omega_e = p\omega \qquad p = \frac{\omega_e}{\omega} = \frac{2\pi \times 60}{2\pi \times 60} = 1$

and using (7.22),

$$r_g{}^2 = \frac{L_m p^2 g}{\mu_0} = \frac{10^{-4}}{2\pi} \times \frac{2 \times 10^{-3}}{4\pi \times 10^{-7}} = \frac{1}{4\pi^2}$$

$$r_g = \frac{1}{2\pi} \text{ m} = 15.9 \text{ cm}$$

(a) Completion of the Circuit Model

We may now complete our circuit model in a very simple way. The left part or terminal pair of the gap circuit of Fig. 7.3a always has an

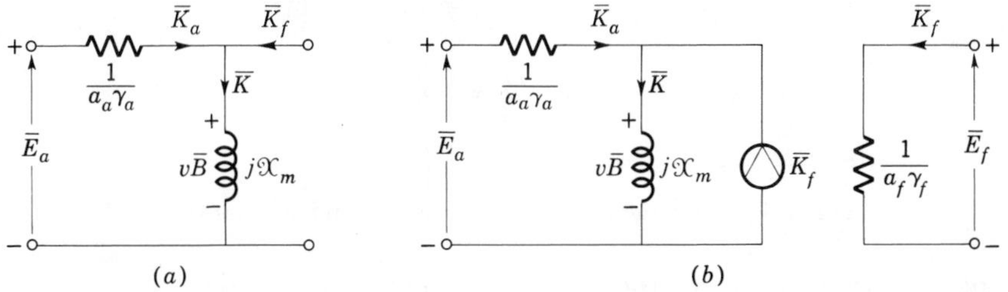

Fig. 7.4 Equivalent circuit of a synchronous converter in terms of the electro magnetic waves prevailing in the gap: (a) Overall armature circuit; (b) completed armature and field circuit.

entering current $\bar{K}_a$ and a voltage drop $v\bar{B}$, and these terminal conditions are identical with the current and voltage drop in the controlled source $v\bar{B}$ in Fig. 7.2. It follows, then, that we may combine the two circuits by replacing the $v\bar{B}$ source in Fig. 7.2 by the circuit of Fig. 7.3a. The result, which is shown in Fig. 7.4a, then portrays the introduction of the armature reaction and the field excitation into the equation expressing the generalized Ohm's law for the armature conductor.

To complete our picture, we must include the field circuit. This is very easy to do, since there is no time variation in the stator reference frame. Thus there can be no magnetic induction effect back from the armature to the field in the steady state. This means that the K_f which we impress when the armature is open-circuited, remains the same when load current does flow. In circuit terms, this steady-state situation amounts to having forward coupling from field to armature but no backward coupling from armature to field. (We shall see in Chaps. 8 and 9 that this condition results from the synchronous speed of the rotor, and no longer obtains in the transient case of the synchronous converter or in the general case of the induction converter.)

Keeping the above in mind, we write the axial or y component of the generalized Ohm's law for the *field* conductor in the stator reference frame. It will be recalled that the sinusoidal K_f wave is actually achieved from a single d-c exciting source by varying the distribution of the individual field conductors, as we have noted in Sec. 6.4. It is more convenient, however, to represent the actual field conductors by an equivalent uniform distribution having an equivalent thickness a_f and conductivity γ_f, and the single source by a source array as in Fig. 6.13*b*. Since the field conductors are at standstill in the stator reference frame,

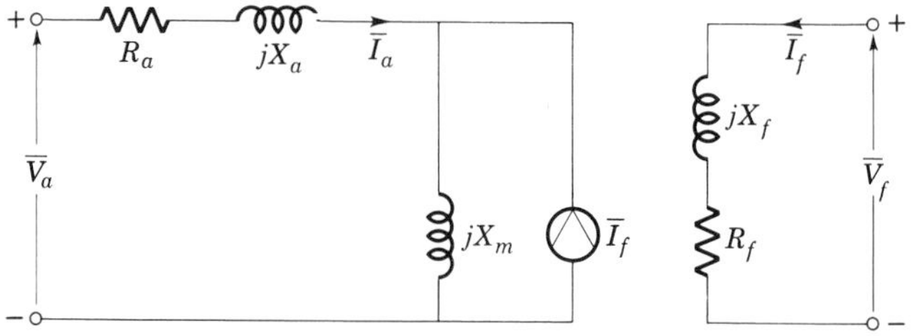

Fig. 7.5 Equivalent circuit in terms of terminal quantities.

the phasor equation for the equivalent field conductor is

$$\bar{E}_f = \frac{\bar{K}_f}{a_f \gamma_f} \tag{7.23}$$

According to our discussion above, the $\bar{K}_f$ wave that excites the right-hand port of the circuit of Fig. 7.4*a* holds constant as $\bar{K}_a$ varies with the operating condition. Consequently, it must be a *current source.* Moreover this $\bar{K}_f$ is determined by the d-c excitation of the field winding. This is formally stated by the simple Ohm's law relationship of Eq. (7.23). These facts are depicted in Fig. 7.4*b* which shows $\bar{K}_f$ as a *controlled current source.* If we compare Fig. 7.4 showing the equivalent circuit in terms of the electromagnetic waves prevailing in the gap, with Fig. 7.5 showing the equivalent circuit in terms of terminal voltages and currents which we will derive in Chap. 9, we observe that the latter differs only because of the presence of additional reactances in series with the resistances of the armature and field circuits. These reactances have very little effect on the performance of synchronous converters and can be either neglected or incorporated into the circuits external to the converter, as we have already done for the homopolar converter. This bit of information, when utilized jointly with the normalization method discussed in the next section, allows us to extend the scope of the circuit which we have derived here to the whole converter, so that our further treatment of the synchronous machines will be on the basis of this circuit.

It will be noted that the circuit of Fig. 7.4 does not show the coupling to the mechanical side of the converter, in contrast to the circuits of the earlier chapters. The reasons for this are plain:

1. We are dealing here with steady-state or constant v, so that there are no mechanical transients which affect the $v\bar{B}$ source in Fig. 7.2; consequently, there is no particular need to establish a circuit model which portrays the mechanical coupling.
2. It is $\bar{B}$, instead, which is not constant but, as we have seen, depends on $\bar{K}_a$ as well as on $\bar{K}_f$. Therefore, it is this dependency which we need to portray. As a matter of fact, we succeeded in obtaining a representation in terms of the constant-parameter circuits of Figs. 7.3 and 7.4 only because we exploited the steady-state condition. Thus, when v is constant, $v\bar{B}$ is linearly dependent on $\bar{B}$ and hence on $\bar{K}_f + \bar{K}_a$, so that the constant impedance representation becomes possible.

7.5 THE PERFORMANCE OF SYNCHRONOUS CONVERTERS IN TERMS OF INTERACTING WAVES

(a) Phasor Diagram

With our complete circuit model and phasor notation established, we seek still further means to display clearly and tersely the inherent relationships which govern the steady-state performance of the synchronous converter. Along these lines, a procedure that is of great value in helping us perceive the wave interrelationships as a single entity is the phasor diagram which expresses the relations given by Eqs. (7.15) and (7.17) to (7.19). Such a phasor diagram is shown in Fig. 7.6 for a particular case of overall generating operation. The phasor diagram and the circuit model of Fig. 7.4 are, of course, alternative ways of conveying the *same* information. The specific advantage of the phasor diagram is that it depicts graphically the magnitudes and relative angular displacements of the several waves as they appear along the periphery of the gap, while at the same time portraying their relationships.

Shown in the diagram are the four angles δ, σ, α, φ, which are defined as follows:

$$\delta = \text{angle by which } \bar{K}_f \text{ leads } \bar{K} \tag{7.24a}$$
$$\sigma = \text{angle by which } \bar{K}_f \text{ leads } \bar{K}_a \tag{7.24b}$$
$$\alpha = \text{angle by which } v\bar{B} \text{ leads } \bar{K}_a \tag{7.24c}$$
$$\varphi = \text{angle by which } \bar{E}_a \text{ leads } \bar{K}_a \tag{7.24d}$$

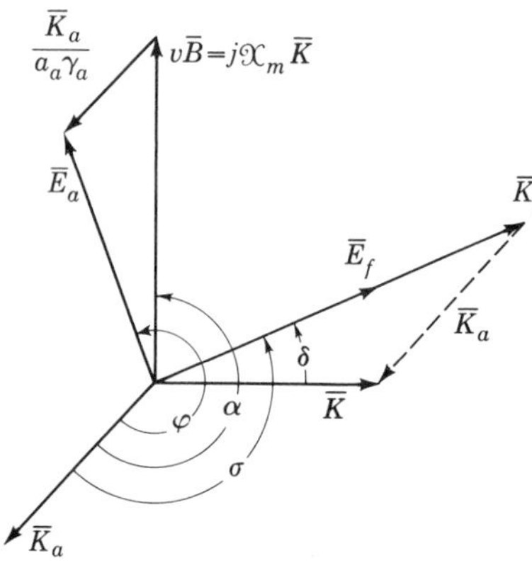

Fig. 7.6 Phasor diagram.

In connection with these angles, we may note that:

1. The angle δ is identical with the angle denoted by the same symbol in Eq. (6.15), Sec. 6.6, since the angle from $\bar{B}$ to $\bar{B}_f$ is plainly the same as the angle from $\bar{K}$ to $\bar{K}_f$; also, the angle σ is related to the angle λ previously defined in Eq. (6.19*a*), Sec. 6.6, since $\bar{B}_f$ leads $\bar{K}_f$ by 90°. Thus,

$$\lambda = \sigma + \frac{\pi}{2} \tag{7.25}$$

[The angle β of Eq. (6.16), Sec. 6.6, may also be related to the angles defined in this section. We shall not, however, have very much occasion to use this angle subsequently.]

2. In the generating case the equivalent impedance connected to the E_a terminal has a phase angle which by convention is equal to the angle by which $\bar{E}_a$ leads $-\bar{K}_a$. It follows that this impedance angle is then $\varphi \pm \pi$.
3. The three angles δ, α, σ are not independent but are linearly related by

$$\alpha = \sigma - \delta + \frac{\pi}{2} \tag{7.26a}$$

or

$$\sigma = \delta + \alpha - \frac{\pi}{2} \tag{7.26b}$$

This relationship is illustrated in the triangle of phasors (Fig. 7.7).

The phasor diagram and the angles defined in Eq. (7.24) also specifically relate to the local regions of operation which we have investigated in Sec. 6.6. To see this we turn to Fig. 7.8. Here part (*a*) shows the phasors $\bar{E}_a$, $v\bar{B}$, and $\bar{K}_a/a_a\gamma_a$ as in Fig. 7.6; part (*b*) the corresponding local variations for a half-cycle along the stator periphery. The figure also shows that the angles φ and α are sufficient to define the phase displacements of interest in both diagrams. The fact that clearly emerges from this presentation is that each of the operating zones per pole pitch is respectively *identical (in angular measure) to one of the interior angles of the triangle;* thus the braking zone is the angle between the $\bar{E}_a$ and $v\bar{B}$ phasors,

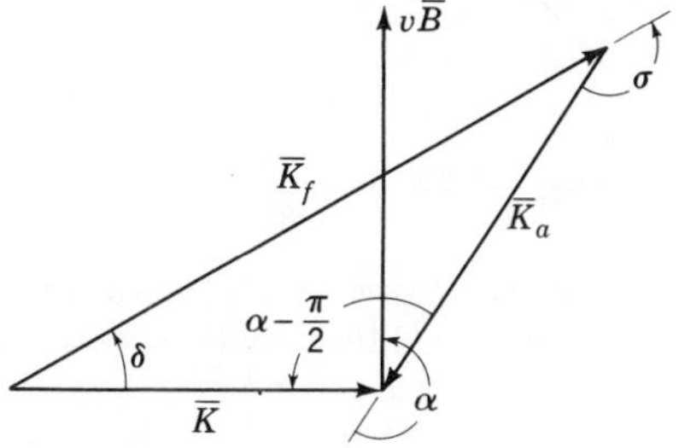

Fig. 7.7 Triangle of phasors.

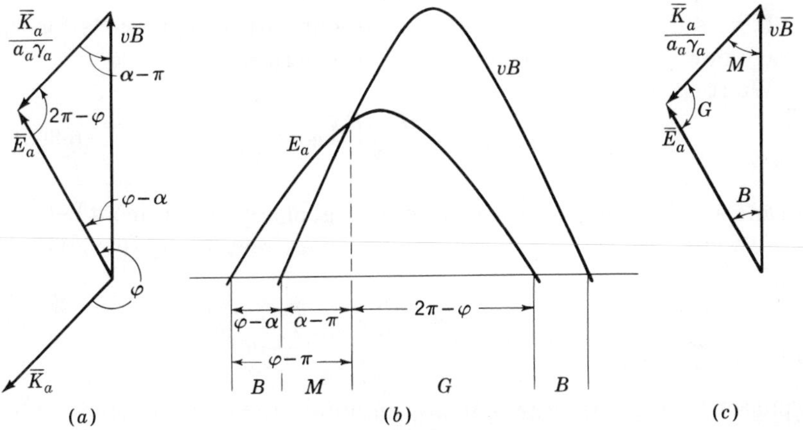

Fig. 7.8 Relation of local regions to phasor diagram.

the motoring zone is the angle between the $v\bar{B}$ and $\bar{K}_a/a_a\gamma_a$ phasors, and the generating zone is the angle between the $\bar{E}_a$ and the $\bar{K}_a/a_a\gamma_a$ phasors. This correspondence holds in each of the several modes of overall operation, and so we may, in general, draw the triangle as shown in Fig. 7.8*c*, with the angles marked as braking, motoring, or generating, respectively.

Example 7.3

A synchronous machine operates as a motor with negligible losses and a power factor of 0.707. What portion of the armature conductor operates in each of the conversion modes?

Solution

Since the losses are negligible, the $\bar{K}_a/a_a\gamma_a$ drop is very small, and so the angle between $\bar{E}_a$ and $v\bar{B}$ is negligible, i.e., $\alpha = \phi$. Since the average operation is motoring, the angle between $\bar{K}_a$ and $\bar{E}_a$ must be less than 180°, and is therefore arccos 0.707 = 45° (lead or lag is not specified, but plays no part in this problem). The phasor diagram is then as shown below. The interior angle between $v\bar{B}$ and $\bar{K}_a/a_a\gamma_a$ is then

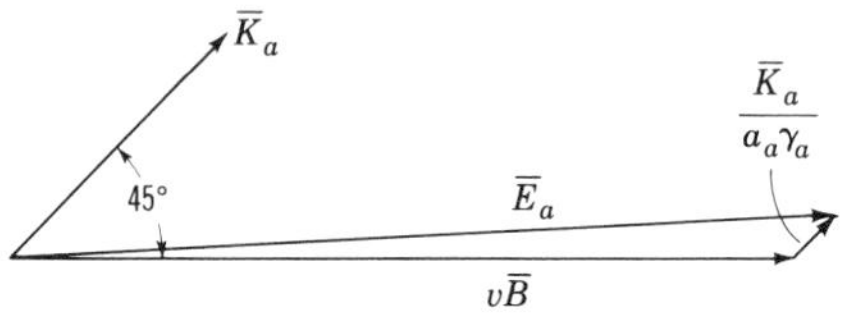

180° − 45° = 135°. Consequently, we see that 0 percent of the armature operates in the braking region, $\frac{45}{180}$ or 25 percent in the generating region, and $\frac{135}{180}$ or 75 percent in the motoring region.

(b) Alternative Expressions for the Average Power and Force Densities

It will also be useful to reformulate our earlier expressions for the average power and force densities in phasor terms.

We recall that

$$\langle p_{s,\text{conv}} \rangle = \frac{vK_{am}B_m}{2} \cos \alpha \tag{6.36b}$$

The angle α, defined as $\lambda - \delta$, is the electrical phase displacement between the K_a and E_a waves; to emphasize this, we may rewrite Eq. (6.36*b*) in the form

$$\langle p_{s,\text{conv}} \rangle = \frac{vK_{am}B_m}{2} \cos \angle_{v\bar{B}}^{\bar{K}_a} \tag{7.27}$$

In phasor terms, it is clear that we can obtain the required phase difference by adding the phase angle of one phasor to the negative of the phase angle of the other. To do this we use the *conjugate* phasor denoted by a star; i.e., if

$$\bar{K}_a = |\bar{K}_a|e^{-j\lambda} \tag{7.28a}$$

then

$$\bar{K}_a^* = |\bar{K}_a|e^{+j\lambda} \tag{7.28b}$$

It follows that we can write in phasor notation

$$\langle p_{s,\text{conv}} \rangle = \frac{K_{am}vB_m}{2} \cos \alpha = \frac{K_{am}}{\sqrt{2}} \frac{vB_m}{\sqrt{2}} \cos (\lambda - \delta)$$

$$= |\bar{K}_a| \times |v\bar{B}| \operatorname{Re} [e^{j\lambda} \times e^{-j\delta}] = \operatorname{Re} [\bar{K}_a^* v\bar{B}] = \operatorname{Re} [\bar{K}_a v\bar{B}^*] \tag{7.29}$$

In words this equation reads: "$\langle p_{s,\text{conv}} \rangle$ is given by the projection of the phasor $\bar{K}_a$ upon the phasor $v\bar{B}$ multiplied by the magnitude of the phasor $v\bar{B}$." Keeping this in mind, we see from the triangle of Fig. 7.7 that the projection of $\bar{K}_a$ and $v\bar{B}$ is exactly the same as the projection of $-\bar{K}_f$ on $v\bar{B}$; consequently, it is clear that we may alternatively write

$$\langle p_{s,\text{conv}} \rangle = |-\bar{K}_f|\,|v\bar{B}| \cos \angle_{v\bar{B}}^{-\bar{K}_f} = \text{Re}\,[(-\bar{K}_f^*)v\bar{B}] \qquad (7.30)$$

The identity of the expressions (7.29) and (7.30) has an immediate physical interpretation in terms of the tangential force densities. The surface tangential density on the armature conductor occurs from the interaction of the K_a and B waves as previously noted in Eqs. (6.33) and (6.34), and consequently has an average value given by

$$\langle f_{sx,a} \rangle = \text{Re}\,[\bar{K}_a\bar{B}^*] = \frac{1}{v}\langle p_{s,\text{conv}} \rangle \qquad (7.31)$$

which from Eq. (7.30) may be written

$$\langle f_{sx,a} \rangle = \text{Re}\,[(-\bar{K}_f^*)\bar{B}] \qquad (7.32)$$

In the same way, the average surface tangential force on the *field* conductor must be

$$\langle f_{sx,f} \rangle = \text{Re}\,[\bar{K}_f\bar{B}^*] = \text{Re}\,[\bar{K}_f^*\bar{B}] \qquad (7.33)$$

It follows directly from Eqs. (7.32) and (7.33) that

$$-\langle f_{sx,f} \rangle = \langle f_{sx,a} \rangle \qquad (7.34)$$

so that the forces on field and armature are equal and opposite, as we might indeed have expected from Newton's law of action and reaction.

The average converted power density may be written in several alternative forms. Thus we note that, from the definition of the angle δ and Fig. (7.6),

$$\angle_{v\bar{B}}^{-\bar{K}_f} = -\frac{\pi}{2} + \delta + \pi = \frac{\pi}{2} + \delta \qquad (7.35)$$

so that $$\langle p_{s,\text{conv}} \rangle = |\bar{K}_a|\,|v\bar{B}| \cos \alpha = -|\bar{K}_f|\,|v\bar{B}| \sin \delta \qquad (7.36)$$

Furthermore, by making use of Eq. (7.19*b*) and by applying the law of sines to the phasor triangle of Fig. (7.7), we obtain the additional identity

$$\langle p_{s,\text{conv}} \rangle = -\mathfrak{X}_m|\bar{K}_a|\,|\bar{K}_f| \sin \sigma \qquad (7.37)$$

In fact, the area of this phasor triangle measures the power since

$$\langle p_{s,\text{conv}} \rangle = 2\mathfrak{X}_m \times (\text{area of triangle}) \qquad (7.38)$$

Next, recalling that $\varphi = \lambda - \beta$ is the electrical phase displacement between the K_a and the E_a waves, we may rewrite Eq. (6.36a) in the form

$$\langle p_{s,\text{elec}}\rangle = \frac{K_{am}E_m}{2}\cos \angle_{E_a}^{\bar{K}_a} = \text{Re}\,[\bar{K}_a\bar{E}_a^*] = \text{Re}\,[\bar{K}_a^*\bar{E}_a] \tag{7.39}$$

The average dissipated surface power density may likewise be written in phasor terms by simply using the amplitude of $|\bar{K}_a|$. Thus

$$\langle p_{s,\text{diss}}\rangle = \frac{|\bar{K}_a|^2}{a_a\gamma_a} \tag{7.40}$$

Explicit formulas such as Eqs. (7.29) and (7.39) are often useful in providing insight and quick solutions to problems. As an illustration we consider the following example.

Example 7.4

Determine the efficiency of power conversion in the armature conductor for the conditions of Examples 6.3 and 7.1.

Solution

From the statement of the problem, we know that in mks units

$$\bar{E}_a = \frac{50.5}{\sqrt{2}} \qquad \bar{K}_a = \frac{K_{am}}{\sqrt{2}}e^{-j60^\circ} \qquad v = 50 \qquad \bar{B} = \frac{1}{\sqrt{2}}e^{-j(\delta-\beta)}$$

Also we have previously found $\delta - \beta = \sqrt{3}/100$ rad $= -0.992°$. Now

$$\langle p_{s,\text{elec}}\rangle = \text{Re}\,[\bar{K}_a^*\bar{E}_a] = \frac{50.5}{2}K_{am}\cos 60^\circ$$

$$\langle p_{s,\text{conv}}\rangle = \bar{K}_a^*v\bar{B} = \tfrac{50}{2}K_{am}\cos(60^\circ - \delta + \beta)$$

This is a *motoring* case, and

$$\eta_m = \frac{\langle p_{s,\text{conv}}\rangle}{\langle p_{s,\text{elec}}\rangle} = \frac{50}{50.5}\frac{\cos(60^\circ - \delta + \beta)}{\cos 60^\circ}$$

or

$$\eta_m = \frac{50}{50.5}\frac{\cos 60^\circ\cos(\delta-\beta) + \sin 60^\circ \sin(\delta - \beta)}{\cos 60^\circ}$$

$$= \frac{50}{50.5}[\cos(\delta-\beta) + \sin(\delta-\beta)\tan 60^\circ]$$

Since $\delta - \beta$ is small, we may use the approximation

$$\eta_m = (1 - \tfrac{1}{101})[1 + (\delta - \beta)\tan 60^\circ]$$

$$= \left(1 - \frac{1}{101}\right)\left(1 - \frac{\sqrt{3}}{100}\frac{1}{\sqrt{3}}\right)$$

$$= 1 - 0.02 = 0.98$$

(c) Per-unit System of Normalization

In many instances we shall use a per-unit system of representing the electrical quantities. This system is a particular conventional procedure for referring all quantities to rated values and thus expressing them as nondimensional fractions. Such a procedure has several advantages:

1. All converters, large or small, are described by per-unit parameters in the same ranges.
2. The numerical values of these parameters are convenient numbers of the order of one.
3. The solution of problems is simplified, especially in cases involving a number of machines and interconnected networks.
4. Constant scaling coefficients (such as those resulting from the integrations performed in the transition from field to terminal quantities) are eliminated.

The per-unit system which we adopt here is one in which all quantities are normalized to the magnitude of the rated armature current and voltage. The base quantities are then the rated values $|\bar{K}_a|_R$ and $|\bar{E}_a|_R$, and the per-unit current and voltage are the phasor quantities which are the ratio of the actual values to the respective values. Thus,

$$\bar{K}_{a,\text{p.u.}} = \frac{\bar{K}_a}{|\bar{K}_a|_R} \tag{7.41a}$$

$$\bar{K}_{f,\text{p.u.}} = \frac{\bar{K}_f}{|\bar{K}_a|_R} \tag{7.41b}$$

$$\bar{E}_{a,\text{p.u.}} = \frac{\bar{E}_a}{|\bar{E}_a|_R} \tag{7.41c}$$

Impedances are written per unit by referring them to $|\bar{E}_a/\bar{K}_a|$ under rated conditions: for example,

$$X_{m,\text{p.u.}} = \frac{\mathfrak{X}_m}{|\bar{E}_a|_R/|\bar{K}_a|_R} \tag{7.42}$$

To measure power in per unit in a manner consistent with the above procedure, we note that

$$\frac{\langle p_{s,\text{elec}}\rangle}{\langle p_{s,\text{elec}}\rangle_R} = \frac{|\bar{K}_a|\,|\bar{E}_a| \cos\varphi}{|\bar{K}_a|_R\,|\bar{E}_a|_R \cos\varphi_R} = \frac{1}{\cos\varphi_R}\,(|\bar{K}_a|_{\text{p.u.}}|\bar{E}_a|_{\text{p.u.}} \cos\varphi) \tag{7.43}$$

In Eq. (7.43), the quantity within the parentheses describes the actual power normalized against the base quantities in our per-unit system. It is natural and convenient to call this the per-unit power, although it is clear from the equation that we need to multiply by the additional constant factor $1/\cos\varphi_R$ to obtain the true ratio of average power to average rated power. Thus we define

$$\langle p_{s,\text{elec}}\rangle_{\text{p.u.}} = |\bar{K}_a|_{\text{p.u.}}|\bar{E}_a|_{\text{p.u.}} \cos\varphi \tag{7.44}$$

with the understanding that the value of this per-unit power is not unity under rated conditions, but rather is cos φ_R, so that the actual power ratio is obtained by dividing by cos φ_R, i.e.,

$$\frac{\langle p_{s,\mathrm{elec}}\rangle}{\langle p_{s,\mathrm{elec}}\rangle_R} = \frac{1}{\cos \varphi_R} \langle p_{s,\mathrm{elec}}\rangle_{\mathrm{p.u.}} \tag{7.45}$$

Example 7.5 illustrates the use of the per-unit system and the phasor diagram.

Example 7.5

A synchronous machine operates as a generator with negligible losses. Under rated conditions, the power output is 100 kw, the load is inductive with a power factor of 0.8, and the surface current density in the field is twice that in the armature. If the operating conditions (double excitation) are such that $|\bar{K}_f|$ is fixed and $|\bar{K}|$ cannot vary appreciably, find the per-unit gap reactance and the maximum overload power that can be drawn from the generator.

Solution

We first draw the per-unit phasor diagram for rated conditions. Choosing the

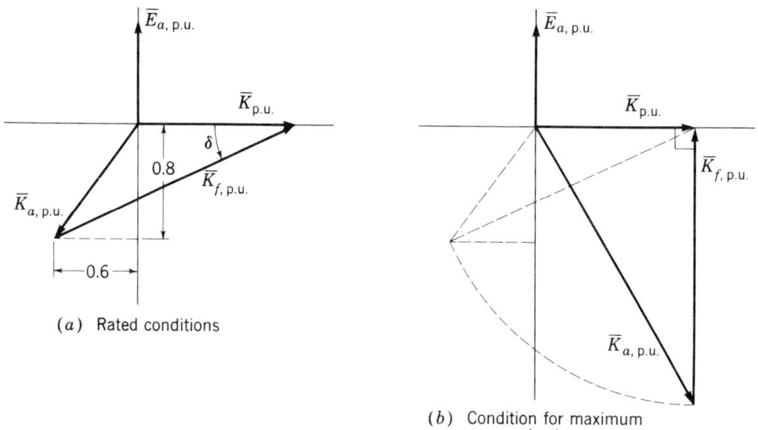

(a) Rated conditions

(b) Condition for maximum overload power

phase of $\bar{E}_a$ as zero, we then have

$$\bar{E}_{a,R,\mathrm{p.u.}} = \bar{E}_{a,R}e^{j0°} = 1 \qquad \bar{K}_{R,\mathrm{p.u.}} = -jK$$

Moreover

$$\cos(\varphi + \pi) = 0.8 \qquad \sin(\varphi + \pi) = \sqrt{1 - \cos^2(\varphi + \pi)} = 0.6$$

so that

$$\bar{K}_{a,R,\mathrm{p.u.}} = -0.8 + 0.6j$$

and

$$\bar{K}_{f,R,\mathrm{p.u.}} = \bar{K}_{R,\mathrm{p.u.}} - \bar{K}_{a,R,\mathrm{p.u.}} = -j(K + 0.6) + 0.8$$

Since we are told that $|\bar{K}_f|_R = 2|\bar{K}_a|_R$, it follows that $|\bar{K}_f|_{R,\mathrm{p.u.}} = 2$, and

$$4 = (K + 0.6)^2 + (0.8)^2$$

Thus, rejecting the negative root, we obtain $K = 1.23$ and $\bar{K}_{R;\text{p.u.}} = -j1.23$. Now

$$X_{m;\text{p.u.}} = \frac{\mathfrak{X}_m|\bar{K}_a|_R}{|\bar{E}_a|_R}$$

and since, for negligible losses, $\bar{E} \doteq v\bar{B}$,

$$X_{m;\text{p.u.}} = \frac{\mathfrak{X}_m|\bar{K}_a|_R}{|v\bar{B}|_R} = \frac{\mathfrak{X}_m|\bar{K}_a|_R}{\mathfrak{X}_m|\bar{K}|_R} = \frac{|\bar{K}_a|_R}{|\bar{K}|_R}$$

$$= \frac{|\bar{K}_a|_{R;\text{p.u.}}}{|\bar{K}|_{R;\text{p.u.}}} = \frac{1}{1.23} = 0.81$$

To find the overload power we note that $|\bar{K}_f|$, $|\bar{K}|$, and hence $|\bar{B}|$ are constant, and so it is advantageous to express the power in the form of Eq. (7.36):

$$\langle p_{s;\text{conv}} \rangle = -|\bar{K}_f||v\bar{B}| \sin \delta$$

As we have noted, $\bar{E}_a \doteq v\bar{B}$ when the losses are negligible, so that

$$\langle p_{s;\text{conv}} \rangle = -|\bar{K}_f||\bar{E}_a| \sin \delta$$

These equations show plainly that $\langle p_{s;\text{conv}} \rangle$ varies only because of changes in the angle δ. As will be discussed in the next section, a change in δ can be brought about in this case by increasing the mechanical input power. Since the maximum value of $\sin \delta$ is one for $\delta = 90°$, the maximum value of $\langle p_{s;\text{conv}} \rangle$ is given by

$$\langle p_{s;\text{conv}} \rangle_{\max} = -|\bar{K}_f||\bar{E}_a|$$

and since $\langle p_{s;\text{conv}} \rangle_R = -|\bar{K}_f||E_a| \sin \delta_R$, we have

$$\frac{\langle p_{s;\text{conv}} \rangle_{\max}}{\langle p_{s;\text{conv}} \rangle_R} = \frac{1}{\sin \delta_R}$$

The value of $\sin \delta_R$ is already known from the previous work, since

$$\bar{K}_{f;R;\text{p.u.}} = -j(1.23 + 0.6) + 0.8 = -1.83j + 0.8 = 2e^{-j\arccos(0.4)}$$

so that $\sin \delta_R = 0.4$ and $\delta_R = 23.6°$.
It follows that

$$P_{\max} = P_R \frac{\langle p_{s;\text{conv}} \rangle_{\max}}{\langle p_{s;\text{conv}} \rangle_R} = \frac{-100}{0.4} = -250 \text{ kw}$$

The condition for maximum power is illustrated in the phasor diagram (*b*). In this condition the phasors are $\bar{K}_{f;\text{p.u.}} = 2$ and $\bar{K}_{a;\text{p.u.}} = -2 - 1.23j$. As we see, the change in δ causes both the inphase and the 90° out-of-phase components of current to vary. This implies that the change in input power forces not only a corresponding change in the average output power but also a change in the amount of reactive volt amperes delivered.

7.6 STEADY - STATE OPERATING CHARACTERISTICS OF THE DOUBLY EXCITED SYNCHRONOUS CONVERTER

(a) Preliminary Remarks

Now that we have completed our circuit model and the development of our analytical tools, we are ready to study the performance of the doubly excited synchronous converter. As we have noted previously, the doubly excited converter has active electrical sources in both field and armature circuits. It follows that the average mode of operation may be any one of the three possible modes.

We shall assume that the field is excited by a steady d-c source which may be adjusted to give a desired value of K_f. As for the armature circuit, we shall consider the case of greatest practical interest. Here the armature is excited by the ideal polyphase "infinite bus," previously described in Chap. 6, with given constant voltage and frequency. Consequently, ω_e and $|\bar{E}_a|$ are both fixed and not subject to any variation; and with ω_e specified, it follows from the synchronous tie that the steady-state speed is fixed at $\omega = \omega_e/p$ for all operating conditions.

We shall assume that we have a high-efficiency converter with the ohmic drop so small as to be negligible. This means that the braking regions of power conversion are essentially missing, and only motoring or generating can occur.

With the ohmic drop neglected, the equation for the generalized Ohm's law in phasor notation reduces to

$$\bar{E}_a = v\bar{B} \tag{7.46}$$

and since $|\bar{E}_a|$ and v are fixed, this means that the magnitude $|\bar{B}|$ remains constant for all operating conditions. Consequently the magnitude of the total current density $\bar{K}$ must stay constant as well, since $\bar{K}$ and $\bar{B}$ are linearly related by the gap inductance.

(b) The Power Angle

In the presence of all this constancy, the reader may well wonder how the converter adjusts to different operating requirements when speed, armature voltage gradient, gap flux density, and field excitation are all fixed. Specifically, how does the converted power change? To answer this question, let us return to Eq. (7.36):

$$\langle p_{s,\text{conv}} \rangle = -|\bar{K}_f|\,|v\bar{B}| \sin \delta \tag{7.36}$$

We have deliberately chosen this particular form, because $|\bar{K}_f|$ and $|v\bar{B}|$ are the quantities that are here held constant. Thus it is clear that changes in $\langle p_{s,\text{conv}} \rangle$ stem solely from changes in the angle δ, which is the phase displacement between the K and K_f waves. What remains to be seen is how this change in δ is brought about in the converter. The following considerations will make it clear.

The K wave is always 90° out of phase with the vB wave, which, in the high-efficiency approximation as described by Eq. (7.46), is identical with the E_a wave. Now the E_a wave is a wave impressed on the armature conductors by the infinite bus. It moves with respect to the armature, the rotor in our case, with a constant phase velocity $v = (\tau/\pi)\omega_e$. Thus the $E_a = vB$ wave and, consequently, the K wave are completely dependent on the armature excitation, which is invariant to a change in operating conditions. In other words, a particular conductor on the rotor sees exactly the same value of K every $2\pi/\omega_e$ sec independently of the converter performance. It follows that the position taken by the K wave with respect to the rotor at every instant of time is not subject to change. The K_f wave, for its part, is fixed in its position relative to the stator. In order for a change in the angle δ to occur, then, there must actually be a change in the "average" position of the rotor as viewed from the stator, i.e., a shift in the relative displacement of the rotor and stator coordinate origins as viewed synchronously, or every $2\pi/\omega_e$ sec. Physically this shift is readily observable by noting the position of a mark on the rotor shaft under synchronous stroboscopic illumination.

In view of its direct control of the power, in this case the angle δ will be called the *power angle.*

(c) A Mechanical Analog

The dependence of the operating condition on the power angle which we have just noted can be usefully illustrated in terms of a mechanical analog. This analog stems from the expressions for force and torque on the armature. Starting with Eq. (7.31) and introducing Eqs. (7.36) and (7.19*b*), we find

$$\langle f_{sx} \rangle = -\frac{\mathfrak{X}_m}{v} |\bar{K}_f|\,|\bar{K}| \sin \delta \tag{7.47}$$

The total electromagnetic torque on the rotor is obtained by multiplying $\langle f_{sx} \rangle$ by the gap area and the gap radius. Thus,

$$\mathfrak{L} = -2\pi r_g{}^2 b \frac{\mathfrak{X}_m}{v} |\bar{K}_f|\,|\bar{K}| \sin \delta \tag{7.48}$$

which may be rewritten by introducing the gap inductance L_m and the pole pitch 2τ, as

$$\mathfrak{L} = -2p^2\tau b L_m |\bar{K}_f|\,|\bar{K}| \sin \delta \tag{7.49}$$

Suppose now that we had, as shown in Fig. 7.9, two concentric links of length $|\bar{K}_f|$ and $|\bar{K}|$, respectively, free to rotate around the center and connected by a perfectly elastic spring having a spring constant (force per unit elongation) equal to $2p^2\tau b L_m$. Referring to the figure, the spring then constitutes the variable third leg d of the triangle defined by the sides $|\bar{K}_f|$, $|\bar{K}|$, and the included angle δ. The tension in the spring (assuming zero free length) is d times the spring constant, or $(2p^2\tau b L_m)d$. Each link therefore transmits a torque to a normal axis through the center equal to the force times the moment arm $|\bar{K}| \sin \theta$; the clockwise torque transmitted by $|\bar{K}|$ is thus

$$\mathfrak{L} = -(2p^2\tau b L_m) d |\bar{K}| \sin \theta \tag{7.50}$$

Now the altitude upon link $|\bar{K}|$ can be expressed as

$$|\bar{K}_f| \sin \delta = d \sin \theta \tag{7.51}$$

Substituting (7.51) in (7.50), we then get

$$\mathfrak{L} = -2p^2\tau b L_m |\bar{K}| \, |\bar{K}_f| \sin \delta \tag{7.52}$$

which is identical with (7.49).

It follows that the torque associated with the electromagnetic coupling between the armature and field structures in the converter is

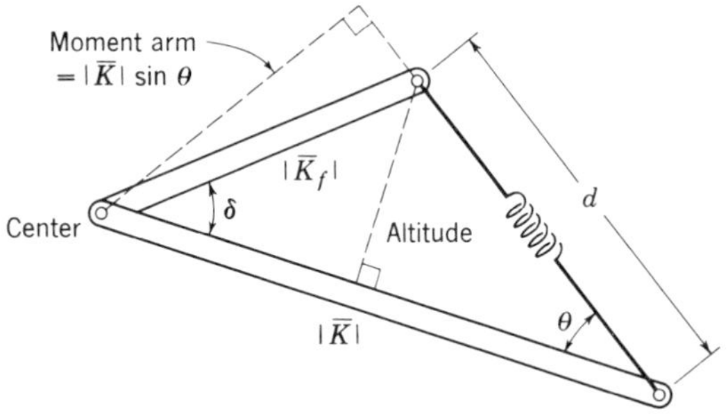

Fig. 7.9 Elastic analog of torque in doubly excited synchronous converter.

completely analogous to that associated with the elastic coupling of Fig. 7.9 between the "phasor links" which represent respectively the K and K_f waves. If we visualize the entire linkage of Fig. 7.9 rotating counterclockwise, as would be seen by an observer on the rotor, then for positive δ ($\bar{K}_f$ leading $\bar{K}$) the $\bar{K}_f$ or field link "pulls" the $\bar{K}$ (or terminal) link. Since the "terminals" are being forced to follow, we interpret this as a generating case. On the other hand, if the power angle δ is negative, the terminal link pulls the field link, and so we interpret this as a motoring case. These interpretations, of course, agree with the actual fact, so that this analog constitutes a correct picture of the electromagnetic torque behavior for all possible steady-state operating conditions.

(d) Mechanical and Electric Controls

We shall now follow through the details of the performance of a doubly excited high-efficiency converter under various conditions of operation. We assume that the rotor is mechanically coupled to a system which can either supply or absorb mechanical power at will. A practical example of such a situation could be a hydroelectric-energy-storage scheme designed to achieve maximum economy by relieving peak load demands on an electric-generating station.[1] In this case the synchronous

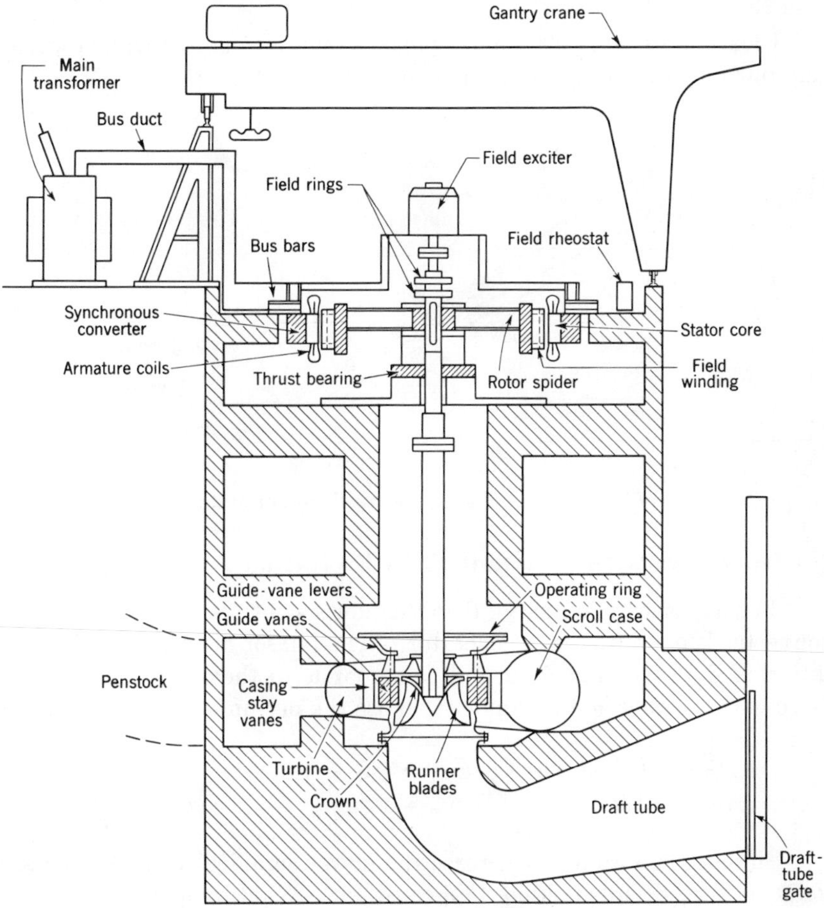

Fig. 7.10 Waterwheel generator and turbine (Francis type).

converter is coupled to a waterwheel which is connected by pipes to an elevated reservoir, as illustrated in Figs. 7.10 and 7.11. During periods of low demand for electricity, the synchronous converter acts as a motor and the waterwheel as a pump delivering water to the reservoir. The energy thus stored can be recovered, during periods of peak demand, by letting the waterwheel function as a turbine and the synchronous converter as a generator.

In such an electromechanical system there are only two possible ways to alter the operating conditions:

1. Control the power output on the mechanical side by appropriate means such as a throttle, a valve, or guide vanes.
2. Control the field current, for example by means of a rheostat.

Clearly both controls can be applied simultaneously; it will, however, help our understanding if we treat them separately.

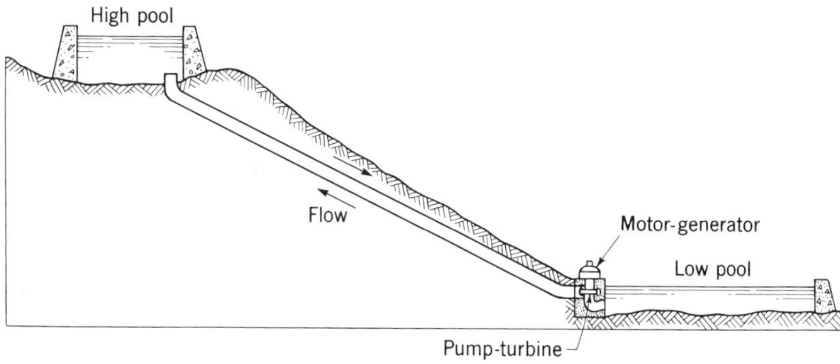

Fig. 7.11 Diagram of pumped storage system.

(e) Operation with Constant Field Excitation

Let us start by assuming that the power controls are set so that the converter is operating as a generator. The phasor diagram for this condition is shown in Fig. 7.12 and corresponds to the operating point P_1. Here we have chosen for simplicity to use the per-unit values of Example 7.5:

$$\bar{K}_{a,1} = -0.8 + 0.6j \qquad \bar{K}_{f,1} = 0.8 - 1.83j \qquad \delta_1 = 23.6°$$
$$\bar{K} = -1.23j \qquad \mathfrak{X}_m = 0.81 \qquad \langle p_s \rangle = -0.8$$

Suppose now that we increase the power supplied to the driver to a value of, say, 1 while holding $|\bar{K}_f|$ constant. What happens to the operating point of the converter? It is clear that the constancy of $\bar{K}$ and $|\bar{K}_f|$ and the change in the power make P move along the arc of a circle centered at the tip of the $\bar{K}$ phasor, from point P_1 to point P_2, as shown in Fig. 7.12.

The new value of δ at point P_2 is given by Eqs. (7.36) and (7.19b) as

$$\sin \delta_2 = \frac{-p_s}{\mathfrak{X}_m|\bar{K}_f|\,|\bar{K}|} = \frac{1}{0.81 \times 2 \times 1.23} = 0.5$$

and $\delta_2 = 30°$.

We may note here that a general relation which obtains in the high-efficiency synchronous converter is

$$X_{m,\text{p.u.}}|\bar{K}_R|_{\text{p.u.}} = 1 \tag{7.53}$$

This may be readily proved by using the definition of the per-unit

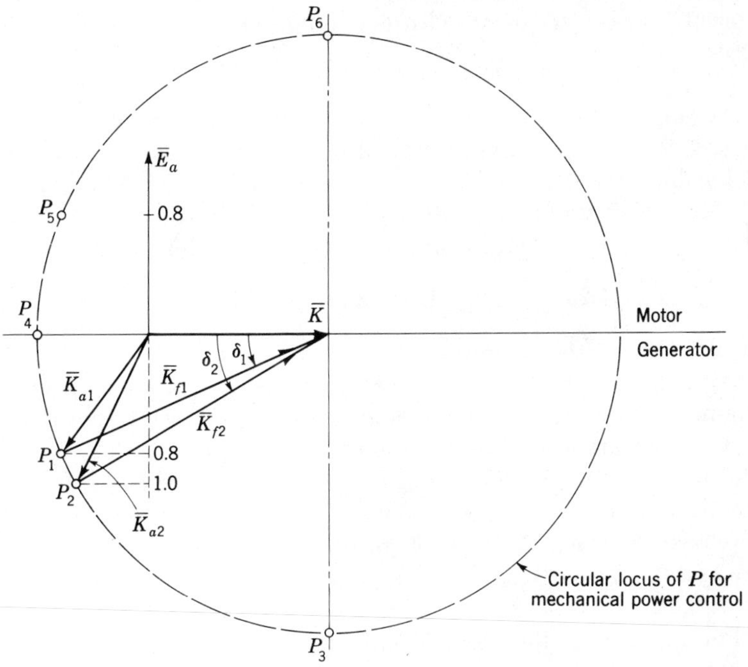

Fig. 7.12 Operation with constant field current.

quantities to give

$$X_{m,\text{p.u.}}|\bar{K}_R|_{\text{p.u.}} = \left(\frac{\mathfrak{X}_m|\bar{K}_a|_R}{|\bar{E}_a|_R}\right)\left(\frac{|\bar{K}|_R}{|\bar{K}_a|_R}\right)$$

$$= \frac{\mathfrak{X}_m|\bar{K}|_R}{|\bar{E}_a|_R}$$

and recalling that in the high-efficiency case,

$$|\bar{E}_a|_R = |v\bar{B}|_R = \mathfrak{X}_m|\bar{K}|_R$$

which establishes Eq. (7.53). Thus in our case $\mathfrak{X}_m|\bar{K}| = 0.81 \times 1.23 = 1$.

At point P_2 we find a new value for $\bar{K}_a$ which is readily determined by phasor subtraction, taking $\bar{K}$ as the reference phasor. Thus,

$$\bar{K}_{a,2} = \bar{K} - \bar{K}_{f,2} = -(1.23 - 2\cos\delta_2)j - 2\sin\delta_2 = -1 + 0.5j$$

This follows from the fact that as the average power is brought to a new level while $|\bar{K}_f|$ is kept constant, $\bar{K}_f$ must change in phase, and $\bar{K}_a$ in phase and amplitude, in such a way that their sum always equals $\bar{K}$.

If we continue to increase the power in this way, we reach a maximum often called *pull-out* power, since it represents a boundary condition for steady-state synchronous operation. As was shown in Example 7.5, this occurs at P_3 for $\delta = 90°$ with maximum power

$$\langle p_s\rangle_{\max} = -|\bar{K}_f|\,|\bar{E}_a| = -2$$

If, on the other hand, we decrease the driver power starting from P_1, δ will decrease. If this process is continued to the point where the power supplied by the driver is zero, then $\delta = 0$, and both $\bar{K}_f$ and $\bar{K}_a$ are collinear with $\bar{K}$ and 90° out of phase with $v\bar{B}$. This is designated as point P_4, the borderline between generator and motor action. Here we plainly have

$$\bar{K} = 1.23 \qquad \bar{K}_f = 1 \qquad \bar{K}_a = -0.77 \qquad \langle p_s\rangle = 0$$

We will return to this condition of operation later.

With $|\bar{K}_f|$ still held constant, we now adjust the power control in the mechanical system so that it can *absorb* power. With the speed and the direction of rotation fixed by the infinite bus, this means that the torque direction must reverse. Thus, our former driver is now being driven as a mechanical load. When this is done, the operating point continues to move clockwise along the circle of constant $|\bar{K}_f|$ into the second quadrant where $\delta < 0$. In particular, if $\langle p_s\rangle = +0.8$, we reach the point P_5 where $\delta = -23.6°$.

For negative δ, the phase displacement between $\bar{K}_a$ and $v\bar{B}$ is less than 90° and we have average motoring operation. Again the power can be increased up to an upper bound only. The power reaches a maximum value of

$$\langle p_s\rangle_{\max} = |\bar{K}_a|\,|E_a| = +2$$

at P_6 where $\delta = -90°$.

(f) Operation with Constant Torque

We now turn to the case in which we hold the power control on the mechanical side fixed and we change the field current. What happens to the operating point in this case? We know that the speed is fixed, because of the fixed frequency and the synchronous tie. Therefore, if we keep the torque constant, the average power must also remain constant. According to Eq. (7.30), this means that the projection of $-\bar{K}_f$ on $v\bar{B}$ (and, consequently, the projection of $\bar{K}_f$ itself on $v\bar{B}$) must maintain a constant value as $|\bar{K}_f|$ is varied. Thus the point P will move along a line drawn through the initial operating point, which is perpendicular to $v\bar{B}$

and parallel to $\bar{K}$. Along this locus the area delimited by the phasor triangle of the current densities remains constant. The locus described by P as the field current is varied, while the power is held constant at a level corresponding to P_2, is thus the lowest horizontal line in Fig. 7.13. Similarly, the variations of field current for the powers of P_4 and P_5 give the other two loci shown. If, for example, starting from P_2, we increase $|\bar{K}_f|$ to a value of 3, the angle δ must decrease, as we see from Eq. (7.36), so as to compensate for the increase in $|\bar{K}_f|$. The value of δ for the point

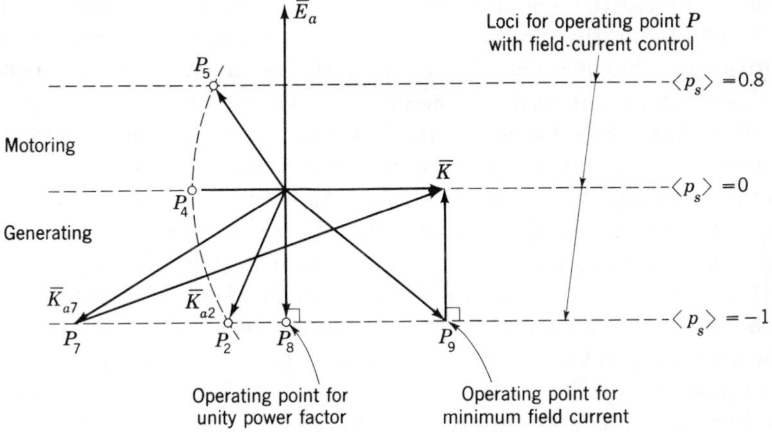

Fig. 7.13 Operation with constant torque.

P_7, which corresponds to $|\bar{K}_f| = 3$ is

$$\sin \delta_7 = \frac{-\langle p_s \rangle}{\mathfrak{X}_m |\bar{K}_f|\, |\bar{K}|} = \frac{1}{0.81 \times 3 \times 1.23} = 0.333$$

and $\delta = 19.5°$.

The new $\bar{K}_a$ is found by phasor subtraction:

$$\bar{K}_{a,7} = \bar{K} - \bar{K}_f = (-1.23 + 3 \cos \delta_7)j - 1 = -1 + 1.59j$$

It is clear that the variation of $|\bar{K}_f|$ changes $\bar{K}_a$ in phase and amplitude in such a way that $|\bar{K}|$ and $\langle p_s \rangle$ stay constant. We can be more specific: When the torque and power, and hence the inphase component of $\bar{K}_f$, are kept constant, the variation of $|\bar{K}_f|$ causes the out-of-phase component of $\bar{K}_f$ to vary. Now the total $\bar{K}$, which is the *magnetizing current*, lags $\bar{E}_a$ by 90°, and is therefore made up of the out-of-phase components of $\bar{K}_a$ and $\bar{K}_f$. Since $\bar{K}$ must remain constant, the variation in the out-of-phase component of $\bar{K}_f$ must be compensated by an appropriate change in the out-of-phase component of $\bar{K}_a$, so that control of the field current means control of the reactive volt-amperes of the converter (which we shall henceforth abbreviate as var).

From the point of view of a generating station, we can look at the change in operation from P_2 to P_7 as being required by the connection of an additional purely reactive load. It appears then, that for a given power, the more inductive the load, the higher the requirement for field-excitation current. This, in turn, sets a requirement for the design of the generator which increases its size and cost. Thus the demand for var affects the investment of capital and is therefore reflected in the fixed charges, whereas the demand for power determines the fuel consumption and is reflected in the running costs of a power plant. As a consequence, utilities not only charge for the actual power consumed but also impose a penalty for operation with low inductive power factor.

Since most electric loads are inductive, a generator is normally called upon to provide a lagging out-of-phase component of $-\bar{K}_a$, i.e., a leading out-of-phase component of $\bar{K}_a$. As it turns out, it is convenient to separate the supply of power from var in practice as well as in concept. This means that inductive electric loads may be supplied by synchronous converters connected in parallel, one or more of which may have an output of pure var and no watts. This zero-power mode of operation is illustrated by point P_4 in Fig. 7.13. Here both $\bar{K}_f$ and $\bar{K}_a$ are purely out of phase with $|\bar{K}_f| > |\bar{K}_a|$, so that the excess $|\bar{K}_f|$ "spills over" in the armature circuit as a leading $\bar{K}_a$. The machine thus appears to the line as a pure capacitance; hence, the name *synchronous condenser* or *synchronous capacitor* for this type of operation. Furthermore, within the limitations imposed by thermal considerations, we can increase the "size" of this capacitor simply by increasing $\bar{K}_f$ without requiring any active power. Operation as a synchronous condenser is used extensively for power-factor correction in large-scale electric-power distribution systems.

Large synchronous motors, likewise, are mostly operated with a leading out-of-phase component of $\bar{K}_a$, for power-factor compensation. This operation is exemplified by P_5 in Fig. 7.13. We conclude then that the synchronous converter normally operates with a $\bar{K}_a$ that leads $\bar{E}_a$ by an angle between 0 and π.

Clearly, although in general we are not interested in this mode of operation, the machine could also be made to represent an inductive load, simply by reducing the field current. In fact, when the out-of-phase component of $\bar{K}_f$ equals $\bar{K}$, as for example in P_8, then the armature current is in phase with the source voltage. Further reduction of the field current yields a reactive component of $\bar{K}_a$ which lags behind $\bar{E}_a$, thus denoting an inductive load. It is important to realize that there exists a lower bound below which $|\bar{K}_f|$ cannot be decreased if synchronous steady-state operation has to be maintained. A little thought will show that this minimum corresponds to the condition where $\bar{K}_f$ and $\bar{E}_a \doteq v\bar{B}$ are perfectly in phase, as, for example, at P_9. Since, then, $\delta = 90°$, this lower bound is, according to Eq. (7.36),

$$|\bar{K}_f| = \frac{|\langle p_s \rangle|}{|\bar{E}_a|} \tag{7.54}$$

and for $\langle p_s \rangle = \langle p_s \rangle_R$, $\bar{E}_a = \bar{E}_{aR}$, Eq. (7.54) becomes, in per unit,

$$|\bar{K}_f|_{\text{min,p.u.}} = \cos \varphi_R \tag{7.55}$$

(g) Concluding Remarks

Let us now summarize what we have learned from the preceding discussion.

1. The doubly excited machine with impressed $|\bar{E}_a|$ is constrained to maintain a constant speed, a constant $|\bar{B}|$, and a constant $|\bar{K}|$, regardless of the amount of power converted or the mode of operation. It therefore adjusts its operating point in a way compatible with these constraints, by varying its power angle δ.
2. The amount of power that is converted is determined entirely on the mechanical side of the converter. Whether the operation is motoring or generating, and how much power is converted, is determined by the mechanical driver or load, as long as $\langle p_s \rangle$ does not exceed an upper bound.
3. Variation of $|\bar{K}_f|$ has no effect on power, as long as a minimum bound in $|\langle p_s \rangle|/|\bar{E}_a|$ is observed. The armature current $\bar{K}_a$ adjusts to variations in $|\bar{K}_f|$ so as to keep the power and the total excitation $\bar{K}$ constant; thus $|\bar{K}_f|$ serves to control the power factor at the armature terminals. A special example of this is the synchronous condenser, which is adjusted for zero power and excess $|\bar{K}_f|$, i.e., $|\bar{K}_f| > |\bar{K}|$: the excess $|\bar{K}_f|$ then "spills over" to the other side of the gap and becomes a leading capacitive $|\bar{K}_a|$.

7.7 OVERLOAD CAPABILITY AND PER - UNIT GAP REACTANCE

In the previous section we have examined how a specific synchronous converter, when doubly excited, performs in the steady state under a variety of operating conditions. Another question of great interest to those who use and design synchronous converters is how to compare the performance of two different machines under identical operating conditions and, in particular, under rated or full-load conditions. We have seen, for example, that for a given field excitation there exists an upper bound for the power output, both as a generator and as a motor. It is important that this upper bound be well in excess of the rated power. This not only enables the machine to cope for a short time with extraordinary load demands but also, as we shall see in Chap. 8, has a great bearing on the problem of stability of operation. We then ask ourselves how we can determine the *overload ratio*, i.e., the ratio of the maximum possible power output to rated power output under conditions of rated field excitation.

It is easy to show that the overload ratio of the high-efficiency synchronous converter is a function only of the power factor and the per-unit gap reactance; in fact,

$$\text{Overload ratio} = \frac{1}{\cos \varphi_R} \sqrt{1 + \frac{1}{X^2_{m,\text{p.u.}}} - \frac{2 \sin \varphi_R}{X_{m,\text{p.u.}}}} \tag{7.56}$$

This relation may be readily derived in a number of different ways. For example, we begin by noting from the previous section that the maximum power for fixed $|\bar{K}_f|$ is

$$\langle p_s \rangle_{\max} = |\bar{K}_f|\,|\bar{E}_a| \tag{7.57}$$

and since

$$\langle p_s \rangle_R = |\bar{K}_a|_R |\bar{E}_a|_R \cos \varphi_R \tag{7.58}$$

we have

$$\text{Overload ratio} = \frac{|\bar{K}_f|_{\text{p.u.}}}{\cos \varphi_R} \tag{7.59}$$

Let us take $\bar{E}_a$ as a reference phasor, i.e., $E_{a,R,\text{p.u.}} = e^{j0}$; then

$$\bar{K}_{R,\text{p.u.}} = -j|\bar{K}_R|_{\text{p.u.}}$$

and $\bar{K}_{a,R,\text{p.u.}} = e^{-j\varphi_R}$ from the definition of the angle φ. It follows that

$$\bar{K}_{f,R,\text{p.u.}} = \bar{K}_{R,\text{p.u.}} - \bar{K}_{a,R,\text{p.u.}} \tag{7.60a}$$

$$= -j|\bar{K}_R|_{\text{p.u.}} - e^{-j\varphi_R} \tag{7.60b}$$

Now from Eq. (7.53) we know that

$$|\bar{K}_R|_{\text{p.u.}} = \frac{1}{X_{m,\text{p.u.}}} \tag{7.53}$$

Thus Eq. (7.60*b*) becomes

$$\bar{K}_{f,R,\text{p.u.}} = -j\frac{1}{X_{m,\text{p.u.}}} + j \sin \varphi_R - \cos \varphi_R \tag{7.60c}$$

so that

$$|\bar{K}_f|_{\text{p.u.}} = |\bar{K}_{f,R}|_{\text{p.u.}} = \sqrt{1 + \frac{1}{X^2_{m,\text{p.u.}}} - \frac{2 \sin \varphi_R}{X_{m,\text{p.u.}}}} \tag{7.61}$$

and Eq. (7.56) follows directly from Eqs. (7.61) and (7.59).

Examination of (7.59) indicates immediately that the price paid for a large overload ratio is a large value of $|\bar{K}_f|_{\text{p.u.}}$, i.e., a relatively large value of field current compared to armature current. Since this means larger losses for a given rating and power factor, a larger machine results. This is the toll that is exacted for large overload capability. Less directly, we also see from Eq. (7.56) that for unity power factor or for leading currents ($-\pi < \varphi_R < 0$), the overload ratio increases as $\mathfrak{X}_m$ decreases. A small value of $\mathfrak{X}_m$ means a large gap which requires a large $|\bar{K}_f|$ to excite the desired voltage level; so this is consistent with the previous conclusion. This is also true for lagging currents ($\pi > \varphi_R > 0$) as long as $X_{m,\text{p.u.}}$ is less than $1/\sin\varphi_R$, which is generally the case. Moreover, for a given $\mathfrak{X}_m$, a larger overload ratio results for power factor leading† rather than lagging. To illustrate these concepts, we consider the following example.

Example 7.6

Determine the necessary per-unit field current and gap reactance if a synchronous motor is to have an overload ratio of 2 when the rated power factor is (*a*) 0.8 leading, (*b*) 0.8 lagging.

Solution

Here

$$\cos\varphi_R = 0.8 \qquad \sin\varphi_R = \mp 0.6$$

so that, from Eq. (7.59),

$$|\bar{K}_f|_{\text{p.u.}} = 2 \times 0.8 = 1.6 \qquad \text{both cases}$$

and, from Eqs. (7.60*c*) and (7.61),

$$(1.6)^2 = \left(\frac{1}{X_{m,\text{p.u.}}} \pm 0.6\right)^2 + (0.8)^2$$

or

$$\frac{1}{X_{m,\text{p.u.}}} = \sqrt{1.92} \mp 0.6 = 1.386 \mp 0.6 = \begin{cases} 0.786 \\ 1.986 \end{cases}$$

or

$$X_{m,\text{p.u.}} = \begin{cases} 1.27 & \text{leading} \\ 0.503 & \text{lagging} \end{cases}$$

7.8 STEADY-STATE PERFORMANCE OF THE SINGLY EXCITED SYNCHRONOUS CONVERTER; VOLTAGE REGULATION

By definition, the singly excited converter has an active electrical source in the field circuit only, and the external armature circuit is completely passive. It follows that the overall mode of power conversion must now be *generating*.

The external armature circuit is again assumed to be of a balanced polyphase nature, as well as being passive; consequently, it consists of several identical passive impedances, equal in number to the number of

† The power factor, being an even function of the phase angle φ, is not sufficient to specify the sense of the reactive component of current. For this purpose we shall henceforth add the adjectives *leading* or *lagging* to indicate whether the out-of-phase component of the current phasor ($\bar{K}_a$ for motoring, $-\bar{K}_a$ for generating), leads or lags by 90°, respectively, the voltage phasor ($\bar{E}_a$).

armature conductors and connected to them through the individual slip-ring pairs, as indicated in Fig. 7.14.

We have heretofore considered only cases in which $\bar{E}_a$ is impressed from an active source, so that the present case is an innovation. Caution might then prompt us to beware of new difficulties, but under the present circumstances of symmetry and uniformity there are none, and we may directly apply the techniques employed in the case of double excitation,

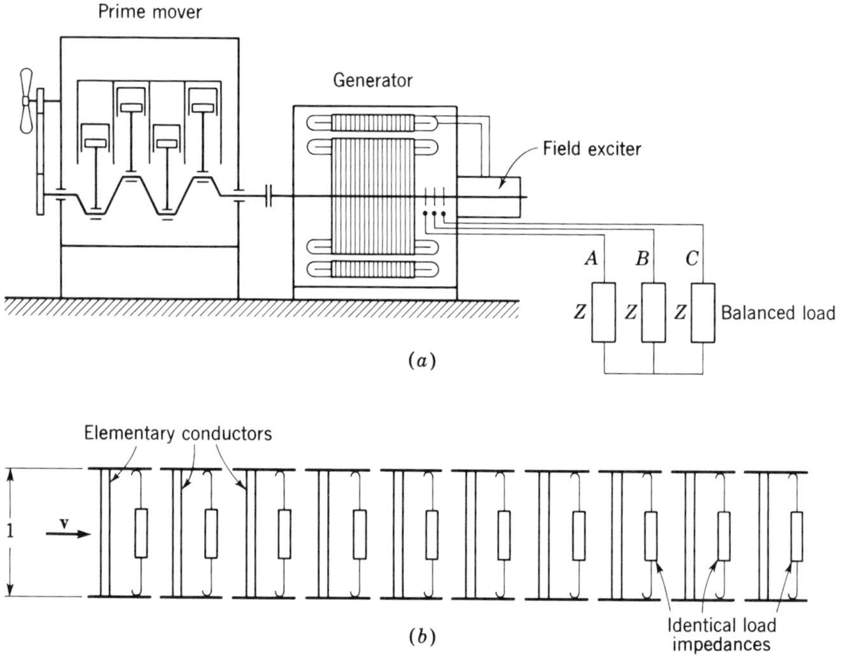

Fig. 7.14 Singly excited synchronous converter: (*a*) Motor-generator set with balanced three-phase load; (*b*) equivalent loading of the conductors per unit length of the armature.

where E_a is kept constant by the infinite bus. To demonstrate that this is so, suppose for a moment that the synchronous converter is connected to an infinite bus and operates as a generator; $\bar{K}_a$ is then a phasor which is more than 90° out of phase with $\bar{E}_a$, and $\varphi > 90°$. The E_a and K_a experienced by a particular phase of the external circuit may then be found by determining E_a and K_a in the particular armature conductor connected by slip rings to the phase in question. We would thus obtain the actual time variations from the phasor quantities by applying Eq. (7.14*c*), and find that E_a and K_a in this phase are indeed sinusoidal time variations which are out of phase by precisely the same angle as the phasors themselves. It follows that the voltages and currents in the converter and the external circuit are completely unchanged if we replace the source in this phase by an impedance whose phasor value in terms consistent with the equivalent circuit of Fig. 7.4 is $-\bar{E}_a/\bar{K}_a$. Since the magnitudes and relative phase displacement of $\bar{E}_a$ and $\bar{K}_a$ are exactly the same for *any* of the phases, it also follows from the above that the active sources in the armature circuit may be replaced by the balanced polyphase array of identical passive impedances without changing any of the conditions in the converter. Conversely, if such a load is used in the singly excited case, we may find the details of the power conversion by solving the circuit model of Fig. 7.4 with the equivalent phasor impedance† replacing the E_a source.

Once we understand the above, we can readily pursue the details of the steady-state performance of the singly excited synchronous converter. It is immediately clear that the speed is *not* necessarily constant, since this is tied to the electric frequency which is no longer dictated by the infinite bus, as in the case of double excitation. Any requirement of constant speed now must be met by auxiliary control devices operating on the driver. Let us suppose that this is done, so that the driver acts as a source of constant mechanical speed, with its power output varied to suit by the control devices. We shall also assume that the field current is not varied.

Under these circumstances, it is typically desired that the armature terminal voltage, as measured by $|\bar{E}_a|$, hold constant for varying electric loads. Actually $|\bar{E}_a|$ varies from no load to full load, and this variation is called *voltage regulation*. A plot of terminal voltage against load current or load admittance is called a *regulation curve*.

The primary reason for the existence of voltage regulation in the synchronous converter is the presence of the armature reaction. In the ideal high-efficiency machine with ohmic drop neglected, the armature reaction is, in fact, the only reason for the voltage regulation. The detailed analysis in this case is easy to perform, and is given below.

In the high-efficiency case we neglect the ohmic drop, and so the air-gap equivalent circuit is reduced as shown in Fig. 7.15, where the equivalent load impedance $-\bar{E}_a/\bar{K}_a$ is written as $Ze^{j(\varphi+\pi)}$, in conformity with the definition of φ given previously. It is clear that

$$\bar{E}_a = \frac{\bar{K}_f}{1/j\mathfrak{X}_m - (1/Z)e^{-j\varphi}} = \frac{j\bar{K}_f\mathfrak{X}_m}{1 - j(\mathfrak{X}_m/Z)e^{-j\varphi}} \tag{7.62}$$

and the no-load condition is $Z \to \infty$, so that

$$\bar{E}_{a,\text{N.L.}} = j\bar{K}_f\mathfrak{X}_m \tag{7.63}$$

† The relation between the equivalent phasor impedance and the actual terminal impedance will be discussed in Chap. 9.

Taking the ratio of (7.62) to (7.63), we have, since $|\bar{K}_f|$ is constant,

$$\left|\frac{\bar{E}_a}{\bar{E}_{a,\text{N.L.}}}\right| = \left|\frac{1}{1 - j(\mathfrak{X}_m/Z)e^{-j\varphi}}\right| = \left|\frac{1}{1 - (\mathfrak{X}_m/Z)(\sin\varphi + j\cos\varphi)}\right|$$

$$= \frac{1}{[1 + (\mathfrak{X}_m/Z)^2 - 2(\mathfrak{X}_m/Z)\sin\varphi]^{\frac{1}{2}}} \tag{7.64}$$

It is clear that the voltage regulation, as measured by $|\bar{E}_a|/|\bar{E}_a|_{\text{N.L.}}$ depends only on two parameters: the load power factor and the ratio $\mathfrak{X}_m/Z$. To illustrate the behavior of the regulation, we calculate a few

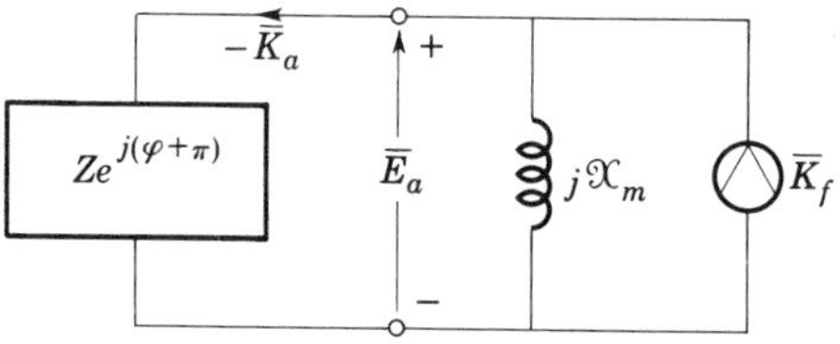

Fig. 7.15 High-efficiency singly excited synchronous converter.

Table 7.1 VALUES OF $|\bar{E}_a|/|\bar{E}_a|_{\text{N.L.}}$

$\sin\varphi$ \ $\mathfrak{X}_m/Z$	0.2	0.5	0.8	1.0	1.2
+1	1.250	2.0	5.0	∞	5.0
$+\frac{1}{2}$	1.090	1.155	1.090	1.0	0.898
0	0.980	0.893	0.780	0.707	0.640
$-\frac{1}{2}$	0.898	0.756	0.640	0.577	0.525
−1	0.833	0.672	0.555	0.5	0.455

values, as listed in Table 7.1. These values are plotted in the universal regulation curves of Fig. 7.16 for $\mathfrak{X}_m/Z$ up to 1.2; the full-load value of $\mathfrak{X}_m/Z$ is, of course, the per-unit gap reactance, which is a number in the vicinity of unity. From an inspection of these curves, we may conclude that:

1. For resistive ($\sin\varphi = 0$) or inductive ($\sin\varphi < 0$, $\varphi - \pi > 0$) loads, the regulation gets worse as $\mathfrak{X}_m/Z$ is increased. For a given Z at full load, one can therefore improve the regulation in the design stage by making $\mathfrak{X}_m$ smaller, through the physical means of increasing the gap size. This, however, entails using a large $\bar{K}_f$ to establish the necessary no-load gap flux, so that there must be more dissipated heat and, consequently, a large gap

surface is required. Thus machine size and cost increase as better regulation is required.

2. For capacitive ($\sin \varphi > 0$, $\varphi - \pi < 0$) loads, the regulation is generally better than for inductive loads, provided the converter operates in the range $\mathfrak{X}_m/Z \doteq 2 \sin \varphi$. In fact, for

$$\mathfrak{X}_m/Z = +2 \sin \varphi$$

$|\bar{E}_a|/|\bar{E}_a|_{\text{N.L.}} = 1$. However, to get good regulation over a large range of Z, it is still necessary to have a small $\mathfrak{X}_m$, and the comments given above for the inductive case apply here as well.

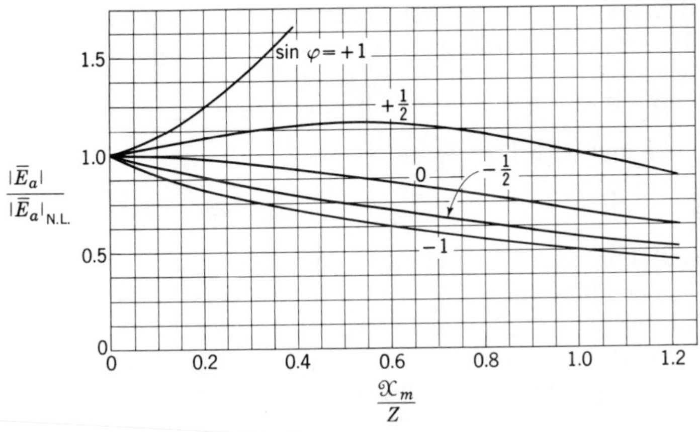

Fig. 7.16 Universal regulation curves.

When the term *voltage regulation* is applied to a numerical value, it conventionally means the quantity $|\bar{E}_a|_{\text{N.L.}}/|\bar{E}_a|_R - 1$, the fractional deviation in output voltage over the full range. From Eq. (7.64), it is clear that the percent regulation is therefore given by

$$\%\ \text{regulation} = 100 \left\{ \left[1 + \left(\frac{\mathfrak{X}_m}{Z_R} \right)^2 - 2 \frac{\mathfrak{X}_m}{Z_R} \sin \varphi_R \right]^{\frac{1}{2}} - 1 \right\} \quad (7.65a)$$

or, in terms of per-unit quantities,

$$\%\ \text{regulation} = 100[(1 + X_{m,\text{p.u.}}^2 - 2X_{m,\text{p.u.}} \sin \varphi_R)^{\frac{1}{2}} - 1] \quad (7.65b)$$

Since it is generally expensive to achieve good regulation by using a large gap, one might seek feasible alternatives. Such an alternative might be to use a smaller gap and keep the terminal voltage constant by controlling the field excitation. In order to hold the terminal voltage perfectly constant, it is easy to show that the field current would have to vary according to

$$\frac{|\bar{K}_f|}{|\bar{K}_f|_{\text{N.L.}}} = \left[1 + \left(\frac{\mathfrak{X}_m}{Z}\right)^2 - 2\,\frac{\mathfrak{X}_m}{Z}\sin\varphi\right]^{\frac{1}{2}} \tag{7.66}$$

If we compare Eqs. (7.65*a*) and (7.66), we see that a machine with inherently poor regulation for constant $|\bar{K}_f|$ will require large variations in $|\bar{K}_f|$ to hold $|\bar{E}_a|$ constant. A fast-acting control system to accomplish this in a large machine is not easy to achieve, and the economics of this possible alternative must be carefully weighed against the more direct expedient of designing the larger air gap.

The preceding considerations should have made evident that regulation and overload ratios are very much related. In fact, if we express Eq. (7.64) for rated conditions in per unit, we obtain

$$|E_{a,\text{N.L.}}|_{\text{p.u.}} = \sqrt{1 + X^2_{m,\text{p.u}} - 2X_{m,\text{p.u.}}\sin\phi_R} \tag{7.67}$$

which compared with Eq. (7.56) gives

$$|\bar{E}_{a,\text{N.L.}}|_{\text{p.u.}} = X_{m,\text{p.u.}}\cos\varphi_R \times \text{overload ratio} \tag{7.68}$$

Both regulation and overload ratio are a measure of the magnetizing reactance and therefore of the degree of coupling between the field and the armature circuit. The smaller $\mathfrak{X}_m$, the smaller the effect of the armature reaction, and the better the performance. The overload ratio is usually given as a design specification when ordering a motor and the regulation when ordering a generator.

Example 7.7

If the generator of Example 6.7 has to be designed for a regulation of 134 percent and the rated power factor is lagging, determine $X_{m,\text{p.u.}}$, g, and K_f for the two- and four-pole machines.

Solution

Introducing $\sin\varphi_R = -\sqrt{1-(0.85)^2} = -0.526$ in Eq. (7.65*b*), we have

$$134 = 100\{[1 + X^2_{m,\text{p.u.}} + 2X_{m,\text{p.u.}}(0.526)]^{\frac{1}{2}} - 1\}$$

Solving for $X_{m,\text{p.u.}}$, we find $X_{m,\text{p.u.}} = 1.654$. From Eq. (7.21),

$$g = \frac{\mu_0 r_g^2}{p^2\mathfrak{X}_m}\,\omega_e = \frac{\mu_0 r_g^2 K_{a,R}}{p^2 X_{m,\text{p.u.}}E_{a,R}}\,\omega_e$$

$$\frac{r_g}{p} = 0.583\ \text{m} \qquad K_{a,R} = \frac{1.81}{\sqrt{2}} \times 10^5\ \text{amp/m}$$

$E_a \doteq vB = 220 \times \dfrac{0.815}{\sqrt{2}}$ volts/m, so that

$$g = \frac{4\pi \times 10^{-7} \times (0.583)^2 \times 1.81 \times 10^5}{1.654 \times 220 \times 0.815}\,377 = 0.098\ \text{m}$$

To find K_f we observe that

$$E_{a,\text{N.L.},\text{p.u.}} = X_{m,\text{p.u.}} K_{f,\text{p.u.}} = 1.34 + 1$$

$$K_{f,\text{p.u.}} = \frac{2.34}{1.654} = 1.4$$

$$K_f = K_{f,\text{p.u.}} K_{a,R} = 1.4 \times \frac{1.81}{\sqrt{2}} \times 10^5 = 1.79 \times 10^5 \text{ amp/m}$$

7.9 SUMMARY

In this chapter we have learned the following:

1. A current distribution, in the form of a current sheet, whose intensity varies sinusoidally along the gap, is related by Ampère's law to a flux-density distribution, whose component perpendicular to the gap is likewise a sinusoidal wave having the same wavelength and displaced in space from the K wave by $\pi/2$ rad. The particular side of the gap on which the current sheet is located is immaterial.
2. Since the interacting waves in the gap of a heteropolar converter all have the same periodicity and are at standstill with respect to each other, only two numbers are required to describe them. We can then conveniently use complex or phasor notation. In this notation, the same phasor can be interpreted to represent a spatial or temporal distribution as well as a traveling wave, depending on the viewpoint taken.
3. In terms of phasors, the relations governing the performance of synchronous converters reduce to algebraic equations which can be represented by equivalent circuits containing three parameters only; two of these characterize the conductivity of the materials used on each side of the gap and the third the reluctance of the gap.
4. A graphical representation which has the advantage of displaying the angular displacements of the several waves as they appear along the periphery of the gap is the *phasor diagram.*
5. Synchronous converters are mostly used with double excitation. In this case the operating condition is determined by two external controls: one acting on the shaft torque sets the level for the conversion of power; the other acting on the field current sets the level for the circulation of var. Any change in the watts or var handled by the converter results in a change of the angular displacement between the waves impressed on the rotor and on the stator. Such a change is observable with stroboscopic illumination of the rotor.

   A synchronous converter can draw its magnetizing current

from both the field and the armature supply; when overexcited, it acts as a "condenser" supplying var to inductive consumers.

6. A doubly excited converter can deliver power up to a certain maximum limit. This depends on the excitation and the magnetizing reactance. Higher overload capability corresponds to lower values of $X_{m,\text{p.u.}}$, so that this parameter offers a convenient index for comparison of different machines.

This same index is also used to compare the performance of different machines when operated with single excitation.

REFERENCES

1. Friedlander, Gordon D.: Pumped Storage: An Answer to Peaking Power, *IEEE Spectrum*, October, 1964, pp. 58–75.

PROBLEMS

7.1 Prove that the homopolar magnetic flux contributed by the constant term in Eq. (7.5*b*) must vanish when the symmetry condition $\partial(\ \ )/\partial y = 0$ is satisfied.

7.2 The winding of a heteropolar converter with cylindrical symmetry and uniform gap consists of identical coils, all carrying the same current I_c and placed three per pole in equidistant slots, as shown.

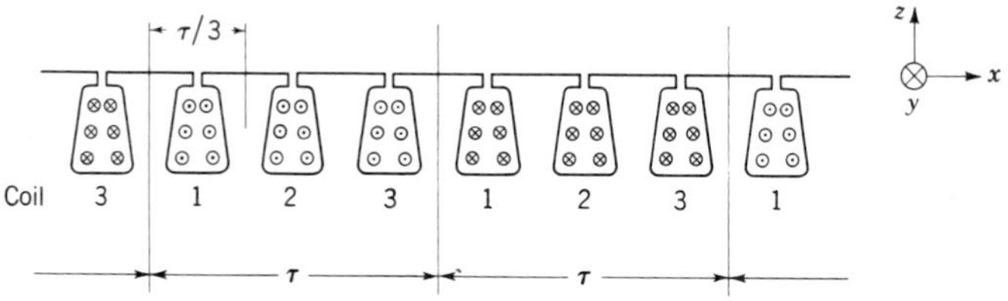

(*a*) Determine the harmonic components K_{mn} in the Fourier expansion of the current density

$$K = \sum_{1}^{n} K_{mn} \cos \frac{n\pi x}{\tau}$$

when the current density contributed at each slot is approximated by an impulse function in x.

(*b*) Substituting K_{mn} for K_m and τ/n for τ in the exact expression for B_z given by Eq. (B.28*b*), Appendix B, evaluate the flux distribution set up by the harmonic current sheet of order n.

(*c*) For $g/\tau = 10^{-2}$ and $n = 11$ compare the value of B_{zn} with that of the fundamental B_{z1}. What conclusion can you draw about the importance of the higher harmonic contribution to the overall flux buildup?

7.3 Determine the amplitude, wavelength, and phase velocity of the traveling B_z waves set up in the uniform gap of a heteropolar converter by a coil of negligible cross section carrying the current $i(t) = I_m \cos \omega t$. For this purpose expand K in a Fourier series, and relate B_z to K by means of the approximate equation (7.7).

7.4 A symmetrical two-phase heteropolar converter has two identical windings displaced along the gap by $\pi/2$ electrical degrees. In each winding the coils are connected in series, and their density n varies sinusoidally along the gap. If i_1 and i_2 are the currents flowing in the first and second coils, respectively, then the surface current densities associated with each winding can be represented as

$$K_1 = i_1 n \cos \frac{\pi}{\tau} x$$

$$K_2 = i_2 n \cos \left(\frac{\pi}{\tau} x - \frac{\pi}{2} \right)$$

(*a*) Prove that if

$$i_1 = I_m \cos \omega t$$

and

$$i_2 = I_m \cos \left(\omega t - \frac{\pi}{2} \right)$$

there exists in the gap only one flux-density wave B_z; determine its amplitude.

(*b*) Generalize the result for a symmetrical m-phase converter.

(*c*) Repeat part (*a*) graphically by representing each of the four constituent traveling waves by phasors appropriately phase-shifted and rotating in the appropriate directions.

7.5 In the generator of Examples 4.5 and 4.6 determine the rated field current density K_f, and draw the complete phasor diagram. Assume that the gap length is $g = 3.5$ cm; note that the value given for B in Example 4.5 is the rms value, and the value obtained in part (*c*) of Example 4.6 is the rms value of K_a.

7.6 (*a*) Determine the required field current density when the generator of the previous problem is feeding an inductive load with a 0.8 power factor and the same $K_{a,\text{rms}}$.

(*b*) What is the extent of the generating motoring and braking regions?

7.7 (*a*) If the motor of Example 6.1*c* is of the synchronous type, under what circumstances can the output power be maintained at the rated level of 1 kw when the motor is connected to a 330-volt supply?

(*b*) If the motor is designed to operate at the rated voltages with a 0.75 power factor leading and a 100 percent overload capability, what will be the maximum power output when connected to the 330-volt supply? Assume that frequency and flux density remain the same. Make the high-efficiency approximation.

7.8 The parameters of a synchronous generator are determined by performing open-circuit and short-circuit tests.

(*a*) Evaluate the magnetizing reactance $\mathfrak{X}_m$ if, on open circuit with $v = 10$ m/sec and $K_{f,\text{rms}} = 5 \times 10^3$ amp/m, the electric field measures $E_{a,\text{rms}} = 2.5$ volts/m.

(*b*) Evaluate the specific resistance $1/\gamma_a a_a$ if, under short-circuit conditions with the same v and K_f, the tangential force density measures $f_s = 80$ newtons/m^2.

(*c*) Determine the rated power output per unit surface of the converter if, under rated conditions as a generator with resistive load

$$v = 100 \text{ m/sec} \qquad K_f = 10^4 \text{ amp/m} \qquad \eta_g = 0.995$$

7.9 Because of the ever-increasing demand for electric power and the economy stemming from the operation with larger units, turbogenerators become obsolescent while still in perfect condition. Therefore the smaller units are often used as synchronous condensers for power-factor correction. Determine the maximum amount of var that a turbogenerator rated 40 Mw with a 0.8 power factor lagging can deliver as a synchronous condenser if its $X_{m,\text{p.u.}} = 1.2$ and K_f cannot exceed the rated value.

7.10 The design specification for a 60-cycle synchronous motor call for:

Output power: 350 hp
Power factor: 0.8 leading
Speed: 250 rpm
Conversion efficiency: 0.9935
Overload capability: 2.5

Considering as limiting factors,

$$K_{a,\mathrm{rms}} = 33{,}500 \text{ amp/m}$$
$$v = 18.5 \text{ m/sec}$$
$$B_{\mathrm{rms}} = 0.63 \text{ weber/m}^2$$
$$\gamma = 5 \times 10^7 \text{ mhos/m}$$

determine p, r_g, b, a, $\mathfrak{X}_m$, g, and K_f.

7.11 A high-efficiency synchronous motor delivers a rated power of 400 hp, when operating with a power factor of 0.8 leading. What is the maximum power that this motor can deliver when the field current and busbar voltage are maintained constant at their rated value? The magnetizing reactance is $X_{m,\mathrm{p.u.}} = 1.2$.

7.12 A synchronous generator delivers a rated power of 200 Mw with a power factor of 0.8 lagging. If, under rated conditions of operations, the surface density of field current is $K_{f,\mathrm{p.u.}} = 1.6$:

(*a*) What is the per-unit value of the magnetizing reactance $X_{m,\mathrm{p.u.}}$?

(*b*) What is the per-unit value of the terminal voltage if the armature circuit is opened while the field current is maintained at its rated full-load value?

7.13 A synchronous generator is designed to operate under rated load conditions with a power factor of 0.85 lagging. The generator is connected on the electrical port to a busbar of rated voltage and is driven at the mechanical port with the rated torque and speed.

(*a*) What is the minimum value of $K_{f,\mathrm{p.u.}}$ that is required for stable operation?

(*b*) Will the maximum value of K_f also be determined by stability considerations?

7.14 A high-efficiency synchronous motor is supplied with power by an identical synchronous generator which is driven by a constant-speed engine. Each machine has a magnetizing reactance of 0.577 per unit. The field currents of the two machines are adjusted so that they operate at rated terminal voltage, rated armature current, and unity power factor when the motor shaft load has its rated value. With the field currents held constant, the shaft load on the motor is then slowly increased. Using a phasor analysis based on the overall circuit model of the two machines, answer the following questions:

(*a*) Does the power factor change?

(*b*) What is the ratio of the maximum overload power that the motor can deliver under these conditions, to rated power?

Hint: Find an expression for the converted power in terms of the field-current phasors $\bar{K}_{f,1}$ and $\bar{K}_{f,2}$.

7.15 A synchronous motor with $X_{m,\mathrm{p.u.}} = 1.2$ is supplied by an identical synchronous generator. Under rated full-load conditions the motor operates with a power factor of 0.8 leading. Determine:

(*a*) The per-unit field current density in both motor and generator at full load,

(*b*) The overload capability of the motor when its field current and terminal voltage are held fixed at the rated value.

(*c*) The overload capability of the motor when the field currents in both motor and generator are held fixed at a value corresponding to rated full-load operation.

Neglect the armature resistance of both motor and generator.

chapter 8
DYNAMIC PERFORMANCE OF SYNCHRONOUS CONVERTERS

8.1 INTRODUCTION

In this chapter we study the performance of the synchronous converter under conditions that involve changes in the converter speed. We shall refer to the converter performance and characteristics under these conditions as the *dynamic performance* and *dynamic characteristics*.

The dynamic characteristics of the synchronous converter do not generally of themselves lead to useful applications (in contrast to the homopolar converter where pulsed operation is useful). They rather create a *stability problem*, that is, a possibility of losing steady-state operating conditions with either a runaway or a stalled machine as the consequence. Thus we shall find ourselves considering questions such as the following:

1. Will a singly excited synchronous converter ever become unstable, and if so, under what circumstances?
2. What is the process whereby the doubly excited synchronous converter changes its power angle from one stable operating point to another? Can this process ever become unstable?
3. Why are some apparently valid steady-state operating points actually unstable?
4. Can a synchronous motor start by itself? If not, why not, and what must be done to cause it to start?

We shall find that the stability problem is associated with the armature reaction and its interaction with the impressed excitation, and we shall encounter the possibility of instability in both the singly and doubly excited cases. We shall see that in the former the unstable region of operation is manifested in the torque-speed characteristic at constant load and K_f; in the latter, instead, it is manifested in the power-angle δ characteristic for given excitations E_a and K_f.

The principal design parameter affecting the dynamic performance turns out to be the per-unit gap reactance. The smaller this reactance, i.e., the larger the gap size, the better the stability of the converter. This means, however, that good stability, along with good regulation, are achieved at the price of a larger and more expensive machine.

8.2 THE QUASI - STEADY STATE

In order to analyze the dynamic performance and answer the questions asked in the introduction, we must, of course, have the analytic tools with which to proceed. At first glance, it does appear that we are indeed inadequately prepared to undertake a transient analysis at this point, since our whole study of the synchronous converter so far has been based on the initial assumptions of constant speed and perfectly sinusoidal time variation.

Strictly speaking, we would have to abandon the phasor approach, go back to the very beginning, and reformulate the entire problem in time-variable or transform terms. Actually, we shall *not* do this. This apparent sleight of hand is made possible by the fact that the electromechanical transient cases with which we will concern ourselves here are actually *slow* or *quasi-steady-state* transients.

To understand what is meant by these descriptions we must keep in mind the factors that govern the dynamic behavior of the converter. These are (1) the inertial effects associated with the change of the kinetic energy stored in the moving mass of the rotor and coupled mechanical systems, and (2) the capacitive and inductive effects associated with the change of the electromagnetic energy stored in the converter and connected electric circuits. A change in operating point then requires changes in these energies, changes that take place in finite times since the available power is finite.

If the characteristic times which describe the duration of these changes were of comparable magnitude with the electrical period $T = 2\pi/\omega_e$, the electromagnetic and inertial effects would couple in a complex way and make the analysis quite difficult. Fortunately, however, this is not the case in the high-power machines, which are the most important among the synchronous converters, because the electromagnetic and mechanical quantities vary only slightly in one electrical period. The mechanical transient is, of course, associated with the rotor inertia, and in large machines this inertia is so large that the time required to change the rotor speed is in the order of seconds, i.e., some two orders of magnitude larger than the electrical period. On the other hand, the characteristic times which describe the rate of change of the energy stored in the electromagnetic field when the operating point changes are much shorter in duration than the mechanical transients. We find that the resulting electrical transients generally last for a few line cycles, i.e., for times in the order of $\frac{1}{10}$ sec in 60-cps converters.

Inasmuch as both the mechanical and electromagnetic variables do not change appreciably in one line cycle, the alternating electromagnetic quantities become sinusoidal functions of time *with phase and amplitude that vary slowly, without much change in one cycle.* Moreover, since there is at least one order of magnitude separating the mechanical and electromagnetic transients, and since the latter are relatively small and of short duration, it is quite accurate to neglect them when considering the mechanical response. In so doing, we are in essence assuming that in the dynamical situation of interest, the electrical steady state is achieved instantaneously, whereas the mechanical transient endures.

Similarly it is quite accurate to evaluate the electrical response of the system separately by assuming that during the transient the speed remains constant. This will not be done here since the problem then reduces to one of ordinary stationary electric networks.[1]

In view of the above discussion, it is clear that we may consequently use the *electrical steady-state analysis*, maintaining the convenience of the equivalent circuit and the phasor representation, in conjunction with the differential equations of the mechanical transient state. This combination of electrical steady state and mechanical transient is what we have denoted as the *quasi-steady state.*

The reader may rightly ask at this point: How accurate is the quasi-steady-state approximation or, in other words, what is the upper bound of the error made by resorting to this type of analysis? To this question there is no simple answer. Since a similar problem arises in connection with the evaluation of the response of time-varying systems with amplitude- or frequency-modulated inputs, the reader is referred to the specialized literature on the subject.[2] In this context we will accept as a "rule of thumb" that the quasi-steady-state analysis is justified when the time constant of the mechanical transients τ_m is an order of magnitude larger than that of the electrical transients τ_e, and we will limit ourselves to formulating this criterion in terms of the relevant system parameters.

We begin by defining $1/\tau_m$ as the logarithmic time derivative† of the angular velocity ω,

$$\left|\frac{1}{\tau_m}\right| = \left|\frac{d}{dt}(\log \omega)\right| = \left|\frac{d\omega/dt}{\omega}\right| \tag{8.1}$$

† This is equivalent to the assumption that the rotor angular velocity changes exponentially: i.e., $\omega = \omega_0 \exp(-t/\tau_m)$.

so that we can write

$$\left| \frac{d\omega/dt}{\omega} \right| \leq \frac{1}{10\tau_e} \tag{8.2}$$

Then assuming, as mentioned, that

$$\tau_e \doteq 10 \frac{1}{f_e} \tag{8.3}$$

where f_e is the electric frequency, we can write

$$\left| \frac{d\omega/dt}{\omega} \right| \leq \frac{f_e}{100} \tag{8.4}$$

so that, since

$$f_e = \frac{\omega_e}{2\pi} = \frac{p\omega}{2\pi} \tag{8.5}$$

we have

$$\left| \frac{d\omega/dt}{\omega^2} \right| \leq \frac{p}{200\pi} \tag{8.6}$$

Now the largest possible acceleration occurs when the peak developed

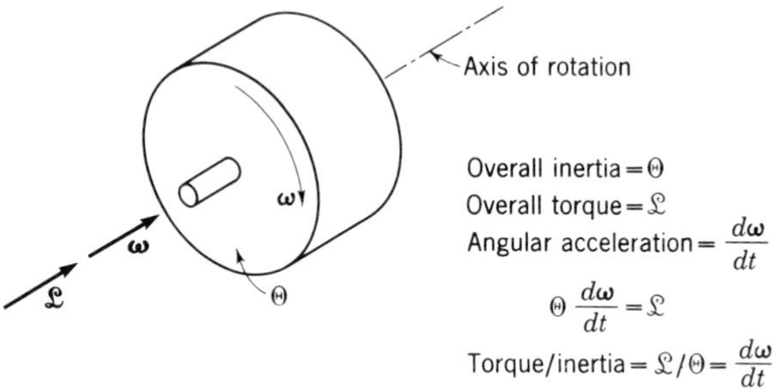

Fig. 8.1 Operation with pure inertia load; significance of the torque/inertia parameter $\mathfrak{L}/\Theta$.

torque $\mathfrak{L}_m$ acts solely on the inertia Θ, of the mechanical system, or, according to Fig. 8.1 and Newton's law, when

$$\left| \Theta \frac{d\omega}{dt} \right| = \mathfrak{L}_m \tag{8.7}$$

Thus a sufficient condition to satisfy Eq. (8.6) results when $d\omega/dt$ is replaced by $\mathfrak{L}_m/\Theta$, i.e., when

$$\frac{\mathfrak{L}_m}{\Theta\omega^2} < \frac{p}{200\pi} \tag{8.8}$$

We may give Eq. (8.8) a physical interpretation by looking ahead a little. As we shall see later, a synchronous machine under double excitation performs slowly decaying oscillations around a stable operating point with radian frequency ω_h, where $\omega_h^2 = p\mathfrak{L}_m/\Theta$. Consequently Eq. (8.8) may be written

$$\frac{\omega_h^2}{\omega^2} < \frac{p^2}{200\pi} \tag{8.9a}$$

or, since

$$\omega = \omega_e/p$$

$$\frac{\omega_h}{\omega_e} < 0.04 \tag{8.9b}$$

Thus the quasi-steady state occurs when the natural frequency of oscillation is sufficiently small compared with line frequency. As shown in Table 8.1 for different types of 60-cps synchronous machines, typical values of this frequency ratio are indeed in this range.

Table 8.1 TYPICAL NORMALIZED NATURAL FREQUENCIES OF OSCILLATIONS IN LARGE 60-CYCLE SYNCHRONOUS CONVERTERS†

Type	Speed, rpm	ω_h/ω_e
250-Mva turbine generators	3,600	0.017
100-Mva turbine generators	3,600	0.015
50-Mva turbine generators	3,600	0.013
250-Mva turbine generators	1,800	0.012
100-Mva turbine generators	1,800	0.011
50-Mva turbine generators	1,800	0.010
100-Mva waterwheel generators	514	0.013
50-Mva waterwheel generators	514	0.015
100-Mva waterwheel generators	120	0.016
50-Mva waterwheel generators	120	0.017
Synchronous condensers	3,600	0.026
Synchronous motors	514	0.020

† These figures include the inertial contributions of the coupled mechanical systems.

8.3 STABILITY OF THE SINGLY EXCITED CONVERTER

(a) Torque-Speed Characteristic

We shall first apply our quasi-steady-state analysis to study the stability of the singly excited synchronous converter and answer question 1 of Sec. 8.1. To do this we shall consider the constant $|\bar{K}_f|$ high-efficiency case of Sec. 7.6*e* and a load characterized by resistance R and inductance L at the $\bar{E}_a$ terminals. Figure 7.4 then becomes Fig. 8.2.

On the mechanical side, we shall assume that the rotor is driven by a *constant-torque* prime mover such as a piston engine operating without speed regulator.

The initial question has a purely steady-state character: What speed does this system operate at, and how do we find it? Since the frequency is not specified, the synchronous tie offers no clue. We must then proceed to express the developed torque actually as a function of speed (or frequency), equate this to the known applied torque, and solve for the speed

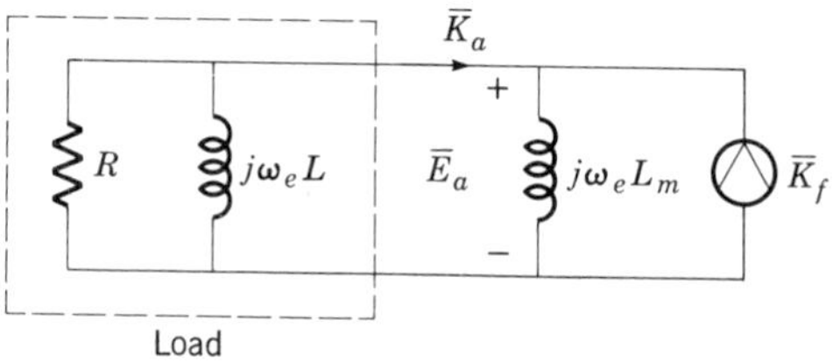

Fig. 8.2 Singly excited generator with RL load.

(or frequency). To do this, we know from Eq. (7.29) that the power converted per unit surface is

$$\langle p_{s,\text{conv}} \rangle = \text{Re}\,[\bar{K}_a^* v\bar{B}] = \text{Re}\,[-\bar{K}_f^* v\bar{B}] \qquad (7.29a)$$

and in the high-efficiency case $\bar{E}_a \doteq v\bar{B}$, so that

$$\langle p_{s,\text{conv}} \rangle \doteq \text{Re}\,[-\bar{K}_f^* \bar{E}_a] \qquad (8.10)$$

Since the surface of the active conductor is $2\pi r_g b$, the overall developed torque $\mathfrak{L}_d$ is then

$$\mathfrak{L}_d = 2\pi r_g b \frac{\langle p_{s,\text{conv}} \rangle}{\omega} = -\frac{2\pi r_g b}{\omega} \text{Re}\,[\bar{K}_f^* \bar{E}_a] \qquad (8.11)$$

Now from Fig. 8.2 we find

$$\bar{E}_a = \frac{\bar{K}_f}{1/R + (1/j\omega_e)(1/L + 1/L_m)} = \frac{\bar{K}_f[1/R - (1/j\omega_e)(1/L + 1/L_m)]}{(1/R)^2 + (1/\omega_e^2)(1/L + 1/L_m)^2} \qquad (8.12)$$

so that

$$\mathfrak{L}_d = -\frac{2\pi r_g b}{\omega} \frac{|\bar{K}_f|^2/R}{(1/R)^2 + (1/\omega_e^2)(1/L + 1/L_m)^2} \qquad (8.13)$$

and this may be simplified to

$$\mathfrak{L}_d = -2\pi r_g p R |\bar{K}_f|^2 \frac{\omega_e}{\omega_e^2 + \left[\dfrac{R}{LL_m/(L + L_m)}\right]^2} \qquad (8.14a)$$

The developed torque turns out to be negative (i.e., opposite to the sense of ω), as we expect in the generating case. By substituting $\omega = \omega_e/p$, we may reexpress $\mathfrak{L}_d$ as

$$\mathfrak{L}_d = -2\pi r_g R|\bar{K}_f^2| \frac{\omega}{\omega^2 + \left[\dfrac{R}{pLL_m/(L + L_m)}\right]^2} \tag{8.14b}$$

and if we define

$$A = 2\pi r_g R|\bar{K}_f^2| \tag{8.15a}$$

$$a = \frac{R}{pLL_m/(L + L_m)} \tag{8.15b}$$

we have

$$\mathfrak{L}_d = -A \frac{\omega}{\omega^2 + a^2} \tag{8.15c}$$

Also if the applied torque of the driver in the direction of ω is $\mathfrak{L}_a$, then the following relations must be satisfied in the steady state:

$$\mathfrak{L}_a + \mathfrak{L}_d = 0 \tag{8.16}$$

and

$$\mathfrak{L}_a = A \frac{\omega}{\omega^2 + a^2} \tag{8.17}$$

Equation (8.17) is the one that must be solved to find ω.

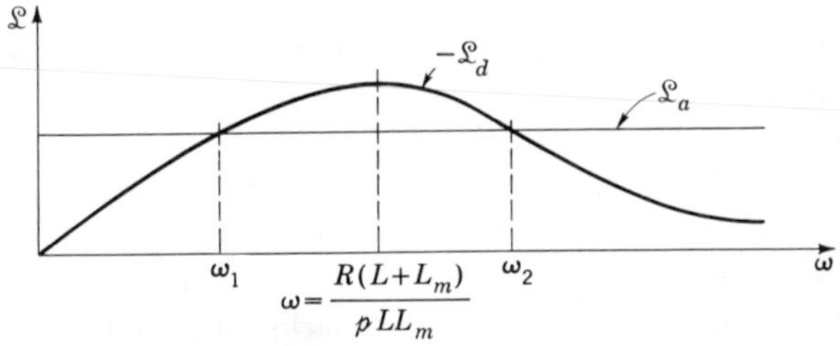

Fig. 8.3 Developed and applied torques as functions of frequency (or speed).

It is particularly instructive to seek a solution in graphical form, as indicated in Fig. 8.3. Let us first plot $-\mathfrak{L}_d$ as a function of ω, from Eq. (8.15*c*). Next, since $\mathfrak{L}_a = -\mathfrak{L}_d$, we seek intersections of the horizontal line $\mathfrak{L} = \mathfrak{L}_a$ and the curve $\mathfrak{L} = -\mathfrak{L}_d$. It is clear from the figure that there will, in general, be *two* intersections or solutions, denoted as ω_1 and ω_2 if there are any at all. This situation comes about because of the nature of the developed torque which, in the usual case of *RL* loads, vanishes for both zero and infinite speed and, consequently, has a maximum at some finite speed. By differentiating Eq. (8.14*a*) and equating to zero we find that this maximum occurs at a speed such that the *resist-*

ance equals the total reactance across the $\bar{E}_a$ terminals, or when

$$\omega_{\text{peak torque}} = \frac{\omega_{e,\text{peak torque}}}{p} = \frac{R(L + L_m)}{pLL_m} \tag{8.18}$$

The developed torque vanishes at zero speed because $\bar{K}_a = 0$ when $v\bar{B} = 0$. At large speeds, on the other hand, the magnetizing and load reactance become very large and the shunt branches of Fig. 8.2 open up. Thus at high speed $\bar{E}_a \doteq v\bar{B} \doteq -\bar{K}_f R$, $B = K_f R/v \to 0$, and so the torque vanishes. In short, at low speed, we have B field, but no armature current, whereas at high speed we have armature current but no B field because of the strong armature reaction; neither condition yields any torque.

The appearance of the multiple solutions ω_1 and ω_2 above now leads to new questions. Can our system operate equally well at two completely different speeds? If so, how does it "know" which one to run at? At this point the steady-state analysis can carry us no further, and we must study the transient stability to find the answer.

(b) Stability Limit

In investigating stability, we inquire how a configuration of equilibrium (not necessarily static) responds to a perturbation. Specifically we ask: If the system is disturbed, will the disturbance die down or will it grow in amplitude with time? We say that the system is, in the former instance, *stable* with respect to the particular disturbance and, in the latter instance, *unstable*. It is possible that a system in stable equilibrium for small perturbations ceases to be so for finite-amplitude disturbances. Similarly it could as well happen that an initially unstable perturbation of small amplitude ultimately may be replaced by an oscillation of a large but limited amplitude. The above remarks about stability are illustrated by the example of the rolling ball in Fig. 8.4.

To determine the stability of a particular operating point we shall, of course, use the quasi-steady-state analysis. Thus Eqs. (8.14) and (8.15) for the developed torque $\mathfrak{L}_d$ are still valid, except that we now consider ω_e and ω as continuous, if slow, variables.

In the transient case, the sum total of the developed and applied torque on the rotor is not zero, but is equal to the inertial torque plus damping torque. Neglecting this latter component, which vanishes as the system approaches steady state, the differential equation of motion becomes

$$\mathfrak{L}_a + \mathfrak{L}_d = \Theta \frac{d\omega}{dt} \tag{8.19}$$

where Θ is the moment of inertia of the rotor. Introducing Eq. (8.15*c*), we now have

$$\mathfrak{L}_a = \Theta \frac{d\omega}{dt} + \frac{A\omega}{\omega^2 + a^2} \tag{8.20}$$

What light can Eq. (8.20) shed on the two steady-state solutions for ω

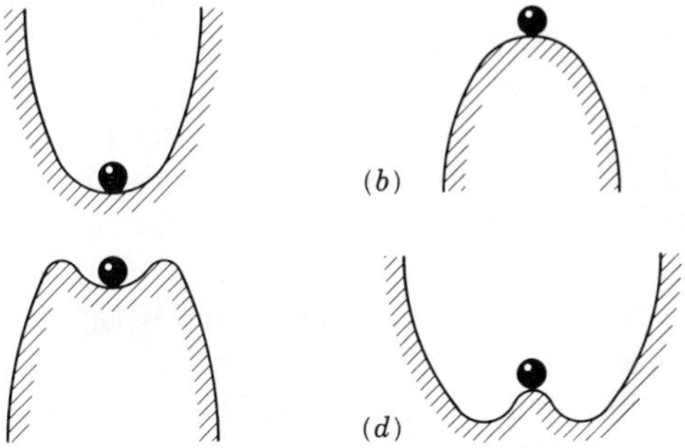

Fig. 8.4 A mechanical example illustrating stable and unstable equilibrium situations: (*a*) Stable; (*b*) unstable; (*c*) stable for small displacement only; (*d*) unstable for restricted amplitude only.

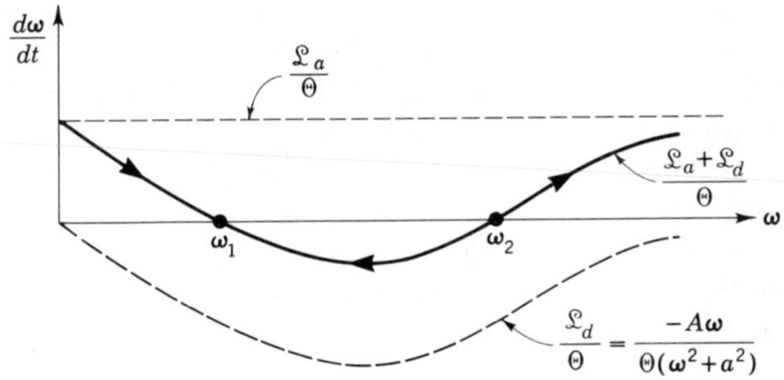

Fig. 8.5 Acceleration-velocity trajectory.

when $\mathfrak{L}_a$ is constant and independent of speed? To answer this, we first solve (8.20) for $d\omega/dt$ in terms of ω,

$$\begin{aligned} \frac{d\omega}{dt} &= \frac{\mathfrak{L}_a}{\Theta} - \frac{A\omega}{\Theta(\omega^2 + a^2)} \\ &= \frac{\mathfrak{L}_a + \mathfrak{L}_d}{\Theta} \end{aligned} \tag{8.21}$$

and plot the result in Fig. 8.5.†

† This type of plot is often called a *phase-plane trajectory*.

From an inspection of this figure, we see the following:

1. $d\omega/dt$ is zero at the ω values ω_1 and ω_2: since these are the points $\mathcal{L}_a + \mathcal{L}_d = 0$, these are obviously the same points determined in the previous Fig. 8.3.
2. For $d\omega/dt > 0$, ω must increase with time: thus portions of the $d\omega/dt$ vs. ω curve above the zero axis are marked with arrows to the right, and, conversely, portions below are marked with arrows to the left, as shown in the plot.
3. The point marked ω_1 is *stable* because the arrows point toward it; and ω_2 is unstable because the arrows point away from it. In other words, if we are operating at ω_1 in the steady state, a small disturbance will move us temporarily to a new speed in the neighborhood of ω_1, but we inevitably return to ω_1. On the other hand, if we operate at ω_2, the tiniest disturbance causes the operation to diverge from this point. Moreover, if this disturbance succeeds in increasing the speed, the system runs away to destruction with ever-increasing speed; whereas if the disturbance lowers the speed, the system moves toward ω_1 and settles there.

From the above discussion, we may conclude that: (1) If we attempt to operate the singly excited converter with a constant field excitation, a constant-torque driver and a given RL load at speeds where the total reactance is greater than the resistance $[\omega_e L L_m/(L + L_m) > R]$, the system is unstable. (2) In the case where the load is purely resistive, the above conclusion still holds. Moreover, we can for this condition restate the stability criterion very neatly by saying that any operating point is unstable if the per-unit gap reactance exceeds unity! In fact, in this case the total reactance $\omega_e L L_m/(L + L_m)$ reduces to $\omega_e L_m = \mathcal{X}_m$, so that the condition for instability becomes $\mathcal{X}_m > R$ or, since R is the rated load impedance,

$$\frac{\mathcal{X}_m}{R} = X_{m,\text{p.u.}} > 1 \tag{8.22}$$

If we desire to operate to the right of the peak of the $\mathcal{L}_d$ curve in the steady state, it is necessary to employ a driver whose torque-speed characteristic "droops" sufficiently. This is illustrated by Fig. 8.6, which shows $\mathcal{L}_d$ and two possible driver torque-speed characteristics $\mathcal{L}_{a,1}$ and $\mathcal{L}_{a,2}$. In (*a*) we see that both these driver characteristics intersect the $-\mathcal{L}_d$ curve at the same point, and in (*b*) we see that only the $\mathcal{L}_{a,2}$ driver gives stable operation. This figure makes clear that a potential operating point is stable if the slope of the $\mathcal{L}_a(\omega)$ curve is a negative number of greater magnitude than the slope of the $-\mathcal{L}_d(\omega)$ curve at this point. In particular, any operating point would be stable if the speed of the prime mover were perfectly constant independent of the torque. In order to obtain suitable slopes in the applied torque-speed characteristic, prime movers are normally equipped with automatically controlled speed regulators. To illustrate the calculations leading to their design specifications consider the following example.

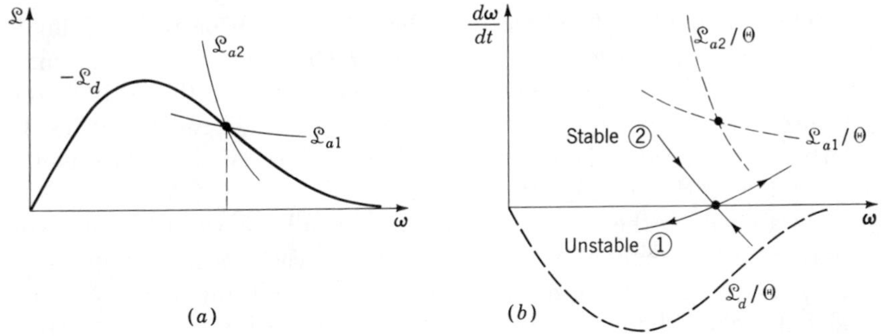

Fig. 8.6 Operation with variable-torque driver.

Example 8.1

A high-efficiency 4-pole 60-cps synchronous generator is to feed a 5-kw lighting load such that the per unit value of the magnetizing reactance is 1.2. Calculate the minimum absolute value of the gradient in the driver torque-speed characteristic which ensures stability at this operating point.

Solution

According to Eq. (8.15c) the slope of the torque-speed curve is

$$\frac{d\mathfrak{L}_d}{d\omega} = A \frac{\omega^2 - a^2}{(\omega^2 + a^2)^2}$$

To eliminate A we use the expression for the output power

$$P_{\text{elec}} \doteq P_{\text{conv}} = \mathfrak{L}_d\omega = -A \frac{\omega^2}{\omega^2 + a^2}$$

and thus obtain

$$\frac{d\mathfrak{L}_d}{d\omega} = -P_{\text{elec}} \frac{\omega^2 - a^2}{\omega^2(\omega^2 + a^2)} = -P_{\text{elec}} \frac{(\omega/a)^2 - 1}{\omega^2[(\omega/a)^2 + 1]}$$

Since the load is purely resistive ($L \to \infty$), we have, according to Eq. (8.15b),

$$\frac{\omega}{a} = \frac{p\omega L_m}{R} = \frac{\mathfrak{X}_m}{R} = X_{m,\text{p.u.}}$$

so that

$$\frac{d\mathfrak{L}_d}{d\omega} = -P_{\text{elec}} \frac{(X_{m,\text{p.u}})^2 - 1}{\omega^2[(X_{m,\text{p.u.}})^2 + 1]}$$

Since this is a generator, $P_{\text{elec}} < 0$, and is

$$P_{\text{elec}} = -5 \times 10^3 \text{ watts} = -5 \times 10^3 \text{ newton-m/sec}$$

Introducing

$$X_{m,\text{p.u}} = 1.2 \qquad p = 2 \qquad \omega = \frac{\omega_e}{p} = \frac{2\pi \times 60}{2} = 60\pi$$

we obtain the minimum value for the magnitude of the negative slope

$$\left|\frac{d\mathfrak{L}_a}{d\omega}\right|_{\min} = 5 \times 10^3 \frac{(1.2)^2 - 1}{(60\pi)^2[(1.2)^2 + 1]} = 0.0254 \text{ newton-m-sec}$$

The previous analysis has considered inductive or resistive loads. If we have a capacitive load, we again find a developed torque curve which possesses a peak at some finite nonzero speed, so that this system can also become unstable if the driver torque-speed gradient is insufficiently steep; the details are quite similar to those of the previous case and are left to the reader (see Prob. 8.2).

As a result of the foregoing analysis, it can be shown that for stable operation of the singly excited synchronous converter *with constant-torque driver,* the power angle δ must be in the first quadrant; i.e., $\bar{K}_f$ cannot lead $\bar{K}$ by more than 90°. In fact, for resistive or inductive load, +45° is the limit for stability! On the other hand, every operating point can be made stable by appropriate speed regulation. When this is done, the power angle is bounded by +90° for resistive or inductive loads and may be anywhere in the first or second quadrants for capacitive loads.

8.4 STABILITY OF THE DOUBLY EXCITED CONVERTER

(a) Armature- and Field-excitation Waves

Here we assume that we have a high-efficiency converter with impressed constant $|\bar{E}_a|$ and ω_e. The only possible *steady-state* speed is then ω_e/p, but departures from this value occur under transient conditions.

Under these circumstances it is useful to distinguish between the actual speed ω and the steady-state value. The latter we shall designate as ω_s; it is often called the *synchronous speed,* since it is related to electric frequency in the infinite bus, by the synchronous tie

$$\omega_s = \frac{\omega_e}{p} \tag{8.23}$$

Because of the double excitation and the deviation from synchronous speed, the transient situation in the doubly excited converter is more complex than that in the singly excited one. The complete picture will become clear only after we study the phenomenon of electromagnetic induction in the next chapter; for the time being we shall content ourselves with a brief, qualitative description, which is all we need for the present development.

We know that the d-c field excitation sets up a group of waves tied to the field conductors, and the armature excitation sets up a group of waves moving with angular velocity ω_s with respect to the armature conductors. Because of the lack of synchronism, $\omega - \omega_s \neq 0$, these two groups are *not* at relative standstill; in fact, they have a relative angular velocity $\omega - \omega_s$ which, small as it might be in the quasi-steady state, is still finite.

In general, all the electromagnetic field quantities consist of contributions from both these groups of waves. This makes the situation quite complicated. In specific instances, however, the electromagnetic quantities relevant to power conversion are predominantly made up of one group of waves. Thus, in our case of the high-efficiency converter, the constant $\bar{E}_a$ impressed by the infinite bus is approximately equal to $v\bar{B}$. Consequently, in this ideal case $\bar{B}$ and therefore $\bar{K} = v\bar{B}/jX_m$ consist solely of waves belonging to the armature-excitation group and traveling with angular velocity ω_s with respect to the armature conductors.

On the other hand, we would naturally expect the field-current surface density $\bar{K}_f$ to be predominantly contributed to from the field-excitation wave group. This is indeed the case, but there is nevertheless a small contribution from the armature-excitation wave group. We shall see how this comes about in the next chapter, where this component takes on great significance since it produces the main steady-state torque. In the present case this torque appears only during transients and acts as a slight viscous friction which tends to damp out oscillations. For simplicity we shall for the time being neglect this effect and approximate the field surface current density $\bar{K}_f$ by a single wave belonging to the field-excitation wave group. We shall, however, subsequently note in a qualitative way how the damping torque modifies the behavior predicted by our simplified model. With these approximations made, we now have, according to Fig. 8.7, which illustrates the position of the waves at a particular instant of time, the following picture of the transient conditions in the doubly excited synchronous converter.

1. The $\bar{K}$ and $\bar{B}$ waves are armature-excitation waves which move with respect to the armature conductors with invariant phase velocity

$$v_{\text{ph}} = -\frac{\omega_e}{\pi/\tau} = -r_g\omega_s \tag{8.24}$$

independently of the relative speed between the armature and field conductors. Since the latter speed is $r_g\omega$ (in the positive direction), the velocity of the $\bar{B}$ and $\bar{K}$ waves with respect to the field conductors is $r_g(\omega - \omega_s)$.

2. The $\bar{K}_f$ wave is a field-excitation wave fixed to the field conductors.
3. The armature- and field-excitation waves have identical wavelength 2τ as dictated by the geometry of the converter, i.e., the connections between the conductors.

We see that for any given time this picture is identical with that of the steady state. The only difference is that the angular displacement between the $\bar{K}$ and $\bar{K}_f$ waves, as denoted by the angle δ, is now a function of time, although in our quasi-steady-state case δ varies very little over the interval of a period $T = 2\pi/\omega_e$. It follows that the average of the surface force density $K_f B$ over the whole periphery of the gap produces a

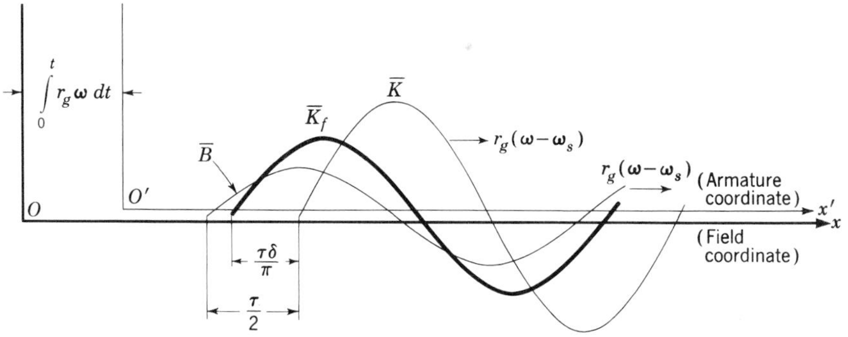

Fig. 8.7 Instantaneous wave position.

net force density on the field conductor at any instant. This force density is

$$\langle f_{sx,f} \rangle = |\bar{K}_f|\,|\bar{B}| \sin \delta = -|\bar{K}_f|\,|jX_m\bar{K}| \sin \delta \qquad (8.25)$$

and similarly the net force exerted on the unit surface of armature conductor is

$$\langle f_{sx,a} \rangle = -|\bar{K}_f|\,|\bar{B}| \sin \delta \qquad (8.26)$$

just as we have previously seen in Eqs. (7.32) and (7.33). The upshot of this discussion is that even when the $\bar{K}_f$ and $\bar{K}$ waves are not at relative standstill, they interact at any instant of time to produce a total torque on the armature conductors. This torque, of course, is a vector parallel to the axis of rotation, as shown in Fig. 8.1, and therefore has only a y component, which is given by

$$\mathfrak{L}_d(t) = -2\pi r_g{}^2 b |\bar{K}_f|\,|\bar{B}| \sin \delta(t) \qquad (8.27)$$

The characteristic curve representing the developed torque as a function of the power angle δ for constant excitation is plotted in Fig. 8.8.

(b) The Equation of Motion

Equation (8.27) above tells us that the developed torque varies with time in proportion to the sine of the power angle δ. The relation between the time variation of the power angle δ and the rotor speed ω is easily determined. In fact, it is clearly seen from Fig. 8.7 that the time rate of change of the linear displacement $(\tau/\pi)\delta$ must be the relative velocity $r_g(\omega - \omega_s)$, so that

$$\frac{d}{dt}\left(\frac{\tau}{\pi}\delta\right) = r_g(\omega - \omega_s) \qquad \text{or} \qquad \frac{d\delta}{dt} = p(\omega - \omega_s) \tag{8.28}$$

In other words $d\delta/dt$ is the radian slip frequency which measures the

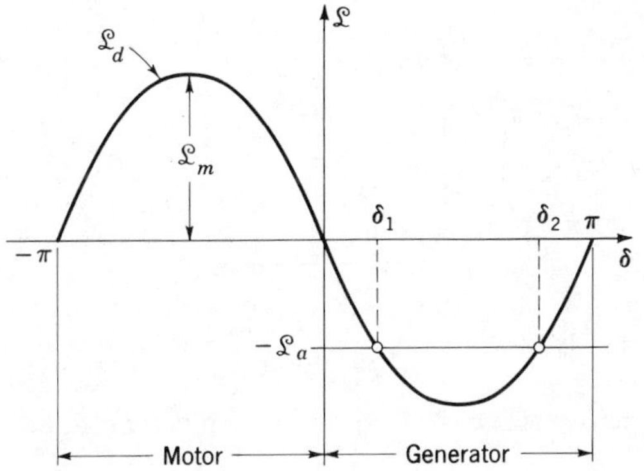

Fig. 8.8 Torque-power angle characteristic of doubly excited synchronous converter with constant excitation.

difference between the actual and synchronous rotor speeds. Also the time derivative of Eq. (8.28) gives

$$\frac{1}{p}\frac{d^2\delta}{dt^2} = \frac{d\omega}{dt} \tag{8.29}$$

We are now in a position to examine how the doubly excited converter undergoes a change of operating point. Suppose we are at a particular steady-state operating point with $\omega = \omega_s$ and $\mathfrak{L}_d + \mathfrak{L}_a = 0$, when a change in load suddenly occurs. This creates a momentary unbalance between applied torque and developed torque. According to Eq. (8.19), this unbalanced torque is absorbed by the moment of inertia of the rotating masses, and results in an angular acceleration $d\omega/dt = (1/p)\, d^2\delta/dt^2$; thus δ begins to change so as to reduce the unbalance in torque. In other words, the change in speed brings about a change in the average rotor position so that the $\bar{K}$ wave shifts with respect to the $\bar{K}_f$ wave.

Eventually, if the system is stable (and if we include some damping torque), the rotor settles to a new average position and thus to a new value of δ such that $\mathfrak{L}_d$ in Eq. (8.27) exactly balances the applied torque.

Suppose now that in the steady state a particular power angle δ satisfies a particular load condition. It is clear from Eq. (8.27) and Fig. 8.8 that its supplement $(\pi - \delta)$ produces the same developed torque, and so also presumably satisfies the load condition. If this is the case, there apparently are two possible solutions when seeking the operating condition for specified $|\bar{K}_f|$ and $\langle p_s \rangle$. These two possibilities are shown in the phasor diagram of Fig. 8.9, distinguished by the subscripts 1 and 2. Steady-state considerations tell us only that both solutions are equally valid, and we need to turn to the transient behavior for further information in this regard.

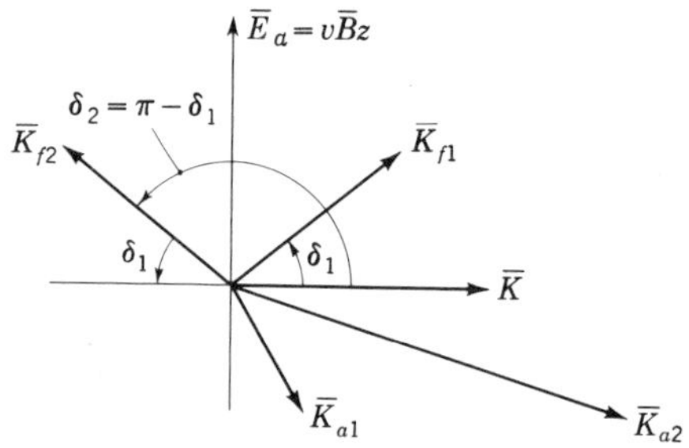

Fig. 8.9 Alternative steady-state operating points for specified $|\bar{K}_f|$ and $\langle p_s \rangle$.

The previous discussion of the stability of the singly excited machine leads us to expect that with constant applied torque one of these points will turn out to be stable, the other not. To prove this we shall again use the quasi-steady differential equations. If $\mathfrak{L}_a$ is the torque applied to the rotor (in the same sense as ω) by the load or driver, then we again have Eq. (8.19)

$$\mathfrak{L}_a + \mathfrak{L}_d = \Theta \frac{d\omega}{dt} \tag{8.19}$$

Since in our case $|\bar{K}_f|$ and $|\bar{B}|$ are fixed,† we may rewrite Eq. (8.27) as

$$\mathfrak{L}_d = -\mathfrak{L}_m \sin \delta \tag{8.30a}$$

where

$$\mathfrak{L}_m = 2\pi r_g{}^2 b |\bar{K}_f|\,|\bar{B}| \tag{8.30b}$$

Using Eq. (8.29), we have then

$$\mathfrak{L}_a = \mathfrak{L}_m \sin \delta + \frac{\Theta}{p}\frac{d^2\delta}{dt^2} \tag{8.31}$$

† Since $B = E_a/v$, B can be considered constant during a mechanical transient only within the range of validity of the quasi-steady-state approximation.

As we might have expected from the discussion of Sec. 7.5c, Eq. (8.31) is identical with the equation of motion of an elastic coupling which transfers a torque $\mathfrak{L}_a$ to a load whose moment of inertia is Θ/p. It is also the equation of a gravity pendulum subjected to a torque $\mathfrak{L}_a$.

(c) Incremental Stability

Equation (8.31) is a nonlinear differential equation whose exact solution is expressed in terms of elliptic integrals. Instead of studying these exact solutions, we shall seek solutions of the linearized equation which describe small displacements around particular operating points.

From the analogy with the pendulum, we know that for $\mathfrak{L}_a = 0$, δ executes periodic oscillations; and for small amplitudes, these oscillations are nearly sinusoidal with radian frequency

$$\omega_h = \sqrt{\frac{p\mathfrak{L}_m}{\Theta}} \tag{8.32}$$

When $\mathfrak{L}_a \neq 0$, but is some constant such that $\left|\dfrac{\mathfrak{L}_a}{\mathfrak{L}_m}\right| < 1$, the solution for small amplitudes is still easy to find. If δ_0 is the steady-state power angle corresponding to $\mathfrak{L}_a$, i.e.,

$$\mathfrak{L}_a = \mathfrak{L}_m \sin \delta_0 \tag{8.33}$$

and ϵ is the deviation of δ from δ_0,

$$\epsilon = \delta - \delta_0 \tag{8.34}$$

then expanding $\sin \delta$ in a power series about $\delta = \delta_0$, we get

$$\sin \delta = \sin \delta_0 + \epsilon \cos \delta_0 - \frac{\epsilon^2}{2} \sin \delta_0 \cdots \tag{8.35}$$

For small ϵ, we may approximate $\sin \delta$ by the first two terms,

$$\sin \delta \doteq \sin \delta_0 + \epsilon \cos \delta_0$$

so that

$$\mathfrak{L}_a = \mathfrak{L}_m \sin \delta_0 + \epsilon \mathfrak{L}_m \cos \delta_0 + \frac{\Theta}{p}\frac{d^2\epsilon}{dt^2} \tag{8.36}$$

In view of Eq. (8.33), this becomes

$$0 = (\mathfrak{L}_m \cos \delta_0)\epsilon + \frac{\Theta}{p}\frac{d^2\epsilon}{dt^2} \tag{8.37}$$

In this equation the coefficient multiplying ϵ is the incremental torque gradient at the operating point $\delta = \delta_0$:

$$\mathfrak{L}_m \cos \delta_0 = \frac{d}{d\delta}(\mathfrak{L}_m \sin \delta)\bigg|_{\delta=\delta_0} = \mathfrak{L}_s \tag{8.38}$$

$\mathfrak{L}_s$ is often called the *synchronizing torque*. We have thus obtained the differential equation governing the time variation of ϵ, and therefore of δ, in terms of the effective moment of inertia Θ/p and the incremental torque gradient at the operating point. This equation is the well-known linear second-order differential equation, without damping, whose characteristic solutions are growing exponentials for $\cos \delta_0 < 0$ or constant-amplitude sinusoidal oscillations of radian frequency

$$\omega_n = \sqrt{\frac{p\mathfrak{L}_m \cos \delta_0}{\Theta}}$$

for $\cos \delta_0 > 0$.

The former of these cases is *unstable*, since the smallest deviation from $\delta \neq \delta_0$ causes a transient which diverges away from δ_0. The latter condition, however, indicates stability, since the inevitable damping terms (which are absent from our simplified model) eventually cause any small sinusoidal oscillation to disappear, just as in the pendulum itself. This oscillatory process about the stable value of δ_0 is called *hunting*.

Even when $\cos \delta_0 > 0$, the synchronous converter may become unstable when its natural oscillation resonates with periodic irregularities in the shaft torque. The latter situation arises when the converter shaft is connected to a piston machine, such as an engine in the case of a generator, or a pump or compressor in the case of a motor. Near resonance the forced oscillations may result in undesirably high pulsations in the power of the converter, as illustrated by the following example.

Example 8.2

A synchronous motor drives a reciprocating compressor, whose torque fluctuates periodically about a steady-state average value. The motor is connected to a 60-cycle supply, rotates at 257 rpm, and draws an average power equal to the rated power of 200 hp with a power factor of 0.75 leading. Its per-unit magnetizing reactance is $X_{m,\text{p.u.}} = 0.8$. The compressor torque pulsation has a significant sinusoidal component of amplitude $\mathfrak{L}_{\text{a.c.}} = 1{,}000$ newton-m and radian frequency equal to the angular velocity. Neglecting Joule losses and friction, find:

(*a*) The maximum values of the power angle δ and delivered power P when the inertia of the motor and load is $\Theta = 400$ kg-m².

(*b*) The inertia which would correspond to resonance.

(*c*) The inertia of the flywheel which has to be added if it is desired to keep the power fluctuation within 10 percent of the average power.

Solution

First we determine the average power angle δ_0. From Eq. (7.53), we know that $|\bar{K}_R|_{\text{p.u.}} = 1/X_{m,\text{p.u.}} = 1.25$. With this information, we may now draw the per-unit phasor diagram for rated conditions.

Here we see immediately that δ_0 is negative, and its tangent is

$$\tan \delta_0 = -\frac{0.75}{1.25 + \sqrt{1 - (0.75)^2}} = -0.393$$

so that

$$\delta_0 = -21.45°$$

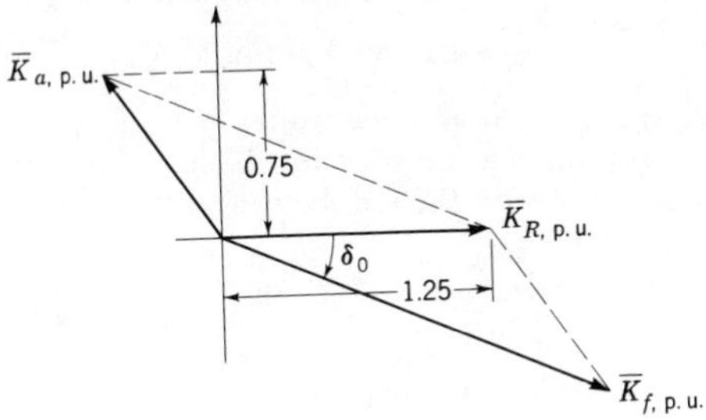

Next we determine the synchronizing torque. This is

$$\mathfrak{L}_s = \frac{d}{d\delta}(\mathfrak{L}_m \sin \delta)\Big|_{\delta_0} = \mathfrak{L}_m \cos \delta_0$$

Now $\mathfrak{L}_{av} = \mathfrak{L}_m \sin \delta_0$

where $\mathfrak{L}_{av} = \dfrac{P_{av}}{\omega} = \dfrac{200 \times 745}{2\pi \times 257/60} = 5{,}550$ newton-m

The synchronizing torque is then

$$\mathfrak{L}_s = \frac{\mathfrak{L}_{av}}{\sin \delta_0} \cos \delta_0 = \mathfrak{L}_{av} \cot \delta_0$$

so that $\mathfrak{L}_s = \dfrac{5{,}550}{0.393} = 14{,}100$ newton-m/electrical degree

With the addition of the forcing term, Eq. (8.37) becomes

$$\mathfrak{L}_{a.c.} \cos \omega t = \mathfrak{L}_s \epsilon + \frac{\Theta}{p}\frac{d^2\epsilon}{dt^2}$$

This equation is identical with that of the LC circuit shown and admits the steady-state solution:

$$\epsilon = \epsilon_m \cos \omega t$$

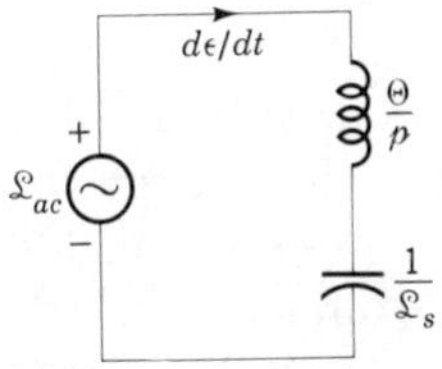

The amplitude of the oscillation can be obtained by direct substitution as

$$\epsilon_m = \left| \frac{\mathfrak{L}_{a.c.}}{\mathfrak{L}_s - \omega^2\Theta/p} \right|$$

Introducing

$$p = \frac{3{,}600}{257} = 14$$

$$\omega = 2\pi \times \tfrac{257}{60} = 27$$

we obtain

$$\epsilon_m = \left| \frac{1{,}000}{14{,}100 - (27)^2 400/1.4} \right| = 0.149 \text{ rad}$$

The maximum δ is then

$$\delta_{\max} = \delta_0 + \epsilon_m = -21.45° - 0.149 \times 57.3° = -30°$$

In practice, the maximum power angle would be slightly smaller because of the damping torque which was not considered, and which in the analogous circuit would appear as a resistance in series with the inductance and the capacitance. The maximum power is

$$P_{\max} = P_{\text{av}} \frac{\sin \delta_{\max}}{\sin \delta_0} = 200 \frac{\sin 30°}{\sin 21.45°} = 274 \text{ hp}$$

This represents a peak overload of 137 percent.

(*b*) The inertia corresponding to resonance is

$$\Theta_r = \frac{p\mathfrak{L}_s}{\omega^2} = \frac{14 \times 14{,}100}{(27)^2} = 270 \text{ kg-m}^2$$

(*c*) If we want to reduce the peak fluctuation to 10 percent then

$$\frac{P_{1,\max}}{P_{\text{av}}} = 1.1 = \frac{\sin \delta_{1,\max}}{\sin \delta_0}$$

This gives

$$\begin{aligned} \delta_{1,\max} &= \sin^{-1} (1.1 \sin \delta_0) \\ &= -23.62° \\ \epsilon_{1,m} &= 2.17° = 3.78 \times 10^{-2} \text{ rad} \end{aligned}$$

Introducing this value of ϵ_m into

$$\begin{aligned} \Theta_1 &= \frac{p}{\omega^2}\left(\mathfrak{L}_s + \frac{\mathfrak{L}_{\text{a.c.}}}{\epsilon_m}\right) \\ &= \frac{14}{(27)^2}\left(14{,}400 + \frac{1{,}000}{3.78 \times 10^{-2}}\right) \end{aligned}$$

we obtain

$$\Theta_1 = 585 \text{ kg-m}^2$$

The additional inertia required is then

$$\Theta_{\text{add}} = \Theta_1 - \Theta = 185 \text{ kg-m}^2$$

We thus see that the amplitude of the deviation ϵ_m is a sensitive function of the inertia Θ. This is symptomatic of the operation of a system in the vicinity of the resonant condition. It is clear that we can avoid reasonance by controlling the inertia of the system. On the basis of Eq. (8.37) we can then state a necessary condition for stability of a synchronous converter with constant field excitation to be $\cos \delta_0 > 0$ or

$$-\frac{\pi}{2} \leq \delta_0 \leq \frac{\pi}{2} \tag{8.39}$$

i.e., the magnitude of the power angle at the operating point must be no more than 90°. The instability that results when this condition is violated causes a continuous increase of δ so that δ has no long-term average value. When this happens, we see from Eq. (8.27) that the developed torque has no average value and net power conversion cannot occur; the converter has then lost synchronism or is said to have "fallen out of step."

(d) Large Transient Stability

On the basis of incremental stability considerations we have seen that it is necessary for the power angle to be confined to the first and fourth quadrants. This, however, is not sufficient to ensure stability under all circumstances, and we may still lose synchronism for large transients. To see qualitatively how this comes about, consider the following sequence of events as depicted in Fig. 8.10.

A synchronous converter is running at synchronous speed and zero load; thus $\delta = 0$. At $t = t_0$ a mechanical load is suddenly applied to the rotor, so that the machine begins to slow down. δ then begins to go

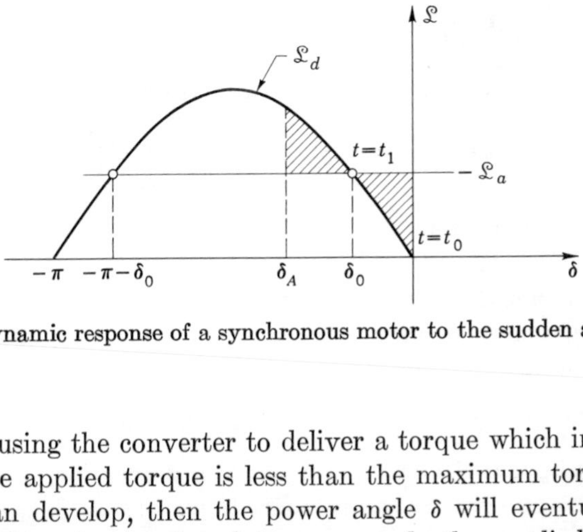

Fig. 8.10 Dynamic response of a synchronous motor to the sudden application of a load.

negative, causing the converter to deliver a torque which increases with time. If the applied torque is less than the maximum torque that the converter can develop, then the power angle δ will eventually reach a value such that the developed torque equals the applied torque. At this instant of time, we let $t = t_1$ and $\delta = \delta_0$, since this point corresponds to a condition of static equilibrium. At $t = t_1$, however, the rotor speed is below synchronism, and, because of the inertia of the rotating masses, continues to remain below synchronism immediately thereafter, so that δ *continues to go negative.* As this happens, excess motoring torque develops, and the rotor starts to speed up; however, if the inertia is large enough, δ may succeed in overshooting past $-90°$ without having regained synchronous speed. In fact, the overshoot may be so far past $-90°$ that the point $-\pi - \delta_0$ is reached, so that the accelerating torque vanishes and then reverses its sign. When this happens, synchronism is lost, and the rotor eventually comes to a stop. It is then apparent that the equilibrium point δ_0 corresponds to the situation of Fig. 8.4*c* where the ball, although stable for small oscillations, will go over the ridge and become unstable if the perturbation is large enough.

We may readily verify the above discussion by analysis. Beginning with Eq. (8.31),

$$\mathfrak{L}_a = \mathfrak{L}_m \sin \delta + \frac{\Theta}{p} \frac{d^2\delta}{dt^2} \tag{8.31}$$

we multiply through by the integrating factor $d\delta/dt$; thus

$$\mathfrak{L}_a \frac{d\delta}{dt} = \mathfrak{L}_m \sin \delta \frac{d\delta}{dt} + \frac{\Theta}{p} \frac{d\delta}{dt} \frac{d^2\delta}{dt^2} \tag{8.40}$$

We recognize the identity

$$\frac{d\delta}{dt} \frac{d^2\delta}{dt^2} = \frac{1}{2} \frac{d}{dt} \left(\frac{d\delta}{dt}\right)^2 \tag{8.41}$$

so that

$$\mathfrak{L}_a \frac{d\delta}{dt} = \mathfrak{L}_m \sin \delta \frac{d\delta}{dt} + \frac{\Theta}{2p} \frac{d}{dt} \left(\frac{d\delta}{dt}\right)^2 \tag{8.42}$$

Integrating this with respect to time, we obtain

$$\mathfrak{L}_a(\delta - \delta_i) = -\mathfrak{L}_m(\cos \delta - \cos \delta_i) + \frac{\Theta}{2p} \left[\left(\frac{d\delta}{dt}\right)^2 - \left(\frac{d\delta}{dt}\right)^2 \Bigg|_i \right] \tag{8.43}$$

where the subscript i refers to the initial conditions at the beginning of the transient.

It is clear that the term in Eq. (8.43) involving the inertia is strongly reminiscent of a change in kinetic energy; in fact, the equation appears to be in the form

$$\text{Work done by } (\mathfrak{L}_a + \mathfrak{L}_d) = \text{change in rotor kinetic energy}$$

and therefore appears to be a statement of conservation of energy. This is indeed the case, since we can conceive of a situation in which the angular variable δ/p corresponds to the actual mechanical displacement of the rotor and $(1/p)(d\delta/dt)$ to its velocity. This occurs when the armature is placed on the stator and the field-excitation wave $\bar{K}_f$ fixed to the rotor is viewed from a frame of reference attached to the impressed $\bar{E}_a$ and $\bar{B}$ waves, i.e., a frame moving with synchronous speed with respect to the stator.

We next rewrite Eq. (8.43) as

$$\frac{\Theta}{2p\mathfrak{L}_m} \left(\frac{d\delta}{dt}\right)^2 = \frac{\Theta}{2p\mathfrak{L}_m} \left(\frac{d\delta}{dt}\right)^2 \Bigg|_i + \frac{\mathfrak{L}_a}{\mathfrak{L}_m} (\delta - \delta_i) - (\cos \delta_i - \cos \delta) \tag{8.44}$$

The reason for using the above form is as follows: We know that $|d\delta/dt|^2$ starts out at zero, and then increases. If the operation is to be stable, $|d\delta/dt|^2$ must then go back to zero, increase again, etc., in a finite-amplitude oscillation (which damping eventually removes). If, however, we can find circumstances such that the right-hand side of Eq. (8.44) *never* goes to zero after the initial condition, we have then found a loss of synchronism.

This can indeed happen here. Our initial conditions are $|d\delta/dt|_i = 0$, $\delta_i = 0$, so that Eq. (8.44) reduces to

$$\frac{\Theta}{2p\mathfrak{L}_m}\left(\frac{d\delta}{dt}\right)^2 = \frac{\mathfrak{L}_a}{\mathfrak{L}_m}\,\delta - (1 - \cos\delta) \tag{8.45}$$

We next investigate the right-hand side of Eq. (8.45) graphically in Fig. 8.11. Here we plot the components $(\mathfrak{L}_a/\mathfrak{L}_m)\delta$ and $(1 - \cos\delta)$, showing three values of $\mathfrak{L}_a/\mathfrak{L}_m$ corresponding to the motoring case. For a value

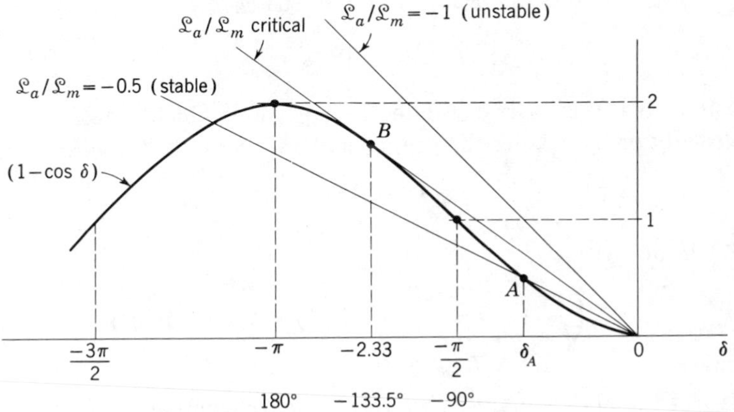

Fig. 8.11 Large transient analysis.

$\mathfrak{L}_a/\mathfrak{L}_m = -0.5$, the line $(\mathfrak{L}_a/\mathfrak{L}_m)\delta$ intersects the $(1 - \cos\delta)$ curve at point A. This means that the right-hand side of (8.45) is positive for $|\delta| < |\delta_A|$, zero for $\delta = \delta_A$, but negative for a large region thereafter where $|\delta| > |\delta_A|$. Since $(d\delta/dt)^2$ *cannot be negative*, this means that the δ value must go from 0 to A, reverse and go back to zero, return to A, etc., giving us a finite oscillation about an average value

$$\delta = \arcsin(-0.5) = -0.52 \text{ rad}$$

For the limiting value $\mathfrak{L}_a/\mathfrak{L}_m = -1$, there is no intersection at all, and it is clear that the right-hand side of Eq. (8.45) is positive and continues to increase for $\delta < 0$. Thus $d\delta/dt$ never returns to 0, ω continues to deviate from ω_s, and synchronism is lost.

From the geometry of the figure, it is clear that there is a critical value of $\mathfrak{L}_a/\mathfrak{L}_m$ such that $(\mathfrak{L}_a/\mathfrak{L}_m)\delta$ is just tangent to $(1 - \cos\delta)$ at point B. For values of $\mathfrak{L}_a/\mathfrak{L}_m$ in the range between this value and -1, there is obviously a loss of synchronism, just as for $\mathcal{L}_a/\mathcal{L}_m = -1$; yet this range is perfectly satisfactory for *incremental* stability!

To determine this critical value of $\mathcal{L}_a/\mathcal{L}_m$ and the corresponding point B, we note that B is on both curves so that

$$\left(\frac{\mathcal{L}_a}{\mathcal{L}_m}\right)_{\text{crit}} \delta_B = 1 - \cos \delta_B \tag{8.46}$$

Also, the slopes are identical, so that

$$\left(\frac{\mathcal{L}_a}{\mathcal{L}_m}\right)_{\text{crit}} = \sin \delta_B \tag{8.47}$$

Substituting Eq. (8.47) in Eq. (8.46), we get

$$\delta_B \sin \delta_B = 1 - \cos \delta_B$$

or

$$\delta_B = \tan \frac{\delta_B}{2} \tag{8.48}$$

Equation (8.48) is a transcendental equation which must be solved numerically or by scaling the graphics of Fig. 8.11. The solution is

$$\begin{aligned} \delta_B &= \pm 2.33 \text{ rad} \\ &= \pm 133.5° \end{aligned} \tag{8.49}$$

so that in our case,

$$\begin{aligned} \left(\frac{\mathcal{L}_a}{\mathcal{L}_m}\right)_{\text{crit}} &= \sin(-133.5°) = \sin(-46.5°) \\ &= -0.725 \end{aligned} \tag{8.50}$$

In view of the above analysis, we reach the following conclusions:

1. If mechanical loads are to be applied suddenly, synchronous operation can be attained only if the rated load is less than 72.5 percent of the maximum developed torque. The converter must then operate in the corresponding steady-state power-angle range

$$-46.5° < \delta < 0 \tag{8.51}$$

2. It is moreover desirable to restrict the operating range of power angle to an even narrower range than that of Eq. (8.51), in order to reduce the magnitude and duration of the disturbances. In fact, for $\delta_0 = -46.5°$ the transient extremes are 0° and $-133.5°$, but for $\delta_0 = -30°$ the extremes are only 0° and approximately $-63.5°$ (point A), a much more desirable situation.

An equivalent graphical procedure for studying large transient stability is called the *equal-area method.* In this method, which is illustrated in Fig. 8.10, the extreme value of δ, $\delta_{\max}$, is determined by making the shaded areas equal. The critical value of applied torque $\mathcal{L}_a$ is then that value for which the equal-area method finds $\delta_{\max}$ at the intersection point of $\mathcal{L}_d$ and $-\mathcal{L}_a$.

It is important to note that the extent of the swing around the steady-state operating point does not depend on the inertia. The limitations in operating range therefore hold as well for very small but finite values of Θ/p, provided the quasi-steady-state analysis is valid.

Disturbances other than the sudden load increase in a motor can also lead to instability and result in the same criterion for large transient stability. An example of such disturbances for synchronous converters operating as generators, are faults in the transmission lines, which suddenly reduce the electric load (see Problems).

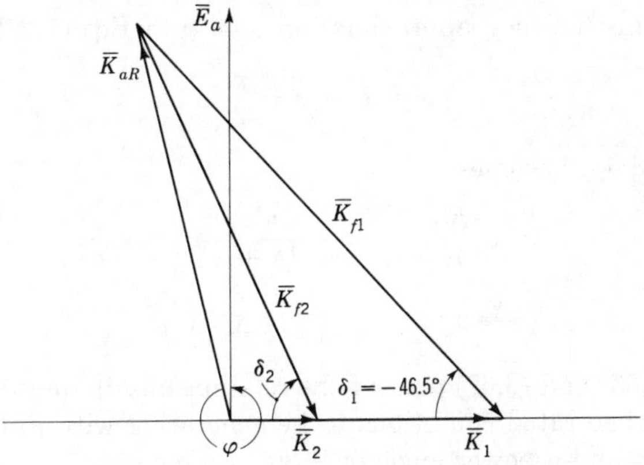

Fig. 8.12 Phasor diagrams of two motors having identical armature current and different power angles.

(e) Economic Import of the Stability Requirements

The restrictions which stability imposes on the operating power angle have important economic consequences. To see how this comes about, consider two synchronous motors with identical power and armature current, but with different power angles, as shown in Fig. 8.12.

Here we see that for a given armature current, the ends of the $\bar{K}_f$ and $\bar{K}$ phasors move to the right as the absolute value of the power angle δ decreases, so that the requirement of a small angle δ necessitates large field current densities. A small value of δ also corresponds to small values of $X_{m,\text{p.u.}}$ since, from Eq. (7.53),

$$X_{m,\text{p.u.}} = \frac{1}{K_{R,\text{p.u.}}} = \left.\frac{K_a}{K}\right|_R$$

and we see from Fig. 8.12 that this ratio decreases as the magnitude of δ decreases.

These facts may be put in completely quantitative terms. Applying the law of sines in the triangle of phasors Fig. 7.7, we find

$$\frac{K_f}{K_a} = -\frac{\cos \alpha}{\sin \delta} \tag{8.52}$$

In the high-efficiency case, $\alpha \approx \varphi$, and Eq. (8.52) becomes

$$\frac{K_f}{K_a} \approx -\frac{\cos \varphi}{\sin \delta} \tag{8.53}$$

Again applying the law of sines in Fig. 7.7, we also find

$$\frac{K_a}{K} = \frac{\sin \delta}{\sin (\pi - \sigma)} = \frac{\sin \delta}{\sin \sigma} \tag{8.54}$$

Using the high-efficiency approximation $\alpha = \varphi$ in Eq. (7.26*b*), we have

$$\sigma = \delta + \varphi - \frac{\pi}{2} \tag{8.55}$$

so that Eq. (8.54) becomes

$$\frac{K_a}{K} \approx -\frac{\sin \delta}{\cos (\delta + \varphi)} \tag{8.56}$$

and

$$X_{m,\text{p.u.}} \approx -\left.\frac{\sin \delta}{\cos (\delta + \varphi)}\right|_R \tag{8.57}$$

Equations (8.53) and (8.57) present the relationships in question. If, for example, we take rated conditions to be generating with a power factor of 0.8 lagging, and a power angle of +30°, we have

$$\begin{aligned} \cos \varphi_R &= -0.8 \qquad & \sin \delta_R &= 0.5 \\ \sin \varphi_R &= -0.6 \qquad & \cos \delta_R &= 0.866 \end{aligned}$$

and, from Eqs. (8.53) and (8.57),

$$K_{f,\text{p.u.}} = \frac{0.8}{0.5} = 1.6 \qquad X_{m,\text{p.u.}} = -\frac{0.5}{0.866(-0.8) - (0.5)(-0.6)} = \frac{0.5}{0.393} = 1.27$$

whereas if we permit a 45° power angle, we have

$$K_{f,\text{p.u.}} = \frac{0.8}{0.707} = 1.13 \qquad X_{m,\text{p.u.}} = -\frac{0.707}{0.707(-0.8) - (0.707)(-0.6)} = \frac{1}{0.2} = 5$$

From these calculations and from the results of Secs. 7.7 and 7.8 it is clear that poor transient stability, poor overload capability, and poor regulation go hand in hand, and all can be ameliorated by using large K_f and small $\mathfrak{X}_m$, or, in other words, by designing the converter with a large gap. The requirement of relatively large gaps and field currents implies large Joule losses in the field conductor. Even though the lower field voltage and the consequent lighter insulation allow for higher specific loss in the field than in the armature conductors, the power dissipated in the field controls the design and ultimately determines the size and cost of the machine.

In arriving at these conclusions, we have assumed that K_f is held constant. If, on the other hand, K_f is varied, we can overcome the transient stability problem (as well as the problems of overload capability and regulation) in machines with larger $\mathfrak{X}_m$, by suitably controlling K_f. Thus, an automatic regulator may adjust K_f so that the ratio between applied and peak developed torque $\mathfrak{L}_a/\mathfrak{L}_m$ is made small during a transient, and larger as steady state is approached. However, the technical problems of constructing such regulators, especially in view of the very stringent reliability requirements which they must satisfy, still lead electric utilities to rely to a considerable extent on the inherent performance characteristic of the converter. Another solution to this problem has recently been proposed by one of the authors.[3] In this method, the armature reaction is directly compensated by feeding a current component through the field coils which is proportional to the armature current. This is achieved by rectifying the output of current transformers whose primaries carry the armature currents. As a result, K_f now varies as the operating point changes. The advantages of this technique are that the range of stable operation is extended far beyond $\delta = \pi/2$, so that the operating point can be chosen in the vicinity of maximum power. This liberates the design of the generator itself from the requirement of a large gap normally imposed by stability considerations. The proposed excitation method may lead to a 30 percent reduction in the cost of large generating units.

8.5 SYNCHRONIZATION

We have seen that the doubly excited synchronous converter operates stably in the steady state only if its speed is the synchronous speed and its power angle δ is confined to a limited range. Under these circumstances, how do we put such a converter into steady-state operation? We shall see in the next section that the converter is brought to the vicinity of steady-state operating conditions by means of appropriate single excitation. Assuming that this has been done, the question that next concerns us is: How near the synchronous speed and the steady-state power angle must we be in order to ensure proper final operation when the second excitation is applied? The transient "pulling in" process as this occurs is called *synchronization*. Plainly if our maximum torque capability is inadequate compared to the effective rotor inertia, such synchronization will not occur.

The answer to our question again may be quickly found from Eq. (8.44). We consider here the case where the applied torque $\mathfrak{L}_a = 0$; the method of solution is easily generalized to the case $\mathfrak{L}_a \neq 0$ (see Prob. 8.11). Our parameters in this case are $\mathfrak{L}_a = 0$; $d\delta/dt|_i$ specified; δ_i to be chosen. Thus we have

$$\frac{\Theta}{2p\mathfrak{L}_m}\left(\frac{d\delta}{dt}\right)^2 = \frac{\Theta}{2p\mathfrak{L}_m}\left(\frac{d\delta}{dt}\right)^2\Bigg|_i - (\cos\delta_i - \cos\delta) \qquad (8.58)$$

As before, we shall investigate graphically by plotting in Fig. 8.13

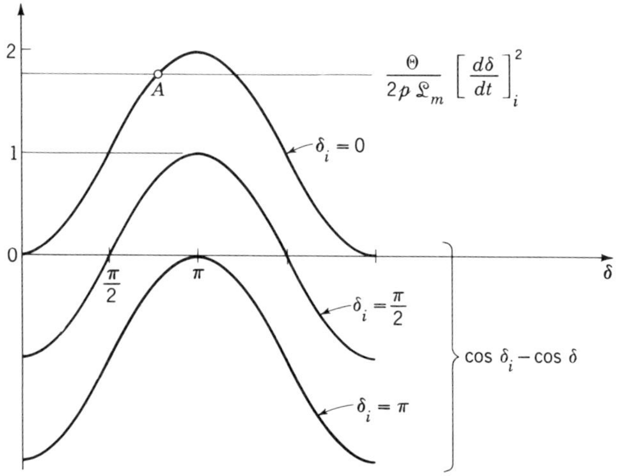

Fig. 8.13 Synchronizing transient analysis.

the components on the right-hand side of Eq. (8.58). The inertial term here is a known positive constant for a given initial speed; the term $(\cos\delta_i - \cos\delta)$ depends on the selection of δ_i as shown. Using the analysis previously applied to Fig. 8.11, we see that:

1. Synchronization occurs when we have an intersection such as point A.
2. The most propitious value of δ_i is plainly $\delta_i = 0$; with this value we can synchronize the largest possible speed deviation under the circumstances. This is understandable, since having $\delta = 0$ at the initial instant makes available the entire range of useful developed torque for accelerating the inertia.
3. If $\delta_i = \pi$, *synchronization is impossible.*

4. If $\delta_i = 0$, the maximum deviation we can synchronize is given by

$$\frac{\Theta}{2p\mathfrak{L}_m}\left(\frac{d\delta}{dt}\right)_i^2 \le 2 \tag{8.59}$$

Using Eqs. (8.28) and (8.32), this may be rewritten as

$$(\omega_i - \omega_s)^2 \le \frac{4\omega_h^2}{p^2} \tag{8.60a}$$

or

$$\left|\frac{\omega_i - \omega_s}{\omega_s}\right| \le 2\,\frac{\omega_h}{\omega_e} \tag{8.60b}$$

where ω_h is the radian frequency of small oscillation around $\delta = 0$. If we call the fractional deviation from synchronous speed the *slip*,† and denote it by S, we can write Eq. (8.60*b*) as

$$S_i \le 2\,\frac{\omega_h}{\omega_e} \tag{8.61a}$$

$$S_{i,m} = 2\,\frac{\omega_h}{\omega_e} \tag{8.61b}$$

i.e., the "maximum slip that can be synchronized (if we switch in at $\delta_i = 0$) is twice the per-unit natural frequency."

Of course, switching at $\delta_i = 0$ implies adequate instrumentation to provide measurement of the power angle, and possibly even automatic control of the switching. The reader is referred to Prob. 8.10 for further details. The condition for synchronization given by Eq. (8.61) has been derived under the assumption that the converter develops no electromagnetic torque besides the synchronous torque. We shall see, however, that most synchronous converters carry on the field structure a second winding. This winding is designed to provide an additional damping torque component which facilitates the synchronization as well as the starting process. It is consequently called the *starting*, *damper*, or *amortisseur* (Fr. "damper") winding.

The relations developed above are illustrated in the following example.

Example 8.3

A 10-pole-pair 60-cps synchronous motor with a pure inertia load has a maximum natural frequency of 1.8 cps. The motor is brought up to a speed of 349.2 rpm before the d-c field excitation is applied.

(*a*) For what range of power angle (at the moment of excitation) will synchronization occur?

(*b*) If the power angle (at the moment of excitation) is 30°, find the limits on the excursions of the power angle and the peak value of the speed.

† This is *not* identical with, although related to, the slip defined in terms of the drift velocity in earlier chapters.

(*c*) Would the motor synchronize if the overall inertia were tripled? Neglect damping; i.e., consider only the synchronous component of electromagnetic torque.

Solution

(*a*) Equation (8.58) can be rewritten in terms of slip S as

$$S^2 = S_i^2 - 2\left(\frac{\omega_h}{\omega_e}\right)^2 (\cos \delta_i - \cos \delta)$$

since

$$f_h = 1.8 \qquad f_e = 60 \qquad \frac{\omega_h}{\omega_c} = 0.03$$

For $p = 10$ and $f_e = 60$, the synchronous speed is 360 rpm, so that

$$S_i^2 = \left(\frac{360 - 349.2}{360}\right)^2 = \left(\frac{10.8}{360}\right)^2 = (0.03)^2$$

and

$$S^2 = (0.03)^2[1 - 2(\cos \delta_i - \cos \delta)]$$

Synchronization for the extreme δ_i occurs for $S = 0$, $\delta = \pi$, $\delta_i = \delta_{i,\max}$; thus

$$\cos \delta_{i,\max} = \tfrac{1}{2} - 1 = -\tfrac{1}{2}$$

Therefore

$$\delta_{i,\max} = \pm 120°$$

(*b*) Now $\delta_i = 30°$, so that

$$\begin{aligned} S^2 &= (0.03)^2[1 - 2(0.866 - \cos \delta)] \\ &= (0.03)^2(2 \cos \delta - 0.732) = 2(0.03)^2(\cos \delta - 0.366) \end{aligned}$$

The peak excursions occur at the zero slip point, which is given by $\cos \delta_{\text{extreme}} = 0.366$, $\delta_{\text{extreme}} = \pm 68.5°$. The peak slip occurs for $\cos \delta = 1$, at $\delta = 0$; therefore;

$$S_{\max}^2 = 2 \times 0.634(0.03)^2 = 1.268(0.03)^2$$

or

$$S_{\max} = 1.12 \times 0.03 = 0.034$$

so that

$$\omega_{\max} = 360(1.034) = 372 \text{ rpm}$$

(*c*) Tripling the inertia causes ω_h/ω_e to decrease by a factor of $\sqrt{3}$ to $0.03/\sqrt{3}$. Thus the critical slip from Eq. (8.61*b*) is $(2/\sqrt{3})(0.03)$. The actual initial slip is 0.03. Since this is less than the critical value, synchronization can still take place.

8.6 MOTOR STARTING

The synchronous machine must be started with single excitation in order to avoid the large pulsations of current and torque which would result if double excitation were employed. The generator is consequently started by using the prime mover to bring the speed up to near the synchronous value, with the armature disconnected. With the d-c field excitation first applied, a propitious instant is selected (see Prob. 8.10), and the armature circuit is then closed.

The starting of a synchronous motor presents a special problem. Normally, the synchronous motor will not start by means of the synchronous mode of power conversion, and it has been said that "the synchronous motor develops no starting torque."

This statement is certainly correct in the sense that there is no *average* starting torque, since for a stationary rotor δ will sweep continuously with time; i.e., $\delta = -p\omega_s t$, and sin $(p\omega_s t)$ has no average value. However, there does seem to be a theoretical possibility that the transient torque might be sufficient, in the same way as in the synchronizing problem just discussed, to cause pull-in from a dead stall. Unfortunately, we cannot perform a simple and accurate analysis of this problem since it is no longer quasi-steady state in character. Thus if $\delta_i = 0$ and we attempt to bring Eq. (8.61) to bear, with $\omega_i = 0$, we find that the starting condition is $\omega_h/\omega_e \geq \frac{1}{2}$, which says that self-starting would be possible for very low inertia rotors. This is, of course, a sensible result, but it does not agree with our condition for quasi-steady state Eq. (8.9*b*), so that we must have doubts about its quantitative validity. In any case, the fact is that in conventional converters the rotors and their coupled loads are simply too ponderous to permit self-starting.

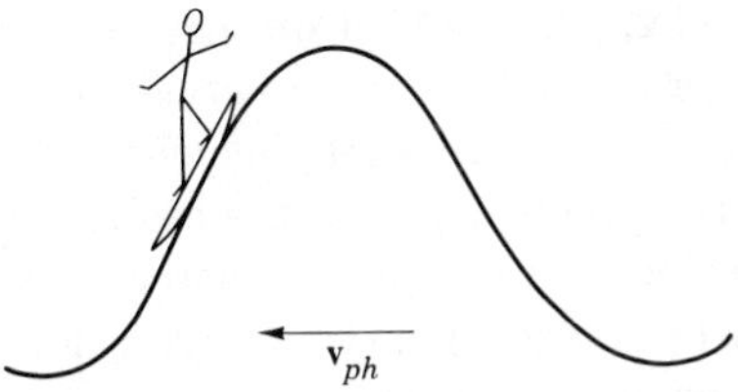

Fig. 8.14 Surf-riding analog of the variable-frequency method for starting synchronous motors.

Another way of looking at the starting "condition" mentioned in the previous paragraph is that self-starting would occur for a given ω_h if the electric frequency were made low. In fact, Eq. (8.61) suggests that we might maintain the slip small and get synchronization by starting off with a very low value of $\omega_e = p\omega_s$ and then subsequently increasing electric frequency at the same rate as the rotor picks up speed, so that the inequality is satisfied during the whole starting period. This indeed turns out to be a feasible method, although it finds relatively limited application since it requires a special variable-frequency power supply. It is used in rayon and other synthetic-fiber mills, where hundreds of spools individually driven by small synchronous motors are not only accelerated but also maintained in absolute synchronism at variable speed by adjusting the frequency of a common generator.

This method of acceleration is reminiscent of surf riding (see Fig. 8.14), in that from the viewpoint of the armature reference frame we see the field conductor phase-locked and carried away by the accelerating armature wave. This same principle is employed in modern high-energy accelerators where a beam of charged particles is brought up to speeds approaching very nearly the speed of light by literally riding on an electromagnetic wave whose phase velocity is made to increase gradually along the accelerator.

The most common method for bringing large synchronous motors close to synchronous speed is to start them using single excitation (i.e., no d-c field) and with the help of the auxiliary starting or damper winding previously mentioned. Its principle of operation will be discussed in the following chapter.

8.7 SUMMARY

In this chapter we have studied the dynamic performance of the synchronous converter. Following are its most important features.

1. The time constants of both the mechanical and electrical transients are, in general, longer than the fundamental period of a-c oscillation. When this situation prevails, the actual speed is adequately represented by its average over a cycle, and it is appropriate to define a single frequency for the alternating quantities and describe them by means of phasors. In addition, the electrical transients are so much faster that the dynamical performance can be viewed as a slow evolution of electrical steady states. This we call *quasi-steady state.*
2. A synchronous converter, when excited with constant field current and connected to a constant passive RL load, has two possible points of operation for each value of shaft torque not exceeding the peak developed torque. If the prime mover develops a constant torque, the point corresponding to the higher speed is unstable. Stable operation can be achieved only when the slope of the torque-speed characteristic of the driven generator exceeds that of the driving prime mover. This is true, in general, for any coupled system of driver and load.
3. The double excitation in a synchronous converter impresses two sets of waves which, during a speed change, are not at relative standstill. The dominant interaction occurs between the $\bar{K}_f$ wave of the field set and the $\bar{B}$ wave of the armature set; as in steady state, the resultant torque is proportional to the sine of the power angle δ which measures the stroboscopically sampled position of the rotor with respect to the stator. However, in contrast with steady state, during a speed change the angle δ and, consequently, the torque vary with time. The dependence of the torque on time, combined with inertial effects, results in a dynamical behavior of the power angle similar to that of an elastic coupling or a gravity pendulum.

4. As in the case of single excitation, for a given shaft torque the doubly excited converter can operate at two different points. The incremental stability analysis shows that: (*a*) With constant field excitation only the range of δ between $-\pi/2$ and $+\pi/2$ is potentially stable. (*b*) The converter "hunts" around stable operating points, performing small oscillations which are usually damped. (*c*) Periodic irregularities in the shaft torque give rise to forced oscillations which near resonance conditions cause undesirably large power fluctuations.
5. Sudden load changes may cause a converter to lose synchronism and fall out of step. In order to accommodate these larger transients, we must further restrict the range of the operating δ. This results in the uneconomical design of synchronous converters with large gaps and large field currents. Since the stability problem in synchronous converters stems from the lack of an intrinsic feedback mechanism capable of controlling the field excitation to suit the armature-circuit requirements, a fruitful endeavor is the development of fast and reliable means of automatic field-current control.
6. Double excitation can be impressed on a synchronous converter only when the rotor speed is very near the synchronous speed and its position (angle δ) is in the appropriate range. Motors are usually started asynchronously from the a-c supply without d-c excitation, and generators are brought up to speed fully excited on the d-c side. The second excitation must be applied at a propitious instant with the help of special synchronizing gear.

REFERENCES

1. Lyon, W. V.: "Transient Analysis of Alternating Current Machinery," MIT Press and J. Wiley & Sons, Inc., New York, 1954.
2. Weiner, D. D., and B. J. Leon: The Quasi-stationary Response of Linear Systems to Modulated Waveforms, *Proc. IEEE*, vol. 53, pp. 564–575 (June, 1965).
3. Levi, E., J. Freidberg, and C. W. Lawrence: Optimizing the Performance of Synchronous Generators, to be presented at the summer Power meeting of the IEEE, New Orleans, July 10–15, 1966, and subsequently published in the *Trans. IEEE* on Power Apparatus and Systems.

PROBLEMS

8.1 Find the maximum speed and frequency possible under stable operating conditions in Example 8.1 if the driver engine has a flat torque-speed characteristic. What is the power delivered to the load under these conditions?

8.2 A 4-pole 60-cps singly excited generator which operates into a constant parameter parallel *RC* load with a power factor of 0.8, has a per-unit gap reactance of 0.9.

(*a*) If the prime mover has a flat torque-speed characteristic, will the system be stable?

(*b*) Find the maximum frequency which can be produced under stable conditions by a prime mover with a flat torque-speed characteristic.

8.3 A doubly excited 60-cps synchronous motor with two-pole pairs and a natural frequency of 2 cps operates at synchronous speed with a mechanical load representing 15 percent of the maximum developed torque of the machine. The load is suddenly increased to 60 percent of the maximum developed torque.

Will the machine subsequently regain synchronous operation? If so, find the extremes of power angle which occur in the transient accompanying the load change.

8.4 The necessary condition for a force interaction between a $\bar{K}$ and a $\bar{B}$ wave is that they have the same wavelength and are at respective standstill. The relative velocity of these waves with respect to the conductors which support them affects the power-conversion process but not the force interaction. This principle can be utilized when there is need to transfer a torque between two shafts which are not in physical contact, but there is no need to convert power. One such device is the synchronous clutch. It consists of two complementary magnetic structures similar to those of the synchronous converter but carrying d-c excitation on both sides.

(*a*) Assuming equal excitation $\bar{K}$ on both sides, determine the relation between the torque and $\bar{K}$.

(*b*) If the clutch is built with two pole pairs and, under rated conditions, the torque is 50 percent of the peak torque developed, determine the maximum angle over which the shaft of the driven part can be rotated with respect to the driver shaft by reducing $\bar{K}$. Determine the percentage reduction in $\bar{K}$ which brings about this change.

(*c*) Determine the maximum swing angle δ_{max} when the rated torque is suddenly applied with rated excitation.

8.5 In normal operation a synchronous generator feeds into an infinite bus through two parallel transmission lines with reactances X_1 and X_2 as indicated.

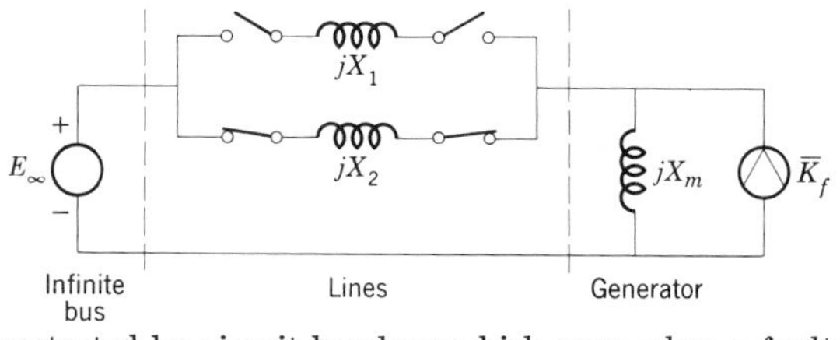

The system is protected by circuit breakers which open when a fault occurs. When one of the parallel branches is disconnected, the overall line reactance increases and the armature current decreases. This causes a decrease in the power and torque developed by the generator. If the torque applied by the prime mover on the shaft of the generator remains constant as the fault occurs, the generator accelerates and may fall out of step. Note that the torque developed by the generator is

$$\mathcal{L}_d = -\frac{2\pi r_g b}{\omega} \operatorname{Re} [\bar{K}_f^* \bar{E}_a] = -\frac{2\pi r_g b}{\omega} \left(\frac{\mathfrak{X}_m}{X_{\text{line}} + \mathfrak{X}_m} \right) \operatorname{Re} [\bar{K}_f^* \bar{E}_\infty]$$

$$= -\mathcal{L}_m \sin \delta'(t)$$

where
$$\mathcal{L}_m = \frac{2\pi r_g b}{\omega} \left(\frac{|\bar{K}_f||\bar{E}_\infty|}{1 + X_{\text{line}}/\mathfrak{X}_m} \right)$$

and $\delta' - \pi/2$ is the angle by which $\bar{K}_f$ leads $\bar{E}_\infty$. If, according to the quasi-steady-state approximation, ω and therefore $\mathfrak{L}_m$ are considered to be constant, then δ' is the only variable quantity in the expression for $\mathfrak{L}_d$. It follows that all the stability considerations discussed in Sec. 8.4*d* apply here with δ' replacing δ.

Assuming that $X_{m,\text{p.u.}} = 0.8$, $X_{1,\text{p.u.}} = X_{2,\text{p.u.}} = 0.3$, $\bar{K}_f$ remains constant, and the power delivered before the fault is 50 percent of the peak power corresponding to the given excitation, determine:

(*a*) The ratio of peak power developed under fault to that developed under normal conditions.

(*b*) The steady-state value of δ' under fault, δ'_0.

(*c*) The maximum swing angle under fault, $\delta'_{\max}$.

Hint: For part (*c*) use the equal-area criterion as shown.

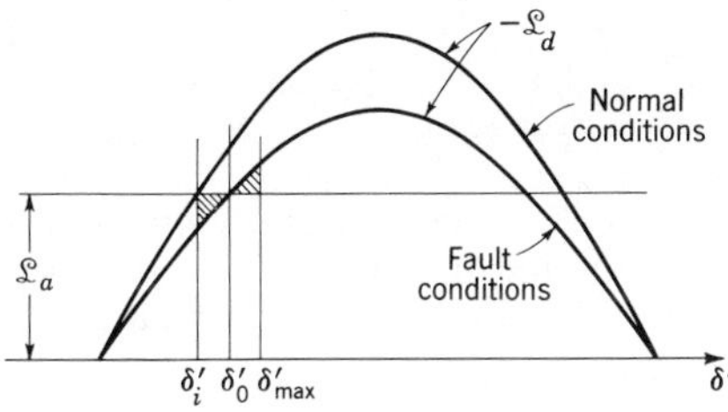

8.6 Consider the situation described in the previous problem but with the following values of the line and generator reactances:

$$X_{m,\text{p.u.}} = 1.2 \qquad X_{1,\text{p.u.}} = 0.2 \qquad X_{2,\text{p.u.}} = 1$$

and assume that at the instant the fault occurs in line 1 the generator is delivering 65 percent of its peak power. Now the peak torque developed under fault is less than the torque applied on the shaft, and the generator will fall out of step unless the fault is cleared and the circuit breaker reclosed within a short time. Stable operation can be reestablished only if the fault is cleared before δ' has reached a critical value δ'_c. Proceeding as in the previous problem, and using the equal-area criterion as shown, determine the critical angle δ'_c for this system.

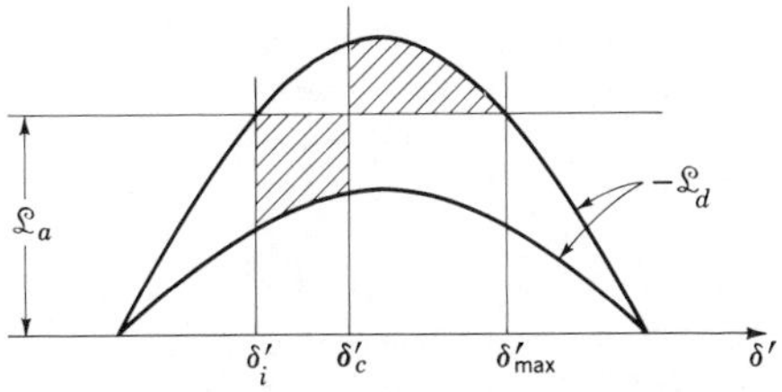

8.7 Lightning strikes the connecting line between a synchronous generator and the infinite bus, causing a dead short circuit as shown. Using the equal-area criterion, determine the critical power angle δ_c which cannot be exceeded during the fault period if stable operation is to be restored. Assume that during the fault K_f

and $\mathcal{L}_a$ remain constant and that $\mathcal{L}_a$ corresponds to 50 percent of the peak torque that the generator can develop with the given value of field excitation.

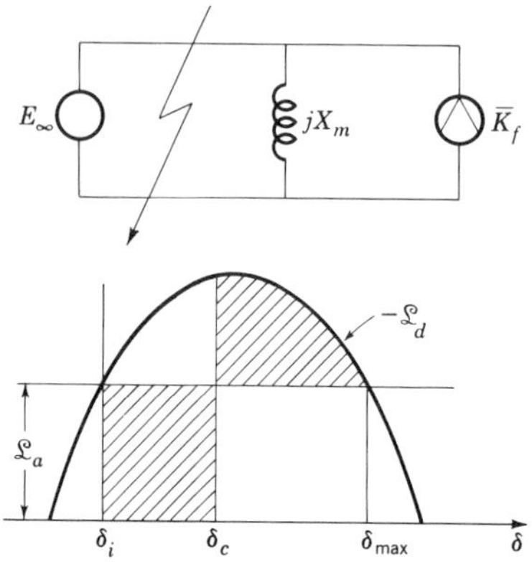

8.8 A 200-Mw generator is connected to an infinite bus and operates with a power angle $\delta_0 = 60°$ when the circuit breaker in the connecting line opens.

(*a*) Determine the critical angle δ_c that the machine is allowed to reach before the circuit breaker recloses.

(*b*) Assuming that the applied torque remains constant in the interval between δ_0 and δ_c, estimate the critical time that the circuit breaker is allowed to stay open. Assume also that the generator has two poles, that its moment of inertia is $\Theta = 8.5 \times 10^3$ kg-m², and that $f_e = 60$ cps.

8.9 A step motor is a servo component which produces a stepwise angular deflection in response to a sequence of pulses. When the pulse-repetition rate is sufficiently large, the rotation becomes continuous, and the motor is then said to operate in the "slewing" mode and performs like a synchronous motor. Determine the maximum rate at which the input frequency can be (*a*) increased, (*b*) decreased, without causing the motor to fall out of step. Assume the most unfavorable operating conditions, and consider a size-5 unit ($\frac{1}{2}$ in. diameter) which has four poles and a moment of inertia $\Theta = 0.5$ gm-cm², develops a peak torque $\mathcal{L}_m = 0.15$ oz-in., and is designed to operate with a load torque up to 50 percent of its peak torque.

8.10 A synchronous generator is brought up to speed and connected to the bus, using the arrangement shown in the figure. Here each phase of the machine armature

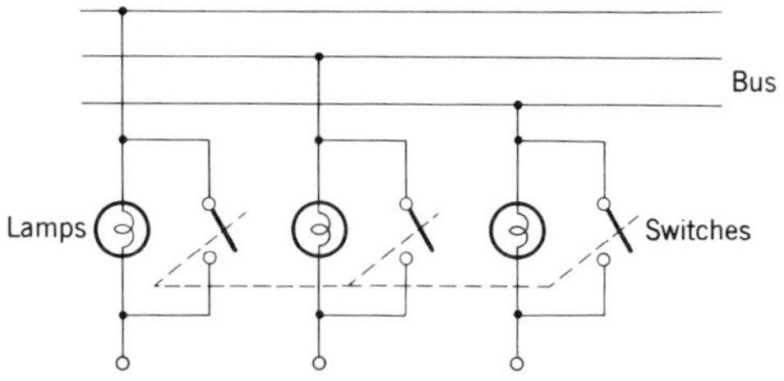

is connected by a switch to an appropriate phase of the bus, with a relatively low-current lamp connected in parallel with each switch. The machine is brought up to speed with the switches open and K_f set so that the open-circuit voltage of the converter armature phases matches the bus voltage in magnitude. As the machine approaches synchronous speed, the lamps are observed to flash in a periodic sequence whose frequency is determined by the speed difference. When the speeds are very nearly equal, the lamps flash very slowly. The switches are then closed at the time when the lamps are dark.

(*a*) What value of the power angle δ results from the above procedure at the instant of switch closure?

(*b*) The lamps are flashing at the rate of once every 5 sec when the switch is closed during the dark interval. If the machine is a 60-cps 10-pole converter with a natural frequency of 2 cps, what maximum δ value ensues (neglecting damping torque)?

(*c*) What must be done to establish the desired power level and power factor of operation? Assume that $\mathfrak{L}_a = 0$ at the instant of synchronization.

8.11 By using the graphical technique of Sec. 8.5, determine:

(*a*) The most propitious power angle δ_i for synchronization of a motor when the applied torque $\mathfrak{L}_a \neq 0$.

(*b*) The limits on the excursion of the power angle δ when the motor of Example 8.3 is synchronized with $\mathfrak{L}_a = -0.3\ \mathfrak{L}_m$ and $\delta_i = 0$.

chapter 9
THE ASYNCHRONOUS HETEROPOLAR CONVERTER; TERMINAL CHARACTERISTICS

9.1 INTRODUCTION

In our study of the heteropolar converter our primary concern so far has been to reach a basic understanding of the power-conversion process itself. For this purpose we have chosen the particularly simple case of synchronous operation, and we have concentrated our attention on the region where this process takes place, the gap. In this chapter we enlarge our scope and take a more comprehensive viewpoint.

We investigate and demonstrate the feasibility of operation at speeds other than the synchronous speed, thus overcoming one of the major limitations of the synchronous converter. In the process we discover an intrinsic feature of the traveling-wave structure: the *transformer action.* This mechanism allows for transfer of power between electric circuits placed on opposite sides of the gap, affords the interchangeability of the stator and rotor windings, and offers the possibility of eliminating sliding contacts.

To trace the course or flow of power in the gap we expand the area of interest to include the terminals of the converter, and we carry out the transition from the local electromagnetic field quantities to the integral circuit quantities in an ideal converter. We find that the transformer action is associated with the time rate of change of the magnetic flux interlinked with the electric circuits; the agency for the transfer of power in the gap is thus that component of electric field which is derivable from a vector potential, i.e., the *solenoidal component.*

At this point, having completed our investigation of the characteristic mechanism for power conversion in traveling-wave converters of the magnetic type, it is appropriate to enter into the details of their physical realization and mechanical structures. We thus study how the conductors, which are finite in number and embedded in discrete slots, are connected to form coils which are grouped into a small number of phases; we learn how to relate the electromagnetic field quantities prevailing in the gap to the observable terminal quantities: the line voltage, current, and power.

We find that the departures from the ideal conditions previously considered result in the excitation of higher-order waves which do not participate in the fundamental power-conversion process but increase the amount of reactive power that circulates between the various parts of the converter and the external networks. We account for their effects on the terminal voltage and the local storage of energy by introducing lumped reactances called *leakage reactances*. We show that these reactances do not affect appreciably the terminal characteristics of the synchronous converters, but we foresee how they will play a more important role in the asynchronous converters which we study in the next chapter.

9.2 STRUCTURE AND OPERATION OF THE GENERAL HETEROPOLAR CONVERTER

The previous chapter on the dynamic performance has demonstrated that a synchronous converter cannot, in general, start as a motor or operate stably over a wide range of power angle. We have found that the two major factors that impair its dynamic performance are:

1. The synchronous tie between the electric frequency and the speed.
2. The unilateral coupling between the armature and the field circuits, or the lack of an intrinsic feedback mechanism to regulate the field current according to the requirements of the armature circuit.

We now wish to determine whether a heteropolar converter can be operated so as to circumvent these difficulties.

It turns out that this is indeed possible. In fact, the reader will recall that we have anticipated the *induction* mechanism in Sec. 8.4, where we studied the transient performance of doubly excited synchronous machines. It was noted that when the converter operates asynchronously, the armature wave group induces a current component which flows in the field conductors and produces an electromagnetic *induction* torque. This suggests that the inductive effect, which itself vanishes at synchronous speed, provides the requisite mechanism for coupling from the armature to field at nonsynchronous speeds. We shall indeed find that it is possible to synthesize a converter based on this mechanism. Such machines are therefore called *asynchronous* or *induction* converters.

To develop this idea in an orderly fashion, let us begin by envisaging a converter whose stator and rotor are heteropolar structures similar to those of the synchronous converter. The active conductor on each side of the gap thus consists of an array of strands lying parallel to one another in the axial direction and embedded in slots as shown in Fig. 6.6.

(a) Wave Frame

As we have previously noted in Chap. 6, we may consider a reference frame "attached" to the electromagnetic waves of the heteropolar converter, i.e., a frame in which by definition the waves are at standstill.

In the synchronous converter operating in the steady state, the wave frame is fixed to the field-conductor array, since the field is excited by direct current. In our new induction converter, this constraint is eliminated, and both conductors are in motion with respect to the wave frame.

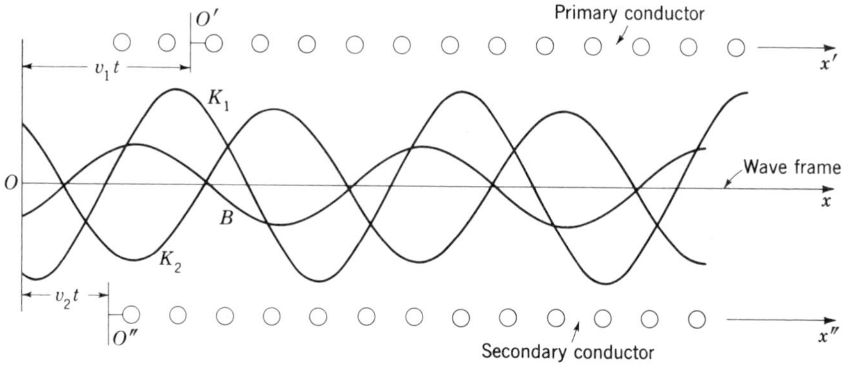

Fig. 9.1 Relative motion of the primary and secondary conductors with respect to the wave frame.

As seen from the wave frame, then, both conductors behave like the armature conductor of a synchronous converter, and may be so treated.

From the viewpoint of the wave frame the distinction between *stator* and *rotor*, or *field* and *armature* has no significance since both conductors are seen to be in motion and behave in the same way. In recognition of this fact, we choose to designate the conductors as *primary* and *secondary*, denoted by the indices 1 and 2, respectively. The motion of the two conductors in the wave frame is shown in Fig. 9.1.

The relative motion with respect to the wave frame sets up a motion-induced electric field in each of the two arrays. If v_1 is the velocity of the primary array with respect to the wave frame, then in this frame the electric field $\bar{E}$, the perpendicular component of flux density $\bar{B}$, and the current density $\bar{K}$ satisfy, according to Eq. (6.13*b*), the phasor relation,

$$\bar{E}_1 - v_1\bar{B} = \frac{\bar{K}_1}{a_1\gamma_1} \tag{9.1}$$

Likewise if v_2 is the velocity of the secondary array with respect to the wave frame, we have

$$\bar{E}_2 - v_2\bar{B} = \frac{\bar{K}_2}{a_2\gamma_2} \tag{9.2}$$

As a result of the flow of current and the presence of the magnetic field, the conductors are stressed by a tangential force density which, for each set, is given on the average by the real part of the phasor product of $\bar{B}$ and $\bar{K}$:

$$\langle f_x \rangle = \text{Re}\,[\bar{K}\bar{B}^*] = \text{Re}\,[\bar{K}^*\bar{B}] \tag{9.3}$$

As we have seen in Sec. 6.7*b*, this product vanishes for all heteropolar converters, unless the $\bar{K}$ and $\bar{B}$ waves have the same wavelength 2τ and are at relative standstill. These conditions are ensured in synchronous converters by connecting the conductor array which is moving with respect to the wave frame (the armature array) to a system of electric circuits consisting of equal impedances and properly phased sources. In this *generalized* version of the heteropolar converter we must duplicate the same scheme for *both* the primary and secondary arrays.

(b) Primary and Secondary Frequencies; Doppler Effect

In the synchronous converter, the radian frequency of the time variation in the armature conductor ω_e is related to the velocity v by the synchronous tie of Eq. (6.8*a*):

$$\omega_e = \frac{\pi}{\tau} v = \frac{p}{r_g} v \tag{6.8a}$$

In the generalized heteropolar converter, however, there are now *two* radian frequencies, $\omega_{e,1}$ and $\omega_{e,2}$ in the primary and secondary, respectively. We can see this very easily. For identical wavelength 2τ, Eq. (6.8*a*) applies equally well to the relationship between each conductor and the wave frame. Thus we have

$$\omega_{e,1} = \frac{v_1 p}{r_g} \qquad \omega_{e,2} = \frac{v_2 p}{r_g} \tag{9.4}$$

To achieve power conversion there must be relative motion between the primary and secondary conductors. It follows that $v_1 \neq v_2$, so that, in general, $\omega_{e,1} \neq \omega_{e,2}$. Thus we have alternating current of different frequencies in primary and secondary, and zero frequency or direct current (time invariance) in the wave frame.

This phenomenon of frequency change from one reference frame to another is a generalization of the effect we noted earlier in the synchronous converter. There an electromagnetic field quantity with periodic spatial variation, which appears to be time-invariant in one frame (the field frame), transforms into a traveling wave when seen from another frame in relative motion (armature frame). In the present instance we have a wave which in *both* the primary and secondary frames appears to be traveling and to have the same wavelength but different frequencies. This change in the frequency which is observed when going from the primary to the secondary is a well-known effect named after Doppler who enunciated the principle in 1842. The *Doppler shift* is independent of the physical nature of the phenomenon; it is merely the result of the relative motion between frames and can be evaluated by applying the Galilean transformation of coordinates, as was done in Sec. 6.5*b*. A commonplace example is the change in pitch of a moving source of sound, such as an automobile horn or a train whistle. Another example is the shift toward the red of the spectral lines emitted by distant stars, which forms the basis for the theory of the expanding universe.

A practical consequence of the Doppler change from $\omega_{e,1}$ to $\omega_{e,2}$ is that if *double* excitation is used, we need two separate polyphase supplies at these frequencies. Moreover, if the rotor speed were to be changed, at least one of the two supply frequencies would have to be changed. These are considerable drawbacks, so that double excitation is not usually employed. Instead, nonsynchronous heteropolar converters are normally operated with single excitation.

In summary, then, it appears that it is possible to construct and operate in the steady state a power converter that is a heteropolar machine having *two* active conductors, both of which carry alternating currents, though of different frequencies. In general, such a machine uses single excitation, although double excitation is possible, if not very common. The rotor speed of this machine differs from the synchronous rotor speed. The analytical description of the asynchronous heteropolar converter is facilitated by choosing as a frame of reference one in which the waves are at standstill so that time invariance obtains.

9.3 IDEALIZED CIRCUIT MODELS

In this section we derive equivalent-circuit representations of the heteropolar converter and begin to study their performance. In addition to the Ohm's law relations for the primary and secondary conductors [Eqs. (9.1) and (9.2)], we need an equation relating the current densities to the magnetic field prevailing in the gap. If we employ the wave frame, the $\bar{K}$ and $\bar{B}$ waves associated with each conductor are stationary, just as in our previous case of the synchronous machine in the field reference frame. Thus Eq. (7.17) applies directly, and we restate it here:

$$\bar{B} = \bar{B}_1 + \bar{B}_2 = j\,\frac{\mu_0\tau}{\pi g}\,(\bar{K}_1 + \bar{K}_2) \tag{9.5}$$

The set of equations (9.1) through (9.5) constitutes the mathematical description of an ideal heteropolar converter in the most general terms, including the synchronous converter as a limiting case when either v_1 or v_2 vanishes.

Rather than formally manipulate the equations, we shall proceed as previously to embody the electromagnetic relationships in appropriate models. Noting that the terms which couple the primary and secondary circuits, i.e., the motion-induced electric fields $v_1\bar{B}$ and $v_2\bar{B}$ in Eqs. (9.1) and (9.2), are not the same in the two equations, we must first reduce these equations to a common base before combining them in a single equivalent representation. This process is called *referring secondary to primary*, or vice versa. In view of the complete symmetry, it is arbitrary which way we choose to go. Usually the choice is associated with the identification of rotor and stator, but inasmuch as we need not concern ourselves with this question at this point, we shall arbitrarily decide to refer the secondary to the primary. The actual process consists simply of multiplying Eq. (9.2) by an appropriate factor so that the term $v_2\bar{B}$ then becomes $v_1\bar{B}$. Obviously the factor required is v_1/v_2; the resulting equation is then

$$\bar{E}_2 \frac{v_1}{v_2} = v_1\bar{B} + \frac{\bar{K}_2}{a_2\gamma_2} \frac{v_1}{v_2} \tag{9.6}$$

Although Eq. (9.6), along with all the previous ones, is written in the wave frame, it is useful to express v_1 and v_2 in terms of velocities relative to a frame attached to one of the conductors, in this case the primary, since we have chosen to refer secondary to primary. Thus we define v_s and v as

$$\begin{aligned} v_s &= \text{synchronous speed, or the velocity of the} \\ &\quad\ \text{wave frame with respect to the primary} \\ v &= \text{velocity of the secondary with respect to the primary} \end{aligned} \tag{9.7}$$

From the previous definitions of v_1 and v_2 it follows that

$$\begin{aligned} v_s &= -v_1 \\ v_2 &= v + v_1 = v - v_s \end{aligned} \tag{9.8}$$

so that

$$\frac{v_2}{v_1} = \frac{v_s - v}{v_s} \tag{9.9a}$$

Equation (9.9*a*) makes it clear that the ratio v_2/v_1 is the measure of the rate at which the secondary slips past the wave frame, normalized to the synchronous speed. As we have previously done in Sec. 8.5, we may define this quantity as the slip S with respect to the synchronous speed:

$$S = \frac{v_2}{v_1} = \frac{v_s - v}{v_s} \tag{9.9b}$$

In terms of S, Eq. (9.6) becomes

$$\frac{\bar{E}_2}{S} = v_1\bar{B} + \frac{\bar{K}_2}{a_2\gamma_2 S} \tag{9.10}$$

and, from Eq. (9.5),

$$v_1\bar{B} = \frac{j\mu_0\tau}{\pi g} v_1(\bar{K}_1 + \bar{K}_2) \tag{9.11}$$

If, in keeping with Eq. (7.20), we let

$$\mathfrak{X}_{m,1} = \frac{\mu_0\tau v_1}{\pi g} \tag{9.12}$$

we see from Eqs. (7.21), (7.22) and (9.4) that

$$\mathfrak{X}_{m,1} = L_m\omega_{e,1} \tag{9.13}$$

i.e., $\mathfrak{X}_{m,1}$ is the gap reactance evaluated at the radian frequency in the primary conductor. Equation (9.11) then may be written

$$v_1\bar{B} = j\mathfrak{X}_{m,1}(\bar{K}_1 + \bar{K}_2) = j\omega_{e,1}L_m(\bar{K}_1 + \bar{K}_2) \tag{9.14}$$

Equations (9.1), (9.10), and (9.14) now may be depicted by the equivalent circuit of Fig. 9.2. Following the approach used in Chap. 7, the relationships of Eqs. (9.1), (9.10), and (9.14) may be alternatively depicted in a phasor diagram, as shown in Fig. 9.3.

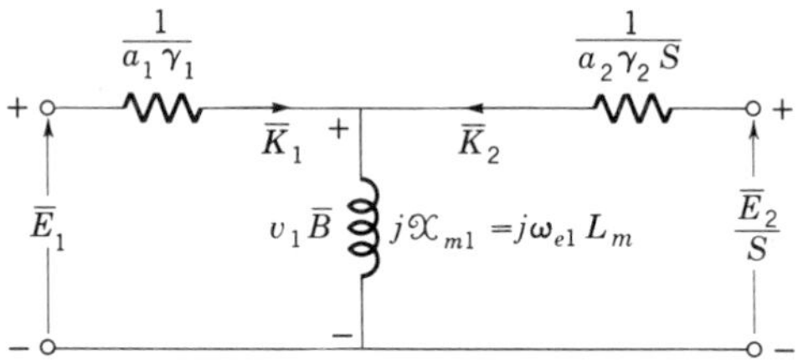

Fig. 9.2 Equivalent circuit of the ideal asynchronous heteropolar converter.

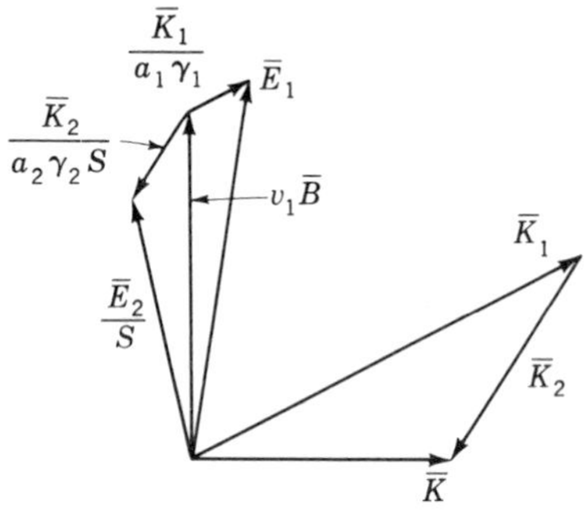

Fig. 9.3 Phasor diagram of the ideal asynchronous heteropolar converter (motoring operation).

(a) Limiting Case of Synchronous Operation

We next wish to see how the wave-frame equivalent circuit depicts several limiting cases. In doing this, we shall find it desirable to relate this circuit to the terminal conditions. Although we have not yet considered the relationship between the wave-frame quantities and those observed in the reference frame of the external circuits, let us look ahead a little and forecast, as was done in Sec. 7.4 for the synchronous converter and as will be proved in the next section, that the electric field in the wave frame is directly applicable to the determination of the actual terminal voltage.

The equivalent circuit of Fig. 9.2 displays the bilateral coupling between the primary and secondary circuits in the general case when

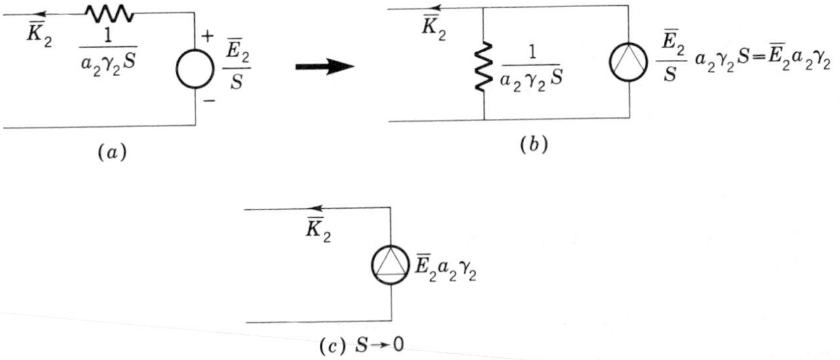

Fig. 9.4 Transition to the equivalent circuit of a synchronous converter.

$S \neq 0$. It is easily seen how the symmetry of the coupling is lost in the limit when $S \to 0$, and the circuit reduces to that of a synchronous machine. As S approaches zero, both the secondary source and its series resistance increase without bound; the secondary current $\bar{K}_2$ therefore becomes insensitive to changes in the primary circuit and can be assumed to originate in an ideal current source. Formally we can perform a source transformation in the secondary circuit and replace the voltage source $\bar{E}_2/S$ and its series resistance $1/a_2\gamma_2 S$ by a current source $(\bar{E}_2/S)a_2\gamma_2 S$ in parallel with a conductance $a_2\gamma_2 S$, as indicated in Fig. 9.4. When the slip S vanishes, the parallel branch opens up and the secondary current $\bar{K}_2$ equals the source current $\bar{E}_2 a_2\gamma_2$; the circuit then reduces to that of the synchronous machine shown in Fig. 7.4.

(b) Single Excitation; Asynchronous Operation

In the case where double excitation is used with fixed radian frequencies ω_{e1} and ω_{e2} in the primary and secondary, respectively, the velocities v_1 and v_2 are determined [Eq. (9.4)] so that the relative velocity $v = v_2 - v_1$ is fixed [(Eqs. (9.7) and (9.8)]. Since the velocity v is also, of course, the relative velocity between rotor and stator, it follows that *fixing the two excitation frequencies constrains the rotor angular velocity to a value*

$$\omega = \frac{\omega_{e,2} - \omega_{e,1}}{p} \tag{9.15}$$

Thus the doubly excited heteropolar machine with prescribed a-c excitation in rotor and stator is again a *synchronous machine*, in the sense that the steady-state speed is fixed. We see that the conventional synchronous machine with d-c field excitation represents a special case of the general class of doubly excited heteropolar machines. There is little practical advantage, however, to building synchronous machines with all

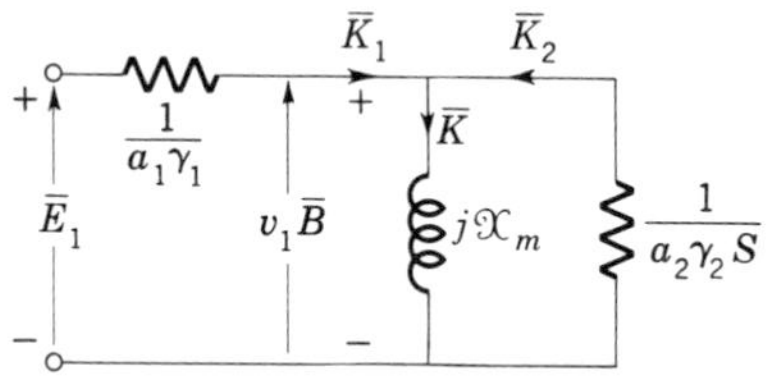

Fig. 9.5 Equivalent circuit of the ideal heteropolar converter singly excited by an a-c supply.

a-c operation at two fixed frequencies; so we normally encounter conventional d-c excitation of the field in synchronous machines.

If we wish to achieve truly asynchronous operation, then we must use single excitation only. In this case $E_2 = 0$; i.e., the secondary conductor is short-circuited, and there is no source which *constrains* the value of $\omega_{e,2}$. The secondary currents are then wholly induced, and their frequency is determined by $\omega_{e,1}$ and the rotor speed. The rotor speed, in turn, is determined by the resulting speed-torque characteristics, as we shall see in Chap. 10.

The equivalent circuit of the heteropolar converter singly excited by an a-c supply can be derived from that of Fig. 9.2 simply by short-circuiting the secondary terminals, as shown in Fig. 9.5. This equivalent circuit clearly indicates that singly excited asynchronous operation bears a greater resemblance to the operation of the homopolar than to that of the synchronous converter. In fact, in contrast with the singly excited synchronous machine the asynchronous machine can operate as a motor as well as a generator. This can be deduced from Fig. 9.5 as follows:

First we note that

$$\text{Re}\,[v_1\bar{B}\bar{K}_1^*] = -\,\text{Re}\,[v_1\bar{B}\bar{K}_2^*] \tag{9.16}$$

is the power that flows into the secondary circuit and is absorbed by the secondary resistance $1/a_2\gamma_2 S$. However, the actual resistance of the conductor is $1/a_2\gamma_2$. It appears that, when $S \neq 1$, or when the rotor conductor is in motion ($v \neq 0$), not all the power is dissipated, and part must be converted. We can put the two parts in evidence by separating from $1/a_2\gamma_2 S$ the actual conductor resistance $1/a_2\gamma_2$, as was done in Fig. 4.7. The result is shown in Fig. 9.6. Here we see that the drop across the resistance $\frac{1}{a_2\gamma_2}\frac{1-S}{S}$ is $v_1(1-S)\bar{B}$, which from Eqs. (9.8) and (9.9) is $-v\bar{B}$. Consequently the power absorbed by this resistance is

$$\begin{aligned} \text{Re}\,[(-\bar{K}_2^*)(-v\bar{B})] &= \text{Re}\,[\bar{K}_2^* v\bar{B}] = \text{Re}\,[-\bar{K}_1^* v\bar{B}] \\ &= (1-S)\,\text{Re}\,[\bar{K}_1^* v_1\bar{B}] \end{aligned} \tag{9.17}$$

and we see from Eq. (9.17) that this resistor power is identical to the converted surface power density in the *rotor*. This is true since if the rotor

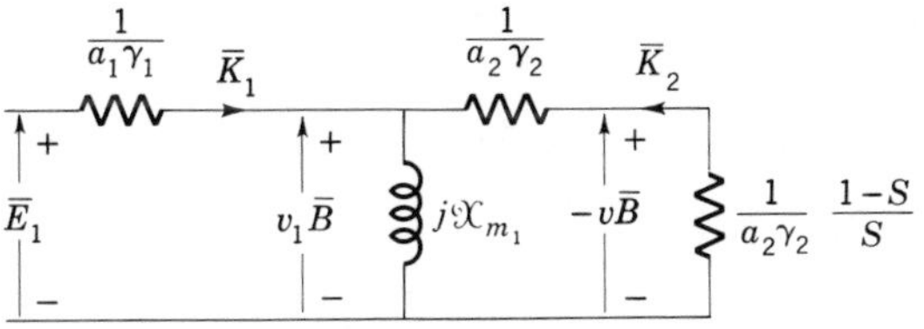

Fig. 9.6 Equivalent circuit, showing allocation of the secondary power.

is the primary, its velocity (seen from the stator) is $-v$, and its surface current density is $\bar{K}_1$; whereas if the rotor is the secondary, its velocity is $+v$, and its surface current density is $\bar{K}_2$.

It is now a simple matter to deduce the conditions attending the different modes of operation. For $S < 0$, the resistance $\frac{1}{a_2\gamma_2}\frac{1-S}{S}$ is negative, so that the rotor converted power is likewise negative; i.e., mechanical power is being delivered to the rotor. Moreover $\left|\frac{1-S}{S}\right| > 1$ so that the amount of power lost in secondary ohmic losses is less than that converted. Consequently, power flows out of the secondary and into the primary and we have overall *generating*. Next, for $0 < S < 1$, the conversion resistance is positive, so that we have overall *motoring*. Finally, for $S > 1$, the conversion resistance is again negative, but is less in magnitude than the secondary ohmic resistance, so that power flows from primary to secondary and we have *braking*. From the definition of the slip S, it follows that generating occurs for rotor velocity greater than synchronous, motoring for velocity less than synchronous, and braking for velocity less than zero, i.e., for the rotor running in a direction opposite to that of the traveling wave impressed by the primary source.

The singly excited asynchronous converter can thus operate in all the three modes, and the power flow is solely controlled by the relative velocity between the primary and secondary conductors.

The relations involving the slip and the mode of operation are illustrated by the following example.

Example 9.1

A heteropolar converter is connected to a 400-cycle polyphase supply. When the converter operates at 18,000 rpm, the frequency in the secondary conductors measures 200 cps.

(*a*) Find the number of pole pairs p.

(*b*) If the secondary is open-circuited and the primary resistance negligible, what is ratio of the magnitudes of the electric fields E_2/E_1, and what is their phase relation?

(*c*) If the secondary conductor is short-circuited, does it operate in the motoring, generating, or braking mode?

(*d*) Under what circumstances will the mode of operation of the whole converter correspond to that of the secondary conductor?

Solution

(*a*) The number of pole pairs is given by the ratio of primary radian frequency to angular velocity at synchronous speed:

$$p = \frac{\omega_1}{\omega_s}$$

To obtain the synchronous speed we can use the relation between the primary and the secondary frequencies:

$$\frac{\omega_2}{\omega_1} = \frac{v_2}{v_1} = S = \frac{\omega_s - \omega}{\omega_s}$$

Solving for ω_s, we get

$$\omega_s = \frac{\omega}{1 - \omega_2/\omega_1}$$

and
$$p = \omega_1 \frac{1 - \omega_2/\omega_1}{\omega} = \frac{\omega_1 - \omega_2}{\omega} = \frac{f_1 - f_2}{\text{rps}}$$

In this case
$$\text{rps} = \frac{18{,}000}{60} = 300 \qquad f_1 = 400 \qquad f_2 = 200$$

If we introduce these numerical values without further consideration, we obtain as a result

$$p = \frac{400 - 200}{300} = \frac{2}{3}$$

This is clearly wrong since the number of pole pairs must be an integer. The source of the mistake is in the sign of the secondary frequency. In fact, when the primary and secondary conductors move in opposite directions with respect to the wave frame,

$$\frac{v_2}{v_1} = S = \frac{\omega_2}{\omega_1} < 0$$

We thus have the alternative of assigning the negative sign to f_2 so that

$$p = \frac{400 + 200}{300} = 2$$

which is the correct result.

(b) When the primary resistance is negligible, we find, from the equivalent circuit of Fig. 9.2,

$$\bar{E}_1 = \frac{\bar{E}_2}{S}$$

Since we have found above that

$$S = \frac{\omega_2}{\omega_1} = -\frac{1}{2}$$

we have

$$\frac{E_2}{E_1} = \frac{1}{2}$$

with $\bar{E}_2$ being 180° out of phase with respect to $\bar{E}_1$.

(c) Since the slip is negative, the conductor operates in the generating mode.

(d) The mode of operation of the whole converter is also generating when the power transferred to the primary exceeds the power dissipated in the primary conductor.

The preceding considerations about the slip allow us to reach another important conclusion. In fact, with very rare exceptions, singly excited converters are fed through the stator, so that the conversion of power occurs in the secondary conductor. In this case we see from the equivalent circuit of Fig. 9.6 and Eq. (9.17) that the power flowing into the secondary divides between power converted and power dissipated within the conductor in the proportion $1 - S$ and S, respectively. It follows that the conversion efficiency of the secondary conductor is

$$\eta_m^{\text{sec}} = 1 - S \tag{9.18a}$$

in the motoring case and

$$\eta_g^{\text{sec}} = \frac{1}{1 - S} \tag{9.18b}$$

for a generator. We thus find that in this case the secondary of the asynchronous converter behaves like the armature of the homopolar machine; we may then apply to its design all the considerations which we derived in Sec. 4.10, simply by substituting the slip referred to the synchronous speed for the slip referred to the drift velocity. The design procedure is illustrated in the following example.

Example 9.2

Determine the dimensions of the secondary conductor in the generator of Example 9.1, if it is placed on the rotor and under rated conditions it delivers 1 Mw at unity power factor with a conversion efficiency $\eta_g = 0.99$. Assume $B_{\text{rms}} = 0.6$ weber/m². $K_{2,\text{rms}} = 10^5$ amp/m², $b/\tau = 6$, $\gamma = 5 \times 10^7$ mhos/m.

Solution

From Sec. 4.10 we have

$$A = 2\pi r_g b = \frac{P_{\text{out}}}{p_{s,\text{elec}}} = \frac{P_{\text{out}}}{Kv_E B}$$

where
$$v_E = v_s = \frac{2\pi r_g f}{p} = 400\pi r_g$$

and
$$b = 6\tau = \frac{6\pi r_g}{p} = 3\pi r_g$$

Solving for r_g, we obtain

$$r_g = \frac{1}{\pi}\sqrt[3]{\frac{10^6}{6 \times 400 \times 0.6 \times 10^5}} = 0.0608 \text{ m}$$
$$b = 3\pi r_g = 0.573 \text{ m}$$
$$v_E = 400\pi \times 0.0608 = 76.4 \text{ m/sec}$$

The thickness of the conductor is then given by

$$a = \frac{p_{s,\text{elec}}}{p_{\text{elec}}} = \frac{-Kv_E B}{(1 - 1/\eta_G)\gamma v_E{}^2 B^2} = \frac{0.99 \times 10^5}{0.01 \times 5 \times 10^7 \times 76.4 \times 0.6}$$
$$= 0.00432 \text{ m} = 4.32 \text{ mm}$$

According to our idealized model, the secondary circuit is purely resistive, and therefore the power factor is unity. In an actual machine the secondary circuit includes the leakage reactance already mentioned. However, its effect on the power factor under rated conditions is negligible because of the low frequency of the secondary currents. As a result, calculations such as those of the preceding example are adequately accurate. When the leakage reactance is taken into account, the power densities of Secs. 6.7*c* and 7.5*b* should be used instead of those of Secs. 4.7 and 4.9.

In the rare case that the converter is fed through the rotor, no power conversion occurs in the secondary conductor, and therefore its conversion efficiency is zero. The design is then based on the overall efficiency of the converter, which will be determined in Chap. 10.

(c) The Homopolar Converter Viewed as a Limiting Case

The similarity in the performance of the rotor conductors of the asynchronous and homopolar converters leads us to speculate that one might conceptually go from one type to the other by using some kind of limiting process in the same way as the doubly excited heteropolar converter reduces to the synchronous converter in the limit when $S \to 0$. We pursue this line of thought because it will help in bringing to light the important mechanism which differentiates between the two converter types.

If we make use of Fig. 4.7 and draw an equivalent circuit for the homopolar converter in terms of the current density K and the slip s, we obtain for the rotor conductor the right-side portion of Fig. 9.7. On the left-hand side of Fig. 9.7 we have introduced the resistance of the stationary shell, which serves as return conductor and compensates for the armature reaction. Comparison between Figs. 9.7 and 9.6 shows that the only difference aside from the different base velocities used in defining the two slips, is the presence in the asynchronous converter of a parallel branch representing the magnetizing reactance $\mathfrak{X}_m$. Formally this branch can be made to disappear, according to Eq. (9.12), by letting the pole-pitch arc τ increase without bound. Clearly, letting the wavelength of alternation become infinite is the same as assuming the structure to be uniform, and accordingly we find from Eq. (6.8*a*) that the electric frequency vanishes. The homopolar device can then be considered as the limiting case of a heteropolar converter with infinite wavelength. Let us see what this implies in terms of the physical structure. In a heteropolar device the active conductors belonging to opposite poles are connected to

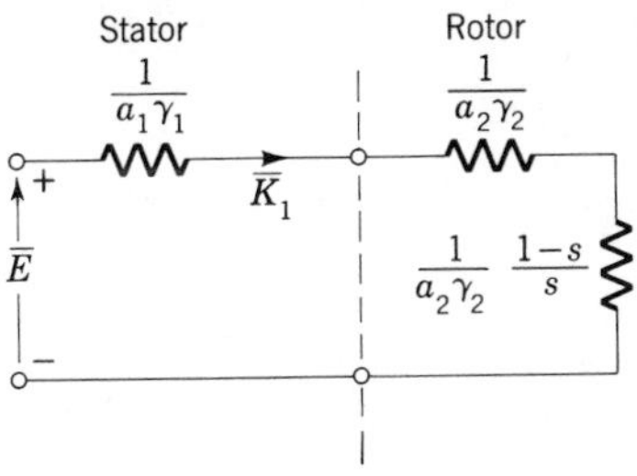

Fig. 9.7 Equivalent circuit of homopolar converter including compensating sleeve.

form coils, as shown in Fig. 6.4. These connections run around the periphery of the gap at both ends; their length is τ. When τ becomes infinite, these connections become endless. As we know from Sec. 5.3, a structure with cylindrical symmetry offers the possibility to realize an endless conductor by closing it back on itself. When this is done, the end connections become separate circular coils, as indicated in Fig. 9.8*b*. If we now look at Fig. 5.10 depicting a twin homopolar converter, we recognize that these coils are the field-excitation coils. Finally, since we have opened up the connections of the active conductors, we must provide an alternative path for the currents. The only path compatible with the symmetry of a uniform structure is the one joining the stator and rotor in a single loop, as shown in Fig. 9.8*c*. Since the two portions of the loop are in relative motion, sliding contacts are required.

The similarity in the macroscopic performance of the rotor conductor in the homopolar and asynchronous converters naturally stems from an identity in the microscopic mechanisms involved. The drift velocity v_E is by definition the velocity for which the electric field as sensed by the charged particles in the conductor vanishes. In a singly excited asyn-

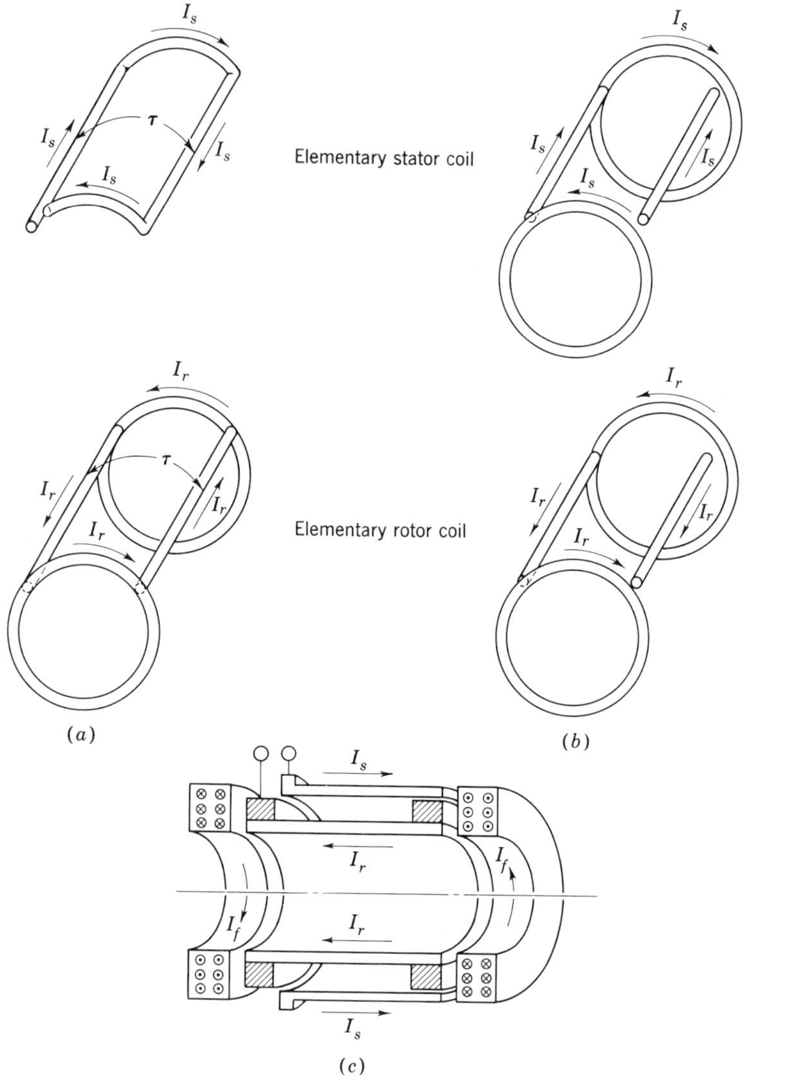

Fig. 9.8 Changes in the connections and currents of the stator and rotor conductors resulting from the limiting process $\tau \to \infty$: (*a*) Finite pole pitch τ; (*b*) infinite pole pitch $\tau \to \infty$; (*c*) twin homopolar converter.

chronous converter, where the rotor conductor is short-circuited ($E_2 = 0$), the only component of electric field is the one induced by the motion with respect to the wave frame. This vanishes when the charged particles reach the synchronous speed, so that v_s corresponds to v_E. A formal proof of this correspondence is obtained by writing the equation of the secondary rotor conductor in the stator frame. Since the stator moves with velocity v_1 with respect to the wave frame, Eq. (9.2) which is referred to the wave frame becomes, in the primed stator frame,

$$\bar{E}'_2 = \bar{E}_2 - v_1\bar{B} = (v_2 - v_1)\bar{B} + \frac{\bar{K}_2}{a\gamma_2} \tag{9.2a}$$

or since $E_2 = 0$, $-v_1 = v_s$, $(v_2 - v_1) = v$, and $\bar{K}_2/a = \bar{J}_2$,

$$\bar{E}'_2 = v_s\bar{B} = v\bar{B} + \frac{\bar{J}_2}{\gamma_2} \tag{9.2b}$$

Introducing for $\bar{J}_2$ the value given by Eq. (4.18), we have

$$\bar{E}'_2 = v_s\bar{B} = v\bar{B} + (v_E - v)\bar{B} = v_E\bar{B} \tag{9.2c}$$

This proves the identity of the synchronous and drift velocities in a singly excited asynchronous converter with a short-circuited secondary placed on the rotor.

It is also interesting to investigate the implications of this identity in connection with the homopolar converter. If, in performing the transition from heteropolar to homopolar structure, we let

$$\omega_e \longrightarrow 0 \qquad \text{as} \qquad \tau \longrightarrow \infty$$

subject to the condition that the synchronous speed

$$v_s = \frac{\tau}{\pi}\,\omega_e = v_E$$

remain constant and equal to the drift velocity, we arrive at the conclusion that in the homopolar device too, the flux-density wave moves with respect to the stator. According to this viewpoint,[1] in the absence of collisions the charged particles remain leashed to the lines of force of B even when an electric field is present, but the B lines themselves move with velocity v_E. Since in a uniform structure there is no way of detecting the motion of the magnetic field, this viewpoint does not violate any of the previously established principles. On the contrary, it allows us to generalize our representation of power conversion in terms of interacting waves traveling with the same velocity and having the same periodicity, to include the homopolar converter as a limiting case.

When the rotor speed does not correspond to the synchronous or drift speed, the motion-induced component of electric field in both the asynchronous and homopolar converter is finite and, if there exists a closed path, it forces a flow of current through the conductor. This current represents organized motion or streaming of the electrons past the ions. As a result, the microfields associated with electron-ion encounters are no longer completely random and produce, as discussed in Sec. 4.4*c*, a net component of electric field. Under ideal symmetry conditions, and when the active conductors are short-circuited with connecting links of negligible resistivity, there is no accumulation of surface charge, and the motion-induced field is exactly balanced by the sum total of the microfields.

We conclude that the essential difference between the heteropolar and the homopolar converter is none other than the feature which originally motivated the realization of the heteropolar structure as discussed in Sec. 6.2. When the conductor elements lying side by side along the gap sense different electric fields, it is possible to form closed loops around which the voltage is nonzero, thus allowing currents to flow entirely within the rotor conductor. When, instead, the electric field is uniform, the voltage around any closed loop lying entirely within the rotor conductor vanishes. Therefore any current-carrying loop must close outside the rotor conductor and thus requires sliding contacts.

The ability of the asynchronous converter to operate without the need for sliding contacts constitutes one of its major technical assets. In addition, it draws our attention to the existence of a mechanism which allows for transfer of power across the gap between circuits electrically insulated from each other. This mechanism for "action at a distance" is called *electromagnetic induction* or *transformer action,* since it is operative in transformers. We shall investigate it in the next sections.

9.4 TERMINAL VOLTAGE

The object of our study here, the transfer of power across the gap, is a process that takes place in the free space separating the electrically insulated circuits; it would be natural and desirable to carry out our investigation in terms of local properties of this space, i.e., by using a field approach. This is best done by introducing the concept of an electric-power flux density, the Poynting vector. By tracing the lines of force of this vector one can then follow the flow of power in the gap. This analysis, which requires more than an elementary knowledge of field theory, is given in Appendix C.

Here instead we will discuss the balance of power in terms of the more familiar circuit terms. For this purpose we need to carry out the transition from field to circuit quantities, as was done in Sec. 5.3*a* for the homopolar device. We begin with the terminal voltage. Since, as we have seen at the end of the previous section, it is the voltage that appears around a loop formed exclusively by conductor elements belonging to the same winding which differentiates between the performance of a homopolar and a heteropolar converter, we expect this calculation to shed some light on the phenomenon of electromagnetic induction. Indeed we shall find that in contrast with the case of the homopolar device, the *terminal* voltage of a heteropolar converter is the same when measured on the stator as on the rotor; in other words, it is invariant to a transformation of reference frames. As a result, the external circuits can be attached to whichever structure is most convenient, on either side of the gap, and the location of the primary and secondary windings can be interchanged. For this reason the heteropolar converter does not require relative motion between two portions of the electric circuit of a single active conductor, and so does not need sliding contacts, as does the homopolar converter.

For the sake of comparison with the results obtained in Chap. 6, we shall first evaluate the terminal voltage of a heteropolar machine, retaining some of the features of the idealized models used up to this point, and we shall then remove these restrictions by successive steps as we proceed in this chapter.

We thus assume that:

1. The magnetic flux density outside the gap is vanishingly small.
2. The magnetic flux density in the gap is sinusoidally distributed along the periphery (x direction) and does not vary along the active conductor (y direction), as indicated in Fig. 9.9.
3. The number of elementary active conductors is very large and equal to the number of phases.
4. All the conductors lie on the surface of the iron structures.
5. The connections between the elementary active conductors, and between the active conductors and the terminals, are perfectly conducting.

Before we proceed with the evaluation of the terminal voltage, we must determine the conditions under which this voltage is uniquely defined. This is particularly important here because we are dealing with time-varying quantities. We note, however, that the terminals are located *outside* the gap, where according to assumption 1 the magnetic field is zero. As a consequence, the electric field in that region ideally has no component due to magnetic induction. It is thus *conservative*, which means that is derivable from a scalar potential ϕ such that

$$\mathbf{E} = -\nabla\phi \qquad (9.19a)$$

This makes the terminal voltage unique as long as it is defined along a path which lies *outside the gap*.

Having assured ourselves of the uniqueness of the terminal voltage, we turn next to the problem of evaluating it. The most direct way is by straightforward application of Faraday's law. Since the procedure involved is essentially the same as was used for the homopolar device in Sec. 5.3*a*, we shall forgo a discussion of this method in the text. The reader will find this approach discussed in Probs. 9.7 and 9.8.

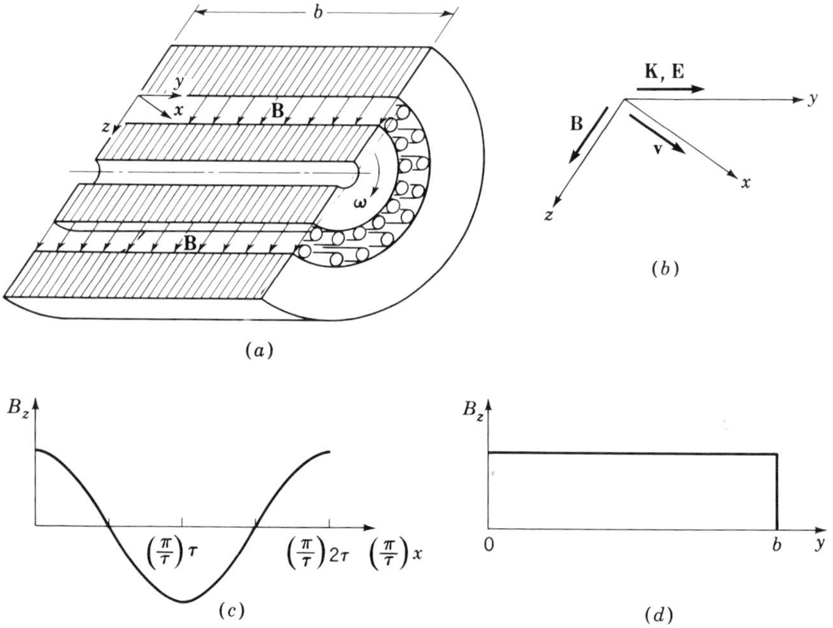

Fig. 9.9 Idealized model of heteropolar converter: (*a*) Cutaway view of ideal converter; (*b*) orientation of axes and main vectors; (*c*) magnetic flux distribution along x; (*d*) magnetic flux distribution in the plane $x = 0$.

We shall present instead another method which, although more sophisticated, is more appropriate to the study of power converters, provides a much greater insight into the fundamental difference between heteropolar and homopolar devices, and thus clears the way for understanding the mechanism for transfer of power across the gap.

(a) Conservative and Solenoidal Field Components

As shown in Fig. 9.10, we consider an elementary loop formed by two arbitrary conductors and their end connection. Such a loop is typically a part of an active conductor in a heteropolar converter, for example, the armature of a synchronous machine. Let us indeed consider the case of the synchronous converter, with the field as the primary and the armature as the secondary. Prime superscripts then refer to the secondary, and unprimed quantities are measured in the primary reference frame (which in this case is also the wave frame). We assume that the two conductors are located on the secondary structure at x_1' and x_2', respectively, as shown. We then define the line-to-line voltage $V_{1,2}$ as the integral of the electric field along any path joining the 1 and 2 terminals and lying wholly outside the gap.

$$V_{1,2} = \int_{\substack{1 \\ \text{outside} \\ \text{gap}}}^{2} \mathbf{E} \cdot d\mathbf{l} \tag{9.20}$$

We now wish to evaluate this voltage and prove that it is the same in either the primary or secondary frame, so that the portion of the circuit external to the armature can be attached to either frame.

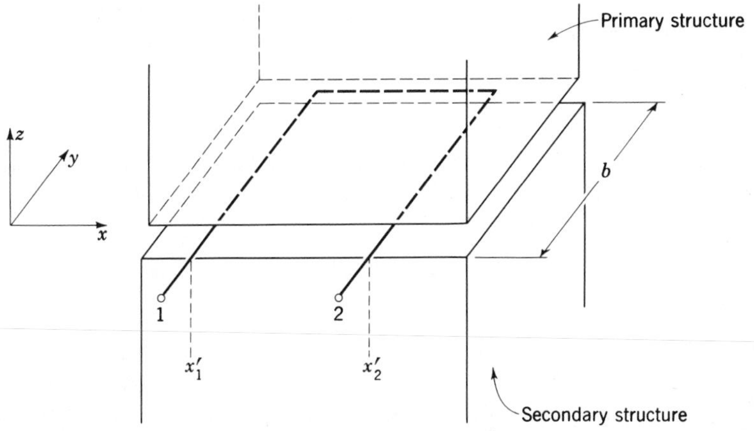

Fig. 9.10 Elementary loop for the evaluation of the terminal voltage in a heteropolar converter.

We start with the secondary frame of reference which we denote by a prime, so that Eq. (9.20) becomes

$$V_{1,2}' = \int_{\substack{1 \\ \text{outside} \\ \text{gap}}}^{2} \mathbf{E}' \cdot d\mathbf{l}' \tag{9.21}$$

Offhand we do not have specific information about the field $\mathbf{E}'$ outside the gap, except for the fact that it is conservative, since in this analysis B is assumed to vanish outside the gap. Instead we do have information about the field inside the gap which, when measured in the secondary frame of reference where the conductors lie ($v = 0$), is given by Eq.

(3.52) as

$$\mathbf{E}' = \frac{\mathbf{J}'}{\gamma} \tag{9.22}$$

Also we know that $\mathbf{E}'$ is certainly *not* conservative, since we are considering an a-c winding in whose frame of reference the magnetic flux is time-varying. We now introduce the technique of decomposing the total electric field into a *conservative component*, which is derivable from a scalar potential,

$$\mathbf{E}_{\text{cons}} = -\nabla\phi \tag{9.19b}$$

and a *solenoidal component*, which is derivable from a vector potential,

$$\mathbf{E}_{\text{sol}} = -\frac{\partial \mathbf{A}}{\partial t} \tag{9.23}$$

where **A** and **B** are related by

$$\mathbf{B} = \nabla \times \mathbf{A} \tag{9.24}$$

We may thus write for the electric field measured within the secondary conductor in a frame of reference attached to the conductor

$$\mathbf{E}' = \mathbf{E}'_{\text{cons}} + \mathbf{E}'_{\text{sol}} = \frac{\mathbf{J}'}{\gamma} \tag{9.25}$$

By its very definition, the line integral of $\mathbf{E}'_{\text{cons}}$ around any closed path must vanish. Taking such a path as the coil itself together with an arbitrary closure between the terminals outside the gap, this means that

$$V'_{1,2} = \underset{\substack{\text{outside}\\ \text{gap}}}{\int_1^2} \mathbf{E}'_{\text{cons}} \cdot d\mathbf{l}' = -\underset{\substack{\text{inside}\\ \text{gap}}}{\int_2^1} \mathbf{E}'_{\text{cons}} \cdot d\mathbf{l}' \tag{9.26}$$

The terminal voltage is then determined once we know the conservative component of the electric field near the conductor *inside* the gap. Moreover, from Eq. (9.25) we see that $\mathbf{E}'_{\text{cons}}$ in the conductor will indeed be expressible in terms of current density, once we know $\mathbf{E}'_{\text{sol}}$ in the conductors. We might then proceed to use Eq. (9.23) and the known distribution of $\mathbf{A}'$ in the gap (as given in Appendix B) to determine $\mathbf{E}'_{\text{sol}}$ (see Prob. 9.9). It is, however, easier and more illuminating to determine $\mathbf{E}'_{\text{sol}}$ by exploiting the technique suggested in Chaps. 1 and 2; we shall observe the system in another more advantageous reference frame and then resort to the field transformations between the two frames.

(b) Invariance to a Transformation of Reference Frames

Our more advantageous reference frame is the one attached to the flux-density wave which we have called the wave frame. If we view our conductor in this frame, we can write

$$\mathbf{E} = \frac{\mathbf{J}}{\gamma} - \mathbf{v} \times \mathbf{B} = \mathbf{E}_{\text{cons}} + 0 \tag{9.27}$$

since the solenoidal component vanishes when the field quantities are constant in time. We shall now demonstrate that in a *heteropolar converter the conservative components of the electric field are identical in the two reference frames;* that is,

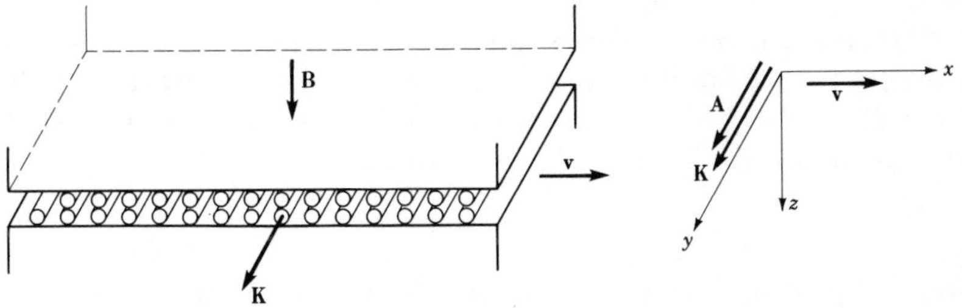

Fig. 9.11 Orientation of the vector potential **A** relative to **K** and **v** (heteropolar converter).

$$\mathbf{E}'_{\text{cons}} = \mathbf{E}_{\text{cons}}$$

To do this we shall refer freely to the results of Appendixes A and B. Note the following facts:

1. A unidirectional distribution of currents results in a vector potential **A** which is identically directed (Appendix B). In our case this is the $\mathbf{y}_0$ direction, as shown in Fig. 9.11.
2. The low-velocity transformation equation for the scalar potentials in the two reference frames which are in relative motion is

$$\phi' = \phi - \mathbf{v} \cdot \mathbf{A} \tag{9.28a}$$

[See Appendix A, Eq. (A.40).]

3. Since in the gap of the ideal heteropolar converter **A** is in the y direction and **v** in the x direction, $\mathbf{v} \cdot \mathbf{A} = 0$ identically. Thus Eq. (9.28a) here reduces to

$$\phi' = \phi \tag{9.28b}$$

Moreover, since $\nabla' = \nabla$ (Appendix A), we immediately see, by applying Eq. (9.19*b*) to Eq. (9.28*b*), that

$$\mathbf{E}'_{\text{cons}} = \mathbf{E}_{\text{cons}} \tag{9.29}$$†

Since in low-velocity transformations,

$$d\mathbf{l} = d\mathbf{l}' \tag{9.30}$$

and since Eq. (9.26) holds for the wave or primary frame as well, we have thus proved that

$$V'_{1,2} = V_{1,2} \tag{9.31}$$

(c) Line-to-Line and Conductor Voltages

Having demonstrated the equality of the conservative components of the electric field in the two reference frames, we again use the results of Appendix A, this time to note that the current-density transformation in our case of electrically neutral conductors,

$$\mathbf{J}' = \mathbf{J} \tag{9.32}$$

Now, introducing Eqs. (9.32) and (9.27) into Eq. (9.25), we have

$$\mathbf{E}'_{\text{sol}} = \mathbf{v} \times \mathbf{B} \tag{9.33}$$

and

$$\mathbf{E}'_{\text{cons}} = \frac{\mathbf{J}}{\gamma} - \mathbf{v} \times \mathbf{B} = \left(\frac{J}{\gamma} + vB\right)\mathbf{y}_0 \tag{9.34}$$

Equation (9.34) is the solution to our problem: It is precisely the relationship which we seek since it expresses $\mathbf{E}'$ in terms of the conductor current density and the gap flux density. By virtue of assumptions 1 and 5 at the beginning of this section, the only contribution to the integral of Eq. (9.21) comes from the portion of the path passing through the active conductors 1 and 2. If we then introduce Eq. (9.34) into Eq. (9.26) and perform the integration, we obtain

$$\begin{aligned} V_{1,2} = V'_{1,2} &= +\int_0^b \left(\frac{J}{\gamma} + vB\right)_{x'=x_1'} dy + \int_b^0 \left(\frac{J}{\gamma} + vB\right)_{x'=x_2'} dy \\ &= b\left[\left(\frac{J}{\gamma} + vB\right)_{x'=x_1'} - \left(\frac{J}{\gamma} + vB\right)_{x'=x_2'}\right] \end{aligned} \tag{9.35a}$$

† It is interesting to compare the present case with that of the homopolar converter. In that former instance the electric fields in both reference frames were both entirely conservative, but markedly different; in fact the electric field is equal to $\mathbf{J}/\gamma$ in the rotor frame and to $\mathbf{J}/\gamma - \mathbf{v} \times \mathbf{B}$ in the stator frame. This condition stems specifically from the fact that $\mathbf{v} \cdot \mathbf{A} \neq 0$. The reader is referred to Prob. 9.10 which deals with the possibility of eliminating the sliding contacts in the homopolar converter.

We next substitute K/a for J, and take notice that, by virtue of assumption 2, the field vectors vary sinusoidally in time. We can express this in terms of the phasor notation of Sec. 7.3:

$$V'_{1,2} = V_{1,2} = b \operatorname{Re}\left[\sqrt{2}\, e^{j\omega_e t} \left\{\left[\left(\frac{\bar{K}}{a\gamma} + v\bar{B}\right) e^{j\pi x'/\tau}\right]_{x'=x_1'} - \left[\left(\frac{\bar{K}}{a\gamma} + v\bar{B}\right) e^{j\pi x'/\tau}\right]_{x'=x_2'}\right\}\right] \tag{9.35b}$$

If we denote the conservative component of E measured along the conductor as $E_{c,\text{cons}}$, we may define the phasor conductor voltage as

$$\bar{V}_c = b\left(\frac{\bar{K}}{a\gamma} + v\bar{B}\right) = b\bar{E}_{c,\text{cons}} \tag{9.36a}$$

As we have noted in Sec. 7.3, our phasors with bar superscript describe quantities ranging over the entire periphery of the gap and hence must be associated with the exponential time and space factors in order to retrieve local time and space information. In view of Eq. (9.35*b*), it will also be convenient for us to define a phasor which itself contains the space information, so as to be able to succinctly express quantities, such as the line-to-line voltage $V_{1,2}$, which refer to specific positions along the gap. Thus we use a dot superscript to define a phasor $\dot{Q}$ in terms of $\bar{Q}$

$$\dot{Q} = \bar{Q}e^{j\pi x'/\tau} \tag{9.37a}$$

The phasor $\dot{Q}$ is none other than the *time phasor* used in a-c network theory, since it needs to be associated only with the exponential $e^{j\omega_e t}$ in order to permit calculation of the local quantity. Thus

$$Q = \operatorname{Re}\left[\sqrt{2}\, \dot{Q}e^{j\omega_e t}\right] \tag{9.37b}$$

Using this approach, we may introduce the time phasor notation into Eq. (9.36*a*) and then into Eq. (9.35*b*) to obtain

$$\dot{V}_c = b\left(\frac{\dot{K}}{a\gamma} + v\dot{B}\right) = b\dot{E}_{c,\text{cons}} \tag{9.36b}$$

$$V'_{1,2} = V_{1,2} = \operatorname{Re}\left[\sqrt{2}\, e^{j\omega_e t}(\dot{V}_{c,1} - \dot{V}_{c,2})\right] \tag{9.35c}$$

where the numerical subscript on the time phasor serves to localize $\dot{V}_c$ to a particular conductor. We may further simplify our notation by defining a time phasor $\dot{V}_{1,2}$ to express the line-to-line voltage of Eqs. (9.35*b*) and (9.35*c*) as

$$\dot{V}_{1,2} = b\left(\frac{\dot{K}}{a\gamma} + v\dot{B}\right)_{x'=x_1'} - b\left(\frac{\dot{K}}{a\gamma} + v\dot{B}\right)_{x'=x_2'} \tag{9.35d}$$

or

$$\dot{V}_{1,2} = \dot{V}_{c,1} - \dot{V}_{c,2} \tag{9.35e}$$

In the rest of the chapter we shall have occasion to use both dot and bar superscripts to distinguish local from general relationships. We shall see, however, that a local relationship may often be restated as a general one, since the relations for a particular group of conductors hold true for any such group along the gap.

By comparing Eqs. (9.35*d*) and (9.36*b*) with Eq. (7.15), we find that we could have obtained the conductor voltage simply by multiplying Eq. (7.15), which gives the electric field as measured in the wave frame (and therefore $\dot{E}_{c,\text{cons}}$ or $\bar{E}_{c,\text{cons}}$), by the length b of the active conductor, and then going over to the time-phasor notation. This justifies the whole treatment of the preceding three chapters.

9.5 POWER FLOW

In this section we shall examine the mechanism for the transfer of power across the gap of the heteropolar converter. To do this, we need first to consider terminal current and power as discussed below.

(a) Ideal Star Connection

In the previous section we assumed that an active conductor is made up of a large number of conductors uniformly distributed along the gap

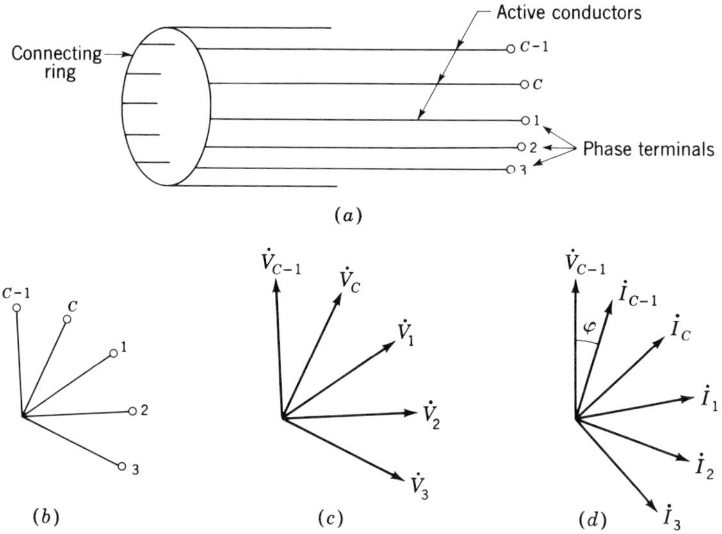

Fig. 9.12 Polyphase winding of heteropolar converter with ideal star connection: (*a*) Construction; (*b*) schematic representation; (*c*) phasor conductor voltages; (*d*) phasor conductor currents.

periphery. If these are all joined at one end (with a perfectly conducting connection) and connected to separate phase lines at the other end, we have an ideal star connection, as shown in Fig. 9.12. We shall assume as before that this polyphase system is connected to a balanced load or balanced busbar.

(b) Terminal Current

Under the balanced conditions outlined above, the line currents in all the conductors will have the same magnitude but a time phase which progresses uniformly along the gap periphery. The current flow in these conductors sets up the traveling-wave surface current density associated with that winding. As in the case of the terminal and conductor voltages, we wish to relate the conductor current $\bar{I}_c$ to the corresponding field quantity in the gap, the current density $\bar{K}$. To do this, let us denote the total number of conductors as c. Then the conductor spacing Δx is

$$\Delta x = \frac{2p\tau}{c} \tag{9.38}$$

and the conductor current, from the definition of the surface current density, is then

$$\bar{I}_c = \bar{K}\,\Delta x = \bar{K}\,\frac{2p\tau}{c} \tag{9.39}$$

(c) Terminal Power

Since the polyphase system is completely balanced, the individual conductor voltages and currents form the respective time-phasor arrays,

$$\dot{V}_c,\ \dot{V}_c e^{j\Delta\theta},\ \dot{V}_c e^{2j\Delta\theta},\ \ldots$$
$$\dot{I}_c,\ \dot{I}_c e^{j\Delta\theta},\ \dot{I}_c e^{2j\Delta\theta},\ \ldots$$

where $\Delta\theta = p\,\Delta x/r_g$ is the phase shift associated with the conductor spacing Δx. The power absorbed by one conductor is Re $[\dot{V}_c\dot{I}_c^*]$; consequently, the total power or terminal power P_t absorbed by the winding is

$$P_t = \text{Re}\,[\dot{V}_c\dot{I}_c^* + \dot{V}_c e^{j\Delta\theta}(\dot{I}_c e^{j\Delta\theta})^* + \dot{V}_c e^{j2\Delta\theta}(\dot{I}_c e^{2j\Delta\theta})^* + \cdots]$$

or $$P_t = \text{Re}\,[\dot{V}_c\dot{I}_c^* + \dot{V}_c\dot{I}_c^* + \cdots]$$

or $$P_t = \text{Re}\,[c\dot{V}_c\dot{I}_c^*] \tag{9.40a}$$

since there are a total of c conductors. From Eq. (9.37*a*), we see that Eq. (9.40*a*) may also be written in terms of space-time or wave phasors as

$$P_t = \text{Re}\,[c\bar{V}_c\bar{I}_c^*] \tag{9.40b}$$

Introducing Eqs. (9.36*a*) and (9.39) into (9.40*b*), we have

$$P_t = 2p\tau b\ \text{Re}\,[\bar{E}_{c,\text{cons}}\bar{K}^*] \tag{9.41}$$

Although Eq. (9.40) was derived on the assumption of an ideal star connection, the same result obtains if we postulate an all-series arrangement of the conductors, i.e., an ideal "mesh" connection. Consequently these results are quite general, and as we shall see at the end of the chapter, also apply to practical windings with only minor modifications.

In observing Eq. (9.41), we note that the factor $2p\tau b$ is the area A of the active conductor. In fact, Eq. (9.41) is very reminiscent of the calculation of the total surface electric power, associated with that winding, since, from Eq. (7.39),

$$\langle P_{\text{elec}} \rangle = A \langle p_{s,\text{elec}} \rangle = A \text{ Re } [\bar{E}\bar{K}^*] \tag{9.42}$$

We must, however, be very careful to note a most significant difference in Eqs. (9.41) and (9.42). In finding the terminal power, we must use the *conservative component* of the electric field, whereas in finding the surface electric power, we use the *total electric field*. Thus, P_t and $\langle P_{\text{elec}} \rangle$ are identical only when the latter is evaluated in the wave frame, where the electric field is completely conservative.

On the other hand, when there is a nonzero solenoidal component of electric field in the conductor reference frame, then P_t and $\langle P_{\text{elec}} \rangle$ evaluated in this frame are plainly unequal. In this case $\langle P_{\text{elec}} \rangle$ is completely absorbed as Joule loss, and the difference between $\langle P_{\text{elec}} \rangle$ and P_t, which is due to the solenoidal component, represents power which transfers across the gap. To clarify the above ideas we shall again consider a synchronous converter and strike a power balance from the viewpoint of the armature frame of reference.

(d) Detailed Power Balance

If according to Eq. (7.23) and Fig. 9.13,

$$\bar{E}_f = \frac{\bar{K}_f}{a_f \gamma_f} \tag{7.23}$$

is the $\bar{E}$ measured near the field conductors in their frame of reference, then in the armature reference frame which moves with velocity $\mathbf{v}$ with respect to the field conductors, we have, according to Eqs. (2.53) and (4.8),

$$\bar{E}'_f = \bar{E}_f - v\bar{B} = \frac{\bar{K}_f}{a_f \gamma_f} - v\bar{B} \tag{9.43}$$

The overall electric power associated with the field conductor is then

$$\begin{aligned} P'_{\text{elec},f} &= 2p\tau b \text{ Re } [\bar{E}'_f \bar{K}'^*_f] \\ &= 2p\tau b \text{ Re } \left[\frac{\bar{K}_f \bar{K}'^*_f}{a_f \gamma_f} - v\bar{B}\bar{K}'^*_f \right] \end{aligned} \tag{9.44a}$$

Observing that, according to Eq. (9.32),

$$\bar{K}_f = \bar{K}'_f \tag{9.32a}$$

we can write Eq. (9.44*a*) as

$$P'_{\text{elec},f} = 2p\tau b \frac{K_f{}^2}{a_f \gamma_f} - 2p\tau b v \text{ Re } [\bar{B}\bar{K}'^*_f] \tag{9.44b}$$

Also, since $-v\mathbf{x}_0$ is the velocity of the field conductor with respect to the armature frame and Re $[\bar{B}\bar{K}_f'^*]$ is the average tangential force density acting on it, we have

$$\begin{aligned} P'_{\text{elec},f} &= A\langle p_{\text{s,diss},f}\rangle + A\langle p'_{\text{s,conv},f}\rangle \\ &= P_{\text{diss},f} + P'_{\text{conv},f} \end{aligned} \tag{9.44c}$$

To evaluate the field terminal power we consider that $\bar{E}_f$ is a phasor by virtue of the array of variable amplitude d-c sources connected to the field

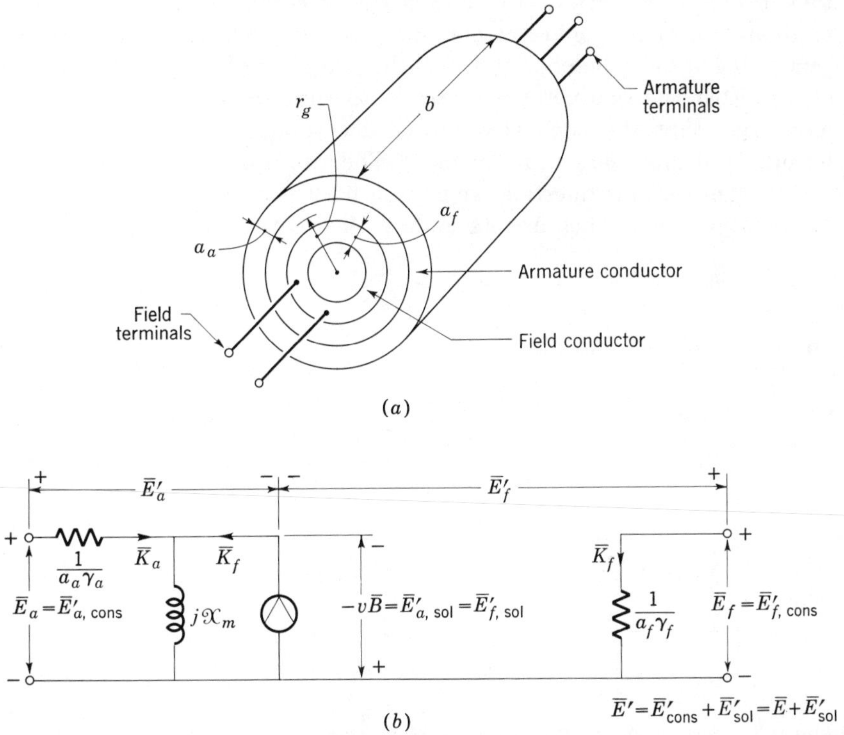

Fig. 9.13 Equivalent circuit of synchronous converter with reference to the armature frame: (*a*) Arrangement of the active conductors; (*b*) equivalent circuit showing the electric fields measured in the armature frame.

conductors, our alternative 1 of Sec. 6.4 and Fig. 6.13. Consequently the field terminal power in the armature frame is, from Eq. (9.41),

$$P_{t,f} = 2p\tau b \text{ Re } [\bar{E}'_{c,\text{cons}}\bar{K}'^*]_f \tag{9.45a}$$

Since the field conductors are at rest in the wave frame, we know that

$$\bar{E}'_{c,\text{cons}} = \bar{E}_{c,\text{cons}} = \frac{\bar{K}_f}{a_f\gamma_f} \tag{9.46}$$

Consequently, the field terminal power is

$$P_{t,f} = 2p\tau b \frac{K_f^2}{a_f \gamma_f} = P_{\text{diss},f} \tag{9.45b}$$

which says that the d-c field power supply furnishes only the power required to provide for the Joule losses in the field winding, a fact which hardly surprises us!

Having identified the path followed by the part of the field conductor power which is dissipated, we are now faced with the problem of tracking the flow of that part of the power which is converted. This power originates in the mechanical port when the conductor operates in the generating or braking mode and ends there in the motoring mode. Let us assume that the conductor operates in the generating mode. Since we have seen that the converted power does not flow through the field terminals, it must flow into the gap. The question is: Whereto?

To answer this question we now turn our attention to the armature conductors. Since they are stationary, their electric field is simply

$$\bar{E}_a' = \frac{\bar{K}_a'}{a_a \gamma_a} \tag{9.47}$$

and their electric power is

$$\begin{aligned} P'_{\text{elec},a} &= 2p\tau b \,\text{Re}\,[\bar{E}_a' \bar{K}_a'^*] \\ &= 2p\tau b \frac{K_a'^2}{a_a \gamma_a} \\ &= A \langle p_{s,\text{diss},a} \rangle \\ &= P_{\text{diss},a} \end{aligned} \tag{9.48}$$

Next we evaluate the power which flows through the armature terminals. This is

$$\begin{aligned} P_{t,a} &= 2p\tau b \,\text{Re}\,[E'_{c,\text{cons}} \bar{K}'^*]_a \\ &= 2p\tau b \frac{K_a'^2}{a_a \gamma_a} + 2p\tau b \,\text{Re}\,[v \bar{B} \bar{K}_a'^*] \end{aligned} \tag{9.49a}$$

Here the first term to the right is the power dissipated in the armature $P_{\text{diss},a}$; the second term can easily be identified with the power converted in the field conductor. In fact, we know from Eqs. (7.31) and (7.32) that

$$\text{Re}\,[\bar{B} \bar{K}_a'^*] = -\text{Re}\,[\bar{B} \bar{K}_f'^*] \tag{9.50a}$$

so that

$$2p\tau b \,\text{Re}\,[v \bar{B} \bar{K}_a'^*] = -2p\tau b v \,\text{Re}\,[\bar{B} \bar{K}_f'^*] \tag{9.50b}$$

This means that the last terms of Eqs. (9.44b) and (9.50b) are identical and equal to $P'_{\text{conv},f}$.

Equation (9.49a) thus becomes

$$P_{t,a} = P_{\text{diss},a} + P'_{\text{conv},f} \tag{9.49b}$$

When the converter operates as a generator, both the terminal and the converted power are negative. We thus conclude that, of the power converted in the rotor conductor, part covers the losses of the armature conductor and the remainder flows directly into the electric circuit connected to the armature conductor. This is exactly what would happen if the armature were on the rotor. The only difference is that, when the armature is placed on the stator, the power that flows through the armature terminals is actually converted in the field conductor.

Equations (9.44*c*), (9.45*b*), (9.48) and (9.49*b*) indicate how the power is balanced in the converter. From these equations one can trace the flow of power, as shown in Fig. 9.14. This schematic diagram corresponds to the plot of the lines of force of the Poynting vector derived in Appendix C.

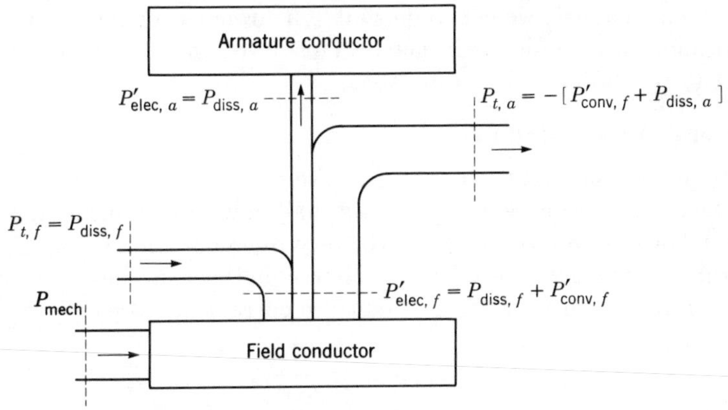

Fig. 9.14 Schematic diagram of the power flow in a synchronous generator viewed from the armature frame of reference ($P_{conv,\,f} < 0$).

The example clearly indicates that in heteropolar converters the mechanism for power transfer between electrically insulated a-c circuits, which we have called transformer action or electromagnetic induction, is provided by the solenoidal field component which results from the relative motion between the conductors and the wave frame. It is also apparent that the reason why this mechanism is not bilateral in synchronous converters is that on the field side the conductors are at standstill with respect to the wave frame. It follows that no power can flow from the armature conductors into the d-c electric circuits connected to the field conductors. We have thus reached a full appreciation of the significance of the statement made in Sec. 7.4 that there exists forward coupling from field to armature but no backward coupling from armature to field, a statement which is corroborated by the presence of a current source on the field side of the equivalent circuit.

In this second look at the operation of the synchronous converter which we have taken here, our viewpoint has shifted from the field frame, where things look pretty much the same as in the homopolar converter, to a frame of reference attached to the armature where the a-c terminals are located. Naturally the new viewpoint does not in any way alter our evaluation of the overall performance of the converter; it does, however, verify the interchangeability of the electric circuits connected to the stator and rotor, which results from the invariance of the terminal voltage.

It is thus quite feasible to eliminate the slip rings on the a-c side, which handles the largest power, by placing the armature active conductors on the same frame to which the external circuits are normally attached: the stator. In addition, since there are means for maintaining the field excitation without power consumption, as, for instance, by using a permanent magnet, we conclude that synchronous converter can operate without any sliding contacts. This is of great advantage with respect to reliability and maintenance.

(e) Overall Power Balance

Having considered the particular case of the synchronous converter from the armature reference frame, we shall now strike a general overall power balance from a completely arbitrary reference frame. To do this, we return to the generalized Ohm's law equations in the wave frame, written in phasor form in terms of surface current densities:

$$\bar{E}_1 - v_1\bar{B} = \frac{\bar{K}_1}{a_1\gamma_1} \tag{9.51a}$$

$$\bar{E}_2 - v_2\bar{B} = \frac{\bar{K}_2}{a_2\gamma_2} \tag{9.51b}$$

Suppose we now consider an arbitrary reference frame which moves with velocity v_3 with respect to the wave frame. In this frame, denoted by a triple-prime superscript, the primary and secondary conductor velocities are seen to be $v_1 - v_3$ and $v_2 - v_3$, respectively. Since $\bar{B}$ and $\bar{K}$ are essentially invariant to the reference-frame transformation, the generalized Ohm's law equations in the new frame become

$$\bar{E}_1''' - (v_1 - v_3)\bar{B} = \frac{\bar{K}_1}{a_1\gamma_1} \tag{9.52a}$$

$$\bar{E}_2''' - (v_2 - v_3)\bar{B} = \frac{\bar{K}_2}{a_2\gamma_2} \tag{9.52b}$$

If we split the electric-field intensities into conservative and solenoidal components, the conservative component remains invariant in all reference frames. Since $\bar{E}$, as measured in the wave frame, is the conservative component, we may subtract Eqs. (9.51) from Eqs. (9.52) to obtain

$$\bar{E}'''_{1,\text{sol}} + v_3\bar{B} = 0 \tag{9.53a}$$
$$\bar{E}'''_{2,\text{sol}} + v_3\bar{B} = 0 \tag{9.53b}$$
$$\bar{E}'''_{1,\text{sol}} = \bar{E}'''_{2,\text{sol}} = -v_3\bar{B} \tag{9.53c}$$

We see, therefore, that the solenoidal component of the electric field is the same on both sides of the gap.

Let us next find the overall electric power in the primary conductor:

$$P'''_{\text{elec},1} = A\ \text{Re}[\bar{K}_1^*\bar{E}_1]''' = A\ \text{Re}\ [\bar{K}_1^*\bar{E}_{1,\text{cons}}] + A\ \text{Re}\ [\bar{K}_1^*\bar{E}'''_{1,\text{sol}}] \tag{9.54a}$$

In Eq. (9.54a), the first term on the right-hand side is the terminal power. Introducing Eq. (9.53), we may then write

$$P'''_{\text{elec},1} = P_{t,1} - A\ \text{Re}\ [v_3\bar{K}_1^*\bar{B}] \tag{9.54b}$$

In the same way, we write for the secondary

$$P'''_{\text{elec},2} = P_{t,2} - A\ \text{Re}\ [v_3\bar{K}_2^*\bar{B}] \tag{9.54c}$$

We have previously noted in Chap. 7 and Sec. 9.3 that

$$\text{Re}\ [\bar{K}_1^*\bar{B}] = -\ \text{Re}\ [\bar{K}_2^*\bar{B}] \tag{9.55}$$

Consequently, if we add Eqs. (9.54b) and (9.54c),

$$P'''_{\text{elec},1} + P'''_{\text{elec},2} = P_{t,1} + P_{t,2} \tag{9.56}$$

Equation (9.56) means that the composite or *total* electric power is identical with the total terminal power, and is therefore the same in any reference frame. This result may also be explained in terms of transformer action. The difference between P_{elec} and P_t in either conductor is due to the solenoidal component of the electric field; this difference represents power transferred through the gap to the other conductor by transformer action. In the sum total, however, the transferred component cancels, since it appears as power out in one conductor, and power in, in the other. This result may also be readily verified from the Poynting-vector approach of Appendix C.

We next take the phasor products of Eq. (9.52a) with $A\bar{K}_1^*$ to obtain

$$A\ \text{Re}\ [\bar{K}_1^*\bar{E}''' - \bar{K}_1^*(v_1 - v_3)\bar{B}] = A\,\frac{K_1{}^2}{a_1\gamma_1} \tag{9.57a}$$

The term-by-term identification of Eq. (9.57a) becomes

$$P'''_{\text{elec},1} - P'''_{\text{conv},1} = P_{\text{diss},1} \tag{9.57b}$$

In the same way for the secondary we have

$$P'''_{\text{elec},2} - P'''_{\text{conv},2} = P_{\text{diss},2} \tag{9.57c}$$

Adding Eqs. (9.57*b*) and (9.57*c*) and using Eq. (9.56), we obtain

$$\Sigma P_t - \Sigma P'''_{\text{conv}} = \Sigma P_{\text{diss}} \tag{9.58}$$

Now in this power balance, the terminal and the dissipated power terms are invariant and independent of the reference frame. It follows then that the converted power term must likewise be invariant. We can see how this comes about by examining this term in detail:

$$\Sigma P'''_{\text{conv}} = A \text{ Re } [\bar{K}_1^*(v_1 - v_3)\bar{B} + \bar{K}_2^*(v_2 - v_3)\bar{B}] \tag{9.59a}$$

As seen from Eq. (9.55), the terms involving v_3 cancel, and we then have

$$\Sigma P'''_{\text{conv}} = A \text{ Re } [\bar{K}_1^* v_1 \bar{B} + \bar{K}_2^* v_2 \bar{B}] \tag{9.59b}$$

In Eq. (9.7) we defined the quantity $v = v_2 - v_1$, the velocity of the secondary with respect to the primary. Introducing v into Eq. (9.59*b*), we obtain

$$\Sigma P'''_{\text{conv}} = A \text{ Re } [\bar{K}_1^* v_1 \bar{B} + \bar{K}_2^* v_1 \bar{B} + \bar{K}_2^* v \bar{B}] \tag{9.60a}$$

From Eq. (9.55) we see that the first two terms on the right-hand side cancel, so that

$$\Sigma P_{\text{conv}} = A \text{ Re } [\bar{K}_2^* v \bar{B}] = A \text{ Re } [-\bar{K}_1^* v \bar{B}] \tag{9.60b}$$

In Eq. (9.60*b*), all the terms on the right-hand side are invariant to transformation of reference frames, since v is a velocity difference which remains constant in any frame. Thus ΣP_{conv} is indeed the same in all frames, and in recognition of this we have dropped the triple-prime superscript in Eq. (9.60*b*). Moreover, it is clear that ΣP_{conv} is the power dissipated in the secondary resistor $\dfrac{1}{a_2\gamma_2}\dfrac{1-S}{S}$ in Fig. 9.6 and, as previously explained, is then the converted power in the rotor as seen from the stator, regardless of whether the stator is primary or secondary.

In view of these facts, we may rewrite Eq. (9.58) in its invariant form

$$\Sigma P_t - \Sigma P_{\text{conv}} = \Sigma P_{\text{diss}} \tag{9.61a}$$

or alternatively

$$\Sigma P_{\text{elec}} - \Sigma P_{\text{conv}} = \Sigma P_{\text{diss}} \tag{9.61b}$$

Eq. (9.61) shows plainly that the *overall* power balance in the entire converter is indeed the same in all frames of reference, and that in the heteropolar as well as in the homopolar converter, the macroscopic relationship is the same as the unit-volume relationship established in Eq. (4.6). This is true even in the presence of the power-interchange mechanism afforded by the transformer action. The general heteropolar converter, incidentally, included as a special case the stationary transformer. This can be seen by making $v = 0$, i.e., by holding the rotor fixed. In this case there is no converted power, and Eq. (9.61*a*) becomes

$$-P_{t,2} = P_{t,1} - P_{\text{diss},1} - P_{\text{diss},2} \tag{9.61c}$$

showing that the secondary output power is equal to the primary input power less ohmic losses.

From the limiting case of the transformer we see that the relative motion between the conductors and a wave is to be considered a sufficient but not a necessary condition for the existence of a solenoidal component of electric field. In fact, Eq. (9.23),

$$\mathbf{E}_{\text{sol}} = -\frac{\partial \mathbf{A}}{\partial t} \tag{9.23}$$

defining the solenoidal component of electric field is simply a restatement of Faraday's law [Eq. (1.3*a*)]:

$$\nabla \times \mathbf{E} = -\frac{\partial \mathbf{B}}{\partial t} \tag{1.3a}$$

Therefore, the solenoidal component and the associated mechanism of electromagnetic induction in magnetic devices result, in more general terms, from the coupling which Faraday's law provides between the electric field and the time rate of change of the magnetic flux density without implying the existence of a traveling wave. This conclusion is borne out in the next section where we discuss departures from the idealized conditions.

9.6 DEPARTURES FROM IDEALIZED CONDITIONS

In our study of the heteropolar converter we have until now assumed that each individual conductor is connected to separate, properly phased ideal voltage sources or to separate identical load impedances. This represents a balanced and symmetrical polyphase system which ideally has an infinite number of phases. Practical considerations, however, limit the number of phases to three for power systems and two for control systems. To achieve this reduction in the number of phases, while at the same time retaining good utilization of the gap surface, a number of conductors are connected in series and assigned to the same phase. The series connection of conductors also serves the purpose of realizing an important feature of the heteropolar converter, which, as was mentioned in Sec. 6.2, is the ability to control impedance level.

A second major departure from the ideal conditions results from the fact that the conductors are not continuously distributed on the surface of the iron structures but are placed in discrete slots. The placing of the conductors in slots, which was originally devised by Pacinotti, facilitates the transmission of the electromagnetic stress to the stator and rotor structures. As mentioned in Sec. 4.8, the slot sides or teeth not only fasten the active conductor to the iron as does a key in a key groove, but also carry most of the magnetic flux so that relatively little flux enters the slot itself. As a result, the force on the conductors themselves is small. For the reasons explained in Appendix C, and as illustrated in Probs. 9.11 and 9.12, the decrease in force exerted on the active conductors is now balanced by forces on the teeth, so that the total force is the same as would be calculated if the conductors were placed in the gap between smooth iron structures. The teeth, then, carry most of the electromagnetic stress.

A third and obvious departure from ideal conditions is that the end connections of the ideal conductor are not lossless. In fact, we have seen in Chap. 6 that the a-c windings conventionally consist of integrally wound whole coils, so that the end connection is simply an extension of the active conductor itself.

These practical modifications disturb the symmetry of the field configurations and are detrimental to the performance of the converter: i.e., the efficiency and the average power output for a given size machine are reduced, while the var requirement is increased.

The decrease in efficiency is largely due to the power dissipated in the end connections between the active conductors and in parasitic torques caused by the higher harmonics of the electromagnetic field.

The decrease in converted power density is the result of an imperfect electromagnetic coupling between the windings on either side of the gap.

Finally the increase in var requirements is caused by a proportionate increase in the energy stored in the alternating fields and the consequent exchange of power among various portions of the gap periphery, as explained in Sec. 6.7*a*.

Our task in the remainder of this chapter will be to arrive at a representation of the converter performance which reflects these departures from the ideal conditions. In particular, we wish to derive equivalent circuits and phasor diagrams which provide a graphical display of the relations between the terminal variables in terms of suitable parameters characterizing the converter.

(a) Leakage Fluxes

As we see from the equivalent circuit of Fig. 9.2, in order to describe an ideal heteropolar converter, we need three parameters only: the two resistances of the active conductors $1/a_1\gamma_1$, $1/a_2\gamma_2$, and the magnetizing reactance $\mathcal{X}_{m,1}$. The latter represents the coupling term between the primary and secondary circuits and relates the current densities K_1 and K_2 to the solenoidal component of electric field $-v_1B$, where v_1 is the velocity of the primary conductor with respect to the wave frame. In the idealized model of the converter, the solenoidal component of voltage arises solely from a flux-density component, which is identical on both sides of the gap, is sinusoidally distributed, and forms a wave having the same wavelength and speed as the current-density waves $\bar{K}_1$ and $\bar{K}_2$. These are the conditions which, according to Sec. 6.7*b*, yield a nonvanishing average power. It follows that, under ideal conditions, *all* the solenoidal components contribute to that power which in the wave frame is considered as converted and, in general, is transferred across the gap by the mechanism of electromagnetic induction discussed in Sec. 9.5.

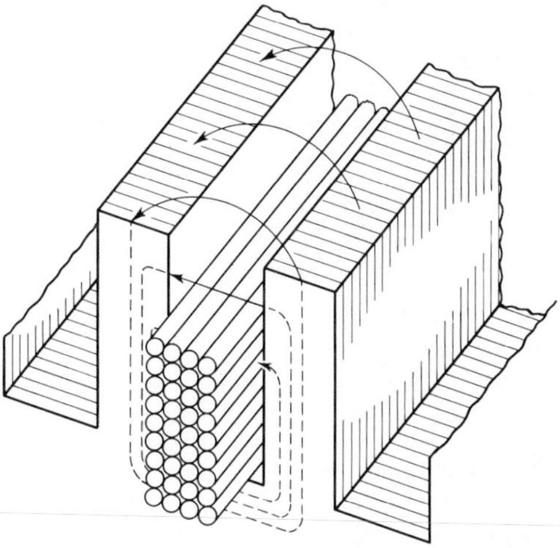

Fig. 9.15 Distribution of the slot leakage flux.

However, in addition to this common or *main flux*, there exist in the practical converter other time-varying fluxes which are interlinked with only one of the electric circuits, either the primary or the secondary, and therefore are called *leakage fluxes.* They give rise to solenoidal components of the terminal voltage which *are not common* to both circuits and *do not contribute* to conversion or transfer of power. The leakage fluxes may be classified as follows:

1. The slot leakage flux which develops around the conductors in the slots without crossing the gap, as indicated in Figs. 9.15.
2. The end-winding leakage flux which develops around the end connections between the active conductors, as shown in Fig. 9.16. This flux includes the flux outside the gap which exists in the heteropolar converter just as in the homopolar, as previously mentioned in Sec. 5.3*a*.

Both the leakage fluxes are portrayed in Fig. 9.16.

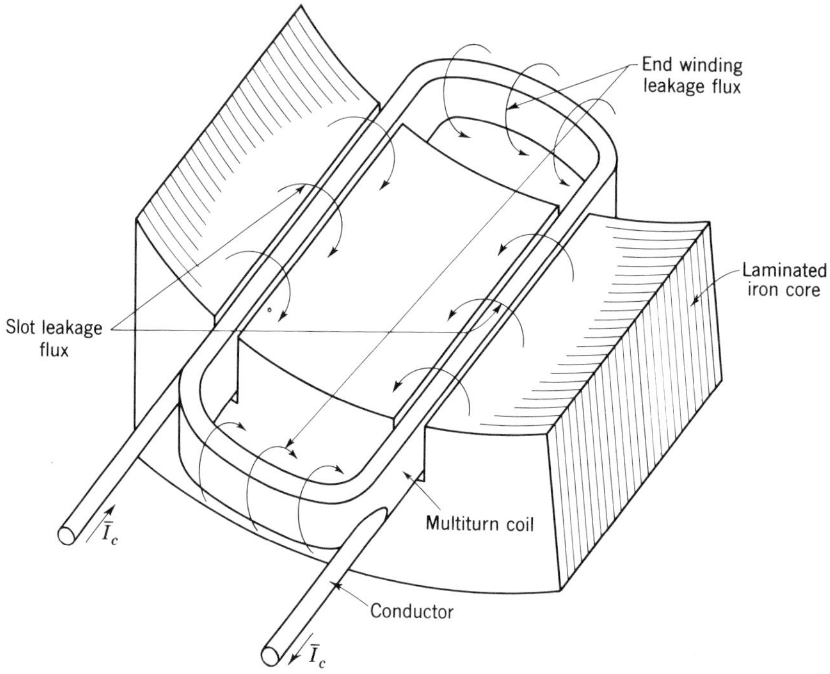

Fig. 9.16 End winding and slot leakage fluxes.

3. The harmonic leakage resulting from the distortion of the flux distribution crossing the gap and including all the harmonics with the exception of the fundamental sinusoidal wave. Figure 9.17 shows, for example, the fundamental and the fifth harmonic. In well-designed polyphase windings this is the lowest-order non-vanishing harmonic which contributes to the leakage flux.

The name *harmonic* in itself implies that the magnetic field prevailing in a practical device is conveniently described by a Fourier expansion in terms of sinusoidal waves. In such a description, the leakage fluxes are said to represent higher-order "modes," some of which form traveling-wave patterns and others standing-wave patterns. We can account for the overall effect of the leakage fluxes by introducing a lumped parameter into the circuit representation which portrays their most important characteristic. Since this is storage of magnetic energy, the appropriate parameter is a *leakage inductance*. The reader familiar with guided-wave theory will recognize the similarity with the procedure used to account for higher propagating and nonpropagating modes in waveguides.

Together with the resistance, the leakage inductance serves to

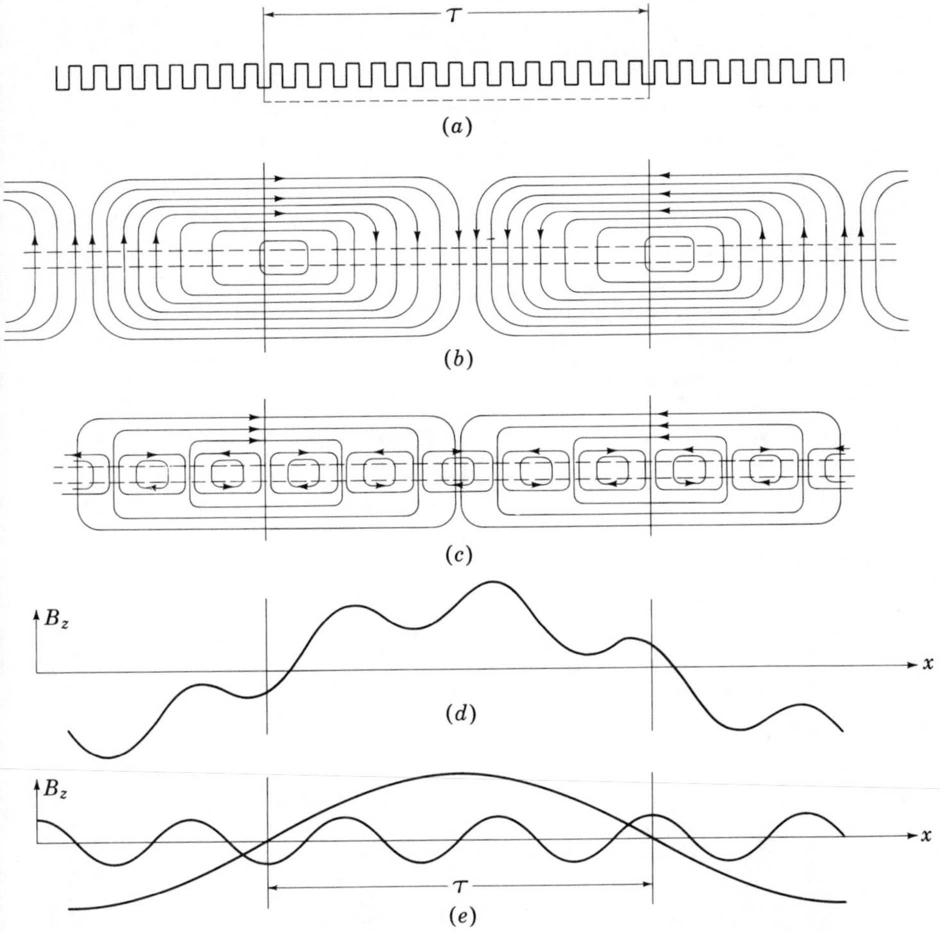

Fig. 9.17 Magnetic flux distribution showing the contribution of the fifth harmonic to the harmonic leakage: (*a*) Slot distribution and full-pitch coil; (*b*) actual flux distribution; (*c*) fundamental and fifth harmonic of the flux distribution; (*d*) flux-density wave; (*e*) fundamental and fifth harmonic of the flux density.

characterize a winding. It also serves to distinguish between the idealized model of the converter and its practical realization.

*9.7 RELATIONS BETWEEN TERMINAL AND FIELD QUANTITIES

(a) Phase Group

We are now ready to evaluate the terminal voltage of a practical heteropolar converter; by this we mean a converter in which the con-

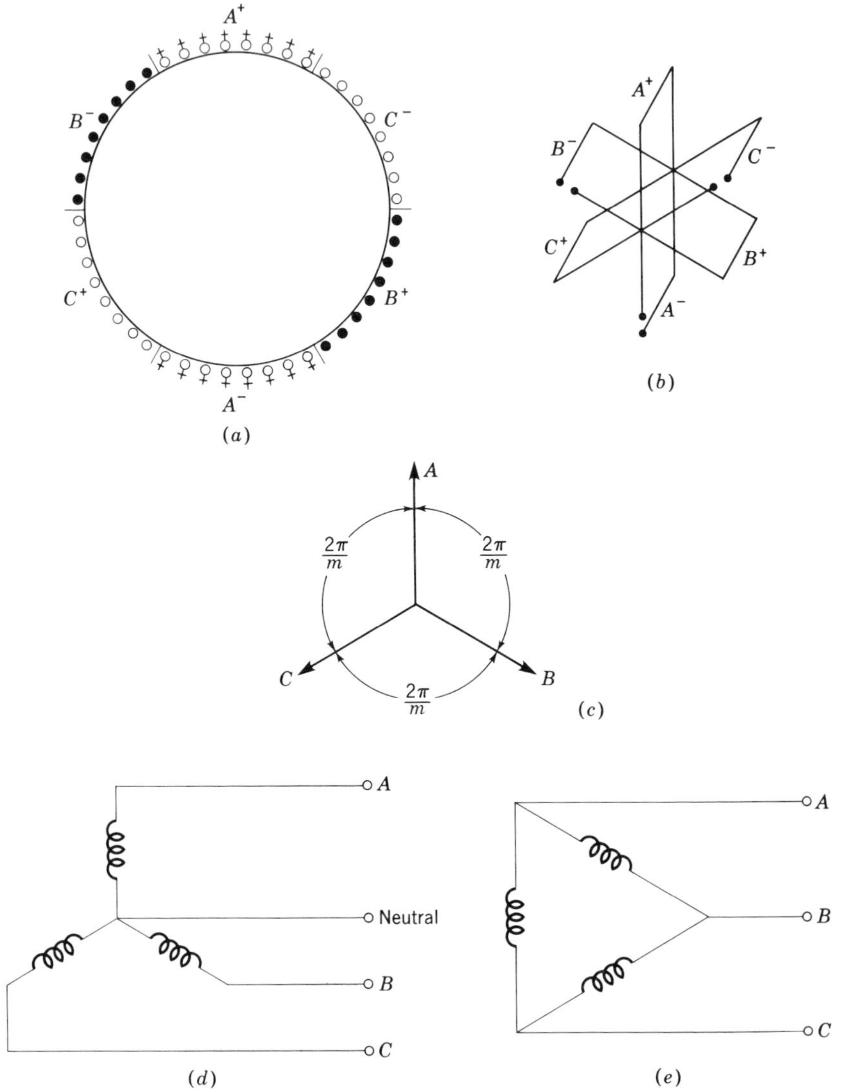

Fig. 9.18 Three-phase winding of two-pole machine with eight slots per pole and phase: (*a*) Actual distributed coil arrangement; (*b*) equivalent concentrated coil arrangement of the phase groups; (*c*) symbolic phasor representation; (*d*) schematic diagram of star connection; (*e*) schematic diagram of mesh connection.

ductors are finite in number, are embedded in slots, and are connected in series to form coils which, in turn, are connected to a small number of phase lines. Windings are usually designed so as to retain as much symmetry as possible; we thus assume that the groups of conductors belonging to each phase, or the so-called *phase groups*, are all equal and equally displaced along the periphery of the gap, as shown in Fig. 9.18.

If there are m phases, the angular displacement between phase groups is $2\pi/m$ electrical degrees, except in the singular case of two phases

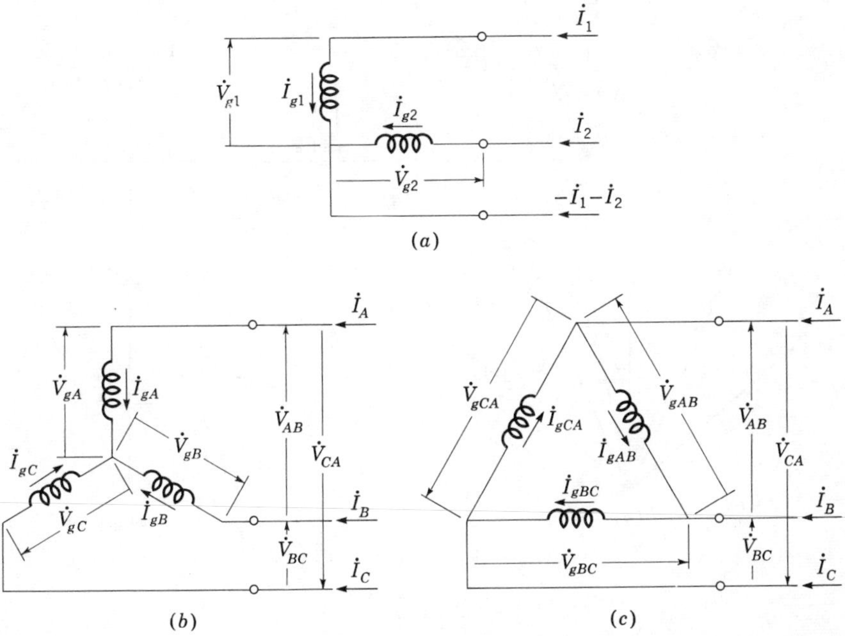

Fig. 9.19 Phase-group connections in two and three-phase windings: (*a*) Two-phase star connection; (*b*) three-phase star connection; (*c*) three-phase mesh connection.

where the phase groups are displaced by $\pi/2$. When $m = 2$, the only possible connection of the phase groups is in star with two of the ends joined together to a common line which carries the return current, as illustrated in Fig. 9.19*a*. When the number of phases exceeds two, both the star and the mesh connections of the phase groups are possible, as indicated in Fig. 9.19*b* and *c*.

In the case of star connection of a balanced system with $m > 2$, the sum of the phase currents vanishes by virtue of symmetry, and the star center point or "neutral" can be left floating.

We recall that when we considered an ideal converter, we found it convenient to relate the terminal and gap quantities via intermediate

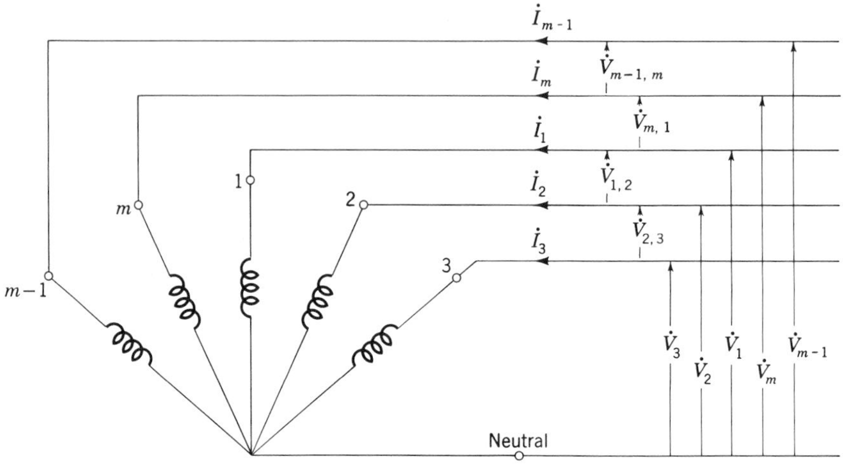

(a)

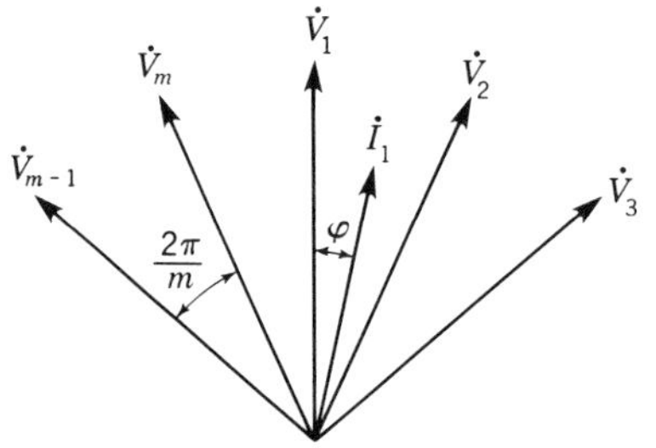

(b)

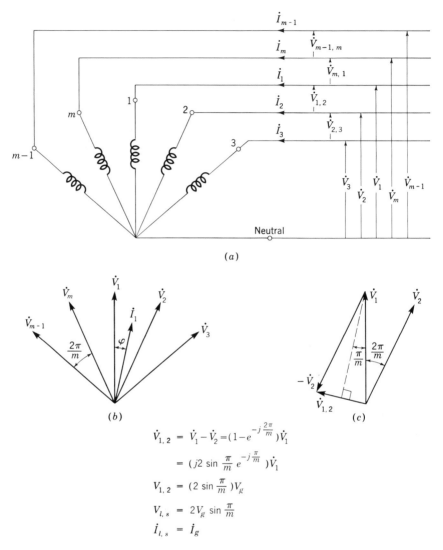

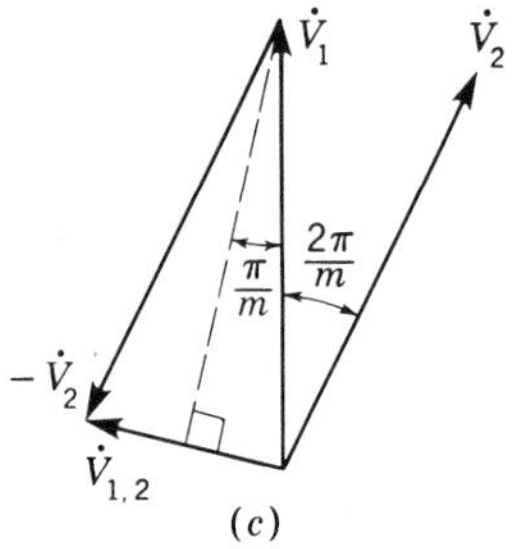

(c)

$$\dot{V}_{1,2} = \dot{V}_1 - \dot{V}_2 = (1 - e^{-j\frac{2\pi}{m}})\dot{V}_1$$

$$= (j2\sin\frac{\pi}{m}\,e^{-j\frac{\pi}{m}})\dot{V}_1$$

$$V_{1,2} = (2\sin\frac{\pi}{m})V_g$$

$$V_{l,s} = 2V_g\sin\frac{\pi}{m}$$

$$\dot{I}_{l,s} = \dot{I}_g$$

Fig. 9.20 Polyphase star connection: (*a*) Schematic representation; (*b*) phasor diagram of phase-group voltages; (*c*) relation between phase-group and line-to-line voltages.

quantities, the conductor voltage and current which represent the terminal voltage and current in each phase of a star-connected winding. We now see from Fig. 9.19*b* that in the case of a practical winding it will be convenient to use, as corresponding auxiliary quantities, the voltage $\dot{V}_g$ which appears across the series-connected conductors belonging to a phase group and the current $\dot{I}_g$ flowing through these conductors.

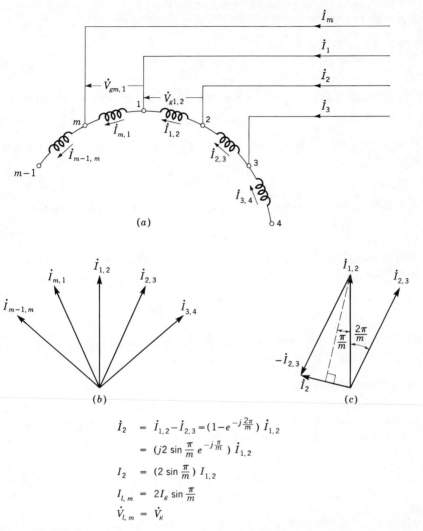

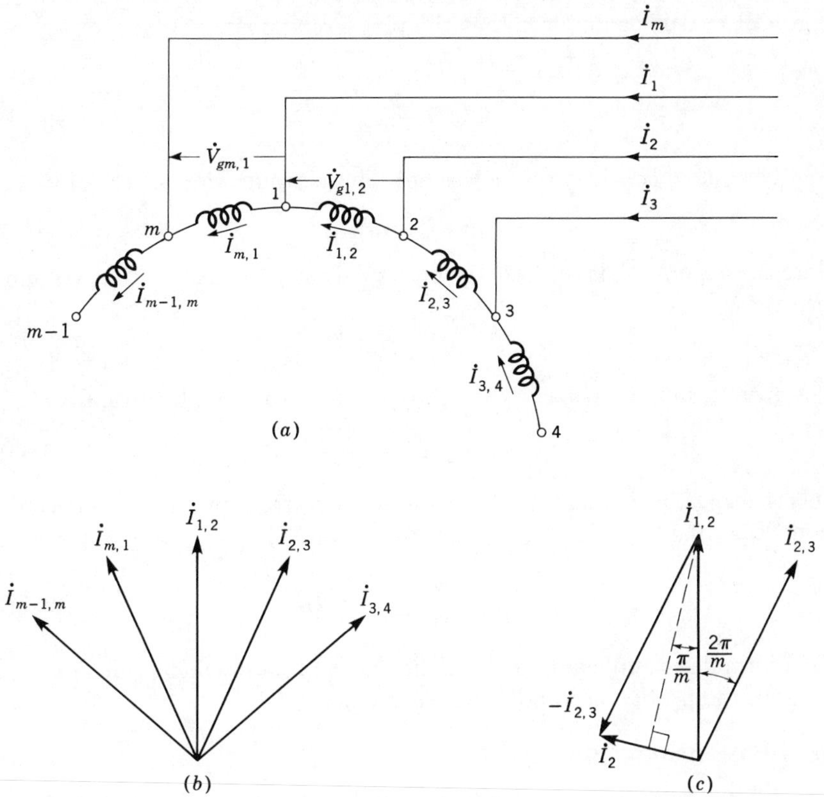

$$\dot{I}_2 = \dot{I}_{1,2} - \dot{I}_{2,3} = (1 - e^{-j\frac{2\pi}{m}})\,\dot{I}_{1,2}$$
$$= (j2 \sin \frac{\pi}{m}\, e^{-j\frac{\pi}{m}})\,\dot{I}_{1,2}$$
$$I_2 = (2 \sin \frac{\pi}{m})\, I_{1,2}$$
$$I_{l,m} = 2I_g \sin \frac{\pi}{m}$$
$$\dot{V}_{l,m} = \dot{V}_g$$

Fig. 9.21 Polyphase mesh connection: (*a*) Schematic representation; (*b*) phasor diagram of phase-group currents; (*c*) relation between phase-group and line currents.

Let us relate the line quantities $\dot{V}_l$, $\dot{I}_l$ to the phase-group quantities $\dot{V}_g$, $\dot{I}_g$. Consider first a balanced m-phase star connection, as shown in Fig. 9.20. It is clear that the relationships are

$$\dot{I}_{l,s} = \dot{I}_g$$
$$V_{l,s} = 2V_g \sin \frac{\pi}{m} \qquad (9.62)$$

We next turn to the mesh connection of the m-phase groups shown in Fig. 9.21. It is again clear that the phase relationships are:

$$\dot{V}_{l,m} = \dot{V}_g$$

$$I_{l,m} = 2I_g \sin\frac{\pi}{m} \qquad m > 2 \tag{9.63}$$

If we now consider the power of a phase group, this is given by

$$P_g = \text{Re}\,[\dot{I}_g\dot{V}_g^*] \tag{9.64a}$$

Here the exponentials containing the displacement cancel, so that we may also write

$$P_g = \text{Re}\,[\bar{I}_g\bar{V}_g^*] \tag{9.64b}$$

The total terminal power is then the sum of m such contributions or

$$P_t = \text{Re}\,[m\bar{I}_g\bar{V}_g^*] \tag{9.65}$$

Substituting for $\bar{I}_g$ and $\bar{V}_g$, the line-to-line voltage and the line current from Eqs. (9.62) and (9.63), we finally obtain

$$P_t = \frac{m}{2\sin(\pi/m)}\,\text{Re}\,[\bar{I}_l\bar{V}_l^*] \tag{9.66}$$

This formula is applicable to both the star and mesh connections and, in general, to any balanced polyphase system.

(b) Phase-group Voltage

Having established the relations between the terminal and the group variables V_g and I_g, we now need to relate the latter to the field variables. For this purpose we use Faraday's law. According to Eq. (5.6b), we can write

$$V_g(t) = -\int_{\substack{-\\ \text{inside}\\ \text{conductor}}}^{+} \mathbf{E}\cdot d\mathbf{l} - \int_S \frac{\partial \mathbf{B}}{\partial t}\cdot d\mathbf{s} \tag{9.67}$$

where the line integral is taken along the loop formed by all the series-connected conductors in the phase group and the surface integral over the total areas circumscribed by this loop.

If we choose a frame of reference attached to the conductors, the only contribution to the electric field within the conductor, according to Eq. (9.22), comes from the resistive drop J'/γ. If we denote by s_c the cross section of the conductors, by l_g the overall length of the phase group, then its resistance is

$$R_g = \frac{l_g}{\gamma s_c} \tag{9.68}$$

and its current density is

$$J = J' = \frac{I_g}{s_c} \tag{9.69}$$

since all the conductors of the phase group are connected in series. We can thus write

$$-\int_{\substack{-\\ \text{inside}\\ \text{conductor}}}^{+} \mathbf{E}' \cdot d\mathbf{l} = -\int_{-}^{+} \frac{\mathbf{J}}{\gamma} \cdot d\mathbf{l} = R_g I_g \tag{9.70}$$

The surface integral on the right-hand side of Eq. (9.67) represents the solenoidal component of voltage or the negative of the time rate of change of the magnetic flux. As mentioned in Sec. 9.6, in a practical converter the solenoidal component can be decomposed into two parts: the main part which is associated with the fundamental flux-density wave which crosses the gap and participates to the conversion or transfer of power, and the part associated with the time rate of change of the leakage fluxes or

$$\int_S \frac{\partial \mathbf{B}}{\partial t} \cdot d\mathbf{s} = \int_S \left(\frac{\partial \mathbf{B}}{\partial t}\right)_{\text{main}} \cdot d\mathbf{s} + \int_S \left(\frac{\partial \mathbf{B}}{\partial t}\right)_{\text{leakage}} \cdot d\mathbf{s} \tag{9.71}$$

Since the leakage fluxes have the same time dependence as the current flowing through the conductors, if ω_e is the radian frequency of I_g, we can write for the contribution of the leakage fluxes to the terminal voltage in phasor notation

$$-\int_S \left(\frac{\partial \mathbf{B}}{\partial t}\right)_{\text{leakage}} \cdot d\mathbf{s} = \text{Re}\,[j\omega_e \dot{\Phi}_l e^{j\omega_e t}] \tag{9.72}$$

In the linear regime $\dot{\Phi}_l$ is proportional to the conductor current $\dot{I}_g$. It is then possible to define, as mentioned in the previous section, an appropriate *leakage inductance* L_l such that

$$\dot{\Phi}_l = L_l \dot{I}_g \tag{9.73a}$$

and a *leakage reactance* X_l such that

$$j\omega_e \dot{\Phi}_l = jX_l \dot{I}_g \tag{9.73b}$$

The exact evaluation of the leakage reactance represents quite a challenging application of field theory; approximate procedures are normally quite adequate (see Prob. 9.13).

Finally, we evaluate the main part of the solenoidal component which is called the *electromotive force* (emf), and which we denote by the symbol $V_{g,m}$. We begin by considering an elementary phase group consisting of a single-turn coil with the two conductors located at x_1' and x_2' respectively. We then have

$$V_{1,2,m} = -\int_{S_{1,2}} \left(\frac{\partial \mathbf{B}}{\partial t}\right)_{\text{main}} \cdot d\mathbf{s} = -\int_0^b dy \int_{x_1'}^{x_2'} \left(\frac{\partial \mathbf{B}}{\partial t}\right)_{\text{main}} dx' \qquad (9.74)$$

where, according to Eq. (6.7)

$$B = B_m \cos\frac{\pi}{\tau}(x' + vt) \qquad (6.7)$$

By taking the time derivative and performing the double integration, we obtain:

$$V_{1,2,m} = vB\left[\cos\frac{\pi}{\tau}(x_1' + vt) - \cos\frac{\pi}{\tau}(x_2' + vt)\right] \qquad (9.75a)$$

or, introducing the time phasor notation of Sec. 9.4*c*,

$$\dot{V}_{1,2,m} = v\dot{B}(x_1') - v\dot{B}(x_2') \qquad (9.75b)$$

If we compare this last equation with Eq. (9.35*d*), we observe that they differ only in the resistive drop term, which in our present derivation is accounted for separately by means of Eq. (9.70).

We see that $V_{g,m}$ can be expressed in terms of the individual contribution of each conductor in the coil. Thus we can easily generalize Eq. (9.75*b*) to calculate $V_{g,m}$ for a phase group. If we assume, as is generally the case, that all the conductors under similar poles are connected in series, we can write

$$\dot{V}_{g,m} = pvb\left[\sum_{\alpha=1}^{c/2mp} \dot{B}(x_\alpha) - \sum_{\beta=1}^{c/2mp} \dot{B}(x_\beta)\right] \qquad (9.76)$$

In this equation, c is the total number of conductors, m the number of phases, and p the number of pole pairs, so that $c/2mp$ is the number of conductors per pole per phase.

The index α refers to all the $c/2mp$ conductors of the phase group which are exposed to the same polarity in B, i.e., belong to one side of the coils, and the index β refers to all the $c/2mp$ conductors of the phase group which are exposed to the opposite polarity, i.e., the other side of the coils.

The contribution of each conductor is a phasor, and therefore in the evaluation of the phase-group voltage we take into account the fact that the voltage of conductors lying in different slots are out of phase with one another by using time phasors in Eq. (9.76).

The summation of the conductor voltages is illustrated in Fig. 9.22 for a phase group consisting of chorded (fractional pitch) coils placed in six slots with two conductors per slot, when the coil span is two-thirds of the pole pitch τ.

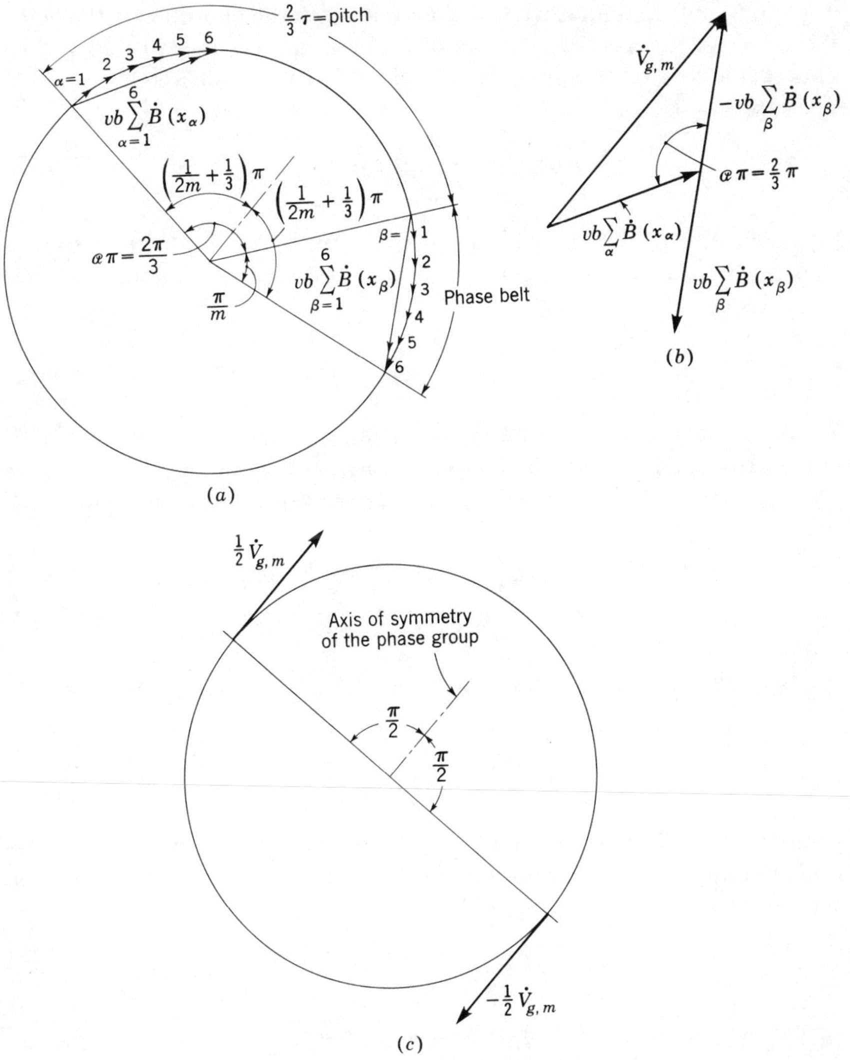

Fig. 9.22 Graphical evaluation of the electromotive force of a phase group with $c/2m = 6$, $q = 3$, $\mathscr{a} = \frac{2}{3}$, and $p = 1$: (*a*) Contribution of the individual conductors; (*b*) final result; (*c*) equivalent full-pitched concentrated coil.

Because of the assumed symmetry, the voltages of all the phase groups have the same magnitude, and their phase displacement is known. Therefore we are really interested only in the magnitude of the phase-group voltage. The graphical construction of Fig. 9.22 suggests that we can arrive at an analytical expression for this magnitude by introducing a trigonometric factor which accounts for the distribution of the conductors in various slots and another which accounts for the chording of the coils. We take as reference the voltage of a phase group concentrated in two slots a full pole pitch apart, so as to form a full-pitched coil. Since in this case

$$\sum_{\alpha} \dot{B}(x_\alpha) = -\sum_{\beta} \dot{B}(x_\beta) = \frac{c}{2mp} \dot{B} \tag{9.77}$$

the magnitude of the no-load phase-group voltage is simply given by the algebraic sum of the contribution of the individual conductors over all the poles or

$$V_{g,m} = \frac{c}{m} vbB \tag{9.78}$$

We then define a distribution factor k_d as the ratio of the actual sum of the contributions of the conductors on one side of the coils to the sum that would result if the conductors were concentrated into a full-pitch coil:

$$k_d = \frac{\left| vb \sum_{\alpha} \dot{B}(x_\alpha) \right|}{vb(c/2mp)B} = \frac{\left| \sum_{\alpha} \dot{B}(x_\alpha) \right|}{(c/2mp)B} \tag{9.79a}$$

We may also define a pitch factor k_p, such that

$$k_p = \frac{\left| \sum_{\alpha} \dot{B}(x_\alpha) - \sum_{\beta} \dot{B}(x_\beta) \right|}{|2\Sigma \dot{B}(x_\alpha)|} \tag{9.80a}$$

From its definition, we see that k_p is the factor that measures the reduction of voltage resulting from the use of coils that do not span a full pitch. We can now write

$$V_{g,m} = pvb \left| \sum_{\alpha} \dot{B}(x_\alpha) - \sum_{\beta} \dot{B}(x_\beta) \right| = \left(\frac{c}{m} k_d k_p \right) bvB \tag{9.81a}$$

In Eq. (9.81*a*) $(c/m)k_d k_p$ represents the *effective number* of conductors in the phase group, i.e., the number of conductors which, when placed in two slots one full pitch apart, would yield the same voltage. Another useful step we can take is to define a phasor $\bar{V}_{g,m}$ by

$$\bar{V}_{g,m} = \left(\frac{c}{m} k_d k_p \right) bv\bar{B} \tag{9.81b}$$

In contrast with the time phasor $\dot{V}_{g,m}$, which is related to the time phasor $\dot{B}$ at the location of the equivalent concentrated full-pitched coil by Eq. (9.76), Eq. (9.81b) defines a phasor quantity of identical magnitude but which represents a traveling wave synchronized with $\bar{B}$.   The phasor $\bar{V}_{g,m}$ thus defined will be of value in the development of the equivalent circuit in Sec. 9.8.   On the other hand, when we desire to focus attention

$$k_d = \frac{\left|\sum\limits_{\alpha} \dot{B}(x_\alpha)\right|}{|q\dot{B}(x_\alpha)|} = \frac{\sin(\pi/2m)}{q\sin(\pi/2qm)}$$

(a)

$$k_p = \frac{\frac{1}{2}\left|\sum\limits_{\alpha} \dot{B}(x_\alpha) - \sum\limits_{\beta} \dot{B}(x_\beta)\right|}{\left|\sum\limits_{\alpha} \dot{B}(x_\alpha)\right|} = \sin \wp \frac{\pi}{2}$$

$$\frac{1}{2}\left|\sum_{\alpha} \dot{B}(x_\alpha) - \sum_{\beta} \dot{B}(x_\beta)\right| = \left|\sum_{\alpha} \dot{B}(x_\alpha)\right| \sin \wp \frac{\pi}{2}$$

(b)

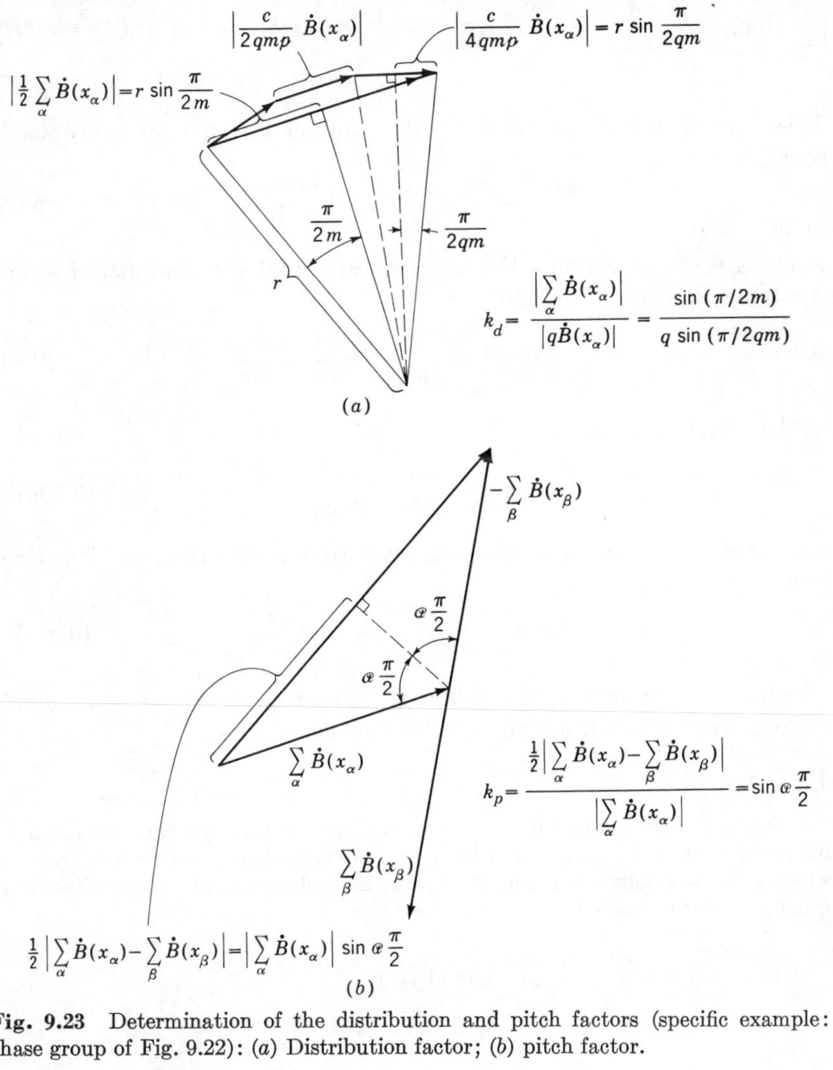

Fig. 9.23 Determination of the distribution and pitch factors (specific example: phase group of Fig. 9.22): (a) Distribution factor; (b) pitch factor.

on the local condition, we use $\dot{V}_{g,m}$.   The relationship between these two phasors is, from Eq. (9.37a), readily seen to be

$$\dot{V}_{g,m} = \bar{V}_{g,m} e^{j\pi x'/\tau}\big|_{x'=x'_{\text{coil}}} \tag{9.81c}$$

The expressions for the distribution and pitch factors can be readily inferred from Fig. 9.23 or derived as follows.   If q is the number of slots per pole per phase, then each slot carries $c/2mqp$ conductors all connected in series in the same phase group, and the electrical phase shift per slot is π/qm rad. Consequently,

$$\left|\sum_{\alpha} \dot{B}(x_\alpha)\right| = \frac{c}{2mqp} |(\bar{B}_1 + \bar{B}_1 e^{j\pi/qm} + \bar{B}_1 e^{j2\pi/qm} + \cdots + \bar{B}_1 e^{j(\pi/m)(q-1)/q})| \tag{9.82}$$

This may be readily summed by the familiar formula for a geometric series,

$$S = \frac{A(1 - r^n)}{1 - r} = A r^{(n-1)/2} \frac{r^{+n/2} - r^{-n/2}}{r^{\frac{1}{2}} - r^{-\frac{1}{2}}} \tag{9.83}$$

where A is the first term, r the common ratio, and n the number of terms. Applying Eq. (9.83), we find

$$\left|\sum_{\alpha} \dot{B}(x_\alpha)\right| = \frac{c}{2mqp} B \frac{\sin(\pi/2m)}{\sin(\pi/2mq)} \tag{9.84}$$

so that (9.79a) becomes

$$k_d = \frac{\sin(\pi/2m)}{q \sin(\pi/2mq)} \tag{9.79b}$$

Also, if α is the fraction of the pole pitch spanned by the coils, it is clear that

$$k_p = \left|\frac{1 - e^{j\alpha\pi}}{2}\right| = \left|\sin\frac{\alpha\pi}{2}\right| \tag{9.80b}$$

The use of these factors in calculating the terminal voltage of a heteropolar converter is illustrated in the following example.

Example 9.3

Determine the no-load line-to-line voltage of the turbogenerator of Examples 6.7 and 7.7 when the generator is built as a 2-pole 3-phase machine, the armature winding has 54 conductors placed in 54 slots, the coil span is 22 slots, and the phase groups are star-connected.

Solution

The number of slots per pole and phase is

$$q = \frac{54}{2 \times 3} = 9$$

and the distribution factor is

$$\frac{\sin[\pi/(2 \times 3)]}{9 \sin[\pi/(9 \times 2 \times 3)]} = \frac{\sin 30°}{9 \sin 3.33°} = 0.96$$

Since there are $\frac{54}{2} = 27$ slots per pole, the fraction of the pole pitch spanned by the coils is

$$\alpha = \tfrac{22}{27} = 0.815$$

and the pitch factor is

$$k_p = \sin 0.815 \frac{\pi}{2} = 0.957$$

From the data of Example 6.7 we know that

$$v = 220 \text{ m/sec} \qquad b = 4.45 \text{ m} \qquad B_m = 0.815 \text{ weber/m}^2$$

and therefore

$$B_{\text{rms}} = \frac{0.815}{\sqrt{2}} = 0.576 \text{ weber/m}^2$$

From Eq. (9.81) we obtain for the voltage $V_{g,m}$ of a phase group

$$V_{g,m} = \frac{c}{m} k_d k_p v b B = \tfrac{54}{3} \times 0.96 \times 0.957 \times 220 \times 4.45 \times 0.576 = 9{,}350 \text{ volts}$$

Since the phase groups are star-connected, the line-to-line voltage is, according to Eq. (9.62),

$$V_{l,s} = 2 \times 9{,}350 \times \sin \frac{\pi}{3} = 9{,}350 \times \sqrt{3} = 16{,}200 \text{ volts}$$

We note that the phase displacement between the individual contributions to the no-load voltage equals the angular displacement between the conductors along the periphery of the gap, times the number of pole pairs p, and therefore increases in proportion to the order of the harmonic wave, since, in effect, the higher harmonic has a smaller τ. It follows that the distribution and pitch factor of the harmonics differ from, and are in general smaller than, those of the fundamental wave. As a result, the series connection of conductors lying in separate slots has the beneficial effect of filtering out of the terminal voltage the higher harmonics which might be present in the flux distribution. Problem 9.14 serves to demonstrate that by exercising ingenuity in the winding design, and at the cost of a slight decrease in output of the fundamental, one can obtain a practically sinusoidal voltage even when the flux density is appreciably distorted. This should not surprise us. In an ideal winding each conductor is connected to a pair of terminals and, except for a scaling factor vb, the voltage is a faithful replica of the flux density B. By connecting the conductors in series and thus economizing on the number of terminals, we are, in effect, sampling the flux distribution at larger intervals. We thus lose the detail in which, fortunately, we are not interested.

(c) Phase-group Current

We now proceed to derive the relation between the current I_g which flows through the series-connected conductors of a phase group and the fundamental current-density wave $\bar{K}$. The surface current density is by definition the current associated with the unit length of an infinitesimal arc along the periphery of the gap. In small machines the slots are semiclosed, as shown in Fig. 6.7. Neglecting the width of the slot opening, the current density associated with a slot can be represented by an impulse.† We consider then a slot placed at $x' = x_1'$. If, as before, we denote the total number of conductors by c, the number of phases by m, the number of pole pairs by p, and the number of slots per pole per phase by q, the number of conductors in the single slot is $c/2pmq$. If we assume that all these conductors belong to the same phase group A and carry the same current $i_{gA}(t)$, then the contribution of this slot to the current density is

$$K(x_1', t) = \frac{c}{2pmq} i_{gA}(t)\delta(x' - x_1') \tag{9.85}$$

If we decompose this spatial distribution into a Fourier series, in the interval from $x' = x_1' - \tau$ to $x' = x_1' + \tau$, the fundamental is

$$K_{s,1}(x',t) = \frac{1}{\tau}\frac{c}{2pmq} i_{gA}(t) \cos\frac{\pi}{\tau}(x' - x_1') \tag{9.86}$$

The total current-density wave is then obtained by summing the contributions of all the slots.

In performing this summation we must take into account the fact that the contributions of different slots are displaced from one another in space. Since the phase displacement of the individual K waves contributed by the various slots of a phase group is equal to the time displacement of the voltages in the same slots, we can express the amplitude factor introduced by this summation as a product of the same distribution and pitch factors derived for the voltage. Since there are $2q$ slots of the phase group in one period or two pole pitches, the *amplitude* of the resultant wave produced by the conductors of the A phase group is

$$K_A(x',t)\big|_m = 2qk_dk_pK_{s,1}(x',t)\big|_m \tag{9.87a}$$

Furthermore, we note that the K produced by a full-pitched concentrated coil is zero at the axis of symmetry, i.e., midway between the coil legs or 90° from each leg. Taking this into account, and letting x_A be the location of the axis of symmetry of the A phase group, we have

$$K_A(x',t) = 2qk_dk_p\frac{1}{\tau}\frac{c}{2pmq} i_{gA}(t) \sin\frac{\pi}{\tau}(x' - x_A')$$

or

$$K_A(x',t) = \frac{c}{pm\tau} k_dk_pi_{gA}(t) \sin\frac{\pi}{\tau}(x' - x_A') \tag{9.87b}$$

The total current density is then found by summing over the contributions of all the phases. Using the fact that the currents are displaced

† This approximation is normally adequate. It is, however, easy to account for the finite width of the slot opening by considering a pulse of finite extent rather than an impulse.

in time by the same phase angle as the individual current waves are displaced in space, we obtain (see Prob. 9.15) the following relations between the total current density K_w contributed by all the phases of a winding and the phase-group current $I_{g,w}$ of one phase group of the winding:

$$\bar{K}_w = \frac{c}{2p\tau} k_d k_p \bar{I}_{g,w} \tag{9.88a}$$

or

$$\bar{I}_{g,w} = \frac{2p\tau}{ck_dk_p} \bar{K}_w = \frac{2p\tau\bar{K}_w}{m[(c/m)k_pk_d]} \tag{9.88b}$$

where we define $\bar{I}_{g,w}$ as a space-timep hasor just as we so defined $\bar{V}_{g,m}$ in Eq. (9.81b).

By comparison with Eq. (9.81), we see that $(c/m)k_dk_p$ represents the effective number of conductors in the phase group with regard to the current as well as the voltage.

In Sec. 9.7b we mentioned that the series connection of conductors is instrumental in suppressing unwanted harmonic from the phase-group voltage. From the duality of the electromagnetic field equations, and the use of the same distribution and pitch factors, we may expect a similar effect on the flux density associated with the phase-group current. Problem 9.16 demonstrates that even with a small number of slots per pole and phase, the amplitude of the higher harmonics of flux density B is relatively small; in fact, the departure from the ideal sinusoidal flux distribution does not amount to more than a few percent when $q = 2$.

This, together with the comment made with regard to the voltage, reassures us that the analysis based on an idealized model is sufficiently accurate and meaningful. All the conclusions reached in the preceding chapters thus apply to practical converters without the need for major modifications.

9.8 CIRCUIT REPRESENTATION OF A PRACTICAL CONVERTER

In this section we shall use the results obtained previously to derive an equivalent circuit for practical heteropolar converters on a phase-group basis.

This procedure requires that we refer secondary quantities to the primary, as we have done in Sec. 9.3. In accomplishing this we must now take into account the difference between primary and secondary conductors with regard to the number of conductors and the number of phases as well. As we shall see, it will not be difficult for us to determine the appropriate parameters, since the performance of the converter is, after all, governed by the field vectors prevailing in the gap, and we have previously established the relations between the field and the terminal quantities.

(a) Transformation Rules

In deriving the circuit model of Fig. 9.2, we found that the process of referring secondary to primary required multiplying the secondary E by $1/S$, whereas the secondary K was left unchanged.

We now wish to determine the relationships that must be used between primary and secondary voltages and currents when the circuit model is to be put in terms of phase-group quantities, or as we shall say, on a "per-phase" basis.

To establish the voltage relationships, we turn to Eq. (9.81a). We shall use subscripts 1 and 2 to denote primary and secondary quantities, respectively. If we write Eq. (9.81a) in turn for a primary phase group and a secondary phase group, and then take the ratio, we find that for a given $\bar{B}$ wave and active length b the ratio of primary to secondary voltage magnitude is

$$\frac{V_{1,m}}{V_{2,m}} = \frac{[(c/m)k_d k_p]_1}{[(c/m)k_d k_p]_2}\frac{v_1}{v_2} = \frac{[(c/m)k_d k_p]_1}{[(c/m)k_d k_p]_2}\frac{1}{S} \tag{9.89}$$

The ratio of Eq. (9.89) is then the ratio by which we have to multiply the secondary voltage in order to obtain the voltage reflected on the primary side. In the case of ideal windings, where $c = m$ and $k_d k_p = 1$, this ratio is simply $1/S$, as we indeed found in Sec. 9.3.

It is customary to denote by V_2' the voltage reflected into the primary by a secondary voltage V_2 at rotor standstill ($S = 1$); thus

$$\bar{V}_2' = \frac{[(c/m)k_d k_p]_1}{[(c/m)k_d k_p]_2}\bar{V}_2 \tag{9.90}$$

so that, in general, the secondary voltage referred to the primary is written as $\bar{V}_2'/S$.

We next turn to the current transformation. The total $\bar{K}$, which of course determines the total $\bar{B}$, is $\bar{K}_1 + \bar{K}_2$. Using Eq. (9.88a), we find

$$\bar{K} = \bar{K}_1 + \bar{K}_2 = \frac{1}{2p\tau} m_1 \left(\frac{c}{m} k_d k_p\right)_1 \left\{\bar{I}_{g,1} + \frac{m_2}{m_1}\frac{[(c/m)k_d k_p]_2 \bar{I}_{g,2}}{[(c/m)k_d k_p]_1}\right\} \tag{9.91}$$

Equation (9.91) makes it clear that the relation between the secondary current $\bar{I}_2$ and its referred-to-primary equivalent $\bar{I}_2'$ is

$$\bar{I}_2' = \frac{m_2}{m_1}\frac{[(c/m)k_p k_d]_2}{[(c/m)k_p k_d]_1}\bar{I}_2 \tag{9.92}$$

Next we consider a secondary impedance $\bar{Z}_2$, carrying current $\bar{I}_2$ (here the bar just means a complex number), and having a voltage drop

$\bar{V}_2$. If, for example, $\bar{Z}_2$ is a series RLC arrangement, we have

$$\frac{\bar{V}_2}{\bar{I}_2} = \bar{Z}_2 = R_2 + j\omega_{e,2}L_2 + \frac{1}{j\omega_{e,2}C_2} \tag{9.93}$$

Now the primary and secondary radian frequencies are related by Eqs. (9.4) and (9.9):

$$\frac{\omega_{e,2}}{\omega_{e,1}} = \frac{v_2}{v_1} = S \tag{9.94}$$

Using Eqs. (9.90), (9.92), and (9.94), we may write

$$\begin{aligned} \frac{\bar{V}_2'}{S\bar{I}_2'} &= \frac{m_1}{m_2}\frac{[(c/m)k_pk_d]_1^2}{[(c/m)k_pk_d]_2^2}\left(\frac{R_2}{S} + j\omega_{e,1}L_2 + \frac{1}{j\omega_{e,1}S^2C_2}\right) \\ &= \frac{R_2'}{S} + j\omega_{e,1}L_2' + \frac{1}{j\omega_{e,1}S^2C_2'} \end{aligned} \tag{9.95}$$

Equation (9.95) incorporates the transformation rules for impedances, which are summarized in Table 9.1.

Table 9.1 TRANSFORMATION RULES FOR IMPEDANCES

Secondary parameter	*Referred-to-primary parameter*
R_2	$\Gamma \dfrac{R_2}{S}$
L_2	ΓL_2
C_2	$\dfrac{S^2C_2}{\Gamma}$

where
$$\Gamma = \frac{m_1}{m_2}\frac{[(c/m)k_pk_d]_1^2}{[(c/m)k_pk_d]_2^2}$$

Next we turn to the magnetizing reactance. This may be expressed as a per-phase quantity by writing it in terms of $V_{g,m}$ and I_g. Thus we introduce the relation between $v\bar{B}$ and $\bar{K}$ given by Eq. (7.16) into Eq. (9.81*b*) for $\bar{V}_{g,m}$, and then substitute $\bar{I}_g$ from Eq. (9.88*b*). Considering any one winding, this procedure yields

$$\begin{aligned} \bar{V}_{g,m} &= j\left(\frac{c}{m}k_dk_p\right)b\mu_0\frac{\tau v}{\pi g}\bar{K} \\ &= j\frac{1}{2p\tau}\frac{1}{m}(ck_dk_p)^2\mu_0\frac{\tau bv}{\pi g}\bar{I}_g \end{aligned} \tag{9.96}$$

Equation (9.96) now serves to define a per-phase magnetizing reactance X_m given by

$$X_m = \frac{\mu_0 bv(ck_dk_p)^2}{2\pi pmg} \tag{9.97}$$

where μ_0 = permeability of free space
g = gap length
b = length of active conductor
v = conductor speed with respect to wave frame
(ck_pk_d) = effective number of conductors
p = number of pole pairs
m = number of phases

Since we are interested in referring all quantities to the primary, we apply Eq. (9.97) to find the primary magnetizing reactance. This is done simply by using the primary velocity and primary winding parameters in the equation.

(b) Equivalent Circuits

We are now ready to write the equations describing the performance of a practical heteropolar converter in terms of terminal variables and to determine overall equivalent circuits. To do this, we begin with Eq. (9.67) for a phase-group voltage, and introduce Eqs. (9.70), (9.71), and (9.74) to obtain

$$V_g(t) = R_gI_g + V_{g,m} - \int_S \left(\frac{\partial \mathrm{B}}{\partial t}\right)_{\text{leakage}} \cdot ds \qquad (9.98a)$$

We now wish to restate Eq. (9.98*a*) on a phasor basis. As a first step, we go to time phasors, and using Eqs. (9.72) and (9.73) we find

$$\dot{V}_g = R_g\dot{I}_g + \dot{V}_{g,m} + jX_l\dot{I}_g \qquad (9.98b)$$

As the next step, we recognize that the relationship of Eq. (9.98*b*) is valid for *any* phase group in the gap, and consequently need not be localized. We can express this fact by resorting to bar-superscript phasors, as we have already discussed. Thus we may write

$$\bar{V}_g = R_g\bar{I}_g + \bar{V}_{g,m} + jX_l\bar{I}_g \qquad (9.98c)$$

Equation (9.98*c*) applies to the primary as well as the secondary winding, once we introduce the appropriate subscripts 1 and 2. To simplify our notation we shall drop the subscripts g and l with the understanding that all quantities are phase-group quantities and reactances are leakage terms unless accompanied by the subscript m. Moreover, we again use a prime superscript to designate the secondary quantities referred to the primary. Introducing $\bar{K}$ from Eq. (9.91) into Eq. (9.96), and using Eqs. (9.92) and (9.97), we thus obtain for the primary winding

$$\bar{V}_1 = (R_1 + jX_1)\bar{I}_1 + jX_m(\bar{I}_1 + \bar{I}'_2) \qquad (9.98d)$$

Similarly, making use of Eq. (9.95), we obtain for the secondary winding referred to the primary

$$\frac{\bar{V}_2'}{S} = \left(\frac{R_2'}{S} + jX_2'\right)\bar{I}_2' + jX_m(\bar{I}_2' + \bar{I}_1) \tag{9.98e}$$

These equations lead to the equivalent circuit of Fig. 9.24, which is the per-phase result for the generalized heteropolar converter. Alternatively

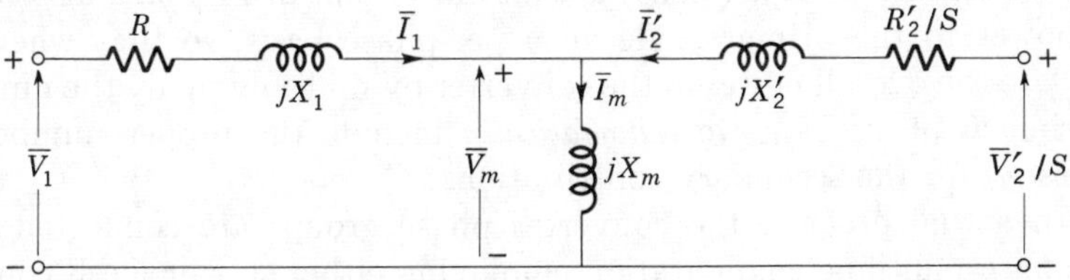

Fig. 9.24 Equivalent circuit of the heteropolar converter.

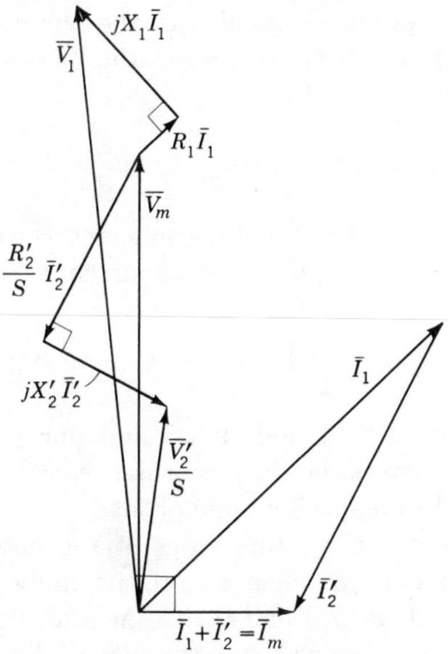

Fig. 9.25 Phasor diagram of the heteropolar converter (motoring operation).

we can depict the phasor relations of Eqs. (9.98*d*) and (9.98*e*) in a phasor diagram, as shown in Fig. 9.25.

The question naturally arises: How does one calculate overall power from the per-phase equivalent circuit of Fig. 9.24 in view of the fact that $m_1 \neq m_2$? The answer is readily obtained if we look at a referred-to-primary power term. Multiplying Eq. (9.92) by $\bar{V}_2'/S$ and using Eq.

(9.90), we have

$$\mathrm{Re}\left[\frac{\bar{V}_2'}{S}\,\bar{I}_2'^*\right] = \mathrm{Re}\left[\frac{m_2}{m_1}\,(\bar{V}_2\bar{I}_2^*)\right] \tag{9.99a}$$

and multiplying both sides of the equation by m_1, we obtain

$$\mathrm{Re}\left[m_1\frac{\bar{V}_2'}{S}\,\bar{I}_2'^*\right] = \mathrm{Re}\,[m_2\bar{V}_2\bar{I}_2^*] \tag{9.99b}$$

The significance of Eq. (9.99*b*) is that our circuit of Fig. 9.24 also refers the power to the primary side on a per-phase basis, so that when we calculate the overall power in the converter by multiplying by the number of primary phases m_1, we *automatically* include the proper number of phases m_2 for the secondary contributions.

In actual practice the converter phase groups are connected in a polyphase multiline configuration employing either star or mesh connections. We are then interested in using our circuit model to calculate actual line voltages and currents: If we have a mesh-connected converter, the line-to-line voltages are identical with the phase-group voltages, but the line-current magnitudes are related to the phase-group voltage magnitudes by Eq. (9.63):

$$I_{l,m} = 2I_g \sin\frac{\pi}{m} \qquad m > 2 \tag{9.63}$$

If, on the other hand, we have a star-connected converter, the line currents are identical with the phase-group currents, but the voltage relationship is

$$V_{l,s} = 2V_g \sin\frac{\pi}{m} \qquad m > 2 \tag{9.62}$$

With the aid of Eqs. (9.62) and (9.63) and our per-phase equivalent circuit, we may thus determine the performance of the physical converter when it is connected to a specified line or load.

Next we consider the limiting cases of the heteropolar converter. With synchronous operation, when $S \to 0$, the equivalent circuit reduces to the one shown in Figs. 7.5 and 9.26. As was already mentioned in Sec. 7.4*a*, a comparison between the circuits of Fig. 9.26 and Fig. 7.4 reveals that the departure from ideal conditions in a synchronous converter results in an additional series impedance in the armature circuit. This impedance, whose per-unit value is normally small (in the order of 0.1 p.u.) is easily absorbed in the load or source impedance. Alternatively the leakage reactance can be absorbed in the magnetizing reactance by introducing the *synchronous reactance* $X_d = X_m + X_1$. This leads to the equivalent circuit shown in Fig. 9.27. Since this circuit is formally identical with that of an ideal machine and $X_m/X_d \doteq 1$, all the considerations based on the idealized model of the previous chapters hold true.

In a similar way we can modify the phasor diagram of Fig. 7.6 into the one shown in Fig. 9.28.

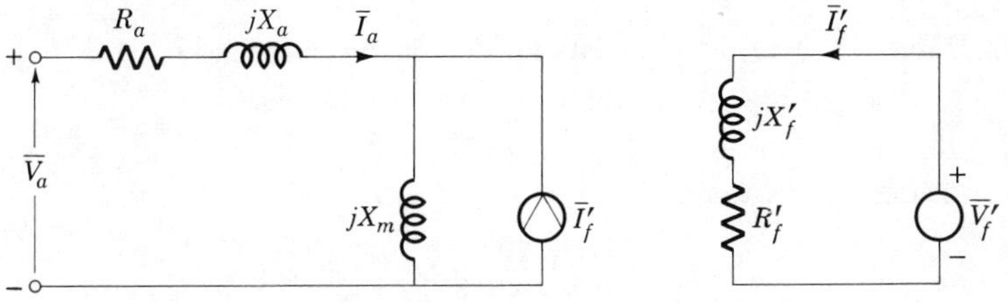

Fig. 9.26 Equivalent circuit of the synchronous converter.

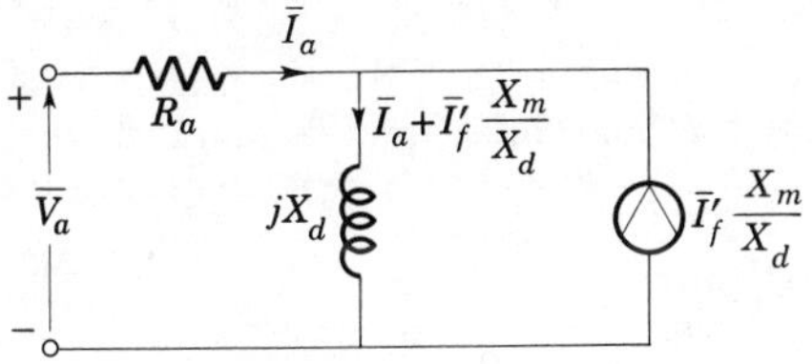

Fig. 9.27 Reduced equivalent circuit of a synchronous converter.

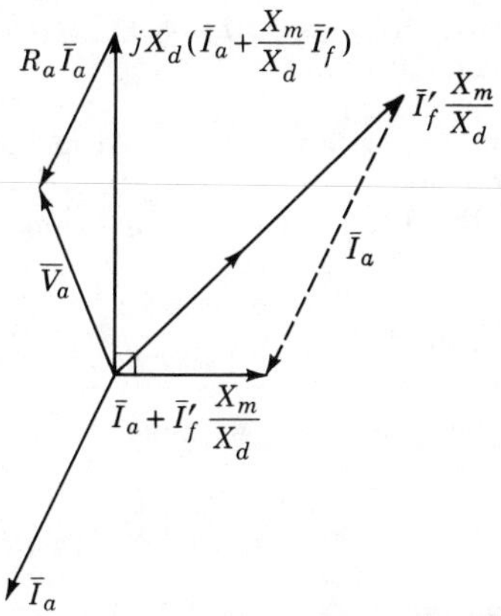

Fig. 9.28 Phasor diagram of a synchronous converter.

The use of the transformation formulas and the application of the equivalent circuit to determine power relations is illustrated in the following example.

Example 9.4

In the generator of Examples 6.7, 7.7, and 9.3:

(*a*) Evaluate the magnetizing reactance.

(*b*) Determine the per-unit value of the magnetizing reactance.

(*c*) Compare the power converted in the practical generator where the conductors are grouped in a small number of phases with the power that would be converted in an ideal machine carrying the same current per conductor but having $c = m$ and $k_d k_p = 1$.

Solution

(*a*) From Eq. (9.97) and the data for the converter we have

$$X_m = \frac{4\pi \times 10^{-7} \times 4.45 \times 220 \times (54 \times 0.96 \times 0.957)^2}{2\pi \times 3 \times 0.098} = 1.63 \text{ ohms}$$

(*b*) The rated phase current is

$$I_a = \frac{225 \times 10^6}{3 \times 9{,}350 \times 0.85} = 9{,}450 \text{ amp}$$

so that

$$X_{m,\text{p.u.}} = \frac{X_m}{V_R/I_R} = \frac{1.63 \times 9{,}450}{9{,}350} = 1.65$$

We observe that the value derived here for the practical converter agrees with the one derived in Example 7.7, assuming ideal flux and current distributions. Indeed, as mentioned in Sec. 7.5*c*, this was one of the main reasons for introducing a per-unit system.

(*c*) The terminal power is

$$P_t = \text{Re}\,[m\bar{V}_a\bar{I}_a^*]$$

and in a practical converter is, according to Eq. (9.98*d*),

$$\begin{aligned} P_t &= m\,\text{Re}\,[(R_a + jX_a)I_a^2 + jX_m(I_a^2 + \bar{I}_f'\bar{I}_a^*)] \\ &= mR_aI_a^2 + \text{Re}\,[jmX_m\bar{I}_f'\bar{I}_a^*] \end{aligned}$$

The first term to the right is the power dissipated in the armature resistance (the leakage reactance, of course, does not absorb power), and the second term is the power converted or transferred through the gap. Introducing Eq. (9.97), the latter can be written as

$$P_{\text{conv},a} = \text{Re}\left[jm\,\frac{\mu_0 bv(ck_dk_p)^2}{2\pi pmg}\,\bar{I}_f'\bar{I}_a'^*\right]$$

In an ideal converter, on the other hand, we have

$$\begin{aligned} P_{\text{conv},a} = A(p_{s,\text{conv}}) &= 2p\tau b\,\text{Re}\,[v\bar{B}\bar{K}^*] \\ &= 2p\tau b\,\text{Re}\,[j\mathfrak{X}_m\bar{K}_f\bar{K}_a^*] \end{aligned}$$

Introducing Eq. (7.20) and Eq. (9.39), we obtain

$$P_{\text{conv},a} = \text{Re}\left[j2p\tau b\,\frac{\mu_0\tau v}{\pi g}\left(\frac{c}{2p\tau}\right)^2 \bar{I}_{cf}'\bar{I}_{ca}^*\right]$$

Since in the per-phase representation

$$I_g = I_c$$

we find that the ratio of the powers converted in the practical and in the ideal converter is

$$(k_dk_p)^2 = (0.96 \times 0.957)^2 = 0.843$$

The preceding example serves to prove two points:

1. Our design procedure based on an idealized model, where the interacting $\bar{B}$ and $\bar{K}$ waves represent the fundamentals of the actual flux and current distributions prevailing in the practical converter, yields the correct value for the power converted. This is demonstrated by the identity of the per-unit values of the magnetizing reactance which relates the two factors in the converted power: $v\bar{B}$ and $\bar{K}$ in the idealized model, and V_m and I in the practical converter.
2. The departures from ideal conditions prevent full utilization of the current flowing in the conductors for the purpose of power conversion. This results in lower attainable densities of converted power p_{conv} since the efficiency and thermal considerations which determine the size of the converter depend on the actual value of the currents and *not* on the fraction which is effective. The effective fraction is given by the product of the distribution and pitch factors $k_p k_d$, and for this reason $(k_d k_p)^2$ represents the fractional power output of a practical converter when compared with an ideal one of the same size.

Finally we consider the special case of the singly excited heteropolar converter. Its equivalent circuit is shown in Fig. 9.29. From this

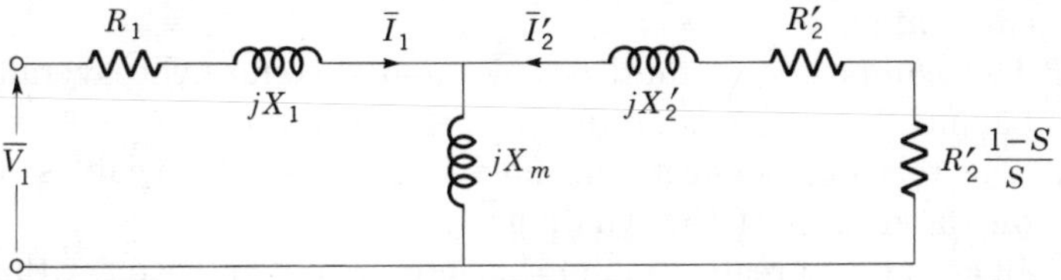

Fig. 9.29 Equivalent circuit of the heteropolar converter singly excited by an a-c supply.

circuit we see that when the converter operates far from synchronism, or with large values of the slip S, the secondary current is governed by the leakage reactance X_2'. Furthermore since the leakage is, in general, only a small fraction of the total flux, X_2' is much smaller than X_m, and the branch consisting of the magnetizing reactance can be considered as an open circuit. This means that the primary as well as the secondary current and, in fact, the whole performance of the converter are largely determined by the leakage reactances. For this reason, although we could neglect the flux leakage in the synchronous converter, we have had to introduce it before the detailed discussion of the singly excited asynchronous converter presented in the next chapter.

9.9 SUMMARY

This chapter has brought to light the following features of the heteropolar converter.

1. It is quite possible to construct a device in which the electromagnetic waves associated with the conductors on both sides of the gap travel with respect to the conductors while remaining at standstill with each other, thus satisfying the conditions for average conversion of power.
2. Such a device represents a generalized version of the heteropolar converter, which includes as special cases the synchronous converter, the asynchronous converter with single excitation on the a-c side, and as a limiting case when the wavelength becomes infinite, the homopolar converter.
3. When the conductors move with respect to the wave frame, power can be transferred between the electric circuits on opposite sides of the gap by transformer action. The agency for this process is the solenoidal component of electric field.
4. The terminal voltage is invariant to a transformation of reference frames in relative motion. As a result, the position of the primary and secondary windings with respect to the external networks can be interchanged, and sliding contacts can be eliminated.
5. The composite or total powers, and therefore the overall power balances, are the same in all reference frames.
6. The relation between the field and terminal variables depends on the details of the windings.
7. In a practical realization of the heteropolar converter with a small number of phases and with conductors embedded in slots, the terminal voltage for a given flux-density wave, and the current-density wave corresponding to given terminal currents are smaller than in an ideal converter.
8. A practical converter designed under the assumption of idealized sinusoidal flux and current-density distributions will convert the expected amount of power. However, an ideal converter of the same size and carrying the same current per conductor will convert more power. The ratio of the two powers is given by the square of the product of the distribution and pitch factors.
9. Even though the converter may depart considerably from the ideal conditions, fairly sinusoidal voltage and current wave shapes can be obtained by exercising ingenuity in the design, at the price of a small reduction in converted power density.

REFERENCE

1. Newcomb, W. A.: Motion of Magnetic Lines of Force, *Ann. Phys.*, vol. 3, no. 4, pp. 347–85 (April, 1958).

PROBLEMS

9.1 A radar system transmits a signal with a frequency of 3×10^9 cps. What is the velocity of the moving target if the frequency in the echo is 10^5 cycles higher than the frequency of the transmitted signal?

9.2 The orbital velocity of the earth is of the order of 3×10^4 m/sec. The frequency of the first spectral line in the Balmer series of hydrogen is $\nu = 4.58 \times 10^{14}$ cps. Evaluate the yearly frequency spread of this hydrogen line in the spectrum of a fixed star as observed on earth.

9.3 The Doppler shift of a spectral line is used as a diagnostic tool to determine the temperature of the ions in a hot plasma. Establish the relation between the spread in the frequency ν of a characteristic spectral line (line broadening) and the random kinetic energy of the ions.

9.4 A heteropolar converter is designed to drive the "coiler" of an aluminum strip mill with a speed ranging between 1,240 and 170 rpm. The motor is commissioned for use in Europe where the standard supply frequency is 50 cps; it is built with eight poles, a per-unit magnetizing reactance referred to the primary $X_{m1} = 3$ p.u., and primary and secondary resistances $1/a_1\gamma_1 = 1/a_2\gamma_2 = 0.01$ p.u. Plot the per-unit magnitude, phase, and frequency of the secondary supply voltage as a function of the speed when the primary voltage and current are kept constant at the rated values with unity power factor.

9.5 The realization of reliable and economical frequency changers is a problem of great technical interest. We have seen how a frequency change results from relative motion by virtue of the Doppler effect. However, a static device is clearly preferable. You are called upon to comment on the validity of the premises and the feasibility of the following invention.

A new static frequency changer: The present invention is motivated by the recognition that relative motion is not essential to a frequency changer, since such a device does not necessarily involve electromechanical power conversion. Accordingly, this new frequency changer consists of a structure similar to that of the heteropolar converter [see sketch (*a*)], but with primary and secondary windings which are at stand-

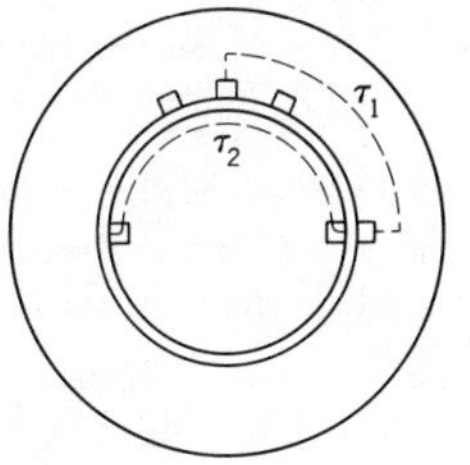

(*a*)

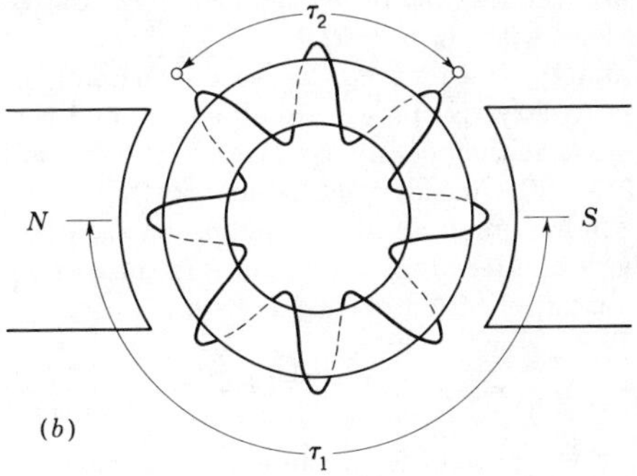

(*b*)

still with each other. The primary winding is connected to a polyphase source which impresses a traveling electromagnetic wave. Its phase velocity v is related to the frequency by the synchronous tie $\omega = \pi v/\tau$. The secondary winding, being at standstill with respect to the primary, senses the wave at the same relative velocity v. By virtue of the synchronous tie the secondary frequency will thus be related to the primary frequency as

$$\frac{\omega_1}{\omega_2} = \frac{\pi v/\tau_1}{\pi v/\tau_2} = \frac{\tau_2}{\tau_1}$$

To satisfy this relation the following two schemes are proposed:

(1) If the desired frequency ratio is an integer, the primary and secondary windings are designed with standard coils but with different pitch, such that the coil-pitch ratio is the inverse of the frequency ratio.

(2) If the desired frequency ratio is not an integer, either the primary or the secondary is designed as a Gramme ring winding [see sketch (*b*)]. It is known that in such a winding the pole pitch is indeterminate and can be chosen at will by making the appropriate connections to the external networks.

9.6 Two induction motors having different numbers of poles and coupled to a common mechanical load, can be made to operate efficiently in three speed ranges by using the arrangement shown in the schematic diagram. According to this arrangement, two of the speed ranges are obtained by energizing the motors one at the time,

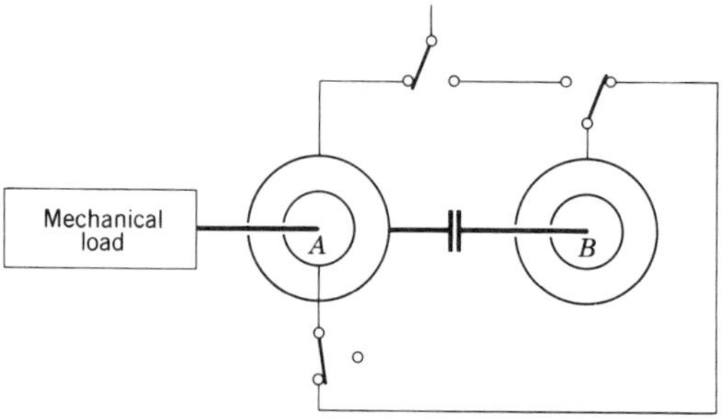

and the third speed range is obtained by connecting the motors in cascade, i.e., by connecting the rotor terminals of motor A to the stator of motor B. The rotor winding of motor B is permanently short-circuited. Determine:

(*a*) The overall efficiency of the drive as a function of the slip S_B in the motor B.

(*b*) The fraction of mechanical power delivered by each motor at no load and at rated load with $S_B = 0.02$.

Assume that motor B has twice the number of poles of motor A, that the primary and secondary resistances are all equal, and that the magnetizing reactances X_m are so large that they can be considered as infinite.

9.7 (*a*) Consider the elementary coil formed by the two series-connected armature conductors of an ideal synchronous converter located at x_1' and x_2', respectively. Evaluate the terminal voltage in a frame of reference attached to the field structure, by direct application of Faraday's law:

$$\oint \mathbf{E} \cdot d\mathbf{l} = -\int_S \frac{\partial \mathbf{B}}{\partial t} \cdot d\mathbf{s}$$

Choose as a path of integration a mathematical loop which coincides with the electric circuit of the coil at the instant of time when the integration is performed. Introduce for $\mathbf{E}$ the value given by Eq. (6.13*b*) and express B and K_a as in Eqs. (6.15) and (6.19*a*), respectively.

(*b*) By using the Galilean transformation of coordinates, express the terminal voltage as a function of time. Note that this is equivalent to following the coil in its

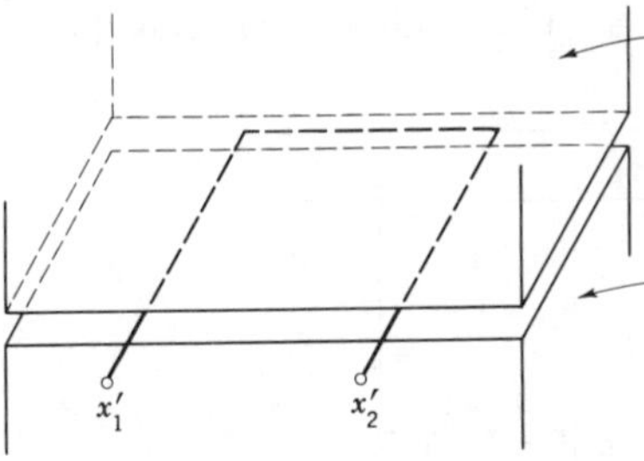

motion, and repeating at each instant of time the integration process along mathematical loops which coincide with the successive positions taken by the coil.

(*c*) Introduce phasor notation, and obtain Eq. (9.35*b*).

9.8 Consider the elementary coil of the preceding problem. Evaluate again the terminal voltage, but this time in the armature reference frame and using Eq. (5.6*b*) instead. Introducing the appropriate values of E_a, $K_a' = K_a$, and $B' = B$, and comparing with the results of the previous problem, verify that the terminal voltage is invariant to a transformation of reference frames.

9.9 Derive Eq. (9.33) directly from the definition

$$\mathbf{E}_{\mathrm{sol}}' = -\frac{\partial \mathbf{A}'}{\partial t'} \qquad (9.23)$$

using the following alternative ways:

(*a*) Evaluate the vector potential $\mathbf{A}'$ in the primed reference frame by following the outline given in Appendix B, and then take its time derivative.

(*b*) Start from the wave frame where $\partial \mathbf{A}/\partial t = 0$, and apply the transformation rules between frames in relative motion given in Appendix A.

9.10 (*a*) Evaluate the terminal voltage of a homopolar converter, using the loop of Fig. 5.3, but choosing a reference frame attached to the conductor. By comparing your result with Eq. (5.6), verify that the terminal voltage is not invariant to a transformation between reference frames in relative motion, and that the sliding contacts cannot be eliminated by placing the armature conductor and its external circuit on the same structure (for instance, the stator).

(*b*) Confirm this result by evaluating the scalar and vector potentials in both reference frames. For this purpose integrate Eq. (9.24) under the assumption of cylindrical symmetry and constant B along the y axis, and also use the transformation law for the scalar potential [Eq. (9.28*a*)].

9.11 The interface between two media of different permeability is subjected to a stress normal to the surface. In the case of iron and air with permeabilities μ_i and μ_o, respectively, the force per-unit area on the bounding surface is found to be (see, for instance, J. A. Stratton, "Electromagnetic Theory," p. 155, McGraw-Hill Book Company, New York, 1941)

$$f_n = \frac{\mu_i - \mu_o}{2}\left(H_{t}^2 + \frac{\mu_i - \mu_o}{\mu_o} H_{ni}^2\right)$$

where H_i is measured just inside the surface in the iron, and the index n stands for normal component. It follows that when the conductor is embedded in a slot, we must consider the force exerted on the slot sides, in addition to the force acting on the conductor. Consider the limiting case in which the iron is highly saturated so that μ_i/μ_o is a constant in the order of unity. In this case the magnetic field is only slightly perturbed by the presence of the iron, and the lines of force may be approximated by straight lines parallel to the z axis. Under this approximation prove that, when the

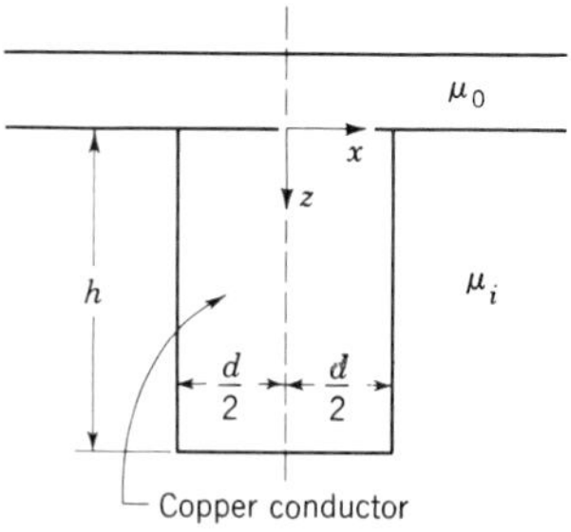

conductor carries a current I uniformly distributed with density $J = I/dh$ and the currents external to the slot impress a uniform magnetic field $H_z{}^0 = B_z{}^0/\mu_i$, then the total force F_x acting on the conductor and on the slot sides is equal to the force that would be exerted by the flux density $B_z{}^0$ on the conductor in the absence of the iron.

Hint: Note that under the approximation made, the magnetic field component contributed by the current in the conductor itself is $|H_z| = I/2h$ and is oppositely directed on the two slots sides.

9.12 Consider the same problem as above but in the limiting case of iron with infinite permeability. In the limit $\mu_i \to \infty$, we have $H_i \to 0$ and

$$f_n = \frac{1}{2}\frac{B^2}{\mu_o}$$

with B in air normal to the interface.

(*a*) Evaluate the impressed magnetic field H^0 in the slot region under the assumption that the conductor carries no current and

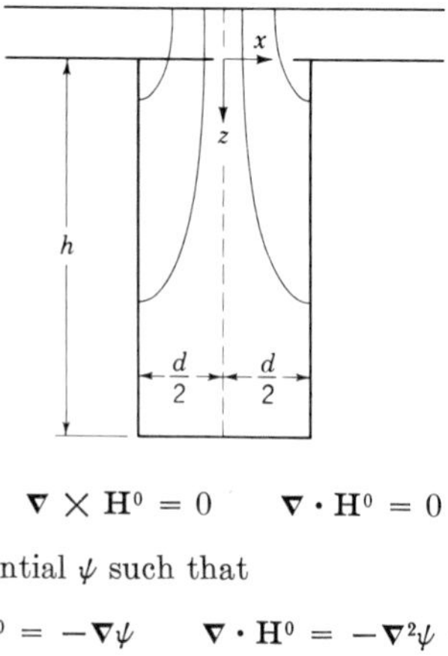

$$\nabla \times \mathbf{H}^0 = 0 \qquad \nabla \cdot \mathbf{H}^0 = 0$$

Introduce a magnetic potential ψ such that

$$\mathbf{H}^0 = -\nabla\psi \qquad \nabla \cdot \mathbf{H}^0 = -\nabla^2\psi = 0$$

and solve the Laplace equation

$$\nabla^2\psi = \frac{\partial^2\psi}{\partial x^2} + \frac{\partial^2\psi}{\partial z^2} = 0$$

(See Appendix B.)

Assume as boundary conditions:

At $z = 0$: $$H_z = -\frac{\partial\psi}{\partial z} = H^0 \cos\frac{\pi}{\tau}x$$

At $z = h$: $$H_z = -\frac{\partial\psi}{\partial z} = 0$$

Assume $h/b > 1$, and approximate the hyperbolic functions.

(*b*) To the same order of approximation evaluate the field associate current I flowing in the conductor. Assume that the current is uniformly distributed with density $J = I/dh$ and the lines of force are straight lines across the slot as sketched.

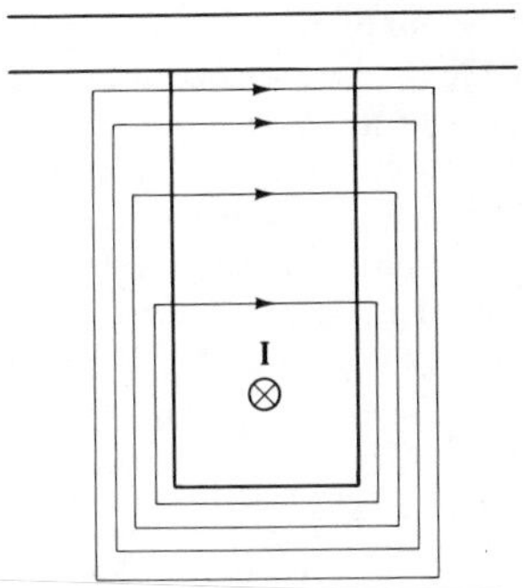

(*c*) By superposing the two components of magnetic field, evaluate the force $F_{x,\text{sides}}$ exerted on the slot sides.

(*d*) Evaluate the force on the conductor F_{xc} and show that the total force is

$$F_{x,\text{sides}} + F_{xc} = I\frac{2}{\pi}B^0 = IB^0_{\text{av}}$$

as it would be in the absence of the iron.

9.13 The armature conductors of the generator of Examples 6.7, 7.7, 9.3, and 9.4 are embedded in slots as shown. Determine the slot leakage reactance of a phase group in ohms and in per-unit. For this purpose, assume:

(1) The current in the conductors is uniformly distributed with density $J = I_g/h_1d$.

(2) The iron has infinite permeability, and the lines of force of the magnetic field associated with the current in the conductor are straight lines across the slots as indicated in the sketch.

(3) $I_g = 9{,}450$ amp $\quad V_g = 9{,}350$ v $\quad \frac{c}{m} = 18 \quad b = 4.45$ m

$h_1 = 0.167$ m $\quad h_2 = 0.03$ m $\quad d = 0.03$ m

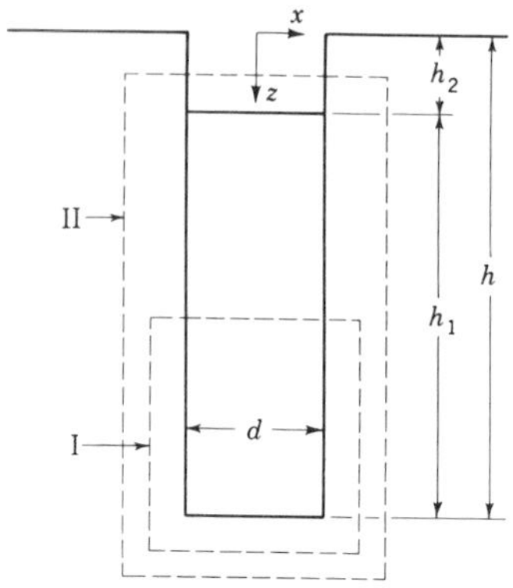

Follow these steps:

(a) Evaluate H_x in the conductor as a function of the distance from the bottom of the slot $h - z$ by applying Ampère's law to loop *I*.

(b) Evaluate H_x above the conductor, using loop II.

(c) Evaluate the leakage flux which crosses the slots per unit length of the conductor, integrating separately over h_1 and h_2.

(d) Evaluate the leakage flux for all the conductors in the phase group, and obtain the slot leakage inductance by dividing by I_g.

9.14 Control synchros are heteropolar converters whose electric output is a prescribed function of the shaft position. Their accuracy, which is subject to very stringent specifications, is strongly dependent on the harmonic content of the voltage

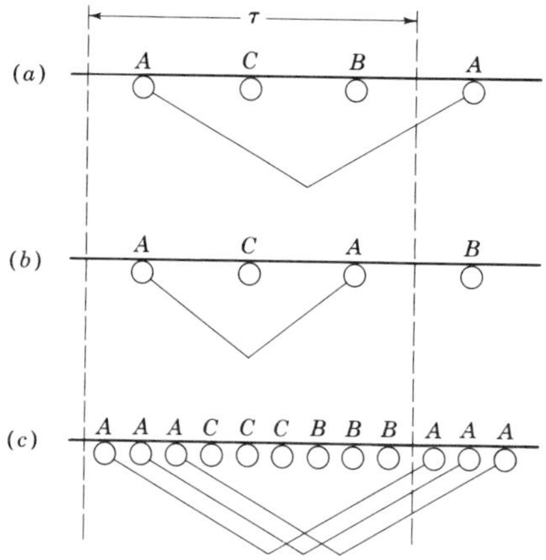

output. Assuming that, because of mechanical and magnetic imperfections, the flux density contains besides the first (fundamental) a second and a third harmonic

$$B = B_1 \cos \frac{\pi}{\tau} x + B_2 \cos 2 \frac{\pi}{\tau} x + B_3 \cos 3 \frac{\pi}{\tau} x$$

compare the harmonic content of the no-load phase voltage in the three alternative designs of a three-phase synchro described below:

(*a*) The armature is wound with full-pitched coils and one slot per pole and phase.

(*b*) The coils are chorded and span two-thirds of the pole pitch τ; there is only one slot per pole and phase.

(*c*) The coils are full-pitched, and there are three slots per pole and phase.

9.15 (*a*) Superposing the current density contributed by the various phases according to Eq. (9.87*b*), and taking into account the relative displacements in space and time, derive Eq. (9.88) for a three-phase converter.

(*b*) Generalize the result for an arbitrary number of phases m.

9.16 A three-phase heteropolar converter is wound with full-pitched coils embedded in semiclosed slots (negligible slot opening). Determine the relative intensity of the first few significant harmonics of the flux density B at the instant at which the current in phase A is at its peak. Neglect saturation in the iron, and assume that:

(*a*) The number of conductors per slot is c_s, and there is only one slot per pole per phase.

(*b*) The overall number of conductors and the current they carry are the same as in part (*a*), but the number of slots is doubled.

Follow these steps:

(1) Expand the flux density K contributed by each slot in a Fourier series.

(2) Note that many terms drop out because of symmetry conditions.

(3) Superpose the contributions of each phase, taking into account the phase displacement between the currents.

(4) Note again that many harmonics are eliminated.

(5) Calculate the distribution factor of the first few significant harmonics.

9.17 (*a*) Determine the no-load line-to-line voltage of the turbogenerator of Examples 4.5 and 4.6 when the generator is built as a 2-pole 3-phase machine, the armature winding has 84 conductors placed in 84 slots, the coil span is 35 slots, and the phase groups are star-connected.

(*b*) Evaluate the magnetizing reactances in ohms and in per-unit when the gap length is $g = 0.035$ m.

chapter 10
THE INDUCTION CONVERTER

10.1 INTRODUCTION

In this chapter we shall consider the performance and design of the most common type of magnetic device, the induction converter. To facilitate our investigation, we begin with a search for approximate representations. Simplified models are obtained by comparing the relative magnitudes of the parameters and by evaluating their effects on the performance. We thus find that in converters employing solid conductors exclusively, the gap is narrow ($g/\tau \ll 1$); therefore, the magnetizing reactance is large, and the current required to establish the magnetic field across the gap can be either neglected or at most taken summarily into account. In contrast, converters such as liquid-metal pumps or plasma accelerators which employ secondary conductors in the fluid state are built with larger gaps, in order to minimize friction losses at the walls. In these converters the primary current consists mainly of the magnetizing component, and can thus be considered independent of the load.

We next consider the dependence of the electromagnetic force on the speed of the secondary conductor and obtain similar characteristics for both narrow and large gaps. As in the case of the synchronous converter with single excitation, these characteristics exhibit a peak, separating stable and unstable speed ranges. Fortunately, the stable range is the one corresponding to larger output power and higher efficiency. The existence of a peak, however, implies that the starting torque of an induction motor is below the peak or pull-out value, unless special provisions are taken. This seems to put the induction motor at a disadvantage with respect to other types such as the homopolar motor where the torque is maximum at stall and, therefore, always higher than the rated torque. It is not difficult, however, to obtain satisfactory starting performance, and for this reason the induction converter is very popular as a motor.

We find that the value of slip at which the pull-out torque occurs shifts toward lower speed as the secondary resistance is increased. It is then apparent that one can get a higher torque at stall by inserting external resistances in the secondary circuit during the starting transient. A more elegant solution, which avoids the necessity for having access to the terminals of the rotor winding by means of slip rings, takes advantage of the *skin effect.* It is known that in the limit of low frequencies the current distributes itself with constant density over the cross section of a massive conductor. At high frequencies, on the other hand, the current tends to concentrate on the surface or skin, so that the effective cross section of the conductor is smaller and its resistance larger. Now, in an asynchronous machine the frequency of the secondary circuit is proportional to the slip and, therefore, in a motor is maximum at stall. The skin effect can then be utilized to achieve the desired dependence of the secondary resistance on the speed automatically, without resorting to unreliable and cumbersome gear.

When the skin effect is appreciable, however, we depart from our fundamental assumption in Chap. 4 that the active conductors are so thin that any variation of the field quantities over their cross section can be neglected. (Under these conditions we find in Appendix D that the frequency of the currents, rather than the velocity, determines the amount of power converted by the active conductor.)

Next we turn our attention to the two other modes of operation, generating and braking, and find that they have relatively limited practical applications.

We then study the accelerating and decelerating transient performance which is characterized by high losses and, consequently, high thermal stresses, and evaluate the import of the latter on the choice of material for the secondary conductor.

We conclude this chapter and this book with a brief review of adjustable-speed drives and commutator machines.

10.2 TYPICAL VALUES OF THE PARAMETERS

Before we proceed to investigate the performance of singly excited asynchronous converters, we want to establish the order of magnitude and the relative importance of the various parameters. This will give us guidelines for the design and suggestions for simplifying the analysis.

We first consider the magnetizing reactance. We recall that in synchronous converters the voltage-regulation requirements discussed in Sec. 7.8 and the stability considerations discussed in Sec. 8.4*d* concur to prescribe an effective decoupling between the armature and the field circuit. As we see from Fig. 7.15, this implies that the impedance of the coupling branch must be, at most, equal to the external terminal impedance: i.e., the per-unit value of X_m must be in the order of unity.

In asynchronous generators, instead, voltage regulation is of no concern since the output terminals are usually connected to a large active network (infinite bus under ideal conditions) even when the machine is singly excited. The output voltage is thus dictated by the polyphase supply system. Likewise the stability problem which hinders the performance of synchronous converters with double excitation does not normally arise in asynchronous converters, since in the case of practical interest the second excitation is obtained, as we shall see at the end of this chapter, via a frequency changer which is controlled by the relative displacement between stator and rotor conductors. This device breaks the tie between the frequency of the external networks and the frequency in the active conductors, so that the latter can attain any arbitrary speed with respect to the wave frame as in the case of single excitation. Since the $\bar{K}$ wave impressed on the rotor is thus disengaged from the position and motion of the rotor conductors, the power angle δ can adjust itself to any sudden change in the load conditions instantaneously, and without the sluggishness which in synchronous converters is caused by the inertia of the rotating masses.

We have thus proved that there is no need to establish an upper bound for X_m. Instead there is a very good reason for limiting X_m from below. In Sec. 7.6*f* we described the mode of operation in which a synchronous device draws all or part of the current required to establish a magnetic flux across the gap from the a-c supply and thus represents an inductive load. In the singly excited asynchronous converter this is the only possibility, since there is only the a-c supply. Inspection of the equivalent circuit of Fig. 9.24 shows that the amount of var absorbed decreases as the magnetizing reactance X_m increases and the leakage reactances X_1 and X_2 decrease. For a given gap surface, as determined by the power-output specifications, the magnetizing reactance is inversely proportional to the gap length g. It then follows that, in order to keep the power factor of asynchronous devices as high as possible, the gap must be chosen as short as mechanical considerations allow. In typical machines the per-unit value of X_m varies between 3.5 and 5.

In the induction converter it is the leakage reactance, instead, which must be minimized. Short connections between the active conductors help in making the end-winding leakage low. The fewer and the shallower the slots, the lower is the slot leakage. However, a small number of slots per pole q causes the flux distribution to depart appreciably from the ideal sinusoidal distribution, and therefore increases the harmonic leakage. In view of these conflicting requirements, q is generally kept in the range from 2 to 15. The leakage reactance also increases with the number of poles, thus setting a practical upper limit of about eight for the number of poles of an asynchronous machine. When a lower speed and, therefore, a larger number of poles are needed, a synchronous machine is used in preference, since there the power factor poses no problem.

In typical machines the per-unit leakage reactances of the primary and secondary vary between the values 0.08 and 0.1.

Efficiency considerations naturally prescribe low values for the primary and secondary resistances. Typical per-unit values vary between 0.01 and 0.02.

10.3 APPROXIMATE EQUIVALENT CIRCUIT AND CIRCLE DIAGRAM

The per-unit values of the relevant parameters not only provide us with guiding principles for the design of asynchronous devices, but they also enable us to simplify the analysis.

For this purpose we consider the terminals a and b of the secondary circuit as shown in Fig. 10.1a, and we replace the primary circuit by an equivalent source $\bar{V}^T$ and a series impedance $\bar{Z}^T$, according to Thévenin's theorem. The equivalent-source voltage $\bar{V}^T$ is then the open-circuit voltage appearing across a and b, when $S = 0$. This is given, according to Fig. 10.1c, by

$$\bar{V}^T = \bar{V}_1 \frac{jX_m}{R_1 + j(X_1 + X_m)} \tag{10.1}$$

The series impedance $\bar{Z}^T$ is the impedance between the terminals a and b looking toward the primary when $\bar{V}_1 = 0$. As shown in Fig. 10.1d, this is the impedance of the primary conductor in parallel with the magnetizing reactance. We now observe that, within an accuracy of a few percent, we can assume that

$$\bar{V}_1{}^T = \bar{V}_1 \tag{10.2a}$$

and

$$\bar{Z}^T = jX_1 \tag{10.2b}$$

Higher accuracy is not warranted since the parameters themselves cannot be determined more accurately. We can thus use the circuit of Fig. 10.1e to find the approximate value of the secondary current $\bar{I}_2'$ as

$$\bar{I}_2' = -\frac{\bar{V}_1}{j(X_1 + X_2') + R_2'/S} \tag{10.3a}$$

Next we wish to determine the primary current. If we denote the current through jX_m as $\bar{I}_m$, we can express this current as $\bar{I}_m = \bar{I}_1 + \bar{I}_2'$, so that $\bar{I}_1$ can be found as the sum of $\bar{I}_m$ and $-\bar{I}_2'$. We note from Fig. 10.1a that, because of the high value of X_m, $\bar{I}_m$ is relatively small and varies between

$$\bar{I}_{m,0} = \frac{\bar{V}_1}{j(X_1 + X_m)} \tag{10.3b}$$

for $S = 0$, and about half this value for $S = \infty$, since X_1 is of the same order of magnitude as X_2'. In the latter case, however, I_2' is large

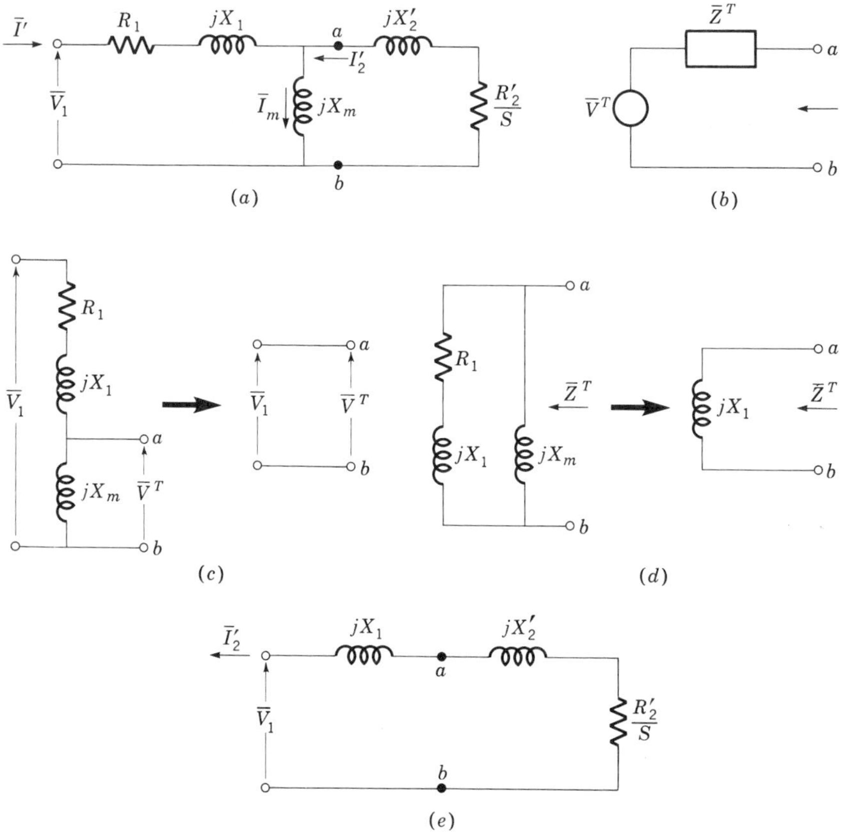

Fig. 10.1 Replacement of the primary circuit by an approximate Thévenin equivalent: (*a*) Circuit representation of a singly excited asynchronous converter; (*b*) Thévenin equivalent of the primary circuit; (*c*) determination of the equivalent source voltage; (*d*) determination of the equivalent source impedance; (*e*) circuit yielding approximate value of secondary current.

because R_2'/S vanishes, so that $\bar{I}_m$ is only a small fraction of $\bar{I}_1$. As a first approximation, then, we can calculate $\bar{I}_1$ as $\bar{I}_m - \bar{I}_2'$ if we simply assume that $\bar{I}_m$ is constant at its no-load value $\bar{I}_{m,0}$ given by Eq. (10.3b).

With these approximations the equivalent circuit of the singly excited asynchronous machine becomes the one shown in Fig. 10.2, and the phasor diagram is the one shown in Fig. 10.3. We observe that in this form the performance of the converters depends, for a given supply voltage $\bar{V}_1$, on the slip S and the three design parameters R_2', X_d, and $X_{s.c.}$. These reactances are defined by

$$\begin{aligned} X_d &= X_1 + X_m \\ X_{s.c.} &= X_1 + X_2' \end{aligned} \tag{10.4}$$

With these approximations the secondary current $\bar{I}_2'$ is given by

$$\bar{I}_2' = -\frac{\bar{V}_1}{R_2'/S + jX_{s.c.}} = -\frac{\bar{V}_1(R_2'/S - jX_{s.c.})}{(R_2'/S)^2 + X_{s.c.}^2} \tag{10.5}$$

It is readily shown from Eq. 10.5 that as S varies, the tip of the $\bar{I}_2'$ phasor describes a circular locus named after Heyland, and therefore called the

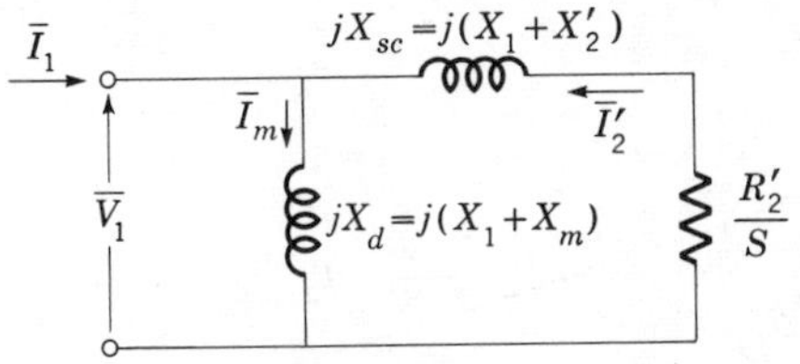

Fig. 10.2 Approximate equivalent of a singly excited asynchronous converter.

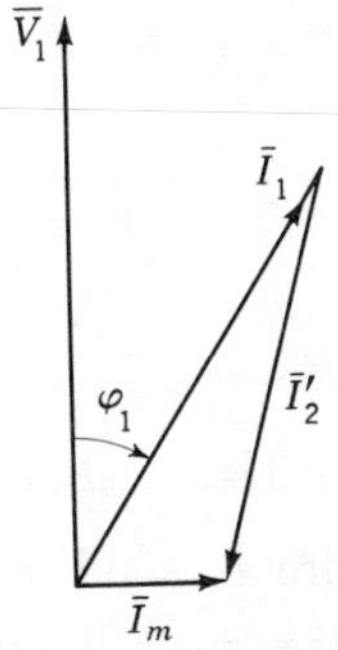

Fig. 10.3 Approximate phasor diagram of a singly excited asynchronous converter.

Heyland diagram or sometimes simply the circle diagram. This is drawn in Fig. 10.4 as the circle which passes through the no-load point $P\Big|_{S=0}$, the ideal short-circuit point $P\Big|_{S=\infty}$, and is symmetric with respect to the horizontal axis for positive and negative values of S. It follows then that the upper half of the circle where $S > 0$ corresponds to the motoring and braking regimes, and the lower half where $S < 0$ corresponds to the generating regime. Besides the points $P\big|_{S=0}$ and $P\big|_{S=\infty}$ one can identify on this diagram other important points. These are:

$P\big|_{S=1}$ which is the point where the rotor is stalled, i.e., at standstill with respect to the stator

$P\big|_{S=S\ \text{rated}}$ which is the rated point of operation

$P\big|_{\cos\varphi_1=\max}$ which is the point for maximum power factor

$P\big|_{S=S_{\text{p.o.}}}$ which corresponds to maximum power output, or as we called it in Sec. 7.6*e*, pullout power as a motor or as a generator

About the location of these points, one can say that, since the per-unit value of the resistance R_2' is much smaller than the per-unit value of $X_{\text{s.c.}}$,

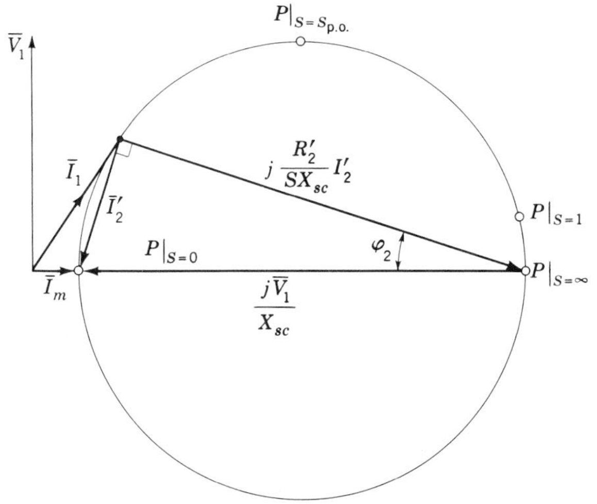

Fig. 10.4 Locus of the primary and secondary currents or Heyland circle diagram.

the reactance under short-circuit conditions ($S = \infty$), then the stall point $P\big|_{S=1}$ is very near to the short-circuit point $P\big|_{S=\infty}$.† The point for rated operation, $P\big|_{S=S\ \text{rated}}$, lies instead in the region where the resistive drop dominates over the reactive drop, because efficiency considerations require S to be low. The point for maximum power factor $P\big|_{\cos\varphi_1=\max}$ corresponds to the point where $\overline{I}_1$ is tangent to the circle.

† As we know from Sec. 9.3*b*, when R_1 is neglected, the converter operates as a motor for $0 < S < 1$ and as a brake for $1 < S < \infty$. Therefore the point $P\big|_{S=1}$ separates the motoring from the braking region of operation.

Since $\bar{I}_m$ is very small (for clarity's sake in Fig. 10.4 $\bar{I}_m$ has been magnified out of proportion), and since near its maximum a function varies slowly, $P\Big|_{S=S\text{ rated}}$ lies in the region where the power factor attains a value very near to its maximum.

From the equivalent circuit of Fig. 10.2 and the diagram of Fig. 10.4 it is apparent that the total electric or terminal power associated with the converter has a maximum which occurs when the resistive drop equals the inductive drop or when

$$S = S_{\text{p.o.}} = \pm \frac{R_2'}{X_{\text{s.c.}}} \tag{10.6}$$

Thus the average electric power at pull-out can be written as

$$P_{\text{elec,p.o.}} = \text{Re}\,[m_1\bar{V}_1\bar{I}_1^*] = -\,\text{Re}\,[m_1\bar{V}_1\bar{I}_2'^*] = \frac{m_1V_1^2}{2X_{\text{s.c.}}} \tag{10.7}$$

and the total converted power which, as we have pointed out in Chap. 9, is the power in the resistance $R_2'(1 - S)/S$, is given by

$$P_{\text{conv,p.o.}} = (1 - S_{\text{p.o.}})P_{\text{elec,p.o.}} = \left(1 \mp \frac{R_2'}{X_{\text{s.c.}}}\right)\frac{m_1V_1{}^2}{2X_{\text{s.c.}}} \tag{10.8}$$

where the minus sign corresponds to motoring and the plus sign to generating.

By dividing Eq. (10.8) by

$$v = (1 - S_{\text{p.o.}})v_s \tag{10.9}$$

we obtain the average force at pull-out as

$$F_{x,\text{p.o.}} = \frac{m_1V_1{}^2}{2X_{\text{s.c.}}v_s} \tag{10.10}$$

Similarly the average torque at pull-out is given by

$$\mathcal{L}_{\text{p.o.}} = \frac{m_1V_1{}^2}{2X_{\text{s.c.}}\omega_s} \tag{10.11}$$

where $\omega_s = |\omega_1/p|$.

(a) The Use of the Circle Diagram

The main advantage of the circle diagram is that all the performance data can be read off directly by measuring appropriate lengths. For instance, if the circle diagram is drawn using per-unit values of the parameters, then the inphase component of $\bar{I}_2'$, given by the segment PC of Fig. 10.5, is the per-unit power flowing from the primary terminals of each phase into the gap. This follows from the fact that we have neglected the primary resistance, and therefore

$$\frac{1}{m_1} P_{\text{elec}} = \text{Re}\,[\bar{V}_1 \bar{I}_1^*] = -\,\text{Re}\,[\bar{V}_1 \bar{I}_2'^*] \tag{10.12a}$$

$$\frac{1}{m_1} P_{\text{elec,p.u.}} = \text{component of } (-\bar{I}'_{2,\text{p.u.}}) \text{ in phase with } \bar{V}_1 \tag{10.12b}$$

Also if we choose ω_s as the unit basis for the measure of angular velocity, the same segment measures the per-unit torque per phase because

$$\frac{\mathfrak{L}}{m_1} = \frac{P_{\text{conv}}}{\omega m_1} = \frac{(1-S)P_{\text{elec}}}{(1-S)\omega_s m_1} = \frac{P_{\text{elec}}}{\omega_s m_1}$$
$$= \frac{\text{Re}\,[\bar{V}_1 \bar{I}_1^*]}{\omega_s} = -\frac{\text{Re}\,[\bar{V}_1 \bar{I}_2'^*]}{\omega_s} \tag{10.13a}$$

$$\frac{\mathfrak{L}_{\text{p.u.}}}{m_1} = \text{component of } (-\bar{I}'_{2,\text{p.u.}}) \text{ in phase with } \bar{V}_1 \tag{10.13b}$$

Moreover, the intersection of the segment PC with the line drawn from P_0

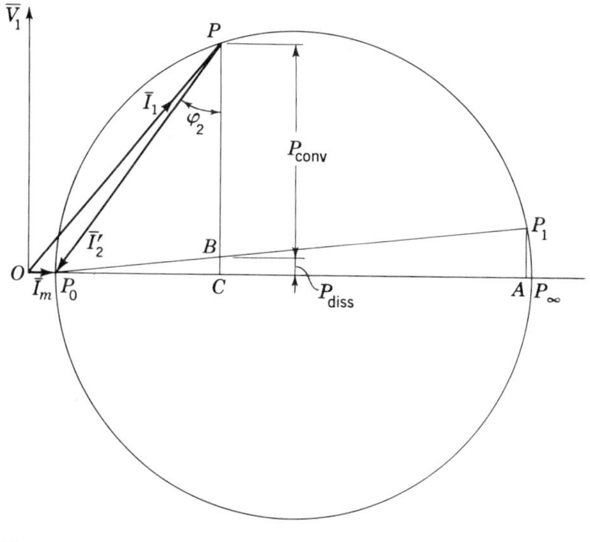

Fig. 10.5 Illustration of the use of the circle diagram in determining performance data.

to the stall point P_1 allows us to determine the converted power, the slip, and the rotor efficiency. This can be seen by the following reasoning:

Since at stall the resistance of the secondary circuit is R_2', then the line P_0P_1 which represents $-\bar{I}'_{2,\text{st}}$ has a slope

$$\cot \varphi_{2,\text{st}} = \frac{R_2'}{X_{\text{s.c.}}} \tag{10.14}$$

This slope is also given by the ratio BC/P_0C, so that we can write

$$BC = P_0C \cot \varphi_{2,\mathrm{st}} = P_0C \frac{R_2'}{X_{\mathrm{s.c.}}} \tag{10.15}$$

We then notice that P_0C represents the 90° out-of-phase component of $\bar{I}_2'$, which, according to the equivalent circuit of Fig. 10.2, can be expressed as

$$P_0C = I_2' \sin \varphi_2 = \frac{I_2'X_{\mathrm{s.c.}}}{\sqrt{(R_2'/S)^2 + X_{\mathrm{s.c.}}^2}} \tag{10.16a}$$

and, since from Eq. (10.5)

$$I_2' = \frac{V_1}{\sqrt{(R_2'/S)^2 + X_{\mathrm{s.c.}}^2}} \tag{10.16b}$$

we have

$$P_0C = \frac{X_{\mathrm{s.c.}} I_2'^2}{V_1} \tag{10.16c}$$

This means that P_0C also represents, in per unit and per phase, the terminal var $X_{\mathrm{s.c.}}I_2'^2$. Introducing Eq. (10.16c) into Eq. (10.15), we thus find that

$$BC = \frac{R_2' I_2'^2}{V_1}$$

is the per-unit dissipated power in each phase when the converter operates at any arbitrary point P. If we subtract this power from the power transferred from the primary, we get the converted power as

$$\frac{1}{m_1} P_{\mathrm{conv}} = PC - BC = PB \tag{10.18}$$

The slip is then given by

$$S = \frac{BC}{PC} \tag{10.19}$$

and the secondary efficiencies are

$$\eta_m^{\mathrm{sec}} = 1 - S = \frac{PB}{PC} \tag{10.20a}$$

and

$$\eta_g^{\mathrm{sec}} = \frac{1}{1 - S} = \frac{PC}{PB} \tag{10.20b}$$

In the case of high X_m, we can find a good approximation for the overall efficiency including the primary losses. Assuming the current in X_m to be zero, we may remove X_m from the circuit of Fig. 10.1a. The result is a simple series circuit, in which the efficiency is plainly the ratio of the mechanical output resistance $R_2'(1 - S)/S$ to the total circuit resistance, $R_1 + R_2'/S$. Thus

$$\eta_m = \frac{R_2'(1 - S)/S}{R_2'/S + R_1} = \frac{R_2'(1 - S)}{R_2' + SR_1} = \frac{1 - S}{1 + SR_1/R_2'} \tag{10.21a}$$

For the practical case of small slip, we may approximate η_m by

$$\eta_m \doteq (1 - S)\left(1 - \frac{SR_1}{R_2'}\right) \doteq 1 - S - \frac{SR_1}{R_2'}$$

$$= 1 - S\frac{R_1 + R_2'}{R_2'} = 1 - \frac{R_1 + R_2'}{R_2'}\frac{BC}{PC} \qquad (10.22a)$$

Similarly,

$$\eta_g = \frac{1 + SR_1/R_2'}{1 - S} \qquad (10.21b)$$

and for small slip

$$\eta_g = \frac{1}{1 - \dfrac{R_1 + R_2'}{R_2'}S} = \frac{1}{1 - \dfrac{R_1 + R_2'}{R_2'}\dfrac{BC}{PC}} \qquad (10.22b)$$

The circle diagram is an ideal tool for obtaining quick answers of adequate technical accuracy, thus circumventing laborious phasor calculations. It can also be used to advantage in deriving the relations between the performance specifications and the converter parameters which are the starting point for the design. This is illustrated by the following example.

Example 10.1

Assuming that the rated point of operation of an induction motor corresponds to the point of maximum power factor, determine, with the help of the circle diagram, analytical expressions for the rated power factor, torque, slip, efficiency, and overload capability.

Solution

If the parameters are expressed in per unit, the power factor $\cos\varphi_R$ corresponds, according to Eq. (10.13b), to the value of torque per phase and is thus given on the circle diagram by the segment P_RC. The analytical expression for $\cos\varphi_R$ is then found by evaluating the area of the triangle OP_RM shown in the accompanying diagram in

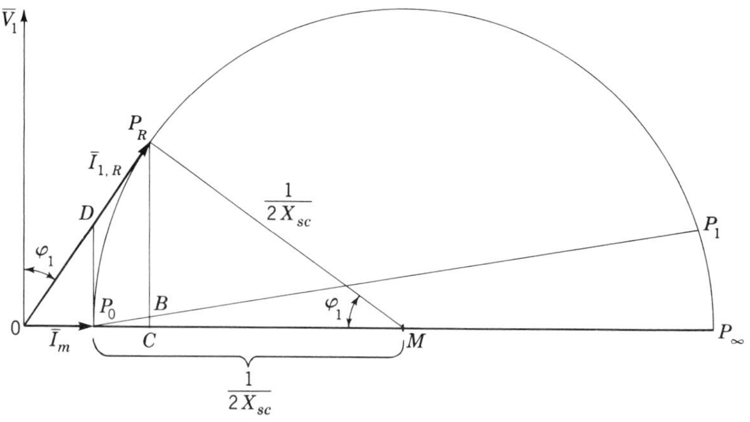

two ways, and equating:

$$2 \times \text{Area} = I_{1,R}\frac{1}{2X_{s.c.}} = \left(I_m + \frac{1}{2X_{s.c.}}\right)P_RC$$

Then, substituting $I_{1,R} = 1$ and $I_m = 1/X_d$ in conformity with Eq. (7.53), we get

$$\cos\varphi_R = \frac{\mathfrak{L}_R}{m_1} = \frac{1}{2X_{s.c.}}\frac{1}{1/X_d + 1/2X_{s.c.}} = \frac{X_d}{X_d + 2X_{s.c.}}$$

The rated slip is

$$S_R = \frac{BC}{P_RC} = \frac{BC}{CP_0}\frac{CP_0}{P_RC}$$

We now observe that the triangles OP_0D and OCP_R are similar, so that

$$\frac{CP_0}{OP_0} = \frac{DP_R}{OD}$$

and

$$\frac{DP_0}{OD} = \frac{P_RC}{OP_R} = \frac{P_RC}{I_{1,R}} = P_RC$$

We also note that

$$DP_R = DP_0$$

so that we can write

$$\frac{CP_0}{OP_0} = P_RC$$

Introducing this identity in the expression for S_R, we get

$$S_R = \frac{BC}{CP_0}OP_0 = \frac{BC}{CP_0}I_m$$

and finally, using Eq. (10.15),

$$S_R = \frac{R_2'}{X_{s.c.}X_d}$$

The secondary efficiency is then

$$\eta_m^{\text{sec}} = 1 - S_R = 1 - \frac{R_2'}{X_{s.c.}X_d}$$

and the overall efficiency, assuming small slip, is

$$\eta_m = 1 - \frac{R_1 + R_2'}{X_{s.c.}X_d}$$

The overload capability is given as the ratio of pull-out converted power to rated converted power:

$$\text{O.C.} = \frac{(1 - S_{\text{p.o.}})\dfrac{1}{2X_{s.c}}}{(1 - S_R)\cos\varphi_R} = \frac{\left(1 - \dfrac{R_2'}{X_{s.c.}}\right)\dfrac{1}{2X_{s.c.}}}{\left(1 - \dfrac{R_2'}{X_{s.c.}X_d}\right)\dfrac{X_d}{X_d + 2X_{s.c.}}}$$

$$= \frac{X_{s.c.} - R_2'}{X_{s.c.}X_d - R_2'}\left(1 + \frac{X_d}{2X_{s.c.}}\right)$$

The relations thus obtained, together with the conditions $R_1 \doteq R_2'$, $X_1 = X_2'$, allow us to express the parameters of the converter R_1, R_2', X_1, X_2', and X_m directly in terms of its rated performance specifications, $\cos \varphi_R$, η_R, and O.C.

10.4 FORCE - SPEED CHARACTERISTICS

(a) Machines with Narrow Gap

To develop the torque-speed relations, we consider Eq. (10.13*a*). This equation makes it clear that the torque varies with speed exactly as does the electric or terminal power, since ω_s is a constant value set by the excitation frequency. Thus we know that $\mathfrak{L}$ develops a maximum or pull-out value, as we have seen from the circle diagram for P_{elec}. The complete picture of how $\mathfrak{L}$ varies with speed is easily obtained by expressing P_{elec} in terms of the slip. Introducing Eqs. (10.12*a*) and (10.5), we find

$$P_{\text{elec}} = \frac{m_1 V_1{}^2 R_2'/S}{(R_2'/S)^2 + X_{\text{s.c.}}{}^2} \tag{10.23}$$

so that

$$\mathfrak{L} = \frac{\dfrac{m_1 V_1{}^2}{\omega_s} \dfrac{R_2'}{S}}{(R_2'/S)^2 + X_{\text{s.c.}}{}^2} \tag{10.24}$$

For generality we normalize the torque and the slip to their pull-out values, as given by Eqs. (10.11) and (10.6). The result is

$$\frac{\mathfrak{L}}{\mathfrak{L}_{\text{p.o.}}} = \frac{2}{S_{\text{p.o.}}/S + S/S_{\text{p.o.}}} \tag{10.25}$$

The normalized torque-slip characteristic given by Eq. (10.25) is plotted in Fig. 10.6.

We note that for small S ($S/S_{\text{p.o.}} \ll 1$) the torque is proportional to the slip; for large S ($S/S_{\text{p.o.}} \gg 1$), the asymptote is a hyperbola.

It is apparent from the torque-slip characteristic of Fig. 10.6 that stable operation with constant torque on the shaft is possible only in the region between the positive and negative peaks. The reason is the same as was given in Sec. 8.3 for a synchronous device. Since the difference between the shaft torque and the torque developed by the converter produces an acceleration, any departure from the equilibrium point is corrected when the difference in torque has the proper sign. It is easily verified that this is not the case in the exterior portions of the torque-slip characteristic by replotting the torque characteristic against speed rather than slip.

Equation (10.25) and the preceding considerations are based on the approximate equivalent circuit of Fig. 10.2, and therefore apply only to machines with narrow gap where the magnetizing reactance X_m is large (a few units). However, even in the case of large-gap devices where X_m is small, the torque- or force-speed characteristics still have the same general nature as those predicted by Eq. (10.25). We shall see an example of this fact in the next section.

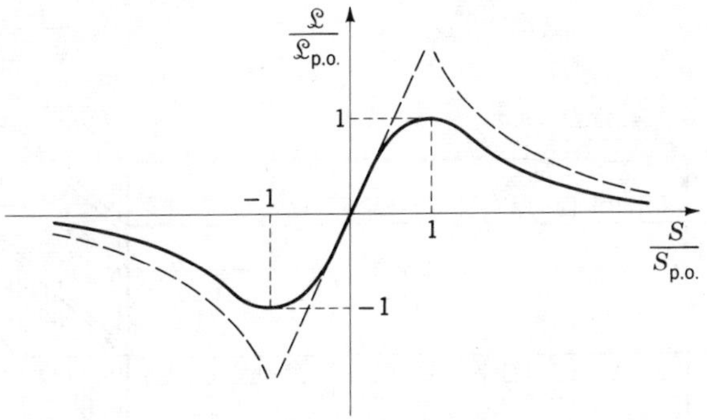

Fig. 10.6 Normalized torque-slip characteristics.

*(b) Induction Pumps

The principle of operation of the asynchronous motor can be applied to pump a conducting fluid. As in the case of the homopolar pump of Sec. 5.7, the fluid itself constitutes the active conductor of the converter, with the difference that there is no need for electrodes, since in an induction motor the secondary currents close within the active conductor. This is a definite advantage, especially in the case of corrosive fluids. The pump thus consists of a completely insulated duct of rectangular cross section placed in the gap between two laminated iron structures, as indicated in Fig. 10.7. The surfaces of these structures facing the duct are slotted in order to accommodate a polyphase primary winding, which is composed of two identical branches connected in parallel, one on each side of the duct. The whole arrangement is then a version of the rotating converter which is developed in rectangular form.

In designing these pumps, an important consideration is the minimization of friction. Since friction is proportional to the area of the channel walls and since, for a given volume of the channel (i.e., a given power), this area is minimized when the dimensions a, b, and $2p\tau$ are equal, it follows that these pumps are constructed with much larger gaps (dimension a) than converters with solid conductors.

We observe that because of the large gap and large magnetizing current required, the primary current is much larger than the secondary current. It follows that the overall efficiency of the pump will be mainly determined by the power dissipated in the primary. There is therefore no reason to operate these converters with a low value of slip.

If we now turn our attention to the circuit representation, we find that as a result of the large gap the magnetizing reactance X_m is very small. As already mentioned at the beginning of this chapter, and as is apparent from Fig. 10.1a, a small magnetizing reactance effectively

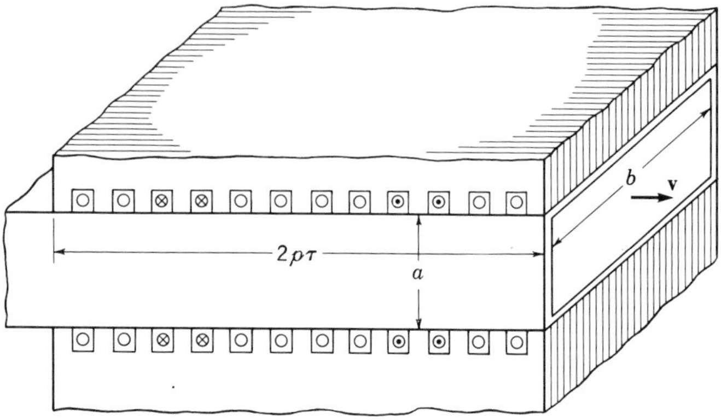

(a)

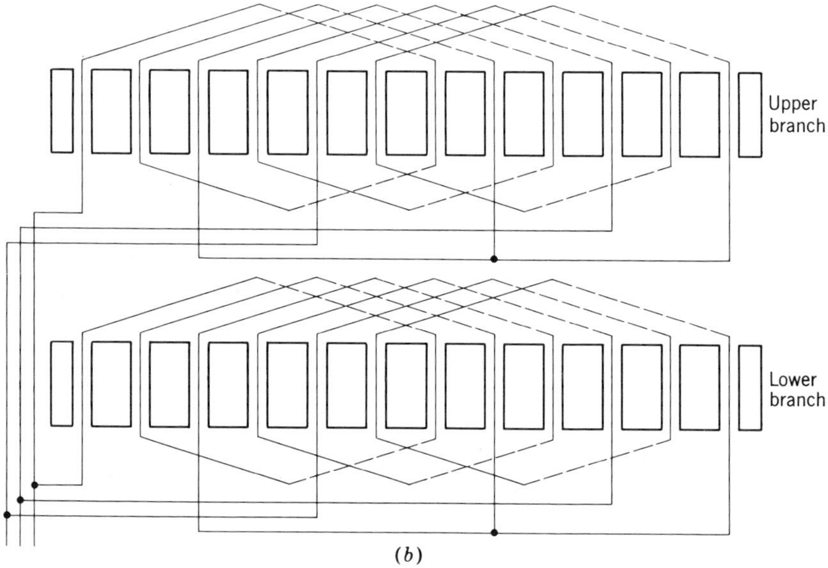

(b)

Fig. 10.7 Sketch of a three-phase induction pump: (a) Cutaway view; (b) schematic winding diagram.

decouples the primary from the secondary circuit. Thus, the primary current becomes essentially independent of the slip S and so does not vary much with the operating point. In the limit when $X_1 \gg X_m$, the primary current is determined by the primary leakage, and we can assume that the pump is fed by an ideal current source

$$\bar{I}_1 = \frac{\bar{V}_1}{R_1 + jX_1} \tag{10.26}$$

Finally we observe that the leakage reactance X_2' will be small since the secondary conductor is not embedded in slots in a ferromagnetic material but fills the gap completely. These considerations lead to the neglect of the secondary reactance X_2' and the approximate equivalent circuit of Fig. 10.8, with R_2' representing the resistance of the liquid conductor referred to the primary.

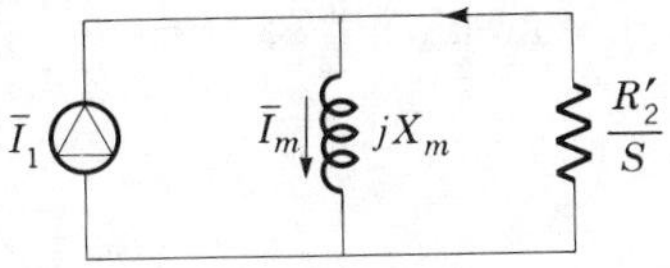

Fig. 10.8 Equivalent circuit of an induction pump.

From this equivalent circuit we can calculate the power absorbed by the fluid conductor as

$$P_2 = \frac{m_1 R_2'}{S} I_2'^2 = m_1 I_1^2 X_m^2 \frac{R_2'/S}{(R_2'/S)^2 + X_m^2} \tag{10.27a}$$

and the output power as

$$P_{\text{out}} = m_1 (1 - S) P_2 = m_1 (1 - S) I_1^2 X_m^2 \frac{R_2'/S}{(R_2'/S)^2 + X_m^2} \tag{10.27b}$$

The latter power can be expressed as the product of the pressure difference (P.D.) times the flow rate Q:

$$P_{\text{out}} = (\text{P.D.}) \times Q = (\text{P.D.}) abv = (\text{P.D.}) abv_s (1 - S)$$

Solving for P.D. from the last two equations, we obtain

$$\text{P.D.} = \frac{m_1}{abv_s} I_1^2 X_m^2 \frac{R_2'/S}{(R_2'/S)^2 + X_m^2} \tag{10.28}$$

The pressure difference is maximum at the pull-out value of slip,

$$S_{\text{p.o.}} = \frac{R_2'}{X_m} \tag{10.29}$$

and attains a maximum value of

$$(\text{P.D.})_{\text{p.o.}} = \frac{m_1 I_1^2 X_m}{2abv_s} \tag{10.30}$$

so that we can write

$$\frac{\text{P.D.}}{(\text{P.D.})_{\text{p.o.}}} = \frac{2}{S/S_{\text{p.o.}} + S_{\text{p.o.}}/S} \tag{10.31}$$

Comparison of this equation with Eq. (10.25) shows that in both limiting cases of short and large gap, the force-speed characteristics are the same.

Equation (10.28) may also be easily derived directly from field considerations, as demonstrated by the following example.

*EXAMPLE 10.2

Starting from the electromagnetic field equations, derive the pressure difference–flow rate characteristic of a linear induction pump. Assume that the dimensions b and c are large enough so that end effects can be neglected, and assume that the split primary winding sets up on each side of the channel a sinusoidal current sheet,

$$K(x,t) = \text{Re}\left[\sqrt{2}\,\frac{\bar{K}_1}{2}\,e^{\,j(\omega_e t - \pi x/\tau)}\right]\mathbf{y}_0$$

as shown.

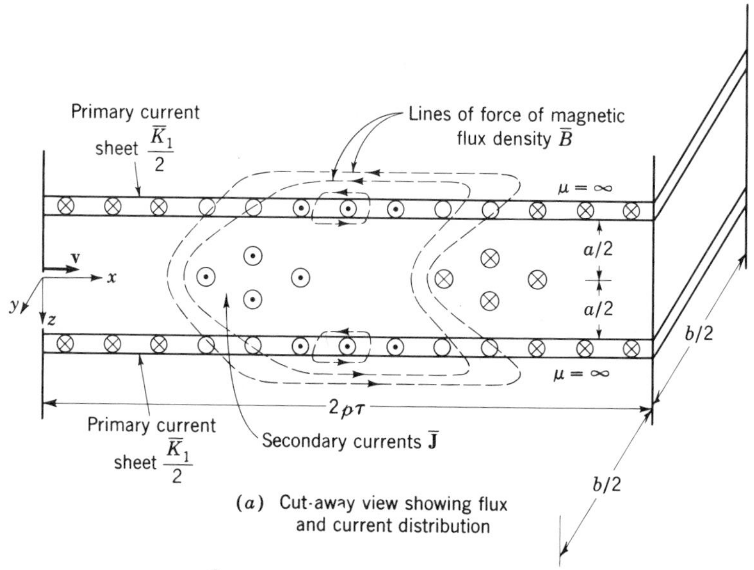

(a) Cut-away view showing flux and current distribution

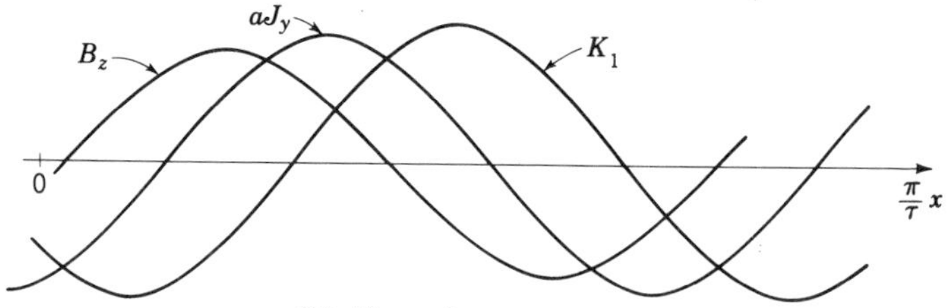

(b) Flux and current density waves

Solution

In steady state the electromagnetic force density balances the pressure gradient, and we have

$$\nabla\mathcal{P} = \mathbf{J} \times \mathbf{B} \qquad \text{or} \qquad \frac{\partial \mathcal{P}}{\partial x} = J_y B_z = \gamma(E_y - vB_z)B_z$$

Assuming that all field vectors have the same traveling-wave dependence on x and t and the velocity is constant,† we can write for the average force density

$$\left\langle \frac{\partial \mathcal{P}}{\partial x} \right\rangle = \text{Re}\,[\bar{J}_y \bar{B}_z^*] = \text{Re}\,[\gamma(\bar{E}_y - v\bar{B}_z)\bar{B}_z^*]$$

To eliminate $\bar{E}_y$ we use Faraday's law:

$$\nabla \times \mathbf{E} = -\frac{\partial \mathbf{B}}{\partial t}$$

Taking into account that $B_y = 0$ and $\partial/\partial y = 0$ because of symmetry conditions and neglect of end effects, this reduces to

$$-\frac{\partial \bar{E}_y}{\partial z} = -j\omega_e \bar{B}_x$$

$$-j\frac{\pi}{\tau}\bar{E}_y = -j\omega_e \bar{B}_z$$

Using the last expression, we get

$$\left\langle \frac{\partial \mathcal{P}}{\partial x} \right\rangle = \text{Re}\left[\gamma\left(\frac{\omega_e \tau}{\pi} - v\right)\bar{B}_z \bar{B}_z^*\right] = \text{Re}\,[\gamma S v_s \bar{B}_z \bar{B}_z^*]$$

since $\omega_e \tau/\pi = v_s$.

To evaluate $\bar{B}_z$ we use Ampère's law,

$$\nabla \times \mathbf{B} = \mu_0 \mathbf{J}$$

which under the assumptions made gives

$$\frac{\partial \bar{B}_x}{\partial z} + j\frac{\pi}{\tau}\bar{B}_z = \mu_0 \gamma S v_s \bar{B}_z$$

Up to this point we have only postulated that the functional dependence of the field vectors on x and t matches the dependence of the excitation; the dependence on z is still unknown. In general, we should allow not only B_z but also v and therefore S to vary across the channel with z, since we are dealing with a fluid, and since friction would tend to retard the motion near the upper and lower walls.

We observe, however, that any variation in v across the channel causes a difference in the motion-induced field vB which gives rise to currents that circulate in planes of constant x. These in turn produce $\mathbf{J} \times \mathbf{B}$ forces which tend to equalize the velocities.

To a first approximation we can thus assume that v and likewise B_z do not vary across the channel. The conditions for which this assumption is valid are discussed in Appendix D. We can now proceed to estimate $\bar{B}_z$.

We observe that, because of symmetry, $\bar{B}_x$ must vanish in the middle of the channel at $z = 0$ and have the value

$$\bar{B}_x \bigg|_{z=a/2} = \mu_0 \frac{\bar{K}_1}{2}$$

---

† This is true when the fluid is incompressible and the channel cross section is constant. In a compressible fluid the pulsations in force density cause velocity fluctuations (see also Sec. 6.7a). The following analysis then applies only if the inertia of the fluid is sufficiently large so that these fluctuations have negligible amplitude.

near the current sheet. On the other hand, integrating Ampère's law from $z = 0$ to $z = a/2$, we have

$$\bar{B}_x\left(\frac{a}{2}\right) = \int_0^{a/2}\left(\mu_0\gamma S v_s - j\frac{\pi}{\tau}\right)\bar{B}_z\,d_z = \frac{a}{2}\left(\mu_0\gamma S v_s - j\frac{\pi}{\tau}\right)\bar{B}_z$$

so that
$$\bar{B}_z = \frac{\mu_0\bar{K}_1}{a}\frac{1}{\mu_0\gamma S v_s - j\pi/\tau}$$

and
$$\bar{E}_y = \frac{\tau}{\pi}\omega_c\frac{\mu_0\bar{K}_1}{a}\frac{1}{\mu_0\gamma S v_s - j\pi/\tau}$$

We note that the impedance per unit surface of the gap looking into the secondary, as given by $\bar{E}_y/\bar{K}_1$, can be put into the form

$$\frac{\bar{E}_y}{\bar{K}_1} = \frac{(1/a\gamma S)(j\mu_0 v_s\tau/\pi a)}{1/a\gamma S + j\mu_0 v_s\tau/\pi a}$$

This is the parallel combination of a resistance $1/a\gamma S$ and a reactance $j\mu_0 v_s\tau/\pi a$, where we recognize $1/a\gamma$ to be the resistance of the secondary conductor, and $j\,\mu_0 v_s\tau/\pi a$ the magnetizing reactance per unit length as given by Eq. (7.21), since in the pump the thickness of the conductor a equals the gap length g. We then arrive at the circuit diagram shown below which indeed agrees with those of Figs. (9.5) and (10.8).

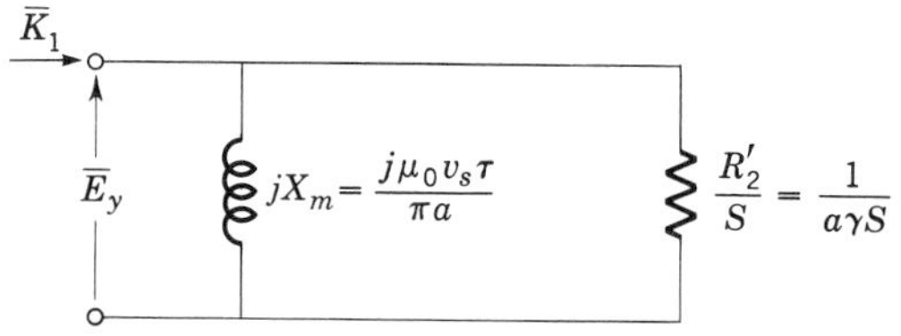

The pressure gradient is

$$\left\langle\frac{\partial\mathcal{P}}{\partial x}\right\rangle = \mu_0\frac{|\bar{K}_1|}{a^2}\frac{\mu_0\gamma v_s S}{(\pi/\tau)^2 + (\mu_0\gamma v_s S)^2}$$

The pressure difference is then obtained by integrating over the whole length of the channel $2p\tau$. The result is

$$\text{P.D.} = 2p\tau\mu_0\frac{|\bar{K}_1|}{a^2}\frac{\mu_0\gamma v_s S}{(\pi/\tau)^2 + (\mu_0\gamma v_s S)^2}$$

This expression is identical with Eq. (10.28), as can be seen by introducing in the latter for I_1, X_m, R_2' the values given by Eqs. (9.88*b*), (9.97), and (9.95) respectively, and by substituting

$$R_2 = \frac{b}{a(2p\tau/m_2)\gamma} \qquad g = a \qquad \left(\frac{c}{m}k_d k_p\right)_2 = 1$$

The desired pressure difference–flow rate characteristic is obtained by eliminating S from the above equation and the expression for the flow rate:

$$Q = abv_s(1 - S)$$

The result is

$$\text{P.D.} = \frac{2p\tau\mu_0|\bar{K}_1|}{a^2}\frac{\mu_0\gamma v_s(1 - Q/abv_s)}{(\pi/\tau)^2 + [\mu_0\gamma v_s(1 - Q/abv_s)]^2}$$

If we then normalize the pressure difference to its maximum value,

$$(\text{P.D.})_{\text{p.o.}} = \frac{2p\tau^2 \mu_0 |\bar{K}_1|^2}{2\pi a^2}$$

which is attained for

$$S = S_{\text{p.o.}} = \frac{\pi}{\tau \mu_0 \gamma v_s}$$

and similarly normalize the flow rate to the flow rate at synchronous speed and zero pressure difference,

$$Q_s = abv_s$$

we can plot the pressure difference–flow rate characteristic as shown. In the dashed

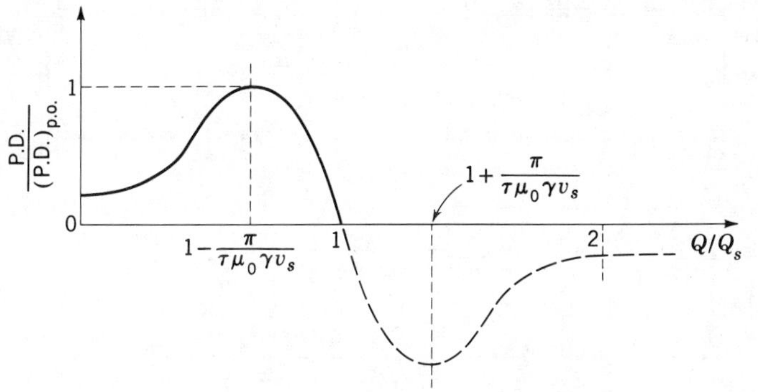

portion of the curve where the pressure difference is negative, the converter operates in the generating mode. Such converters employing liquid metals are presently being considered as possible alternatives to MPD generators. Comparison of this plot with the linear characteristic derived in Example 5.5 for the homopolar pump illustrates the difference in performance of the two converter types. The homopolar type develops its maximum pressure when the flow rate vanishes, whereas in the induction type the maximum occurs for

$$\frac{Q}{Q_s} = 1 - \frac{\pi}{\tau \mu_0 \gamma v_s}$$

This means that some flexibility in the design is afforded by suitable choice of the pole pitch τ and the synchronous speed v_s which, of course, are otherwise related by the synchronous tie,

$$\omega_C = \frac{\pi}{\tau} v_s$$

However, the main advantages of the induction type are the high degree of reliability resulting from the absence of electrodes and the ability to operate from standard a-c power supply at standard voltage instead of the low-voltage d-c supply required by the homopolar converter.

*(c) Plasma Accelerators

If we now turn our attention from liquid to gaseous conductors, we find another interesting application of the asynchronous interaction: This is the acceleration of plasmas by means of a traveling-wave structure.[1,5] Again, the main advantage of the induction type over the homopolar type is that it does not need sliding contacts and, consequently, does not require the flow of current through the low-temperature and, therefore, low-conductivity plasma layers bounding the electrodes. In

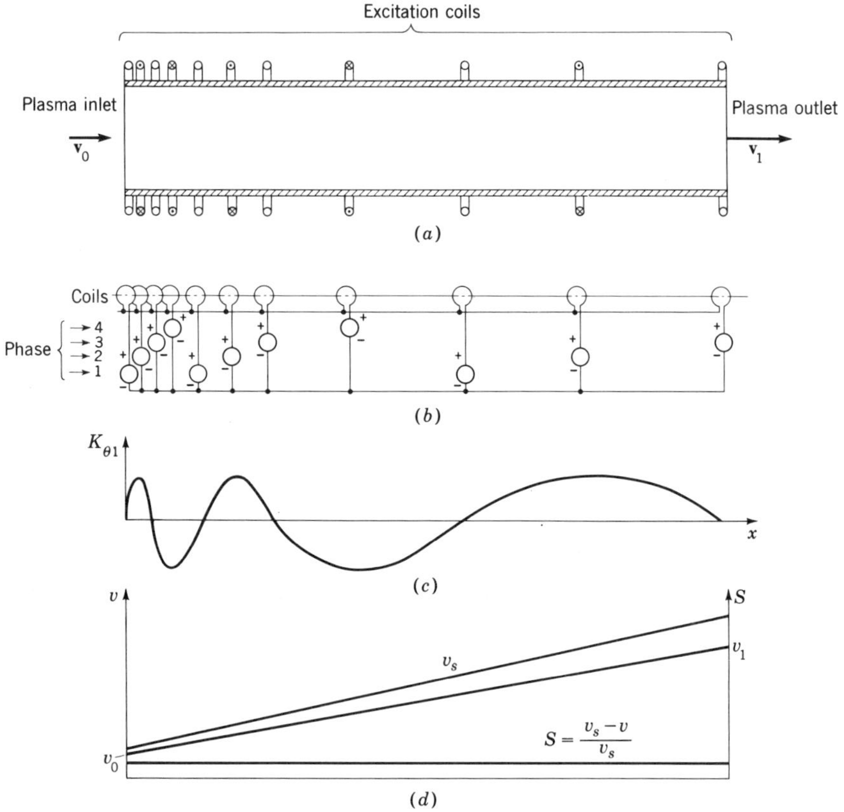

Fig. 10.9 Traveling-wave plasma accelerator: (*a*) Cutaway view; (*b*) winding diagram; (*c*) primary current density; (*d*) velocity and slip.

a typical construction the plasma flows in a cylindrical duct, and the primary excitation is provided by an array of coaxial coils connected to a polyphase supply, as schematically shown in Fig. 10.9.

As we have already mentioned in Sec. 5.4*b* and as we shall show in Sec. 10.7, accelerators are usually plagued by low efficiency because at the low-velocity end the slip is high. The construction of Fig. 10.9 overcomes this limitation by letting the pole pitch and therefore the phase velocity of the traveling wave increase at the same rate as the velocity of the plasma, so that the accelerator can be designed for a constant low value of slip. This is the asynchronous counterpart of the surf-rider accelerator mentioned in Sec. 8.6. For the reasons given in Appendix D, the variable-pitch design leads not only to a reduction in the power dissipated but also to a corresponding increase in the power output. With these devices velocities in the order of 10^5 m/sec can be attained (see Probs. 10.10 and 10.11). For higher velocities the high-frequency polyphase supply required as a source for the traveling wave becomes unwieldy, and is therefore replaced by a transmission line terminated in its characteristic impedance.

10.5 STARTING PERFORMANCE

(a) Wound Rotors

As mentioned before, the *stall* or *starting* torque is of particular importance in the motoring regime. Induction motors are actually classified in terms of their starting performance. A relatively high value of starting torque as well as a low value of starting or inrush current is desirable. By introducing $S = 1$ we get from Eqs. (10.25), (10.6), and (10.11) the starting torque,

$$\mathfrak{L}_{st} = \mathfrak{L}_{\text{p.o.}} \frac{2}{R_2'/X_{\text{s.c.}} + X_{\text{s.c.}}/R_2'} = m_1 \frac{V_1^2}{\omega_s} \frac{R_2'}{R_2'^2 + X_{\text{s.c.}}^2} \tag{10.32}$$

and from Eq. (10.5) the starting current,

$$\bar{I}'_{2,\text{st}} = -\frac{\bar{V}_1}{R_2' + jX_{\text{s.c.}}} \tag{10.33}$$

It appears that, as long as R_2' is less than $X_{\text{s.c.}}$, the starting performance can be improved by increasing R_2'. In fact, with increasing R_2', the starting torque increases, while the inrush current decreases. The increase in R_2' produces, according to Eq. (10.6), a shift in the pull-out slip, but, according to Eq. (10.11), has no effect on the value of the pull-out torque. Naturally a high secondary resistance is detrimental to the rated performance of the converter because, as shown in Fig. 10.10, it shifts the rated operating point toward the region of higher slip and, therefore, lower efficiency. It thus appears desirable to have different values of R_2' during starting and during running conditions.

This can be best achieved by using a rotor in which the conductors are not short-circuited, but rather connected during starting to additional resistances in the rotor circuits. A rotor of this type is called a *wound rotor*. The starting resistances are then gradually short-circuited as the motor picks up speed. Such an arrangement, however, is cumbersome and expensive. If the resistances are attached to the stator, then slip rings and brushes are required. If they are fixed to the rotor, then complex and therefore unreliable gear has to be used. For this reason wound-rotor motors are used in applications such as reciprocating pumps and

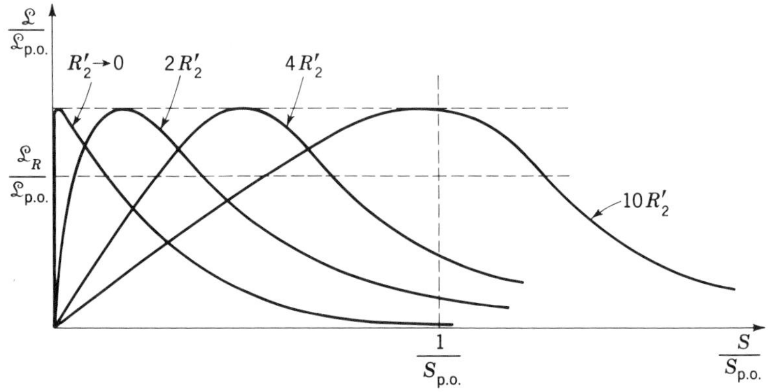

Fig. 10.10 Normalized torque-slip characteristics with R_2' as a parameter.

compressors or elevator drives which have to satisfy stringent starting performance specifications.

(b) Squirrel-cage Rotors; Skin Effect

The wound rotor is by far less common than another type of rotor whose construction resembles a cylindrical cage and is, in fact, usually called a *squirrel cage.* This squirrel-cage rotor takes full advantage of

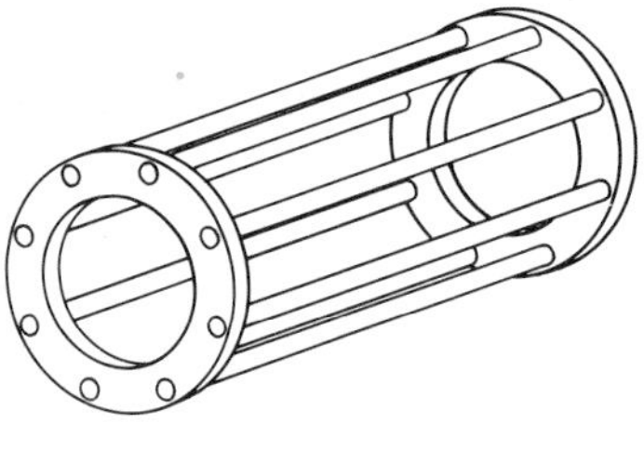

Fig. 10.11 Squirrel-cage rotor winding.

the ability of the asynchronous machine to operate with single excitation and therefore with short-circuited secondary circuit. In this type of winding the active conductors are short-circuited by two end rings, as shown schematically in Fig. 10.11. The result is quite satisfactory from both the mechanical and electrical points of view. Structurally the squirrel-cage winding is rugged, and this is a great advantage in view of the centrifugal forces which act on the rotor structure. Its fabrication is also cheap, especially in small units where it is cast in one piece together with the ventilating fan. The alloy used in this case is aluminum, for reasons that will become apparent in Sec. 10.7*a*.

From the point of view of electrical performance, the squirrel-cage winding needs practically no insulation since all individual conductors are permanently short-circuited. As a consequence, the thin oxide layer which forms naturally at the surface of the conductors provides sufficient insulation. Moreover the leakage flux is low because of the short end connections and the small harmonic content of the current-density wave shape. This results from the large number of phases, as each conductor represents a separate phase, and, consequently, the effective number of conductors $(c/m)k_dk_p$ equals unity.

At first it appears that it is not possible to achieve starting performance with squirrel-cage rotors comparable to that of wound rotors, because there is no access to the secondary circuit. However, adequate starting performance can be secured by taking advantage of the *skin effect*, and various such design schemes have been devised.

For an understanding of the underlying principle of the skin effect we consider the flow of power into the secondary conductors. As we have mentioned in Sec. 9.4, the concept of flow of power originates in electromagnetic field theory where it is associated with the flux of the Poynting vector. Appendix C illustrates the application of field theory to evaluate the power flow in the portion of the gap that is not occupied by the conductor. The same procedure can be applied to study the flow of power within the conductor. This evaluation is carried out in Appendix D. There we show how the absorption of the power which penetrates the conductor corresponds to a progressive decay in the intensity of the electric and magnetic field vectors. Since the characteristic length over which the electromagnetic field decays by one neper is approximately

$$\delta = \sqrt{\frac{2}{\mu\gamma\omega}} \tag{10.34}$$

this length can be taken as an effective depth of penetration of the electromagnetic field within the conductor. As we see, the depth of penetration, or the *skin depth*, as it is called, is inversely proportional to the square root of the magnetic permeability μ, the electric conductivity γ of the medium, and the radian frequency ω of the electromagnetic field.

In induction motors the rotor frequency varies with the slip and undergoes a variation in the order of 100 to 1 when accelerating from stalling to normal operating speed. The skin depth then varies by one order of magnitude. We observe that the skin depth delimits the area of the rotor bars which is occupied by the rotor currents and therefore determines the effective secondary resistance. It is now evident that the skin effect naturally produces the desired dependence of the rotor resistance on speed and is helpful in improving the starting performance. Figure 10.12 shows two typical conductor geometries for skin-effect rotors. In normal operation the rotor moves almost in synchronism with the traveling wave, and therefore the frequency of the induced currents is low; as long as the slot height is less than the skin depth at rated slip frequency, the whole conductor cross section is available to the flow of current, and the resistance R_2' is small. On the other hand, at stall the rotor is at standstill with respect to the stator, and the currents occupy only the shaded area near the gap, which corresponds to the skin depth

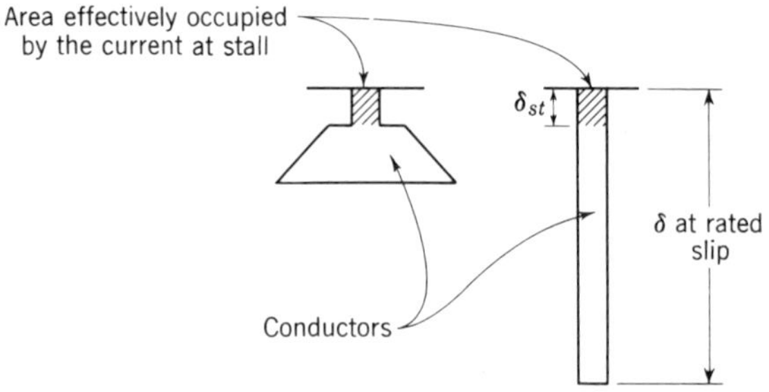

Fig. 10.12 Conductor cross sections used in rotors which utilize the skin effect.

at stator frequency, so that R_2' is large. With copper ($\gamma = 5 \times 10^7$ and $\mu = \mu_0 = 4\pi \times 10^{-7}$) the skin depth is

$$\delta = \sqrt{\frac{2}{4\pi \times 10^{-7} \times 5 \times 10^7 \times 2\pi f}} = \frac{0.07}{\sqrt{f}}\ \text{m} \tag{10.35}$$

and at 60 cycles is about $\frac{3}{8}$ in.

It is now apparent that the skin effect increases the secondary resistance at stall by an amount that is inversely proportional to s_c, the cross section of the conductor effectively occupied by the currents, or

$$R'_{2,\text{st}} = R'_{2,\text{rated}} \frac{(s_c)_{\text{rated}}}{(s_c)_{\text{st}}} \tag{10.36}$$

The skin effect can also be explained in simple terms by considering the slot leakage. At rated speed the frequency is in the order of 1 cps, and the current, being practically direct current, is resistance-limited and so distributes itself evenly in the cross section of the bar. This is not true at standstill when the current is reactance-limited and prefers to take the path of least reactance.

The plot of the slot leakage flux shown in Fig. 10.13 indicates that the current filaments flowing at the bottom of the bar are interlinked with the whole leakage flux, whereas the filaments flowing at the top are interlinked only with their own leakage flux. As a consequence, the bottom of the bar offers a much higher reactance path, and the current filaments tend to crowd themselves at the top of the bar.

Consideration of the leakage reactance shows that the rotor leakage reactance, as well as its resistance, is affected by the distribution of the current in the bar. The leakage reactance is larger at rated speed than

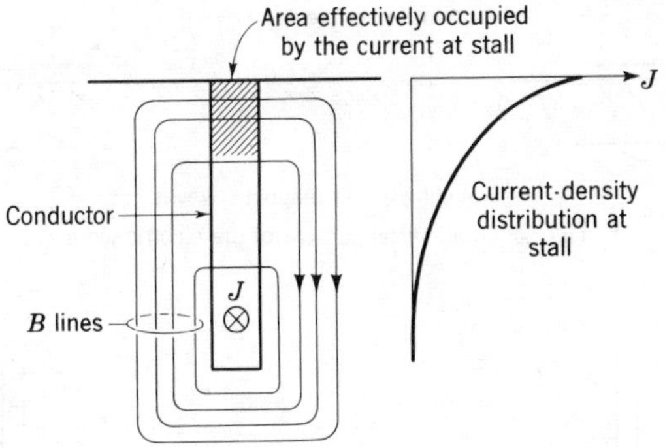

Fig. 10.13 Slot leakage and its relation to skin effect.

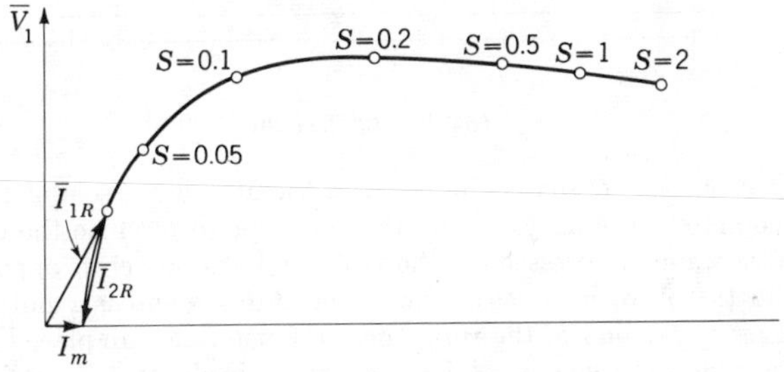

Fig. 10.14 Typical locus of the primary and secondary currents in an asynchronous motor with skin-effect rotor.

at stall, because the slot leakage increases with the effective depth of the bar. This affects the circle diagram, since the radius of the circle $V_1/2(X_1 + X_2')$ is a function of X_2'. For this reason, in skin-effect rotors, the geometric locus of the tip of the primary current $\bar{I}_1$ is no longer a circle, but is shaped more like a portion of an ellipse with the horizontal axis much larger than the vertical, as shown in Fig. 10.14.

It is apparent from this figure that the skin effect greatly expands the speed range over which the inphase component of the current and therefore the power output are practically equal to the pull-out power. The interested reader is referred to Appendix D for a more detailed evaluation of this effect. A particular type of skin-effect motor is presented in the following example.

Example 10.3

In an electric loom the reciprocating motion of the shuttle is the result of the accelerating and decelerating action of two developed polyphase windings placed at both ends of the linear run, as shown in the sketch below. These windings constitute

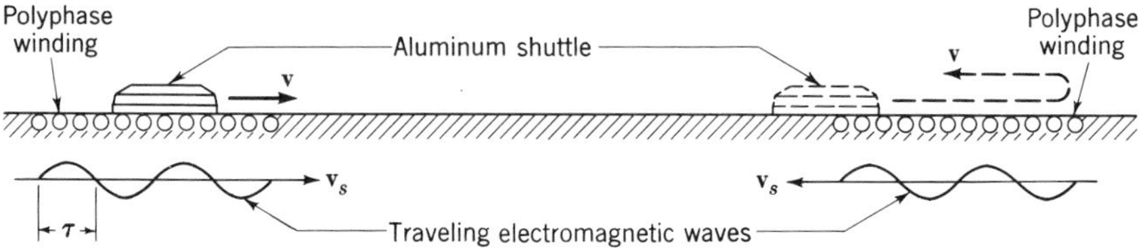

(a) Schematic arrangement of the electric loom

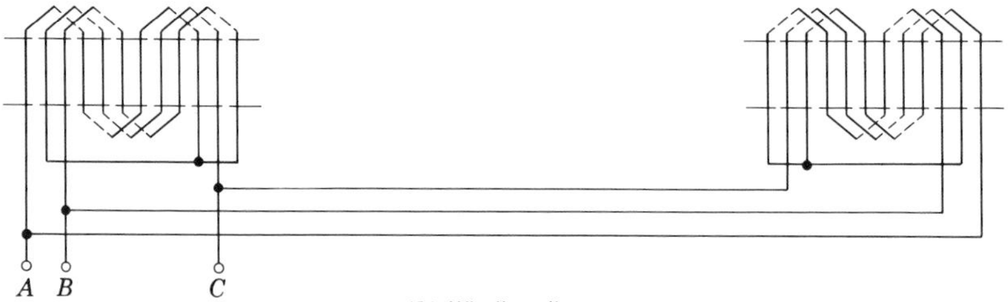

(b) Winding diagram

the primaries of an asynchronous motor, and the aluminum sole of the shuttle constitutes the common secondary. Note that in order to produce the desired motion, electromagnetic waves impressed on the two windings travel in opposite directions, so that the shuttle sole operates as a brake when entering and as a motor when leaving the active zones at the end of the run, where the windings are placed.

(a) Determine the range of variation of the skin depth δ if friction is negligible and therefore the velocity remains constant during the free run with $v = 10$ m/sec, the frequency in the primary is 400 cps, and the pole pitch in the windings is $\tau =$ 1.5 cm.

(b) Determine the required number of poles, knowing that the mass of the shuttle is 0.6 kg and the length and the width of the shuttle sole are 13 and 5 cm, respectively. Assume as a first approximation that the power transferred to the secondary remains constant over the speed range of operation with an average density of 2×10^5 watts/m^2, as one would expect, according to Fig. 10.14, in a skin-effect motor (see also Prob. 10.14).

Solution

(a) To determine the skin depth we must find the Doppler-shifted frequency of the secondary $S\omega_1$. With $\tau = 1.5$ cm and $f_s = 400$ cps the synchronous speed is, according to Eq. (6.8a).

$$v_s = 2\tau f_s = 0.03 \times 400 = 12 \text{ m/sec}$$

The extremes of the slip range occur when the shuttle crosses the active zones at the beginning of the deceleration and at the end of the acceleration periods. The slip is then

$$S_d = \frac{v_s - v}{v_s} = \frac{12 - (-10)}{12} = 1.83$$

$$S_a = \frac{12 - 10}{12} = 0.167$$

The corresponding skin depths are, according to Eq. (10.34) and Table 3.1,

$$\delta_d = \sqrt{\frac{2}{4\pi \times 10^{-7} \times 2.94 \times 10^7 \times 1.83 \times 2\pi \times 400}} = 0.00322 \text{ m}$$

$$\delta_a = 0.00322 \sqrt{\frac{1.83}{0.167}} = 0.0107 \text{ m}$$

(*b*) When the shuttle crosses the active region, its kinetic energy is

$$W_{\text{kin}} = \tfrac{1}{2}Mv^2 = \tfrac{1}{2} \times 0.6 \times 10^2 = 30 \text{ joules}$$

The electromagnetic force acting on the shuttle is, according to Eq. (7.31),

$$F_x = \frac{1}{v_s} \langle p_{s,\text{conv}} \rangle A = \frac{2 \times 10^5 \times 13 \times 5 \times 10^{-4}}{12} = 108 \text{ newtons}$$

The length of the active region is then

$$\tfrac{30}{108} = 0.278 \text{ m}$$

Although F_x is not constant at 108 newtons as the sole moves in and out of the active region, this effect averages out so that the above length is appropriate. To calculate the number of poles, we have

$$2p\tau = 0.278$$

so that the nearest even value of p is 10. Adding 10 percent to account for fringing effects and starting transients, we thus have

$$p = 11 \text{ pole pairs}$$

Electric drive of the shuttle allows for adjustment of the speed by varying the frequency and makes the loom almost vibrationless and therefore noiseless.

A comparison between a shallow- and a deep-bar rotor with the same conductor cross section is illustrated in Fig. 10.15. Here we see that the slot leakage is higher in the deep-bar rotor for all values of speed. This is due to the fact that for a given current the magnetic field intensity across the slot is inversely proportional to the slot width d. The higher slot leakage has an adverse effect on the power factor and efficiency. The price one pays for improved starting performance with deep-bar rotors is thus a lower power factor and a somewhat lower efficiency.

More flexibility in the design and therefore better overall performance can be achieved with *double-cage* or *Boucherot-type* rotors. As indicated in Fig. 10.16, two separate squirrel cages are placed one on top of the other. The upper, which is the only one effective during starting, can then be built with a higher-resistance material. Double cages are also used as starting windings in salient-pole synchronous motors.

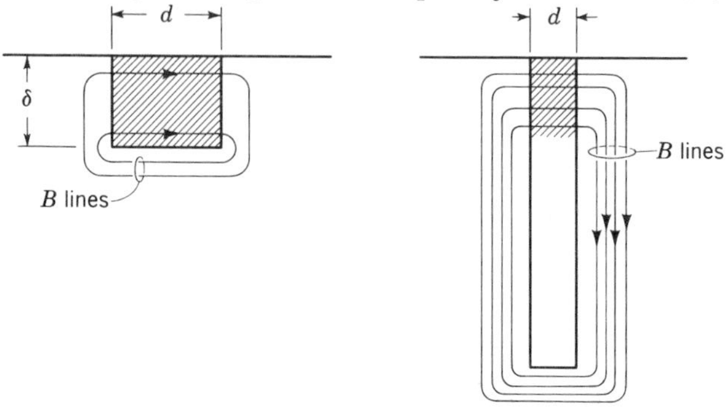

Fig. 10.15 Comparison of slot leakage in shallow- and deep-bar rotors.

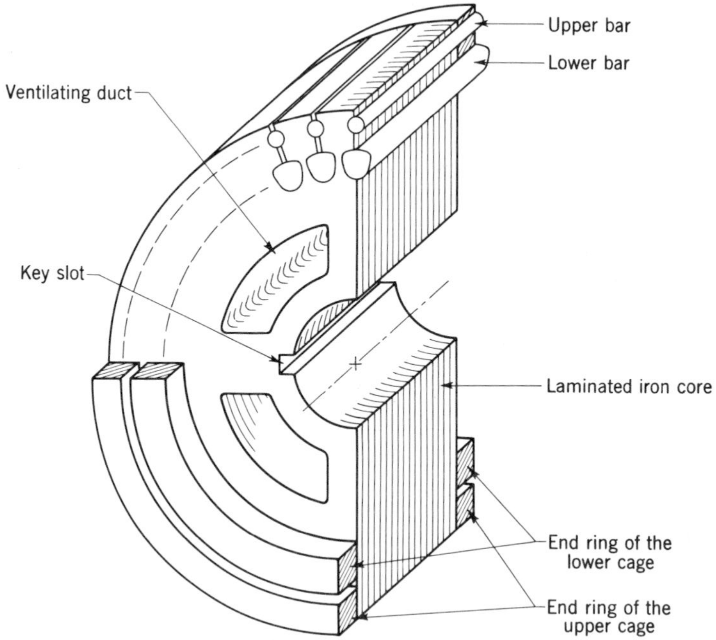

Fig. 10.16 Double-cage rotor.

*(c) Superconducting Rotor Windings

We will later see in Sec. 10.7a how the choice of materials for the squirrel cage is actually determined by thermal considerations. Here we want to consider another question which is related to the skin effect.

What influence does the skin effect have on the losses when comparing materials with different conductivity? One might think that the losses increase with the conductivity because the skin depth and therefore the effective cross section of the conductor decrease as γ increases. This is, however, not true. In fact, the conductor resistance is inversely proportional to γ, whereas the effective cross section is only proportional to the square root of γ. On this score it is clear that high-conductivity materials reduce the overall conductor resistance and hence decrease the losses.

If high γ leads to low losses, why not use $\gamma = \infty$? The development of cryogenic technology has made available perfect conductors in the superconducting state. What would the performance of a squirrel-cage motor be with a superconducting rotor? If the motor were started in the superconducting state, the skin depth δ would be zero, and the magnetic field impressed by the stator would squeeze in the gap, as shown schematically in Fig. 10.17, but it would not penetrate the rotor. The induced currents would concentrate as a thin sheet at the surface of the rotor conductors, but the magnetic flux would not penetrate the conductor. Thus the magnetic flux density would have no component perpendicular to the gap surface. The tangential force would vanish and the motor would not start. This effect is correctly taken into account by our equivalent circuit and circle diagram and is demonstrated by the torque-speed characteristics of Fig. 10.10, where we notice that the starting torque vanishes as R_2' approaches zero. These characteristics also suggest that the resistance and therefore the temperature should be reduced gradually, after the rotor has picked up speed and the magnetic flux has permeated the cage. In this case the operating point moves toward higher velocities, as it would in a wound rotor when the external resistances are short-circuited. When the superconducting state is reached, the magnetic flux lines are trapped between the bars of the cage, the slip vanishes, and the rotor falls into synchronism with the rotating flux wave. In the perfect conductor the rotor current is maintained without the need for relative motion between the conductor and the wave, and without the necessity for a driving electric field. Conversely, an adequate current density would immediately set in to increase the torque and counteract any tendency of the magnetic flux lines to slip past the conductors.

Good, but not necessarily perfect, conductors exhibit a similar behavior. To describe such a situation, which is common in stellar bodies where the diffusion of the magnetic flux through the highly conducting plasmas is negligible, Alfvén first introduced the concept that the magnetic flux lines are "frozen in" the conductor.

To explain further this mode of operation of the heteropolar device

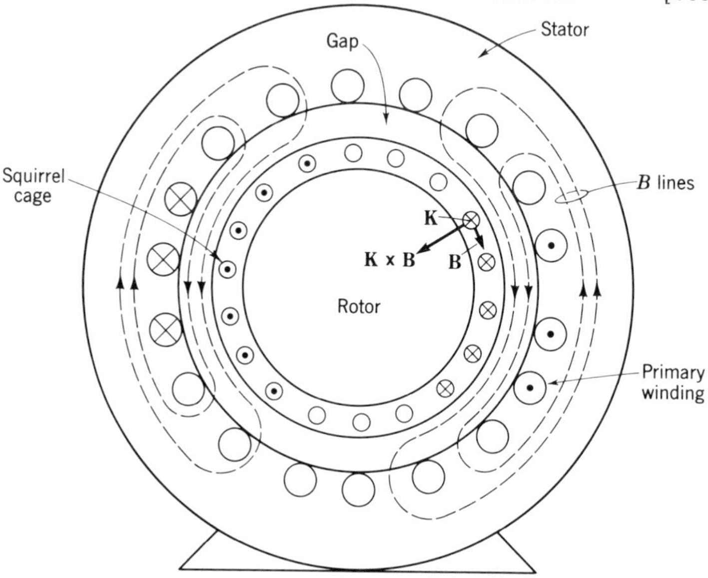

(a)

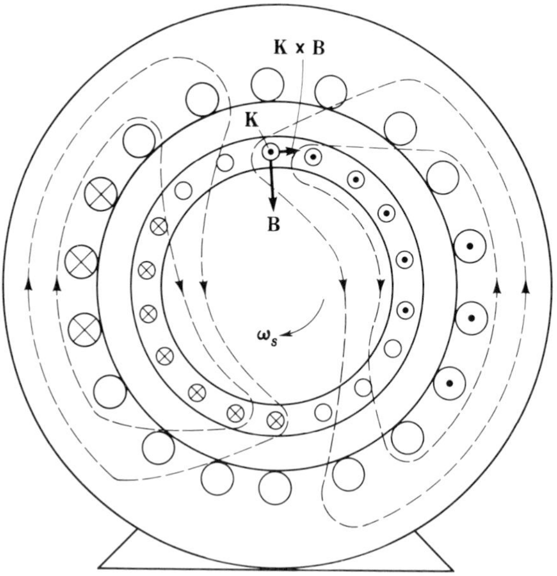

(b)

Fig. 10.17 Instantaneous current and flux distribution in an induction motor with highly conducting squirrel-cage winding: (a) Primary excitation applied with the rotor winding in the highly conducting state (no tangential force component); (b) highly conducting state attained when running (synchronous operation).

we turn to the microscopic picture. In a perfect conductor the electrons move freely past the ions without close encounters or collisions. In the absence of the fluctuating microfields associated with collisions, there is no need for a balancing field. This, however, still does not explain the flow of currents and how the currents adjust to a change in torque requirements. As a matter of fact, if the flux density were uniform, we would

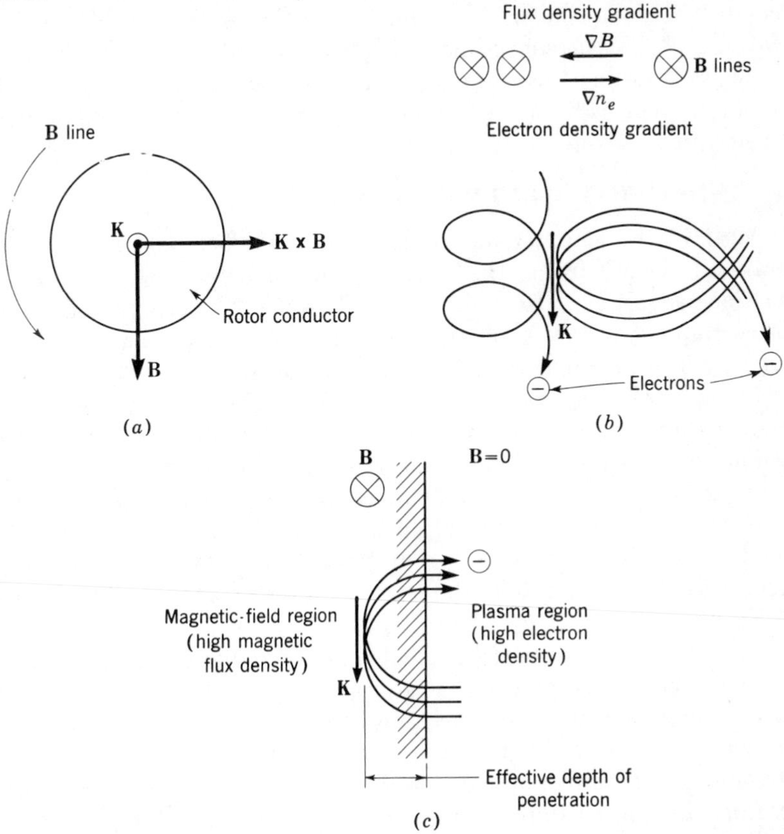

Fig. 10.18 Microscopic model of the currents induced in the high-conductivity rotor: (*a*) Upper portion of figure 10.17*b* expanded; (*b*) microscopic picture at the surface of the conductor, showing density of electrons and their trajectories; (*c*) magnetic wall approximation.

expect the charged particles, electrons included, to be leashed to the flux lines so that no current flows. This is where the heteropolarity of the device enters into the picture: *the flux density is not uniform* along the direction of motion. Since our treatment of the microscopic model of collisionless plasmas in Chap. 2 did not include sinusoidal flux distributions, we first approximate the smooth variation by a sharp discontinuity, a magnetic wall as indicated in Fig. 10.18*c*. In this case we recall from Sec. 3.5*b* that the current is produced by the reflection of the particles at the wall. We also know that, according to Sec. 3.6*b*, this model, crude as it may be, gives the correct one-to-one correspondence between the current and the pressure gradient which is responsible for the tangential force $(\mathbf{K} \times \mathbf{B})_x$ and the torque in the converter. An analysis conducted along similar lines would show[2] that in the case of a smooth variation in **B**, the current results from the combined effect of the electron-density gradient and the asymmetry of the electron orbits caused by the different Larmor radii in the regions of strong and weak magnetic field. This situation is sketched in Fig. 10.18.

10.6 INDUCTION GENERATORS†

Most of this chapter has been devoted to the motoring mode of operation. This is by far the most common and the most important in induction converters. Here we will briefly review the generating regime. This corresponds, as we know, to the condition in which the converter is driven by a prime mover in the direction of synchronous velocity at speeds higher than synchronous speed. The inphase component of the current then reverses its sign with respect to the busbar voltage, and the machine converts the mechanical power supplied at the shaft into electric power, which is fed into the busbar system. The operation as a generator is described by the lower half of the circle diagram of Fig. 10.19 and extends theoretically from $S = 0$ to $S = -\infty$. Because of efficiency considerations, however, only the region of low slip is of practical interest [see Eq. (10.20*b*)].

The main advantage of the singly excited induction generator over the synchronous generator is that no separate d-c supply is required for the rotor, and no brush gear is necessary to carry the current to the rotor. Another advantage is that it operates over the whole velocity range. As a consequence, it can be brought up to speed while connected to the busbar, thus eliminating the need for synchronizing gear. Also, it poses no stability problems since it cannot fall out of step as can the synchronous generator. The intrinsic reliability of the asynchronous generator meets the needs of relatively small and unattended hydraulic plants.

On the other hand, the induction converter is capable of generating only with leading power factor. In view of the fact that the majority of electric-power loads are inductive in character, this is a serious drawback. In addition, the induction generator relies on other sources for its own var consumption. When connected to a busbar system, the induction generator draws the magnetizing var required for its excitation from the synchronous machines connected to that system.

† This name is sometimes erroneously applied to a-c tachometers which are normally operated as rotating transformers without power conversion as such.

For the above reason induction generators are practical only when the gap length and therefore the magnetizing current requirements are small. As a consequence, it is not feasible to undertake MPD generation using the induction principle with presently available plasmas. If, however, higher plasma conductivities and velocities could be allowed, the volume of active conductor and thereby the magnetizing-current requirements could be substantially reduced. Research in this direction is extremely worthwhile, since an induction MPD generator would provide highly desirable practical features (i.e. the elimination of electrodes and a-c output).

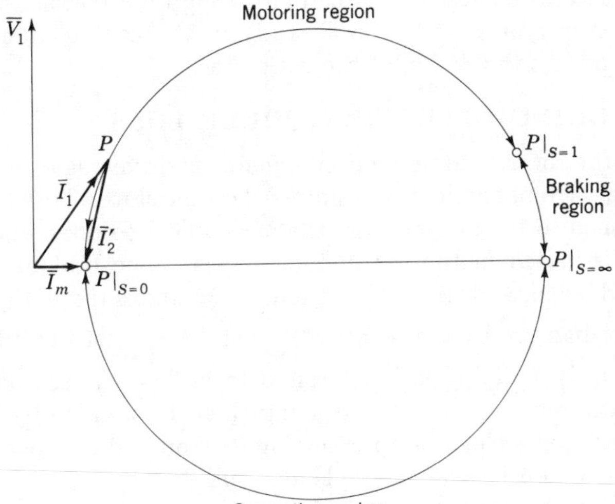

Fig. 10.19 Regions of operation in the circle diagram.

It is even possible to operate an induction generator connected to a passive load without external active excitation at all. The load must be capacitive, since the generator can only supply a leading power factor. In this case, the converter "builds up" a voltage as a result of the residual magnetic field in its pole structure, and operates with an output frequency that is determined by the resonance of the circuit seen from the secondary resistance R_2'/S.

During the Second World War the Swiss company Oerlikon developed an interesting application for such a system, which utilizes the great ability of the inertia of rotating masses to store high values of energy per unit volume, as noted in Chap. 5. Oerlikon developed a city bus capable of operating on long stretches of road from one end of the line to the other without depending on chemical fuel or any other form of energy storage in chemical form as electric batteries.[3] In this bus the energy-storage element consists of a flywheel coupled to an induction machine, which is operated as a motor at the terminal station to accelerate the flywheel and as a tuned generator during the running period to supply electric power to the traction motors.

Under the assumption that the flux density is kept constant during the "charge" and "discharge," the efficiency of electromechanical energy conversion is given by the relations developed in Sec. 5.4*b*. In fact, the only difference between a-c and d-c circuits is the leakage inductance which, on the average, does not absorb power. It follows that all the conclusions derived there about the optimum range of speed variation for energy-storage applications hold for the Oerlikon drive. The same is true with respect to the energy dissipated in high-inertia drives not necessarily used for energy storage. We shall study in the next section how this energy loss affects the design of the converter.

10.7 PLUGGING OPERATION; JOULE LOSS

When the rotor of an induction machine is driven against the direction of the electromagnetic wave impressed on the stator, both the electric power supplied to the primary and the mechanical power supplied to the shaft are dissipated in the conductors. This is the braking regime of operation which extends from $S = 1$ to $S = \infty$ and is therefore delimited in the circle diagram by the points $P\Big|_{S=1}$ and $P\Big|_{S=\infty}$ of Fig. 10.19. Use of this region is made when it is desired to brake or plug a motor, i.e., decelerate the moving masses and bring them to standstill. Examples of such cases are an elevator approaching its stop and the reversal of the direction of motion in machine tools and mill drives.

To achieve braking, the connections between the stator conductors and the busbar system are changed so as to reverse the direction of travel of the impressed field wave. The amount of energy dissipated during braking is so large that, unless special precautions are taken in the design stage, the temperature in the conductors will rise beyond the limit allowed by the insulation. In this section we shall develop the relationship describing this temperature rise and then turn to the design considerations which follow.

To evaluate the energy dissipated in the rotor, we note that, at every instant of time, the following relation holds:

$$P_{2,\text{diss}} = \frac{SP_{\text{conv}}}{1 - S} \tag{10.37}$$

Also during an accelerating or decelerating transient with negligible friction torque and no power supplied at the mechanical port, we have

$$P_{\text{conv}} = \frac{d}{dt} W_{\text{kin}} = \frac{d}{dt}\left(\frac{1}{2} Mv^2\right) \tag{10.38}$$

where $M = \Theta/r_g^2$ is the equivalent mass, referred to the gap radius r_g of the rotor and the coupled mechanical system with total moment of inertia Θ.

For the energy dissipated in the rotor conductor up to the time t, we can therefore write

$$\Delta W_{2,\text{diss}} = \int_0^t P_{2,\text{diss}}\, d\tau = \int_0^t \frac{S}{1-S} P_{\text{conv}}\, d\tau \tag{10.39}$$

and introducing the expression for the slip [Eq. (9.9*b*)] and for P_{conv} [Eq. (10.38)], we obtain

$$\begin{aligned}\Delta W_{2,\text{diss}} &= \int_0^t \frac{v_s - v}{v} \frac{d(\frac{1}{2}Mv^2)}{dt}\, d\tau = \int_{v_0}^{v} M(v_s - v)\, dv \\ &= \tfrac{1}{2}M(v_0{}^2 - v^2) + Mv_s(v - v_0)\end{aligned} \tag{10.40}$$

where v = instantaneous velocity at time t
v_0 = initial velocity at time $t = 0$
v_s = synchronous speed

We observe that we would have arrived at the same conclusions simply by substituting M for ξ and v_s for v_E in the relations obtained in Sec. 5.4*b* in terms of a single volume element of the conductor. This again indicates the generality of the approach we have taken.

We have noted that the rotor and the impressed wave travel in opposite directions during plugging. This means that v_s and v have opposite signs. As a result, the energy dissipated in plugging the motor from normal operating speed ($v_0 \cong -v_s$) to standstill ($v = 0$) is found to be

$$\Delta W_{2,\text{diss}} = \tfrac{3}{2}Mv_s{}^2 = 3\Delta W_{\text{kin}} \tag{10.41}$$

If, after standstill is achieved, we now let the motor remain connected to the supply, it will accelerate to full speed in the opposite direction and dissipate in the rotor the additional energy:

$$\Delta W_{\text{diss}} = \tfrac{1}{2}M(0 - v_s{}^2) + Mv_s(v_s - 0) = \Delta W_{\text{kin}} \tag{10.42}$$

We thus see that for a full reversal of speed, the rotor conductor must be designed so as to stand the temperature rise resulting from the dissipation of an amount of energy equivalent to four times the kinetic energy stored in the coupled mechanical system at full speed. We also note that this result is independent of the type of rotor, its resistance, and the time required for the acceleration. Naturally, however, if the rotor is of the wound type and is connected to external resistances, most of this power is dissipated there. For this reason this type of rotor is mostly used where the mechanical load is characterized by large inertia.

(a) Temperature Rise in Rotor and Stator Conductors

We now proceed to calculate the temperature rise in the conductor of a squirrel-cage rotor. Since the accelerating and decelerating transients occur in times that are short compared with the thermal time constant of the converter, it is quite adequate to assume that the rotor conductor heats up adiabatically, that is, without exchange of heat with the ambient surroundings. Under these conditions the temperature rise ΔT is given simply by

$$\Delta T = \frac{\Delta W_{2,\mathrm{diss}}}{c(\mathrm{Vol.})} \tag{10.43}$$

where c is the specific heat per unit volume of the conductor's material and Vol. the volume of the rotor conductor. If l_c is the total length of the rotor conductor and s_c its cross section, this volume is

$$\mathrm{Vol.} = l_c s_c \tag{10.44}$$

If we now observe that the total resistance is

$$R_c = \frac{l_c}{\gamma s_c} \tag{10.45}$$

we can write for the temperature rise:

$$\Delta T = \frac{\Delta W_{\mathrm{diss}} R_c}{l_c^2} \frac{\gamma}{c} \tag{10.46}$$

Suppose we are faced with the design of an induction machine according to a given set of specifications, and have in fact completed the design on the basis of steady-state considerations. The quantities ΔW_{kin}, R_c, and l_c are now established constants. We may next find upon checking Eq. (10.46) that the temperature rise ΔT during transient operation exceeds allowable limits because of insufficient heat capacity during the adiabatic transient.

Under these circumstances we can alter our design by changing the rotor conductor material. Equation (10.46) shows us that ΔT is a function only of the ratio γ/c when ΔW, R_c, and l_c are specified; thus we may sacrifice high conductivity in favor of lower values of γ/c, so as to bring ΔT within acceptable limits, at the same time keeping R_c constant. This is done by increasing the effective conductor thickness a, so as to keep $a\gamma$ constant. Thus the steady-state performance is left unchanged, while the transient ΔT is brought within proper bounds. The price we pay for this procedure is, of course, the requirement of a larger volume of conducting material at the expense of magnetic material. In extreme cases, of course, it may not be possible to achieve sufficiently small ΔT in this way, and we may have to use larger gap surfaces. In other cases, the application is such that no steady state exists, and transient considerations alone determine the gap surface.

In order to aid in these design considerations, we have presented in Table 10.1 values of γ/c for various materials used in squirrel-cage rotors. The value for copper

$$\left(\frac{\gamma}{c}\right)_{\text{copper}} = \frac{5.6 \times 10^7}{3.47 \times 10^6} = 16.1(°\text{C})(\text{m}^2)/(\text{joule})(\text{ohm})$$

is chosen as base for comparison.

Table 10.1 CONDUCTIVITY AND SPECIFIC HEAT OF TYPICAL CONDUCTING MATERIALS

Material	γ, mhos/m	c, joules/(m^3)(°C)	$\frac{\gamma/c}{(\gamma/c)_{\text{copper}}}$
Copper.............	5.6×10^7	3.47×10^6	1
Aluminum (cast)....	2.8×10^7	2.22×10^6	0.79
Brass..............	1.5×10^7	3.2×10^6	0.3
Phosphor bronze....	9×10^6	3.23×10^6	0.17

From Table 10.1 we learn that if, assuming R_2 constant, we use aluminum instead of copper, the temperature rise is only 79 percent, and if we use brass, only 30 percent. This explains why in small motors, which are subject to greater thermal stress, the squirrel cage is usually cast in aluminum or fabricated with brass bars.

The following example illustrates the design procedure applicable to motors driving high-inertia loads, where the gap surface is determined by the thermal stresses occurring during starting, rather than during steady state.

Example 10.4

An artificial-gravity centrifuge for the training of astronauts is driven by a 60-cps double-cage induction motor. Estimate the gap surface if the centrifuge rotates at 60 rpm and has a moment of inertia $\Theta = 3 \times 10^4$ kg-m^2 and friction is negligible.

Solution

From Eq. (10.40) we know that the energy dissipated in the rotor during acceleration from stall to full speed equals the kinetic energy stored in the rotating masses. This is

$$\tfrac{1}{2}\Theta\omega^2 = \tfrac{1}{2} \times 3 \times 10^4 \left(\frac{2\pi \times 60}{60}\right)^2 = 5.9 \times 10^5 \text{ joule}$$

The volume of the rotor conductor for an allowable temperature rise of 250°C is then given by Eq. (10.43):

$$\text{Vol.} = \frac{5.9 \times 10^5}{250c} = \frac{2{,}360}{c}$$

We note that, except for aluminum, the materials of Table 10.1 have approximately the same value of specific heat. Copper would require the least volume; however, we are interested in the surface rather than in the volume of the conductor. Since the effective thickness during starting is determined by the skin depth, we choose the material that has the maximum skin depth or, as we see from Eq. (10.34), the least conductivity; therefore we pick phosphor bronze. Since the rotor is designed with a double cage, the low conductivity does not impair the performance in the steady state. At 60 cps and with $\gamma = 9 \times 10^6$ mhos/m, δ is, according to Eq. (10.34),

$$\delta_{PB} = \sqrt{\frac{2}{4\pi \times 10^{-7} \times 9 \times 10^6 \times 2\pi \times 60}} = 0.0217 \text{ m}$$

The surface of the conductor facing the gap is thus with $c = 3.23 \times 10^6$ joule/(m³)(°C):

$$A_C = \frac{2{,}360}{3.23 \times 10^6 \times 0.0217} = 3.35 \times 10^{-2} \text{ m}^2$$

This is not the actual gap area since the conductor is embedded in slots, and therefore we must account for the width of the teeth separating the slots. If, as shown in the sketch, we allow for the tooth 90 percent of the slot width, we arrive at an estimate of

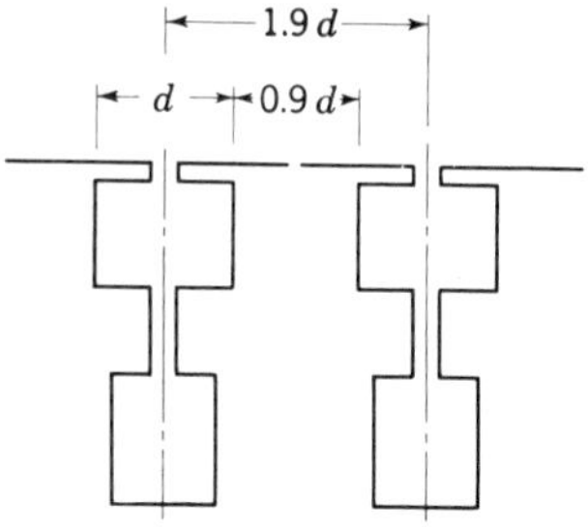

the gap surface

$$A = 1.9 \times 3.35 \times 10^{-2} = 6.4 \times 10^{-2} \text{ m}^2$$

This gives an effective conductor thickness,

$$a = \delta \frac{A_c}{A} = 0.0217 \times \frac{1}{1.9} = 0.0114 \text{ m}$$

We observe that the gap surface thus found does not depend on the torque or power delivered by the motor. These affect only the acceleration time. For further details of this design the reader may see Prob. 10.13.

We now turn our attention to the stator and the temperature rise in its conductor. Since the magnetizing current is small, we can assume that the primary current equals the secondary current. The energy dissipated in Joule loss is then

$$\Delta W_{1,\text{diss}} = \Delta W_{2,\text{diss}} \frac{R_1}{R_2'} \tag{10.47}$$

In rotors with negligible skin effect the rotor resistance is of the same order of magnitude as that of the stator. Thus the losses are also comparable. However, because of the larger volume and more efficient cooling, the temperature rise of the stator winding is about 50 percent of that of the rotor. On the other hand, because of the insulation, the allowable temperature rise is, according to Table 4.4, Sec. 4.10, much lower than in the rotor conductor. In general, we cannot decide in advance which temperature rise determines the design, and this question must be investigated in each instance.

The situation with respect to skin-effect rotors is much better. Here the resistance ratio R_1/R_2' and therefore the loss ratio $\Delta W_{1,\text{diss}}/\Delta W_{2,\text{diss}}$ are smaller because we can assign to the secondary resistance the high value attained at low speed, when most of the losses occur.

10.8 VARIABLE - SPEED DRIVES

As we have seen, the asynchronous machine shares with the homopolar the advantage over the synchronous converter that it operates at all speeds. However, despite the fact that the mechanical angular velocity is not rigidly tied to the frequency of the primary circuit, efficiency considerations limit the economical range of operation in singly excited induction motors to velocities very near the synchronous speed. Nevertheless, such are the advantages with respect to low cost, ruggedness, and reliability which induction machines offer, when compared with all other adjustable-speed drives, that one is frequently willing to sacrifice the efficiency.

When the speed of the induction machine is controlled, we can distinguish between stator and rotor speed control, as follows.

(a) Stator Control

Stator control is the cheapest because it can be applied to squirrel-cage motors, but it is the most inefficient; it consists of a variation of the impressed voltage level. From Eq. (10.11) and from Fig. 10.20 it appears that the torque developed by the motor is proportional to the square of the primary voltage. Note that stable operation with constant load torque can be maintained only in the region $0 < S < S_{\text{p.o.}}$, as stated in Sec. 10.4*a*. Since $S_{\text{p.o.}} = R_2'/X_{\text{s.c.}}$, this quantity is therefore independent of the impressed voltage. Thus stable operation with constant load torque and constant voltage can only be achieved for speeds above the pull-out speed. Lower speeds can only be maintained on the average by means of automatic control of the primary voltage and by relying on the inertia of the rotating masses in order to keep the departure from the desired average speed and the frequency of the control cycle within reasonable limits.

With respect to power dissipation, the same considerations hold as in the previous section. For instance, according to Eqs. (10.37) and

(10.47), the power dissipated in both the stator and rotor winding is

$$P_{\text{diss}} = \left(1 + \frac{R_1}{R_2'}\right) \frac{S}{1 - S} P_{\text{conv}} \tag{10.48}$$

It follows that these motors should be designed with a low ratio of stator to rotor resistance and with enhanced skin effect, in order to make R_1/R_2' small. For this reason solid-iron rotors with no cage at all are often employed.

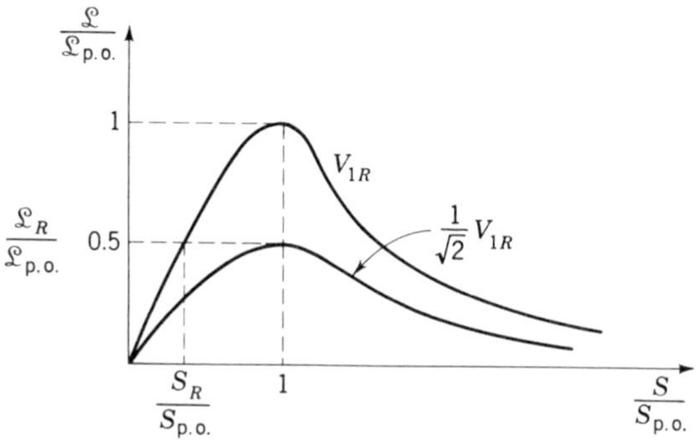

Fig. 10.20 Torque-slip characteristics with the primary voltage as a parameter.

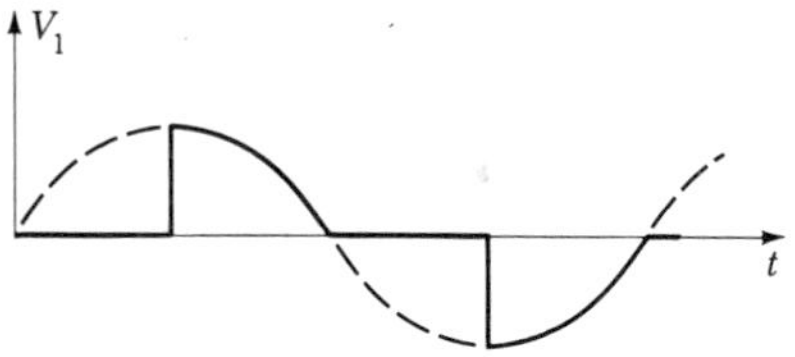

Fig. 10.21 Voltage control by pulse width modulation.

With respect to the control of the primary voltage level, this has been achieved in recent years, not by changing the amplitude but by chopping off part of the sinusoid, as shown in Fig. 10.21. This special type of pulse-width modulation is obtained by means of solid-state switching elements such as saturable reactors, silicon-controlled rectifiers, and transistors. A full discussion of these drives is beyond the scope of this book. It will suffice here to observe that the distorted voltage function can be expanded in a Fourier series. Besides the fundamental, whose amplitude is decreased by the modulation process, thus providing the desired speed control, there exist a large number of higher time harmonics. These set up in the gap waves which are similar to the synchronous wave but which travel at speed

$$v_s{}^n = n \frac{\omega_1 r_g}{p} = n v_s \tag{10.49}$$

where n is the order of the harmonic. For each one of these harmonics we can write a power relation,

$$P^n_{\text{diss}} = \left(1 + \frac{R_1}{R'_{2,n}}\right) \frac{S^n}{1 - S^n} P^n_{\text{conv}} \tag{10.50}$$

where $S^n = (v_s{}^n - v)/v_s{}^n$ is the slip of the rotor with respect to the nth wave. In view of the large value of $v_s{}^n$ when compared to v for all these harmonics, the slip S^n approaches unity. As a consequence, practically all the electric power associated with the higher harmonic waves is dissipated. This lowers still further the efficiency of the drive.

(b) Rotor Control

For higher power drives, where efficiency becomes important, one resorts to rotor control. This is achieved by varying the value of external resistances inserted in the rotor circuit and results in the torque-speed characteristics of Fig. 10.10. For this purpose the terminals of the secondary circuit must be accessible, and therefore the rotor must be of the more expensive and less reliable wound type. This disadvantage is offset by the fact that the drive is stable over the whole speed range since the pull-out speed decreases as the secondary resistance is increased. The drive is also more efficient, because in the power relation of Eq. (10.48), the term contributed by the stator resistance becomes negligible. Here again solid-state switching elements can be used to advantage in eliminating the need for variable resistances and associated gear. Rather than physically short-circuit part of the voltage which builds up across the external secondary resistances, this voltage is pulse-width-modulated, as shown for the stator in Fig. 10.21.

*10.9 DOUBLY EXCITED HETEROPOLAR CONVERTERS WITH FREQUENCY CHANGERS

The preceding discussion has demonstrated that singly excited induction converters cannot provide satisfactory efficiency and stability over a wide range of speeds. In some applications which require wide speed ranges, considerable amounts of power are involved. Examples are the variable-speed motor drives which are used in fabricating tubing, wires, and sheets, and the asynchronous airborne generators which are driven from variable-speed jet engines. Because of the importance of these applications, great effort has been devoted to devise means for improving the efficiency of asynchronous converters at high values of slip. We will consider these means in the following.

At the heart of the problem is the question: Is it possible to avoid dissipating all the power that in singly excited converters has to be wasted in the secondary resistance? This power, which is the difference between the power transferred to the secondary and the converted power, we shall call the *slip* power P_{slip}. From our discussion in Sec. 9.5e and the above definition, we see that P_{slip} is given by

$$P_{slip} = P_{t,1} - P_{diss,1} - P_{conv} = P_{diss,2} - P_{t,2} \qquad (10.51)$$

Equation (10.51) above gives us the answer to our question. We see that in the general case of double excitation some of the slip power is not dissipated but appears as $P_{t,2}$. If we then arrange for the secondary port to *absorb* terminal power by proper selection of V_2' so as to make $P_{t,2}$ negative, $P_{diss,2}$ can be reduced to a small fraction of P_{slip}. In circuit terms, we see from Fig. 10.22 that the power transferred to the secondary flows through the port *ab*. Part of this is the converted power which flows into the port *cd*; the rest is the slip power which divides between ohmic losses in R_2' and the secondary terminal power. In the motoring case, the overall conversion efficiency P_{conv}/P_t can now be much higher,

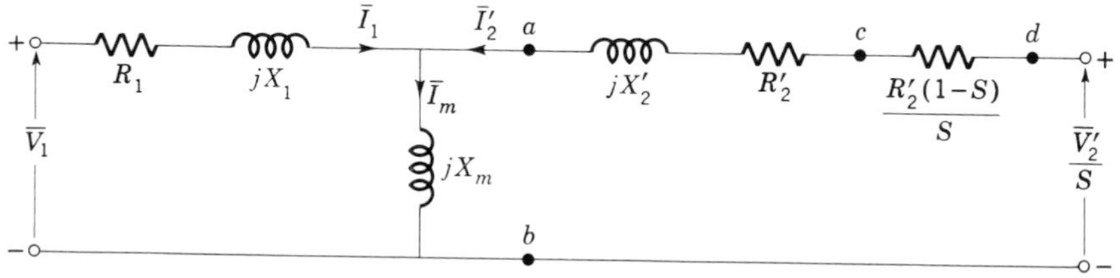

Fig. 10.22 Complete equivalent circuit for double excitation.

since for a given P_{conv}, P_t is smaller than the value in the case of single excitation. This is true because $P_t = P_{t,1} + P_{t,2}$, and $P_{t,2}$ is negative, as previously explained. The efficiency P_t/P_{conv} is similarly increased in the generating case, since $|P_t|$ is increased for a given $|P_{conv}|$, with both primary and secondary now delivering power.

The drawback in this scheme of using double excitation for increasing the efficiency at high slip values is that the Doppler-shifted secondary frequency $S\omega_1$ varies with speed. Thus a change in the frequency of the secondary voltages and currents is a prerequisite for transfer of the secondary power to circuits having the primary frequency. Consequently we need a special device, a *frequency changer*, to make the secondary power useful.

A frequency changer consists of an array of switching elements called a *commutator*. The elements most commonly used in a commutator are mechanical switches mounted on the rotor, in the form of multiple-conducting segments set in a ring and contacted by collecting *brushes*. Alternatively, vacuum or gas-filled electron tubes, or solid-state switches, can be used. All commutators, regardless of type, are faced with the difficulty of having to interrupt large currents in inductive circuits, and thus must provide means for the disposal of the stored magnetic energy. This general problem is called *commutation*. No completely satisfactory solution to the commutation problem has yet been found.

Using a frequency changer, we may actually feed the secondary terminal power back into the primary circuit and thus usefully rechannel the slip power. This amounts to the arrangement described by the power-flow diagram of Fig. 10.23. In this scheme, the feedback loop must also include a device capable of adjusting the voltage, i.e., a *variable transformer*, so that, at all speeds, the power derived from the rotor can be supplied to the primary not only at the proper frequency, but also at the proper phase and voltage level. Both the frequency changer and the

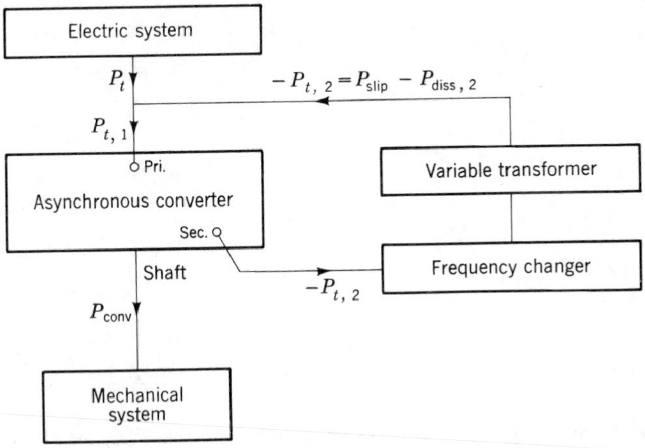

Fig. 10.23 Power-flow diagram in a doubly excited asynchronous converter connected to a single-frequency electric system. (The losses in the frequency changer and in the variable transformer have been neglected.)

variable transformer are passive devices and not power converters. For this reason we will not be concerned with their operation here. We will mention only that the variable transformer itself usually consists of a doubly fed asynchronous converter with blocked rotor.

Of all machines employing commutators, the only ones that have achieved a large degree of reliability and usage are the d-c machines. From the point of view of power conversion, these are heteropolar converters, operating at synchronous speed, in which the terminal frequency is changed to zero by means of a mechanical commutator. Because of the important role that d-c machines have played in the historical development of power converters, they are often studied in great detail as a separate machine type. This will not be done here since, as seen from the gap where the power-conversion process takes place, they do not differ from synchronous converters.

(a) Commutators

To understand how a commutator performs the desired frequency change, we consider first an elementary coil connected to a split ring as shown in Fig. 10.24. We observe that as the coil rotates, the brushes make connection with alternate sides of the coil in such a way that their polarity remains constant. As a result, the output of such an elementary generator is a rectified full wave. Better utilization of the converter and practically ripple-free current is obtained with the multicoil, multi-segment arrangement shown in Fig. 10.25, which was originally developed by Pacinotti and Gramme. In many applications, and especially in outer space, the intrinsic low-reliability and maintenance requirements of sliding contacts is objectionable. For these purposes the segments of the mechanical commutators can be replaced by photodiodes or other photoelectric components.[4]

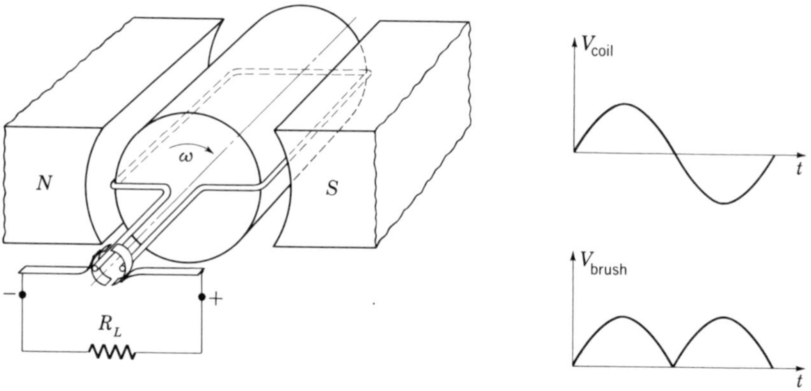

Fig. 10.24 Rectification of the voltage output of an elementary coil by means of a split ring.

(b) Brush Voltage

In general, commutator machines, whether with d-c or a-c output, consist of heteropolar structures with all the conductors on the rotor side of the gap series-connected to form a mesh similar to those discussed in Sec. 9.7. The difference is that the phase terminals, instead of making permanent connection with separate lines as in the heteropolar converters considered so far, make sliding contact with a set of brushes as indicated in Figs. 10.25 and 10.26. We now wish to evaluate the brush voltage. If

$$B(x) = B_m \cos \frac{\pi}{\tau} x \tag{10.52}$$

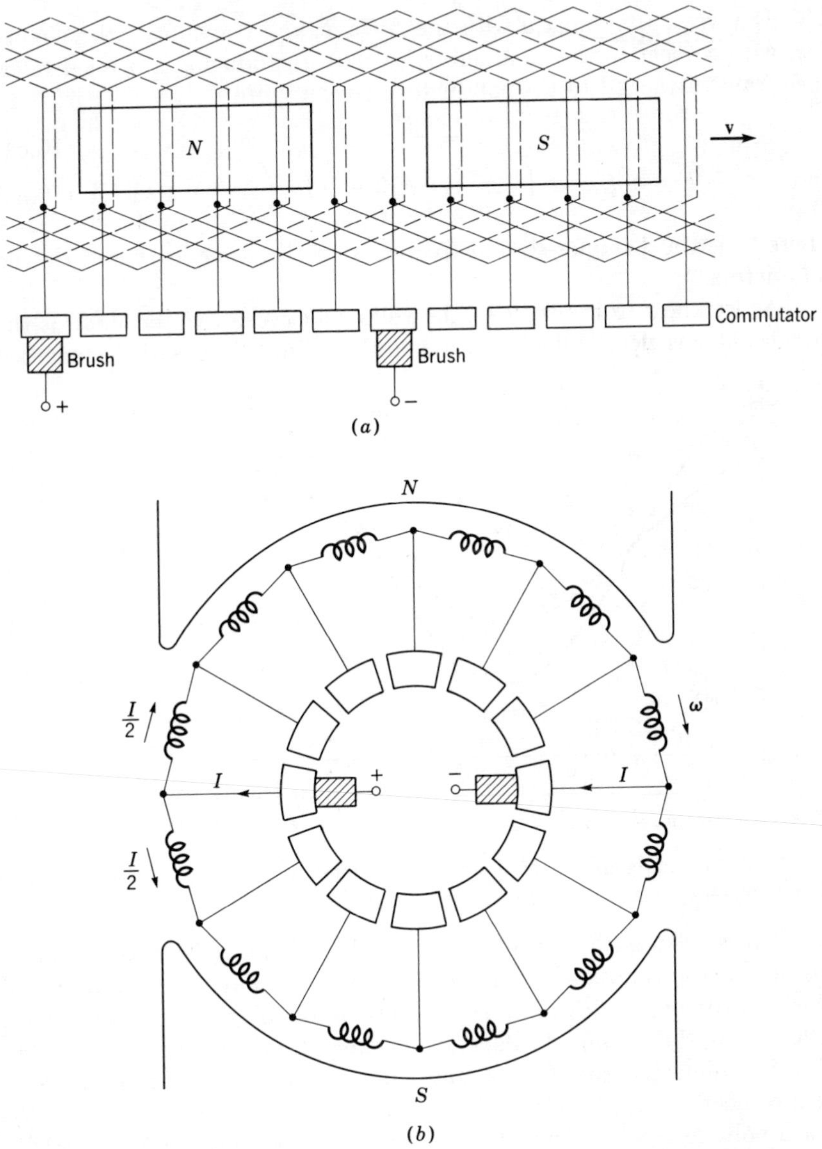

Fig. 10.25 Direct-current heteropolar motor: (a) Developed winding; (b) schematic representation.

is the magnetic flux density as measured in the wave frame (unprimed), and if the velocity of the conductor with respect to the wave frame is v_c, then the conductors sense a motion-induced electric field. At no load we can write, according to Eq. (6.14b),

$$E = v_c B_m \cos\left(\frac{\pi}{\tau} x\right) \tag{10.53}$$

This is a wave at standstill with the B wave, and traveling with velocity $-v_c$ with respect to the conductors, so that, introducing a primed reference frame attached to the conductor, we can write

$$x = x' + v_c t \tag{10.54}$$

and

$$E = v_c B_m \cos\left(\frac{\pi}{\tau}x' + \frac{\pi}{\tau}v_c t\right) = v_c B_m \left(\frac{\pi}{\tau}x' + \omega_c t\right) \tag{10.55}$$

where ω_c is the Doppler-shifted frequency of the wave as sensed by the conductors.

As we know from Sec. 9.4*c*, the voltage between two terminals is the integral of this electric field over a loop threading all the series-connected

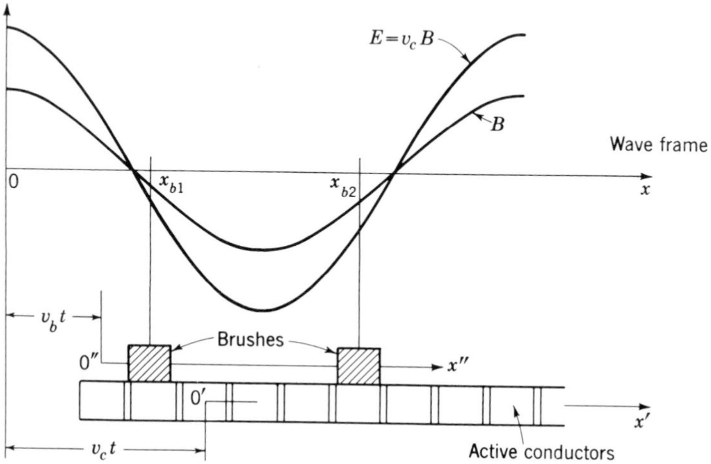

Fig. 10.26 Relative motion of the active conductors and brushes with respect to the wave frame.

conductors. At each instant of time this voltage reflects the relative position of the conductors with respect to the E wave. Since a pair of brushes provides an instantaneous sampling of this voltage, the voltage collected by the brushes V_b depends on the arc spanned, i.e., the number of series-connected conductors, and the relative position of the brushes with respect to the E wave. However, at any given instant of time, the brush voltage *does not* depend on the state of motion of the brushes with respect to the wave frame, because, as we know from Sec. 9.4*b*, the terminal voltage is invariant to a transformation of reference frames. It can be shown (see Prob. 10.17) that if we denote by $x_{b,1}$ and $x_{b,2}$ the instantaneous position of the terminals connected to the brushes in the wave frame, we can write

$$V_b = \mathcal{Q} v_c B\left(\sin\frac{\pi}{\tau}x_{b,1} - \sin\frac{\pi}{\tau}x_{b,2}\right) \tag{10.56}$$

where $\mathcal{A}$ is a proportionality factor which depends on the number of conductors spanned and their length. Using a trigonometric identity, we can rewrite the brush voltage as a function of the arc spanned $(x_{b,1} - x_{b,2})$ and the position of the axis $[(x_{b,1} + x_{b,2})/2]$:

$$V_b = 2\mathcal{A}v_cB \sin\left(\frac{\pi}{2}\frac{x_{b,1} - x_{b,2}}{\tau}\right)\cos\left(\frac{\pi}{\tau}\frac{x_{b,1} + x_{b,2}}{2}\right) \tag{10.57}$$

If we now assume that the two brushes are both attached to a double-primed frame which moves with velocity v_b with respect to the wave frame, we have

$$\begin{aligned} V_b &= 2\mathcal{A}v_cB \sin\left(\frac{\pi}{2}\frac{x''_{b,1} - x''_{b,2}}{\tau}\right)\cos\frac{\pi}{\tau}\left(\frac{x''_{b,1} + x''_{b,2}}{2} + v_bt\right) \\ &= 2\mathcal{A}v_cB \sin\left(\frac{\pi}{2}\frac{x''_{b,1} - x''_{b,2}}{\tau}\right)\cos\left(\frac{\pi}{\tau}\frac{x''_{b,1} + x''_{b,2}}{2} + \omega_bt\right) \end{aligned} \tag{10.58}$$

We conclude that the brush voltage is, in general, a function of time; its frequency is independent of the motion of the conductors but reflects only the motion of the brushes with respect to the wave frame. The amplitude of the brush voltage, instead, is independent of the brush motion but is proportional to the conductor velocity with respect to the wave frame.

In a mechanical commutator the brushes are fixed to the stator and slide with respect to the rotor conductors. It follows that the stator conductors and the brushes have the same velocity with respect to the wave frame and therefore the same frequency. This is indeed what is required in order to realize the scheme of Fig. 10.23 for the utilization of the slip power. The d-c machine represents the particular case in which the stator and the brushes are at standstill with respect to the wave frame.

10.10 SUMMARY

In this chapter we have studied the induction converter. The major points that have been brought to light are the following:

1. In contrast with synchronous converters, the gap of induction devices employing solid conductors is made as small as mechanical considerations allow. Consequently the per-unit value of the magnetizing reactance X_m is larger than unity, larger than the leakage reactances X_1 and X_2' by at least one order of magnitude, and larger than the resistance R_1 and R_2' by at least two orders of magnitude.
2. These parameter values justify the use of approximate representations for the converter, such as the circle diagram. This is par-

ticularly convenient in that it provides a visual display of the performance and avoids laborious phasor calculations.

3. The electromagnetic torque developed by rotating converters with narrow gap is a function of the slip; it exhibits a peak or pull-out value which separates the stable from the unstable branch of operation. The same general trend is shared by converters employing fluid conductors, such as induction pumps and plasma accelerators, which of necessity are built with large gaps.
4. Changes in the resistance of the secondary circuit shift the speed at which the pull-out torque occurs without changing the value of the pull-out torque itself. Insertion of adjustable resistances thus affords improved starting performance, i.e., higher torque with lower inrush current. This, however, requires a rotor of the wound type and sliding contacts or complex gear.
5. Squirrel-cage rotors are rugged, reliable, and cheap. Satisfactory starting performance can be achieved by taking advantage of the skin effect, which for high values of slip increases the resistance of the secondary winding while lowering its leakage reactance. As a result, the electromagnetic force developed by the converter remains fairly constant at the peak value over a wide range of speeds. However, in the limit of perfect conductivity the converter would develop a nonvanishing torque only at synchronism.
6. Induction converters are seldom used in the generating mode because they cannot supply var to inductive loads, not even to provide their own magnetizing currents.
7. Induction converters operate at practically constant B. During acceleration from stall to full speed with negligible applied torque, they dissipate as much energy in the rotor conductor as is stored in kinetic form, just as in their homopolar counterpart. During braking from full speed to stall they dissipate three times the stored kinetic energy, and in reversing the direction of motion four times this energy.
8. The resulting temperature rise can be curbed by using for the rotor conductors materials with lower conductivity and larger heat capacity than copper. Cast aluminum is often employed in low-power squirrel-cage rotors.
9. Operation of singly excited converters at adjustable speed is obtained by controlling either the primary voltage or the secondary impedance. The efficiency is low.
10. Utilization of the slip power and consequently higher efficiency with adjustable speed are made possible by double excitation at variable frequency. The common drawback of the many schemes devised is the problem of commutation, i.e., disposal of the magnetic energy stored at the instant the circuit is broken.

REFERENCES

1. Jones, R. E., and R. W. Palmer: Traveling Wave Plasma Engine Program at NASA Lewis Research Center, *Proc. 3d Symp. Eng. Aspects of MHD*, University of Rochester, Mar. 28–29, 1962.
2. Sutton, G. W., and A. Sherman: "Engineering Magnetohydrodynamics," McGraw-Hill Book Company, New York, 1965.
3. The Oerlikon Electrogyro, *Automobile Eng.*, vol. 45, pp. 559–566 (December, 1955).
4. Studer, P. A.: Development of a Sealed Brushless DC Motor, *NASA Tech. Note* TN D-2819, May, 1965.
5. Bieger, W., P. Graff, H. L. Jordan, and H. Tuczek: Electrodeless Acceleration of Plasma, *Proc. of Euratom Symp. of Plasma Physics*, part I, vol. III, p. 105, Varenna, Oct. 12–17, 1964.

PROBLEMS

10.1 An 8-pole 60-cycle squirrel-cage motor delivers 800 hp under rated conditions. Its parameters in per unit are:

$$X_m = 4.8 \qquad X_1 = 0.125 \qquad R_1 = 1.2 \times 10^{-2} \qquad X_2' = 0.103 \qquad R_2' = 1.11 \times 10^{-2}$$

Determine:

(*a*) The maximum power output.

(*b*) The slip, speed, power factor, torque, and efficiency under rated conditions.

10.2 A 6-pole 60-cycle wound-rotor motor delivers 600 kw under rated conditions. Its magnetizing impedance is $X_m = 3.75$ p.u., and, under rated conditions, the power factor is P.F. = 0.91 and the slip $S = 1.28$ percent. Determine:

(*a*) The maximum output power.

(*b*) The resistance and leakage reactance of the stator and rotor winding, assuming that they have equal per-unit values in the stator and in the rotor.

10.3 A 4-pole 60-cycle 10-hp motor has, at rated voltage and frequency, a starting torque of 160 percent and a maximum torque of 200 percent of full-load torque. Determine:

(*a*) The full-load speed.

(*b*) The speed at maximum torque.

(*c*) The current density in the rotor at starting in percent of the full-load rotor current.

10-4 A squirrel-cage induction motor runs with a slip of 5.0 percent at full load. The rotor current density at starting is five times the rotor current density at full load.

(*a*) Compute the starting torque in percent of the rated torque.

(*b*) Compute the maximum torque in per cent of the rated torque and the slip at which maximum torque occurs.

10.5 A 4-pole 60-cycle wound-rotor induction motor delivers 500 kw under rated conditions with a power factor P.F. = 0.9 and an overall conversion efficiency $\eta = 0.98$. In per unit,

$$X_1 = 0.9 \qquad X_2' = 0.11 \qquad R_1 = 1.2 \times 10^{-2} \qquad R_2' = 1.2 \times 10^{-2}$$

Compute:

(*a*) The per-unit torque and rotor current density when the motor is started with the rotor circuit short-circuited.

(*b*) The per-unit value of the additional resistance that must be inserted in the rotor circuit in order to obtain a starting torque equal to the pull-out torque.

(*c*) The per-unit starting current with the additional resistance inserted.

(*d*) The per-unit value of the additional resistance to be inserted if the rated torque is to be delivered at 50 percent synchronous speed, and the overall efficiency under these conditions.

10.6 A squirrel-cage motor must be so designed as to operate at variable speed by control of the input voltage. If the motor must be capable of delivering the rated torque in steady state over the speed range between $0.5\omega_s$ and $0.9\omega_s$:

(*a*) What is the minimum value that $S_{\text{p.o.}} = R_2'/X_{\text{s.c.}}$ can have?

(*b*) What is the required ratio of rated to pull-out torque $\mathfrak{L}_{\text{rated}}/\mathfrak{L}_{\text{p.o.}}$?

(*c*) What is the range over which the impressed voltage must vary?

(*d*) Assuming that $R_1 = 10^{-2}$ p.u. and $X_{\text{s.c.}} = 2 \times 10^{-1}$ p.u., what is the efficiency under rated conditions and at half-speed?

10.7 A two-phase servomotor is designed so that the pull-out slip is $S_{\text{p.o.}} = 2.5$.

(*a*) Plot the normalized torque $\mathfrak{L}/\mathfrak{L}_{\text{p.o.}}$ as a function of the slip.

(*b*) Plot the torque developed at half speed, as a function of the terminal voltage.

10.8 A 4-pole 60-cycle induction motor delivers 15 kw with a slip $S = 0.03$ when the mechanical load is suddenly removed.

(*a*) Determine the ensuing transient behavior; i.e., plot the speed-time characteristic, knowing that the inertia of the rotating masses is $\Theta = 1$ kg-m^2 and assuming that the torque varies linearly with the speed.

(*b*) Sketch the transient characteristic of a synchronous motor under the same circumstances.

(*c*) Compare the two characteristics, and explain the reason for the difference.

10.9 Design a wound-rotor induction motor to satisfy the following specifications:

$$P_{\text{out}} = 500 \text{ kw} \qquad V = 1{,}730 \text{ volts} \qquad f = 50 \text{ cps} \qquad m = 3$$

$$p = 3 \qquad \text{P.F.} = 0.92 \qquad \eta_m = 0.975 \qquad \frac{\mathfrak{L}_{\text{p.o.}}}{\mathfrak{L}_R} > 2$$

(*a*) Assuming

$$K_{1,\text{rms}} = 4 \times 10^4 \text{ amp/m} \qquad B_{\text{rms}} = 0.5 \text{ weber/m}^2 \qquad b = 1.5\tau$$

determine the main dimensions of the motor.

(*b*) Assuming that in each winding the overall leakage is equal to twice the slot leakage and that the minimum gap length allowed by mechanical considerations is $g = 10^{-3}$ m, determine the parameters of the motor.

10.10 A traveling-wave structure of the type shown in Fig. 10.9 is used as the second stage of a plasma accelerator. The primary winding is built with 12 coils and is supplied from a four-phase generator at 150 kc.

(*a*) If the plasma is accelerated at constant rate from $v_0 = 10^4$ m/sec to $v_1 = 5 \times 10^4$ m/sec with a constant slip $S = 0.95$, determine the spacing of the coils and the length of the duct.

(*b*) Determine the power transferred to the plasma when the mass flow rate is 10^{-5} kg/sec.

10.11 The conductivity of the plasma in the accelerator of the previous problem is $\gamma = 10^5$ mhos/m.

(*a*) If the velocity can be assumed to remain constant within a skin depth only, what is the maximum allowable diameter of the duct?

(*b*) With this diameter and using Eq. (D.30*b*), what is the required K_1?

(c) What is then the average value of the phase current $I_{1,g}$ if each coil has 20 turns?

10.12 An electric catapult is used to launch a small seaplane from the deck of a ship. The catapult consists of an arrangement similar to that discussed in Example 10.3 for linear motion; the sledge of the catapult has a sole of laminated iron containing the secondary winding of an induction motor whose primary is a developed polyphase winding embedded in the runway.

(a) Determine the density of power transferred to the sledge at stall when the supply frequency is 60 cps and the primary current density is $K_1 = 10^6$ amp/m. Assume that the secondary conductor is solid copper, so that you can use Eq. (D.30b).

(b) Determine the length and width of the energized runway (primary structure), assuming that, as in Example 10.3, the power transferred to the sledge remains constant at the initial value during the whole accelerating period. The sledge (secondary structure) is twice as long as it is wide; together with the plane it weighs one metric ton; the plane becomes airborne after a quarter of a second at a speed of 50 mph (22.4 m/sec).

(c) Determine the temperature rise of the copper secondary. Considering that the energy dissipated is in the same order of magnitude as that of Example 10.4, how do you explain the large difference in temperature rise?

10.13 For the motor of Example 10.4:

(a) Determine the initial value of the primary current density K_1 if the centrifuge reaches 80 percent of the final speed in 3 min. Assume that the torque remains constant during the acceleration period, and apply Eq. (D.30b).

(b) Estimate the required effective thickness a of the primary conductor if its insulation is class B.

(c) Which considerations would guide you in the choice of r_g, b, and p?

10.14 For the loom of Example 10.3:

(a) Plot B_z, E (see Appendix D), and the in- and out-of-phase components of $\bar{K}_1$ as a function of the slip S.

(b) Plot the in- and out-of-phase components of $\bar{K}_1$ as a function of E_0.

(c) Taking the linear approximation of the last plot, determine the magnitude and phase of the electric field impressed on the primary and the primary leakage reactance per unit length, under the assumption that the primary resistance is negligible.

10.15 A passenger elevator is driven by an induction motor with a solid-iron rotor, whose torque is practically independent of speed. Acceleration control is achieved by means of saturable reactors which regulate the effective voltage applied to the stator and when required reverse the sequence of the phases.

(a) Determine the voltage-regulation program during the acceleration and deceleration periods; i.e., plot V_1/V_{1R} vs. t, knowing that for passenger comfort the maximum allowable rate of acceleration is $da/dt = 8$ m/sec^3, the steady-state velocity is 5 m/sec, friction is negligible, and the loaded elevator cage is fully counterweighed.

(b) Determine the distance from the floor at which the switch initiating the deceleration cycle should be located.

10.16 In the elevator drive of the preceding problem, the fully loaded cage weighs 2 metric tons and is fully counterweighed.

(a) Determine the gap surface A of the motor on the basis of power considerations, using Eq. (D.29b) and knowing that at stalling and with the rated voltage impressed on the primary $E_0 = 12$ volts/m.

(b) Repeat part (a) on the basis of the temperature rise during the deceleration period and under the assumption that the skin depth at stalling represents the effective thickness of the solid-iron rotor conductor.

(c) Determine the effective thickness of the primary conductor if its insulation is class B.

Assume that the permeability of the iron is $\mu = 2 \times 10^{-3}$ henry/m and $\gamma = 5 \times 10^6$ mhos/m.

10.17 Determine the no-load voltage of a d-c commutator generator as a function of the brush position:

(a) When the brushes are spaced a full pole pitch apart.

(b) When the brushes span only $\frac{2}{3}\tau$.

Assume that

$$r_g = 0.25 \text{ m} \qquad b = 0.2 \text{ m} \qquad v_c = 15 \text{ m/sec} \qquad p = 2 \qquad B_{\text{rms}} = 0.8 \text{ weber/m}^2$$

and the armature has 128 conductors placed in 64 slots arranged to form an ideal mesh winding with all the conductors connected in series.

appendix A
ELECTROMAGNETIC FIELD TRANSFORMATIONS BY GALILEAN RELATIVITY

The formulation of Maxwell's electromagnetic field equations stimulated the experimental and theoretical investigations that led to the Lorentz transformation and Einstein's postulates of special relativity. Although it is not appropriate to discuss this development in any detail here, we may briefly note that the invariance of the characteristic velocity of propagation in vacuo of the electromagnetic phenomena, $c = 1/\sqrt{\mu_0\epsilon_0}$, could not be reconciled with the invariance of the laws of classical Newtonian mechanics under the Galilean transformation between coordinate frames in uniform relative motion. After considerable experimental and theoretical study, the necessity for modifying the laws of Newtonian mechanics through the Lorentz transformation and special relativity became firmly established.†

There are, however, some practical objections to the use of the Lorentz transformation in low-velocity engineering applications where the coordinate frames are in relative motion with $|\mathbf{v}| \ll c$. One of these is that often $|\mathbf{v}|$ is *not* constant, as required for special relativity, so that strictly speaking the Lorentz transform is not applicable. In addition, in the same way as Newtonian mechanics serve as the very first accurate approximation for relativistic mechanics in the low-velocity case, there also exists in this case a set of simple first-order approximations to the electrodynamic transformation laws of special relativity. As a result, it is possible to contemplate the achievement of greater flexibility and simplicity by using a generalized Galilean relativity to derive approxi-

† See for example, Panofsky, W. K. H., and Melba Phillips: "Classical Electricity and Magnetism," chap. 14, Addison-Wesley Publishing Company, Inc., Reading, Mass.

mate field-vector transformations which are quite accurate for the accelerated low-velocity case.

Inasmuch as the Galilean relativity transformation of the complete electromagnetic field cannot possibly be exact, some modus operandi must be found. Generally, there are two schemes which are employed:

1. Recognizing that Galilean relativity is inconsistent with the exact field equations, appropriate approximations are found for the *Maxwell equations themselves* so as to render them consistent with Galilean relativity. This is a logical procedure, as long as the approximate equations constitute an accurate representation of the physical system to be studied. As a consequence of the modification of the Maxwell equations, however, this procedure has the disadvantage of discarding some useful results which are of interest.
2. The pragmatic, commonsense, or "hide-the-skeleton-in-the closet" approach: Here the assumptions of Galilean relativity are applied to the field equations, and the local inconsistencies can be noted and disregarded. In fact, it is often possible to devise techniques which derive the desired results without specifically calling attention to the inconsistencies, as, for example, our derivation of the transformation between **H** and **H′** given in Sec. 2.11*b*.

We shall use both schemes 1 and 2 in order.

1 Approximate Electromagnetic Models

First, we note that the displacement current is often much smaller than the conduction current in low-frequency power converters. Consequently, we can neglect $\partial \mathbf{D}/\partial t$ in

$$\nabla \times \mathbf{H} = \mathbf{J} + \frac{\partial \mathbf{D}}{\partial t} \tag{A.1}$$

giving

$$\nabla \times \mathbf{H} = \mathbf{J} \tag{A.2}$$

Rather than regard the displacement current as simply being "dropped," let us take the viewpoint that this term is omitted as the first step in a procedure which is to make the resulting field equations compatible with the Galilean coordinate transformation. Noting that there is no privileged finite velocity with respect to the Galilean coordinate transformation, whereas Maxwell's equations give $c = 1/\sqrt{\mu_0\epsilon_0}$ as a characteristic propagation velocity, we seek an approximation which makes this propagation velocity infinite, in order to bring the electrodynamical system into compatibility with the Galilean transformation. This can be begun by imagining $\epsilon_0 \to 0$, so that the approximate $c \to \infty$; and this also removes the displacement current $\epsilon_0\, \partial \mathbf{E}/\partial t$ as desired.

We cannot, however, let the matter stand at this point. If we are in effect considering that $\mathbf{D}$ vanishes in the presence of finite $\mathbf{E}$ because $\epsilon_0 \to 0$, we must not forget that $\mathbf{D}$ cannot possibly vanish in the presence of nonzero space charge, since charges give rise to electric flux directly, i.e.,

$$\nabla \cdot \mathbf{D} = \rho \tag{A.3}$$

Consequently, we must for consistency's sake be content with

$$\rho = 0 \tag{A.4}$$

but this is precisely the case of a neutral plasma or a metallic conductor, so that instead of being unduly restrictive, (A.4) is actually the case of interest in this volume.

With these modifications, the set of approximate Maxwell equations is

$$\nabla \times \mathbf{H} = \mathbf{J} \tag{A.2}$$

$$\nabla \cdot \mathbf{B} = 0 \tag{A.5}$$

$$\nabla \times \mathbf{E} = -\frac{\partial \mathbf{B}}{\partial t} \tag{A.6}$$

The preceding set is *not* the only one that approximates Maxwell's equations so as to render them consistent with Galilean relativity. In fact, we note that formally we can make the speed of light become infinite by letting $\mu_0 \to 0$ rather than $\epsilon_0 \to 0$. When this is done, we must for consistency's sake make

$$\mathbf{B} = 0 \tag{A.7}$$

so that Eq. (A.6) reduces to

$$\nabla \times \mathbf{E} = 0 \tag{A.6a}$$

and Eq. (A.5) can be dropped. Instead we must now retain ρ and $\mathbf{D}$ and the relation between them, Eq. (A.3); otherwise, in the absence of charges, and with $\mathbf{B} = 0$, $\mathbf{E}$ would vanish as well. Since $\mathbf{H}$ is no longer a significant variable, we eliminate it from Eq. (A.1) by taking the divergence of both sides,

$$\nabla \cdot \nabla \times \mathbf{H} = \nabla \cdot \mathbf{J} + \nabla \cdot \frac{\partial \mathbf{D}}{\partial t} = 0 \tag{A.8}$$

Using Eq. (A.3), we then obtain the continuity equation,

$$\nabla \cdot \mathbf{J} + \frac{\partial \rho}{\partial t} = 0 \tag{A.8a}$$

The alternative set of approximate Maxwell equations is then

$$\nabla \times \mathbf{E} = 0 \tag{A.6a}$$

$$\nabla \cdot \mathbf{D} = \rho \tag{A.3}$$

$$\nabla \cdot \mathbf{J} + \frac{\partial \rho}{\partial t} = 0 \tag{A.8a}$$

$$B = 0 \tag{A.7}$$

This set is descriptive of nonrelativistic situations where the predominant interaction is between systems of charges, as is the case in most of the power converters which will be covered in the second volume.

Next, we write the Galilean coordinate transformation, generalized to include the accelerated case, for two coordinate systems that undergo relative translation. Thus if $\mathbf{v}$ is the velocity of an origin O', as measured with respect to the origin O, then the position vectors from the two origins to any point P are related by the Galilean transformation

$$\mathbf{r}' = \mathbf{r} - \int_0^t \mathbf{v}\, d\tau \tag{A.9a}$$

In component form, this is equivalent to

$$\begin{aligned} x' &= x - \int_0^t v_x\, d\tau \\ y' &= y - \int_0^t v_y\, d\tau \\ z' &= z - \int_0^t v_z\, d\tau \end{aligned} \tag{A.9b}$$

where the x, y, z and x', y', z' axes are mutually parallel. In addition, time is universal or

$$t' = t \tag{A.9c}$$

Because of the coordinate relationships (A.9), the field-vector quantities may be considered functions of either primed or unprimed coordinates. Consequently, the formal rules of chain differentiation apply, and we may express the operator $\partial/\partial x$ as

$$\frac{\partial}{\partial x} = \frac{\partial}{\partial x'}\frac{\partial x'}{\partial x} + \frac{\partial}{\partial y'}\frac{\partial y'}{\partial x} + \frac{\partial}{\partial z'}\frac{\partial z'}{\partial x} + \frac{\partial}{\partial t'}\frac{\partial t'}{\partial x} \tag{A.10}$$

From Eq. (A.9) this reduces to

$$\frac{\partial}{\partial x} = \frac{\partial}{\partial x'} \tag{A.11}$$

and similarly

$$\frac{\partial}{\partial y} = \frac{\partial}{\partial y'} \qquad \frac{\partial}{\partial z} = \frac{\partial}{\partial z'} \tag{A.12}$$

Thus, when the coordinate axes of the two systems remain parallel, we may conclude that the del operator relationship is

$$\nabla = \nabla' \tag{A.13}$$

In addition, we may write

$$\frac{\partial}{\partial t} = \frac{\partial}{\partial x'}\frac{\partial x'}{\partial t} + \frac{\partial}{\partial y'}\frac{\partial y'}{\partial t} + \frac{\partial}{\partial z'}\frac{\partial z'}{\partial t} + \frac{\partial}{\partial t'}\frac{\partial t'}{\partial t} \tag{A.14}$$

and, from Eq. (A.9),

$$\frac{\partial x'}{\partial t} = -v_x, \qquad \frac{\partial y'}{\partial t} = -v_y, \qquad \frac{\partial z'}{\partial t} = -v_z \tag{A.15}$$

Thus (A.14) becomes

$$\frac{\partial}{\partial t} = -v_x\frac{\partial}{\partial x'} - v_y\frac{\partial}{\partial y'} - v_z\frac{\partial}{\partial z'} + \frac{\partial}{\partial t'} \tag{A.16}$$

or in vector form

$$\frac{\partial}{\partial t} = -(\mathbf{v}\cdot\nabla') + \frac{\partial}{\partial t'} = -(\mathbf{v}\cdot\nabla) + \frac{\partial}{\partial t'} \tag{A.17}$$

We shall apply Eqs. (A.13) and (A.17) to the low-frequency set of equations first. From Eq. (A.6) we have

$$\nabla\times\mathbf{E} = -\frac{\partial\mathbf{B}}{\partial t}$$

$$\nabla'\times\mathbf{E} = -\frac{\partial\mathbf{B}}{\partial t'} + (\mathbf{v}\cdot\nabla')\mathbf{B} \tag{A.18}$$

We now make use of the vector identity,

$$(\mathbf{v}\cdot\nabla')\mathbf{B} = \mathbf{v}(\nabla'\cdot\mathbf{B}) - \mathbf{B}(\nabla'\cdot\mathbf{v}) + (\mathbf{B}\cdot\nabla')\mathbf{v} - \nabla'\times(\mathbf{v}\times\mathbf{B}) \tag{A.19}$$

In this identity, all terms involving space derivatives of **v** may be dropped since the O' origin velocity has no variability with respect to space. Also, from (A.5) and (A.13),

$$\nabla'\cdot\mathbf{B} = \nabla\cdot\mathbf{B} = 0 \tag{A.20}$$

Thus (A.19) simplifies to

$$(\mathbf{v}\cdot\nabla')\mathbf{B} = -\nabla'\times(\mathbf{v}\times\mathbf{B}) \tag{A.21}$$

Substituting in (A.18), we get

$$\nabla'\times(\mathbf{E}+\mathbf{v}\times\mathbf{B}) = -\frac{\partial\mathbf{B}}{\partial t'} \tag{A.22}$$

We are now ready to apply the relativity principle which *demands that the field laws have the same form in both reference frames.* We therefore expect that

$$\nabla'\times\mathbf{E}' = -\frac{\partial\mathbf{B}'}{\partial t'} \tag{A.23}$$

By comparing (A.22) and (A.23) we see that

$$\mathbf{E}' = K(\mathbf{E} + \mathbf{v} \times \mathbf{B}) \tag{A.24a}$$
$$\mathbf{B}' = K\mathbf{B} \tag{A.24b}$$

where K is an arbitrary constant. If, however, we transform *the other way around*, it is clear from symmetry that we would find

$$\mathbf{E} = K(\mathbf{E}' - \mathbf{v} \times \mathbf{B}') \tag{A.25a}$$
$$\mathbf{B} = K\mathbf{B}' \tag{A.25b}$$

where the *same* K is again used, because of the relativity principle which demands that the transformation laws be the same in either direction. From (A.24b) and (A.25b) we get

$$\mathbf{B} = K\mathbf{B}' = K^2\mathbf{B} \tag{A.26}$$

We see then that $K = \pm 1$, and it is clear on physical grounds that we must select $K = +1$, since we must be in the same reference frame if $\mathbf{v}$ vanishes. Thus we get

$$\boxed{\begin{aligned}\mathbf{E}' &= \mathbf{E} + \mathbf{v} \times \mathbf{B} \\ \mathbf{B}' &= \mathbf{B}\end{aligned}} \qquad \begin{aligned}&(A.27)\\ &(A.28)\end{aligned}$$

as the vector transformation laws. We note that in our approximate system, although the electric field changes, the magnetic field does not.

Next, from (A.2), (A.13), and (A.28),

$$\nabla \times \mathbf{H} = \nabla' \times \mathbf{H} = \nabla' \times \mathbf{H}' = \mathbf{J} \tag{A.29}$$

But in the primed frame we must have

$$\nabla' \times \mathbf{H}' = \mathbf{J}' \tag{A.30}$$

Consequently, we see that

$$\mathbf{J} = \mathbf{J}' \tag{A.31}$$

This lack of change of the current density we shall later see to be consistent with our assumption $\rho = 0$.

Finally we shall obtain the transformation laws for the scalar potential ϕ and vector potential $\mathbf{A}$. Since

$$\mathbf{E} = -\nabla\phi - \frac{\partial \mathbf{A}}{\partial t} \tag{A.32}$$

using (A.13) and (A.17), this becomes

$$\mathbf{E} = -\nabla'\phi - \frac{\partial \mathbf{A}}{\partial t'} + (\mathbf{v} \cdot \nabla')\mathbf{A} \tag{A.33}$$

We now use the vector identity

$$(\mathbf{v} \cdot \nabla')\mathbf{A} = \nabla'(\mathbf{v} \cdot \mathbf{A}) - (\mathbf{A} \cdot \nabla')\mathbf{v} - \mathbf{A} \times \nabla' \times \mathbf{v} - \mathbf{v} \times \nabla' \times \mathbf{A} \tag{A.34}$$

As before, the space derivatives of $\mathbf{v}$ vanish; also we have, from the definition of $\mathbf{A}$ and (A.13),

$$\nabla' \times \mathbf{A} = \nabla \times \mathbf{A} = \mathbf{B} \tag{A.35}$$

Thus (A.34) reduces to

$$(\mathbf{v} \cdot \nabla')\mathbf{A} = \nabla'(\mathbf{v} \cdot \mathbf{A}) - \mathbf{v} \times \mathbf{B} \tag{A.36}$$

Introducing (A.36) into (A.33) and collecting terms,

$$\mathbf{E} + \mathbf{v} \times \mathbf{B} = -\nabla'(\phi - \mathbf{v} \cdot \mathbf{A}) - \frac{\partial \mathbf{A}}{\partial t'} \tag{A.37}$$

In the primed system we must have

$$\mathbf{E}' = -\nabla'\phi' - \frac{\partial \mathbf{A}'}{\partial t'} \tag{A.38}$$

Therefore by comparison, as before, we see that

$$\mathbf{E}' = \mathbf{E} + \mathbf{v} \times \mathbf{B} \tag{A.39}$$

$$\boxed{\begin{aligned} \phi' &= \phi - \mathbf{v} \cdot \mathbf{A} && \text{(A.40)} \\ \mathbf{A}' &= \mathbf{A} && \text{(A.41)} \end{aligned}}$$

We have already encountered (A.39), which is here merely a by-product of the potential transformation laws (A.40) and (A.41).

In summary, we see that the approximate Maxwell equations,

$$\boxed{\begin{aligned} \nabla \times \mathbf{E} &= -\frac{\partial \mathbf{B}}{\partial t} \\ \nabla \cdot \mathbf{B} &= 0 \\ \nabla \times \mathbf{H} &= \mathbf{J} \\ (\rho &= 0) \end{aligned}} \tag{A.42}$$

give through the application of Galilean relativity the *self-consistent* low-velocity transformation laws:

$$\boxed{\begin{aligned} \mathbf{E}' &= \mathbf{E} + \mathbf{v} \times \mathbf{B} \\ \mathbf{B}' &= \mathbf{B} \\ \mathbf{J}' &= \mathbf{J} \\ \phi' &= \phi - \mathbf{v} \cdot \mathbf{A} \\ \mathbf{A}' &= \mathbf{A} \end{aligned}} \tag{A.43}$$

We note that the electromagnetic model of Eq. (A.42) is, in fact, the approximation that fits the low-speed, low-frequency MPD regime, as discussed in Chap. 1.

Next we turn our attention from the low- to the high-frequency model. Applying Eqs. (A.13) and (A.17) to Eq. (A.8a), we have

$$\nabla' \cdot \mathbf{J} + \frac{\partial \rho}{\partial t'} - (\mathbf{v} \cdot \nabla')\rho = 0 \tag{A.44}$$

Making use of the vector identity

$$(\mathbf{v} \cdot \nabla')\rho = \nabla' \cdot (\rho \mathbf{v}) - \rho \nabla' \cdot \mathbf{v} \tag{A.45}$$

and dropping the last term, since it involves the space derivative of **v**, we get

$$\nabla' \cdot (\mathbf{J} - \rho \mathbf{v}) + \frac{\partial}{\partial t'} \rho = 0 \tag{A.44a}$$

or by the same arguments used with Eq. (A.22),

$$\begin{aligned} \mathbf{J}' &= \mathbf{J} - \rho \mathbf{v} \\ \rho' &= \rho \end{aligned} \tag{A.46}$$

Equation (A.46) together with

$$\mathbf{E} = \mathbf{E}' \qquad \phi = \phi' \qquad \mathbf{D} = \mathbf{D}' \tag{A.47}$$

constitutes the set of transformation laws for the high-frequency model.

2 Pragmatic Approach

In the second approach, we do not make any attempt to select compatible approximations of the Maxwell equations, but instead apply Galilean relativity directly to the exact equations. If we select the Maxwell equations,

$$\nabla \times \mathbf{E} = -\frac{\partial \mathbf{B}}{\partial t} \tag{A.6}$$

$$\nabla \cdot \mathbf{B} = 0 \tag{A.5}$$

and transform these, the procedural details are exactly as before, so that we again get

$$\mathbf{E}' = \mathbf{E} + \mathbf{v} \times \mathbf{B} \tag{A.27}$$

$$\mathbf{B}' = \mathbf{B} \tag{A.28}$$

as well as the same potential transformations (A.40) and (A.41).

We again accept (A.27) as in accord with experiment and the limiting case of the Lorentz transformation. Now, however, our viewpoint of (A.28) alters. Since we desire to transform the *exact* Maxwell equations, we do indeed expect to find some change in the magnetic field. Consequently, we must now view (A.28) as a slight inconsistency which arises from the basic incompatibility of the Maxwell equations and Galilean relativity. To get a better approximation, we disregard (A.28), and turn to the other Maxwell equations. These are

$$\nabla \times \mathbf{H} = \mathbf{J} + \frac{\partial \mathbf{D}}{\partial t} \tag{A.1}$$

$$\nabla \cdot \mathbf{D} = \rho \tag{A.3}$$

In addition,

$$J = \rho_i v_i + \rho_e v_e \qquad \rho = \rho_i + \rho_e \tag{A.48}$$

We transform (A.1) with the by now familiar procedure. In applying the vector identity (A.19), we introduce (A.3). The result is

$$\nabla' \times (\mathbf{H} - \mathbf{v} \times \mathbf{D}) = \mathbf{J} - \rho\mathbf{v} + \frac{\partial \mathbf{D}}{\partial t'} \tag{A.49}$$

Comparing with

$$\nabla' \times \mathbf{H}' = \mathbf{J}' + \frac{\partial \mathbf{D}'}{\partial t'} \tag{A.50}$$

we see that

$$\boxed{\begin{aligned} \mathbf{H}' &= \mathbf{H} - \mathbf{v} \times \mathbf{D} & \text{(A.51)} \\ \mathbf{J}' &= \mathbf{J} - \rho\mathbf{v} & \text{(A.52)} \end{aligned}}$$

$$\mathbf{D}' = \mathbf{D} \tag{A.53}$$

Equations (A.51) and (A.52) are appropriate low-velocity approximations. Equation (A.53) is, of course, inconsistent, and again we may disregard it.

We note that (A.52) agrees with (A.46) as well as with (A.31) for $\rho = 0$. This transformation law may also be derived from (A.48) if we postulate the invariance of charge density, or, conversely, we may use (A.52) and (A.48) to demonstrate this invariance. Thus, by differentiating (A.9a), we obtain

$$\mathbf{v}_i = \mathbf{v}_i' + \mathbf{v} \tag{A.54}$$

$$\mathbf{v}_e = \mathbf{v}_e' + \mathbf{v} \tag{A.55}$$

Substituting in (A.48), there results

$$\mathbf{J} = \rho_i \mathbf{v}_i' + \rho_e \mathbf{v}_e' + \rho\mathbf{v} \tag{A.56}$$

Now (A.52) may be written

$$\mathbf{J} = \mathbf{J}' + \rho\mathbf{v} \tag{A.57}$$

so that by comparison we see

$$\mathbf{J}' = \rho_i \mathbf{v}_i' + \rho_e \mathbf{v}_e' \tag{A.58}$$

Since the current law in the primed frame must be

$$\mathbf{J}' = \rho_i' \mathbf{v}_i' + \rho_e' \mathbf{v}_e' \tag{A.59}$$

we see that $\rho_i' = \rho_i$, $\rho_e' = \rho_e$, or generally

$$\rho = \rho' \tag{A.60}$$

Thus the approximate, not quite consistent (but practical!) Galilean transformations for the complete set of Maxwell equations are:

$$\begin{aligned}
\mathbf{E}' &= \mathbf{E} + \mathbf{v} \times \mathbf{B} \\
\mathbf{H}' &= \mathbf{H} - \mathbf{v} \times \mathbf{D} \\
\mathbf{J}' &= \mathbf{J} - \rho\mathbf{v} \\
\phi' &= \phi - \mathbf{v} \cdot \mathbf{A} \\
\mathbf{A} &= \mathbf{A}' \\
\rho &= \rho'
\end{aligned}$$

These are good approximations for $|v|/c \ll 1$ and are also valid for translatory motion with time-varying **v**.

appendix B
DETERMINATION OF THE MAGNETIC FIELD ASSOCIATED WITH A SINUSOIDAL CURRENT SHEET ON THE SURFACE OF A RECTILINEAR AIR GAP

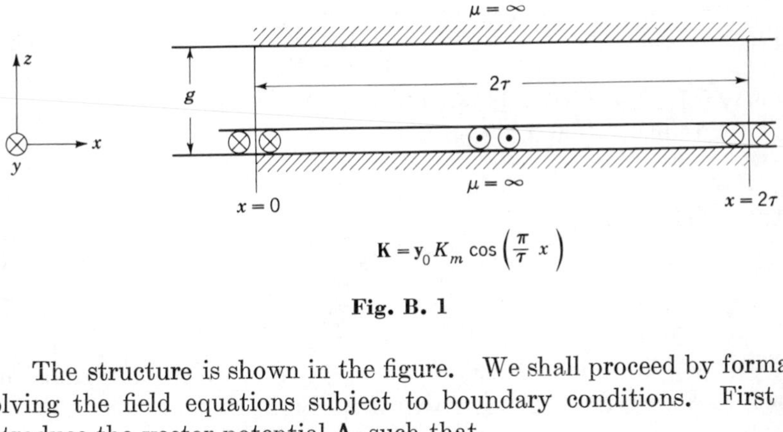

$$\mathbf{K} = \mathbf{y}_0 K_m \cos\left(\frac{\pi}{\tau} x\right)$$

Fig. B. 1

The structure is shown in the figure. We shall proceed by formally solving the field equations subject to boundary conditions. First we introduce the vector potential **A**, such that

$$\mathbf{B} = \nabla \times \mathbf{A} \qquad \nabla \cdot \mathbf{A} = 0 \tag{B.1}$$

Note that since all the currents are directed along the y axis, only the y component of **A** exists in this system.

Taking the curl of Eq. (B.1), and using Maxwell's equations, we find

$$\nabla \times \mathbf{B} = \mu_0\left(\mathbf{J} + \frac{\partial \mathbf{D}}{\partial t}\right) = \nabla \times \nabla \times \mathbf{A} \tag{B.2}$$

In the gap proper, $\mathbf{J} = 0$; moreover we neglect the displacement current, if any. Thus everywhere in the gap except on the surface $z = 0$, we have

$$\nabla \times \nabla \times \mathbf{A} = 0 \tag{B.3}$$

Now we write the identity

$$\nabla \times \nabla \times \mathbf{A} = \nabla(\nabla \cdot \mathbf{A}) - \nabla^2\mathbf{A} \tag{B.4}$$

where ∇^2 is the *vector Laplacian*. In rectangular coordinates $\nabla^2\mathbf{A}$ may be expressed in terms of the Laplacians of its rectangular components. Thus, in such coordinates, Eq. (B.3) becomes

$$\mathbf{x}_0\nabla^2 A_x + \mathbf{y}_0\nabla^2 A_y + \mathbf{z}_0\nabla^2 A_z = 0 \tag{B.5}$$

since $\nabla \cdot \mathbf{A}$ has been chosen to be zero.

Since $\mathbf{K}$ has only a y component, $A_x = A_z = 0$, and Eq. (B.5) reduces to

$$\frac{\partial^2 A_y}{\partial x^2} + \frac{{}_y\partial^2 A}{\partial y^2} + \frac{\partial^2 A_y}{\partial z^2} = 0 \tag{B.6}$$

We shall postulate complete uniformity in the axial or y direction, so that

$$\frac{\partial^2 A_y}{\partial y^2} = 0 \tag{B.7}$$

giving

$$\frac{\partial^2 A_y}{\partial x^2} + \frac{\partial^2 A_y}{\partial z^2} = 0 \tag{B.8}$$

We may solve the partial differential Eq. (B.8) by the method of separation of variables. Suppose that

$$A_y = X(x)Z(z) \tag{B.9}$$

Then Eq. (B.8) gives

$$X''Z + XZ'' = 0 \tag{B.10}$$

or

$$\frac{X''}{X} = -\frac{Z''}{Z} \tag{B.11}$$

The only way in which a function of x only can be everywhere equal to a function of z only is if each function is constant; thus we must have

$$\frac{X''}{X} = -\frac{Z''}{Z} = -\frac{1}{L^2} \tag{B.12}$$

where L is a parameter to be determined. Equation (B.12) gives the two ordinary differential equations:

$$X'' + \frac{1}{L^2}X = 0 \tag{B.13a}$$

$$Z'' - \frac{1}{L^2}Z = 0 \tag{B.13b}$$

Solutions of Eq. (B.13a) are known to be of the type

$$X = K_1 \sin \frac{x}{L} + K_2 \cos \frac{x}{L} \tag{B.14}$$

Since the excitation **K** is periodic in x with a period 2τ, it follows that all the system vectors will be likewise periodic. Thus $1/L$ may take on any of the real values

$$\frac{1}{L} = n \frac{2\pi}{2\tau} = \frac{n\pi}{\tau} \tag{B.15}$$

In particular, since in our case K is purely sinusoidal, we must have $n = 1$, $L = \tau/\pi$, and

$$X = K_1 \sin \frac{\pi}{\tau} x + K_2 \cos \frac{\pi}{\tau} x \tag{B.16}$$

Next, the solution of (B.13b) is known to be

$$Z = K_3 \sinh \frac{z}{L} + K_4 \cosh \frac{z}{L} \tag{B.17}$$

$$= K_3 \sinh \frac{\pi}{\tau} z + K_4 \cosh \frac{\pi}{\tau} z \tag{B.18}$$

To complete the solution we must specifically satisfy the boundary conditions. First we find from the components of $\mathbf{B} = \nabla \times \mathbf{A}$,

$$B_x = -\frac{\partial A_y}{\partial z} = -XZ' \tag{B.19a}$$

$$B_z = \frac{\partial A_y}{\partial x} = +X'Z \tag{B.19b}$$

We know that H_x vanishes in the ideal iron for $z \geq g$. Consequently

$$Z'(g) = 0 \tag{B.20}$$

or

$$K_3 \cosh \frac{\pi}{\tau} g + K_4 \sinh \frac{\pi}{\tau} g = 0 \tag{B.21}$$

Also, for $z = 0$, H_x must be identical with the surface current density itself; thus

$$-XZ'(0) = \mu_0 K_m \cos \frac{\pi}{\tau} x \tag{B.22}$$

or

$$-\left(K_1 \sin \frac{\pi}{\tau} x + K_2 \cos \frac{\pi}{\tau} x\right) \frac{\pi}{\tau} K_3 = \mu_0 K_m \cos \frac{\pi}{\tau} x \tag{B.23}$$

Since Eq. (B.23) must be true for all x, we conclude that

$$K_1 = 0 \tag{B.24a}$$

$$-\frac{\pi}{\tau} K_2 K_3 = \mu_0 K_m \tag{B.24b}$$

Now

$$A_y = XZ = K_2K_3\left(\cos\frac{\pi}{\tau}x + \frac{K_1}{K_2}\sin\frac{\pi}{\tau}x\right)\left(\sinh\frac{\pi}{\tau}z + \frac{K_4}{K_3}\cosh\frac{\pi}{\tau}z\right) \tag{B.25}$$

Introducing Eqs. (B.21) and (B.24), we have immediately

$$A_y = -\frac{\tau}{\pi}\mu_0 K_m \cos\frac{\pi}{\tau}x\left(\sinh\frac{\pi}{\tau}z - \coth\frac{\pi}{\tau}g\cosh\frac{\pi}{\tau}z\right) \tag{B.26}$$

which may be written as

$$\boxed{A_y = +\frac{\tau\mu_0 K_m}{\pi}\,\frac{\cos\frac{\pi}{\tau}x}{\sinh\frac{\pi}{\tau}g}\cosh\frac{\pi}{\tau}(g-z)} \tag{B.27}$$

and using (B.19), we find

$$B_x = \mu_0 K_m \frac{\cos\frac{\pi}{\tau}x}{\sinh\frac{\pi}{\tau}g}\sinh\frac{\pi}{\tau}(g-z) \tag{B.28a}$$

$$B_z = -\mu_0 K_m \frac{\sin\frac{\pi}{\tau}x}{\sinh\frac{\pi}{\tau}g}\cosh\frac{\pi}{\tau}(g-z) \tag{B.28b}$$

Equations (B.28) constitute our solution.

Approximations

For $(\pi/\tau)g \ll 1$, it will also be true that $\pi z/\tau \ll 1$ everywhere in the gap. For this condition

$$B_x = \mu_0 K_m\left(1 - \frac{z}{g}\right)\cos\frac{\pi}{\tau} \tag{B.29a}$$

$$B_z = -\frac{\mu_0\tau}{\pi g}K_m\left[1 + \frac{\pi^2}{2\tau^2}(g-z)^2\right]\sin\frac{\pi}{\tau}x \tag{B.29b}$$

It is clear that in this case:

1. $B_{z,\max}/B_{x,\max} = \tau/\pi g \gg 1$.
2. B_z hardly varies across the gap. For example, if $g/\tau = 10^{-2}$, then from Eq. (B.29*b*) B_z only varies by about 0.05 *percent* across the gap.

Note that in the interest of brevity we have here chosen the origin of the coordinate system to coincide with the point at which the current density is maximum. The results can always be generalized by performing a transformation of coordinates; in particular, to conform with the origin chosen in Sec. 6.4 we can shift the origin along the axis by the transformation

$$x = x_1 - \frac{\tau}{2} \tag{B.30}$$

where x_1 corresponds to the coordinate origin used in Sec. 6.4, and x to the origin used here.

appendix C
POYNTING'S THEOREM: THE POWER FLOW IN HETEROPOLAR CONVERTERS

It was mentioned in Secs. 4.10 and 5.6 that the concept of electric surface power density and electric-power flow are strictly related to the concept of Poynting vector. We now use this viewpoint to investigate the balance of power in a heteropolar converter.

According to the theorem first enunciated by Poynting in 1884, the flux of the vector

$$\mathbf{N} = \mathbf{E} \times \mathbf{H} \tag{C.1}$$

into a closed surface is partly accounted by the electric power expended and partly by the rate of increase of the energy stored in the electric and magnetic fields within the volume. If we assume a sinusoidal time variation with radian frequency ω_e, this theorem can be stated by the following equation:[1]

$$-\int_S \bar{\mathbf{N}} \cdot d\mathbf{s} = \int_V [\bar{\mathbf{E}} \cdot \bar{\mathbf{J}}^* + 2j\omega_e(\tfrac{1}{2}\mu|\bar{\mathbf{H}}|^2 - \tfrac{1}{2}\epsilon|\bar{\mathbf{E}}|^2)]\, dv \tag{C.2}$$

where $\bar{\mathbf{N}} = \bar{\mathbf{E}} \times \bar{\mathbf{H}}^*$ = complex Poynting vector†

V = volume enclosed by the surface S

In order to be able to compare the results obtained here with those obtained in Sec. 9.5 from circuit considerations, we shall apply the Poynting's theorem to the particular case of an ideal synchronous machine. For simplicity in the bookkeeping and for clarity in plotting the power flow, we assume that the terminals in the armature and field windings are situated on opposite sides, although this is not necessarily the most common construction. The steps involved in the determina-

† Note that the bar used in $\bar{\mathbf{N}}$, and subsequently in its components $\bar{N}$, here simply denotes a complex number rather than a phasor.

tion of the power flow and a sketch of the lines of force of the Poynting vector for the generating mode of operation are shown in Fig. C.1. Here again, as in the sketch accompanying Prob. 5.10, the gap length g has been grossly exaggerated.

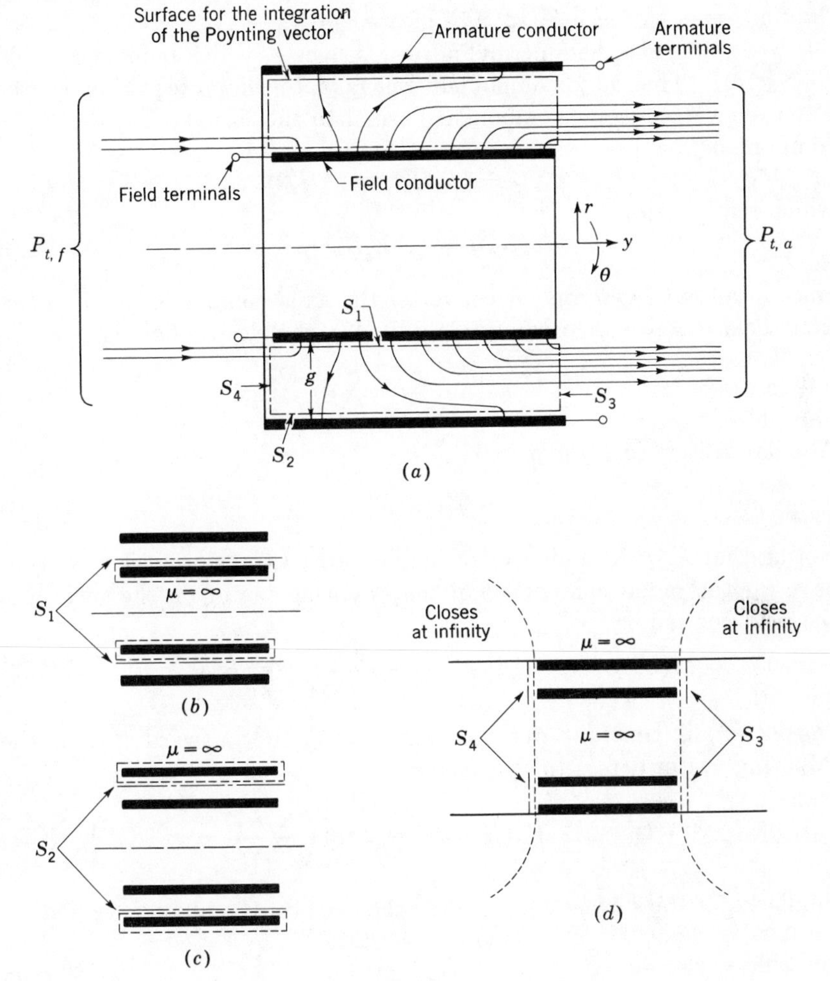

Fig. C. 1

As a first step we must choose a frame of reference, because power and therefore the Poynting vector are not invariant to a transformation of frames of reference in relative motion.

We choose a frame of reference attached to the armature, as was done in Sec. 9.5, and we leave as an exercise to the reader to prove that in any other arbitrary frame the integrations yield the same results although the physical interpretation of the individual terms may vary.

Since we are interested in the transfer of power through the gap, we choose as the volume of integration the volume of the gap with the exclusion of the active conductors. The bounding surface S then consists of the four open surfaces S_1 to S_4 indicated in Fig. C.1.

We start with the inner cylindrical surface S_1 which bounds the field conductor. The only component relevant to the integration of the Poynting vector is the component normal to the surface, i.e., the radial component,

$$(\bar{N}'_r)_f = (\bar{E}'_\theta \bar{H}'^*_y - \bar{E}'_y \bar{H}'^*_\theta)_f$$

which reduces to

$$(\bar{N}'_r)_f = (-\bar{E}'_y \bar{H}'^*_\theta)_f \tag{C.3}$$

since in an ideal heteropolar converter the axial component of the magnetic field is zero. According to Eq. (9.43), the electric field is

$$\bar{E}'_{yf} = \frac{\bar{K}_f}{a_f \gamma_f} - v\bar{B} \tag{C.4}$$

Also, from Eqs. (5.30) and (5.33),

$$\bar{H}'_{\theta f} = \bar{K}'_f \tag{C.5}$$

Noting that $\bar{K} = \bar{K}'$ and $\bar{B} = \bar{B}'$ in a low-speed transformation, we thus have for the radial component of the Poynting vector on the surface of the field conductor

$$(\bar{N}'_r)_f = (-\bar{E}'_y \bar{H}'^*_\theta)_f = -\frac{\bar{K}'_f \bar{K}'^*_f}{a_f \gamma_f} + v\bar{B}'\bar{K}'^*_f \tag{C.6}$$

Since $(N'_r)_f$ is constant over the surface S_1, the outward flux of the Poynting vector across this surface is

$$\int_{S_1} \bar{\mathbf{N}}' \cdot d\mathbf{s}' = -\int_{S_1} (\bar{N}'_r)_f \, ds' = 2p\tau b \left(\frac{\bar{K}'_f \bar{K}'^*_f}{a_f \gamma_f} - v\bar{B}'\bar{K}'^*_f \right) \tag{C.7}$$

Similarly for the surface S_2 bounding the armature conductor we find

$$\bar{E}'_{ya} = \frac{\bar{K}'_a}{a_a \gamma_a} \tag{C.8}$$

$$\bar{H}'_{\theta a} = -\bar{K}'_a \tag{C.9}$$

and

$$\int_{S_2} \bar{\mathbf{N}}' \cdot d\mathbf{s}' = \int_{S_2} (\bar{N}'_r)_a \, ds' = \int_{S_2} (-\bar{E}'_y \bar{H}'^*_\theta)_a \, ds' = 2p\tau b \frac{\bar{K}'_a \bar{K}'^*_a}{a_a \gamma_a} \tag{C.10}$$

Next we consider the annular surface S_3 to the right where the armature conductor is connected to the polyphase transmission line. Again we are interested only in the component of $\bar{\mathbf{N}}'$ normal to the surface, i.e.,

$$\bar{N}'_y = \bar{E}'_r\bar{H}'^*_\theta - \bar{E}'_\theta\bar{H}'^*_r \tag{C.11}$$

From the case of the homopolar device which, when we are interested in symmetry, can be connected to a coaxial transmission line (see Prob. 5.10), we would expect $\bar{E}'_\theta$ to be zero and the term $\bar{E}'_r\bar{H}'^*_\theta$ to be the only significant term in $\bar{N}'_y$. The situation, however, is quite different in a heteropolar converter which must be connected to a polyphase line where in the symmetrical case all the conductors lie on the same cylindrical surface. In this latter case $\bar{E}'_\theta \neq 0$. The exact evaluation of $\bar{N}_y$ is a tough problem. We shall therefore at this point make some seemingly justifiable approximations, and later on we will verify the consistency of the results. We already know that $\bar{\mathbf{H}}'$ is primarily in the radial direction since, according to Eq. (7.8),

$$\frac{H'_\theta}{H'_r} = \frac{\pi g}{\tau} \ll 1 \tag{C.12}$$

In contrast, we expect $\bar{E}'_\theta$ to be predominant over $\bar{E}'_r$. We arrive at this conclusion by observing first that $\bar{\mathbf{E}}'$ has no solenoidal component in the θr plane. In fact, according to Eq. (9.33) or Eq. (9.23) and Appendix B, $\bar{\mathbf{E}}'_{\text{sol}}$ has only a y component. We then only need the θ and r components of $\bar{\mathbf{E}}'_{\text{cons}}$. These can be derived from a scalar potential ϕ by solving the Laplace equation, as was done in Appendix B. If we use boundary conditions which are dual of those used there for the magnetic field, we find

$$\frac{E'_r}{E'_\theta} = \frac{\pi g}{\tau} \ll 1 \tag{C.13}$$

and

$$\frac{H'_\theta E'_r}{H'_r E'_\theta} = \left(\frac{\pi g}{\tau}\right)^2 \ll 1 \tag{C.14}$$

so that $H'_\theta E'_r$ can be neglected.

To the same order of approximation we assume that $\bar{E}'_\theta$ as well as $\bar{H}'_r$ does not vary across the gap. Also we eliminate fringing effects by prolonging the ideal magnetic structures ($\mu = \infty$) to the right of the converter. Finally we get rid of the end effects produced by the field windings by taking the surface of integration itself slightly beyond the end of the field conductor.

We are now ready to proceed with the evaluation of $\bar{N}'_y$ on the surface S_3. Under the previous assumptions the electromagnetic field has no contribution due to the field conductor; therefore the radial component of $\mathbf{H}'$ depends only on the armature current and is given, according to Eq. (7.16), by

$$\bar{H}'_r = \frac{\bar{B}'_a}{\mu_0} = j\frac{\tau}{\pi g}\bar{K}'_a \tag{C.15}$$

In order to evaluate $\bar{E}'_\theta$ we choose the winding type which has the greatest symmetry and the simplest connections between the conductors, i.e., the ideal star winding considered in Sec. 9.5*a* and shown in Fig. 9.12. If $\Delta x' = r_g\,\Delta\theta$ is the linear displacement between two adjacent conductors, then the terminal voltage of the elementary loop formed by these conductors and the connection is, according to Eq. (9.26),

$$V'(x',t) = E'_{\theta,a}\,\Delta x' = \int_{-\,\text{along loop}}^{+} \mathbf{E}'_{c,\text{cons}} \cdot d\mathbf{l}' \tag{C.16}$$

Then, using Eqs. (9.26) and (9.35*a*),

$$\begin{aligned} E'_{\theta,a}\,\Delta x' &= \int_0^b \left(\frac{J'_a}{\gamma_a} + vB'\right)_{x'} dy + \int_b^0 \left(\frac{J'_a}{\gamma_a} + vB'\right)_{x'+\Delta x'} dy \\ &= b\left[\left(\frac{J'_a}{\gamma_a} + vB'\right)_{x'} - \left(\frac{J'_a}{\gamma_a} + vB'\right)_{x'+\Delta x'}\right] \end{aligned} \tag{C.17}$$

where v is the velocity of the armature conductor as seen from the wave frame and $\bar{B}'$ is the radial component of $\bar{\mathbf{B}}'$ measured along the conductor. Introducing

$$J'_a = \frac{K'_a}{a_a} \tag{C.18}$$

and passing to the limit when the number of conductors is very large and $\Delta x' \to 0$, we obtain

$$E'_{\theta,a} = -b\frac{\partial}{\partial x}\left(\frac{K'_a}{a_a\gamma_a} + vB'\right) \tag{C.19a}$$

or, in phasor notation,

$$\bar{E}'_{\theta,a} = -jb\frac{\pi}{\tau}\left(\frac{\bar{K}'_a}{a_a\gamma_a} + v\bar{B}'\right) \tag{C.19b}$$

The component of the Poynting vector normal to the annular surface S_3 is then

$$\begin{aligned} (\bar{N}'_y)_{S_3} &= -(\bar{E}'_\theta\bar{H}'^*_r)_a = +jb\frac{\pi}{\tau}\left(\frac{\bar{K}'_a}{a_a\gamma_a} + v\bar{B}'\right)\left(-j\frac{\tau}{\pi g}\bar{K}'^*_a\right) \\ &= +\frac{b}{g}\left(\frac{\bar{K}'_a\bar{K}'^*_a}{a_a\gamma_a} + v\bar{B}'\bar{K}'^*_a\right) \end{aligned} \tag{C.20}$$

and the total flux across the whole surface S_3 is

$$\int_{S_3} \bar{\mathbf{N}}' \cdot d\mathbf{s}' = -\int_{S_3} (\bar{N}'_y)_{S_3}\,ds' = -2p\tau b\left(\frac{\bar{K}'_a\bar{K}'^*_a}{a_a\gamma_a} + v\bar{B}'\bar{K}'^*_a\right) \tag{C.21}$$

Finally we evaluate the flux of the Poynting vector across the annular surface to the left S_4, where the field conductors are connected to the feeder lines. As we have done with the armature, we assume that the field winding is connected in star according to alternative 1 of Sec. 6.4*a* and Fig. 6.13*b*. Proceeding as before for the surface S_3, we find

$$\bar{H}'_{r,f} = j\frac{\tau}{\pi g}\bar{K}'_f \tag{C.22}$$

$$\bar{E}'_{\theta,f} = jb\frac{\pi}{\tau}\frac{\bar{K}'_f}{a_f\gamma_f} \tag{C.23}$$

In this case the contribution of the solenoidal component is missing since the field conductor has zero velocity with respect to the wave frame. The flux of $\bar{\mathbf{N}}'$ across the surface S_4 is then

$$\int_{S_4} \bar{\mathbf{N}}' \cdot d\mathbf{s}' = +\int_{S_4} (\bar{N}'_y)_{S_4}\, ds' = -2p\tau b\,\frac{\bar{K}'_f\bar{K}'^*_f}{a_f\gamma_f} \tag{C.24}$$

Adding up the contributions of the various surfaces S_1 to S_4 given by Eqs. (C.7), (C.10), (C.21) and (C.24) and changing sign, we obtain the total inwardly directed flux of the Poynting vector,

$$\begin{aligned} -\int_S \bar{\mathbf{N}} \cdot d\mathbf{s}' &= -2p\tau b\left(\frac{\bar{K}'_f\bar{K}'^*_f}{a_f\gamma_f} - v\bar{B}'\bar{K}'^*_f + \frac{\bar{K}'_a\bar{K}'^*_a}{a_a\gamma_a}\right.\\ &\qquad \left. - \frac{\bar{K}'_a\bar{K}'^*_a}{a_a\gamma_a} - v\bar{B}'\bar{K}'^*_a - \frac{\bar{K}'_f\bar{K}'^*_f}{a_f\gamma_f}\right)\\ &= 2p\tau bv\bar{B}'(\bar{K}'_f + \bar{K}'_a)^* \end{aligned} \tag{C.25}$$

Making use of Eqs. (7.19*b*) and (7.18*b*), this last equation reduces to

$$-\int_S \bar{\mathbf{N}} \cdot d\mathbf{s}' = j(2p\tau b\mathfrak{X}_m)\bar{K}'\bar{K}'^* = j2p\tau b\mathfrak{X}_m|\bar{K}'|^2 \tag{C.26}$$

We observe that the total flux has no real part, as we would expect, since in the volume considered $\mathbf{J} = 0$ and no real power is absorbed. The imaginary part of the total flux gives, as we can see, the var absorbed by the overall magnetizing reactance $2p\tau b\mathfrak{X}_m$.

According to the right-hand side of Eq. (C.2), the var which flow into V through its surface equal the var absorbed by the sources located within V plus a term equal to $2\omega_e$ times the difference between the average magnetic energy and the average electric energy stored within V. Since we wish to check the validity of our approximations, we shall now proceed with a direct evaluation of the right-hand side of Eq. (C.2). In our case, where $\mathbf{J} = 0$ and the energy stored in the electric field is negligible, the right-hand side of Eq. (C.2) reduces to

$$\int_V 2j\omega_e(\tfrac{1}{2}\mu_0|\bar{\mathbf{H}}'|^2)\,dv \tag{C.27}$$

The integration is easily performed because of the traveling-wave character of $\mathbf{H}'$ and its constancy along the y axis. If in addition we neglect the contribution of the azimuthal component H'_θ and assume for consistency that $\mathbf{B}'$ does not vary across the gap, we then have

$$\int_V 2j\omega_e(\tfrac{1}{2}\mu_0|\bar{\mathbf{H}}'|^2)\,dv = 2j\omega_e V\left[\frac{1}{2}\frac{\bar{B}'\bar{B}'^*}{\mu_0}\right] \tag{C.28}$$

Introducing in this equation the volume of the gap $V = 2p\tau bg$, using the definitions of ω_e [Eq. (6.8a)] and of $\mathfrak{X}_m$ [Eq. (7.20)], and finally substituting for $v\bar{B}'$ and $\bar{B}'^*$ from Eq. (7.19b), we find that the right-hand side of Eq. (C.2) is

$$j2p\tau b\mathfrak{X}_m|\bar{K}'|^2$$

This expression is identical with the flux of Poynting vector over the surface bounding the gap. This identity serves to reassure us that the approximations on which our calculations are based do not introduce serious errors. It is important to realize that this flow of var into the gap does not necessarily imply a flow of var through the armature terminals. In fact, as we know, in normal operation the synchronous converter draws its magnetic field excitation from the d-c supply. In particular, there exists a nonvanishing flow of var even when the a-c side is open and $\bar{K}_a = 0$. It would therefore be very difficult to explain the significance of these var if we were to restrict our interpretation of phasors to the time domain. Of course, we have no trouble in visualizing out-of-phase components of current density when we think of these phasors as representing sinusoidal distributions in space.

What now remains to be proved is that the flux of the Poynting vector across each of the constituent surfaces S_1 to S_4 taken individually truly represents power flowing through these areas. This is easily done with the help of the additional auxiliary surfaces shown in Fig. C.1. These surfaces are closed, so that the surface integral of the Poynting vector indeed represents the flow of power across them. In addition, they have been so chosen that each one of them has an area in common with one of the open surfaces S_1 to S_4. Over this common area the Poynting vector is finite, but vanishes everywhere else, because of the screening effect of the perfect magnetic material (for $\mu = \infty$, $H = 0$). As a result we can attach physical significance to the flux of $\bar{\mathbf{N}}$ across each of the open surface S_1 to S_4, since it corresponds to the total power flowing into one of the closed surfaces. In conclusion, we can draw the same picture for the flow of real power in the converter that was arrived at in Sec. 9.5*d*. As indicated in Fig. 9.14 and C.1*a*, we find:

1. The power that flows through S_1 is, according to Eqs. (C.7), (9.44), and Fig. C.1*b*, the power associated with the field conductor:

$$\begin{aligned}\text{Re}\left[\int_{S_1} \bar{\mathbf{N}}' \cdot d\mathbf{s}'\right] &= 2p\tau b(\langle p_{s,\mathbf{diss}}\rangle_f + \langle p'_{s,\mathbf{conv}}\rangle_f) \\ &= P_{\mathbf{diss},f} + P'_{\mathbf{conv},f} = P'_{\mathbf{elec},f} \qquad (\text{C.29})\end{aligned}$$

2. Of this power the portion that is dissipated comes, as expected, from the d-c supply line on the left since, according to Eqs. (C.24), (9.45) and Fig. C.1*d*,

$$\begin{aligned}\text{Re}\left[\int_{S_4} \bar{\mathbf{N}}' \cdot d\mathbf{s}'\right] &= -2p\tau b\langle p_{s,\mathbf{diss}}\rangle_f = -P_{\mathbf{diss},f} = -P'_{\mathbf{elec},f} \\ &= -P_{t,f} \qquad (\text{C.30})\end{aligned}$$

3. Of the converted power, which in a generator originates in the mechanical port, part flows into the armature conductor where it covers the Joule losses, since, according to Eqs. (C.10), (9.48), and Fig. C.1*c*,

$$\begin{aligned}\text{Re}\left[\int_{S_2} \bar{\mathbf{N}}' \cdot d\mathbf{s}'\right] &= 2p\tau b\langle p_{s,\mathbf{diss}}\rangle_a = P_{\mathbf{diss},a} \\ &= P'_{\mathbf{elec},a} \qquad (\text{C.31})\end{aligned}$$

The remainder must then flow through the armature terminals. This is indeed true if we observe that, using Eqs. (7.31) and (7.32), we can write

$$\text{Re}\,[v\bar{B}'\bar{K}_a'^*] = -\,\text{Re}\,[v\bar{B}'\bar{K}_f'^*] = \langle p'_{s,\mathbf{conv}}\rangle_f$$

so that, according to Eqs. (C.21) and (9.49) and Fig. C.1*d*, we obtain

$$\begin{aligned}\text{Re}\left[\int_{S_3} \bar{\mathbf{N}}' \cdot d\mathbf{s}'\right] &= -2p\tau b(\langle p_{s,\mathbf{diss}}\rangle_a + \langle p'_{s,\mathbf{conv}}\rangle_f) \\ &= -P_{\mathbf{diss},a} - P'_{\mathbf{conv},f} = -P_{t,a} \qquad (\text{C.32})\end{aligned}$$

Once the distribution of $\bar{\mathbf{N}}$ is known at the surface of the gap, it is an easy step to sketch the lines of force of $\bar{\mathbf{N}}$ in the gap, as indicated in Fig. C.1*a*. The example of the synchronous machine thus illustrates how the Poynting vector can be used to map the flow of power in the converter. When applied to the general case, the same procedure would lead to the results obtained in Sec. 9.5*e*.

It is now apparent that the Poynting theorem has served as a guiding principle all along in our study of power converters. In fact, from the moment we first introduced the surface power densities in Chap. 4, we have consistently been viewing the conversion process in terms of flow of power across mathematical surfaces enshrouding the active conductors. In order to facilitate the calculations, we have chosen simple cylindrical surfaces and idealized the conductor arrangements, so as to attain the greatest degree of symmetry for the resultant field configurations. In so doing, we have relied on the Poynting theorem, which is in effect a statement of the principle of conservation of energy, to guarantee that our calculations were applicable even to practical designs, where, for instance, the conductors are embedded in slots. The structural details have a great influence on the local field configurations, and therefore have great practical importance when the local distributions of electromagnetic and mechanical stresses among the conductors, the insulators, and the ferromagnetic cores are of interest. However, these have hardly any effect on the interactions across the gap. In other words, the lines of force of the Poynting vectors may undergo complex contortions in the proximity of their terminations within the conductors, insulators, or magnetic structures, but they straighten out as they reach the gap. Since in evaluating the overall power flow, all we have to do is to count how many of these lines of force pierce a closed surface, we choose to count them on a smooth surface in the gap where they are reasonably straight. Similar procedures are used, for instance, in radiation problems where it would be a hopeless as well as a needless task to evaluate the near field of an antenna.

REFERENCE

1. Stratton, J. A.: "Electromagnetic Theory," McGraw-Hill Book Company, New York, 1941.

appendix D
SKIN EFFECT IN INDUCTION CONVERTERS

In order to study the skin effect in induction converters, we consider the linear structure shown in Fig. D.1. The secondary conductor may represent either the developed conductor of a rotating device according to the realization of alternative 1 in Sec. 4.8 or the liquid conductor in an induction pump of the type discussed in Sec. 10.4*b*. It is assumed to be moving with constant velocity **v** with respect to a coordinate system fixed to the primary winding. The primary winding itself is assumed to impress a traveling wave with functional dependence $e^{j[\omega_e t-(\pi/\tau)x]}$.

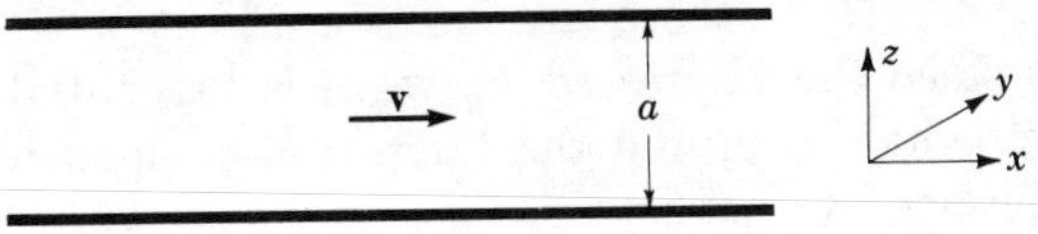

Fig. D. 1

We will consider both limiting cases of impressed electric field and impressed current-density waves. These represent the boundary conditions which the solution of the field equations in the conductor must satisfy. This implies that the unknown field vectors themselves must have the same functional dependence in x and t as the traveling waves impressed at the boundary. For this reason we shall treat all field variables as phasors.

We follow here the procedure indicated in Example 10.2, and we assume that, because of symmetry, $\partial/\partial y = 0$ and $B_y = 0$. Under these conditions Faraday's law reduces to

$$-\frac{\partial \bar{E}_y}{\partial z} = -j\omega_e \bar{B}_x \tag{D.1a}$$

$$-j\frac{\pi}{\tau}\bar{E}_y = -j\omega_e \bar{B}_z \tag{D.1b}$$

and Ampère's law to

$$\frac{\partial \bar{B}_x}{\partial z} + j\frac{\pi}{\tau}\bar{B}_z = \mu\bar{J} = \mu\gamma S v_s \bar{B}_z \tag{D.2}$$

Taking the derivative of Eqs. (D.2) and (D.1*b*) with respect to z and using Eq. (D.1*a*), we obtain

$$\frac{\partial^2 \bar{B}_x}{\partial z^2} + j\frac{\pi}{\tau}\left(j\frac{\pi}{\tau} - \mu\gamma S v_s\right)\bar{B}_x = 0 \tag{D.3}$$

This equation admits as a solution,

$$\bar{B}_x = \bar{B}^+ e^{+\alpha z} + \bar{B}^- e^{-\alpha z} \tag{D.4}$$

where

$$\alpha = \sqrt{j\frac{\pi}{\tau}\left(\mu\gamma S v_s - j\frac{\pi}{\tau}\right)}$$

and $\bar{B}^+$ and $\bar{B}^-$ are constant phasors to be determined by the appropriate boundary conditions. We consider the following limiting cases.

Case 1:

Impressed $\bar{E}$ wave $= \bar{E}_0\mathbf{y}_0$, $a = \infty$. We assume that the $\bar{E}_y$ wave is impressed at the upper surface of the conductor which we choose to be the $z = 0$ plane. Since there are no sources at $z = -\infty$, $\bar{B}^-$ must vanish. Also since the impressed $\bar{E}_y$ wave is tangential to the surface of the conductor at $z = 0$, and the tangential component is continuous across the interface, we have

$$\bar{E}_y \Big|_{z=0} = \bar{E}_0 \tag{D.5}$$

Integrating Eq. (D.1*a*), we get

$$\begin{aligned} \bar{E}_y \Big|_{z=0} &= j\omega_e \int_{-\infty}^{0} \bar{B}_x \, dz = j\omega_e \bar{B}^+ \left[\frac{e^{\alpha z}}{\alpha}\right]_{-\infty}^{0} \\ &= j\omega_e \frac{\bar{B}^+}{\alpha} \end{aligned} \tag{D.6}$$

and, according to Eq. (D.1*b*),

$$\bar{B}^+ = \frac{\alpha}{j\omega_e}\bar{E}_0$$

We thus obtain for $z < 0$,

$$\begin{aligned} \bar{B}_x &= \frac{\alpha}{j\omega_e}\bar{E}_0 e^{\alpha z} \\ \bar{B}_z &= \frac{\pi}{\tau\omega_e}\bar{E}_0 e^{\alpha z} \\ \bar{E}_y &= \bar{E}_0 e^{\alpha z} \end{aligned} \tag{D.8}$$

Case 2:

Impressed $\bar{E}$ wave $= \bar{E}_0\mathbf{y}_0$, $a \neq \infty$ and the lower surface at $z = -a$ is bounded by a material with $\mu = \infty$ and $\gamma = 0$. In this case $\bar{B}_x\Big|_{z=-a} = 0$, or

$$\bar{B}^+e^{-\alpha a} + \bar{B}^-e^{\alpha a} = 0 \tag{D.9}$$

This gives

$$\bar{B}^- = -\bar{B}^+e^{-2\alpha a} \tag{D.10}$$

Next we use the condition on $\bar{E}$ as before,

$$\bar{E}_y\Big|_{z=0} = j\omega_e \int_{-a}^{0} \bar{B}_x\,dz = j\omega_e\bar{B}^+\left[\frac{e^{\alpha z}}{\alpha} + e^{-2\alpha a}\,\frac{e^{-\alpha z}}{\alpha}\right]_{-a}^{0}$$

$$= j\omega_e\frac{\bar{B}^+}{\alpha}(1 - 2e^{-\alpha a} + e^{-2a}) = \bar{E}_0 \tag{D.11}$$

or

$$\bar{B}^+ = \frac{\alpha\bar{E}_0}{j\omega_e}\,\frac{1}{(1 - e^{-\alpha a})^2} \tag{D.12}$$

and obtain for $z < 0$

$$\bar{B}_x = \frac{\alpha\bar{E}_0e^{\alpha z}}{j\omega_e}\,\frac{(1 - e^{-2\alpha(z+a)})}{(1 - e^{-\alpha a})^2}$$

$$\bar{B}_z = \frac{\pi\bar{E}_0e^{\alpha z}}{\tau\omega_e}\left(\frac{1 - e^{-\alpha(z+a)}}{1 - e^{-\alpha a}}\right)^2 \tag{D.13}$$

$$\bar{E}_y = \bar{E}_0e^{\alpha z}\left(\frac{1 - e^{-\alpha(z+a)}}{1 - e^{-\alpha a}}\right)^2$$

Case 3:

Impressed $\bar{K}$ wave $= \bar{K}_1\mathbf{y}_0$, $a = \infty$. In this case the boundary conditions are

$$\bar{B}^- = 0 \qquad \bar{B}_x\Big|_{z=0} = \mu\bar{K}_1 \tag{D.14}$$

Equation (D.4) thus becomes

$$\bar{B}_x = \mu\bar{K}_1e^{\alpha z} \tag{D.15a}$$

Integrating Eq. (D.1*a*), we obtain

$$\bar{E}_y = \frac{j\omega_e\mu\bar{K}_1e^{\alpha z}}{\alpha} \tag{D.15b}$$

and from Eq. (D.1*b*)

$$\bar{B}_z = j\frac{\pi}{\tau}\frac{\mu}{\alpha}\bar{K}_1e^{\alpha z} \tag{D.15c}$$

Case 4:

Impressed $\bar{K}$ wave $= (\bar{K}_1/2)\mathbf{y}_0$ at both surfaces of the conductor, $a \neq \infty$. In this case we let the $z = 0$ plane coincide with the middle plane of the conductor. We note that because of symmetry $\bar{B}_x = 0$ at

$z = 0$. We thus have

$$\bar{B}_x^+ = -\bar{B}_x^- \tag{D.16a}$$

We also note that $\bar{B}_x = \mu \bar{K}_1/2$ for $z = a/2$ or

$$\mu \frac{\bar{K}_1}{2} = \bar{B}^+(e^{\alpha a/2} - e^{-\alpha a/2}) = 2\bar{B}^+ \sinh \alpha \frac{a}{2} \tag{D.16b}$$

which gives

$$\bar{B}^+ = \mu \frac{\bar{K}_1}{4} \frac{1}{\sinh \alpha \frac{a}{2}} \tag{D.16c}$$

We thus obtain for $-a/2 < z < +a/2$

$$\begin{aligned} \bar{B}_x &= \mu \frac{\bar{K}_1}{2} \frac{\sinh \alpha z}{\sinh \alpha \frac{a}{2}} \\ \bar{B}_z &= j \frac{\pi \mu \bar{K}_1}{2\alpha\tau} \frac{\cosh \alpha z}{\sinh \alpha \frac{a}{2}} \\ \bar{E}_y &= j \frac{\omega_e \mu \bar{K}_1}{2\alpha} \frac{\cosh \alpha z}{\sinh \alpha \frac{a}{2}} \end{aligned} \tag{D.17}$$

We observe that when $|\alpha a/2| \ll 1$, $\bar{B}_z$ reduces to

$$\bar{B}_z = j \frac{\pi \mu \bar{K}_1}{a\alpha^2\tau} = \frac{\mu \bar{K}_1}{a} \frac{1}{\mu\gamma S v_s - j\,\pi/\tau} \tag{D.18}$$

as obtained in Example 10.2. It follows that $\bar{B}_z$ can be considered independent of z only in the central region near $z = 0$ where the variation of the hyperbolic cosine is small or when $|\alpha a/2| \ll 1$.

We pause now to examine the significance of these results in the light of the fact that α is a complex number and a function of the slip S.

First we consider the condition of synchronous operation when $S = 0$ and no current flows in the conductor. We then have

$$\alpha = \frac{\pi}{\tau} \tag{D.19}$$

We observe that if we account for the shift in the coordinate system and we substitute g for $a/2$ and $\bar{K}$ for $\bar{K}_1/2$, the results of case 4 agree with Eqs. (B.28*a*) and (B.28*b*) of Appendix B. The condition $S = 0$ leads to the minimum value of α for a given τ and therefore to the maximum uniformity in B_z. With a good degree of approximation this condition may be assumed to prevail when

$$|\mu\gamma S v_s| \ll \frac{\pi}{\tau} \qquad \text{or} \qquad \left|\mu\gamma S v_s \frac{\tau}{\pi}\right| \ll 1 \tag{D.20a}$$

The nondimensional expression $|\mu\gamma S v_s \tau/\pi|$ is thus a measure of the perturbation which the armature reaction introduces in the impressed magnetic field. It is called the *magnetic Reynolds number*. We now turn to the other extreme of a large magnetic Reynolds number or a strong armature reaction:

$$\left|\mu\gamma S v_s \frac{\tau}{\pi}\right| \gg 1 \tag{D.20b}$$

This condition normally prevails at stall or for $|S| > 1$. We then have

$$\alpha = (1 + j)\sqrt{\frac{\mu\gamma S v_s \pi}{2\tau}} \tag{D.21}$$

or, if we introduce the Doppler-shifted frequency sensed by the secondary conductor,

$$\omega_2 = S\omega_e = S\frac{\pi}{\tau}v_s \tag{D.22}$$

we have

$$\alpha = (1 + j)\sqrt{\frac{\mu\gamma\omega_2}{2}} \tag{D.23}$$

If we consider the simplest cases 1 and 3 where the amplitudes of the field vectors decay exponentially with an equal rate, we note that these amplitudes are reduced by one neper at a distance

$$\delta = \sqrt{\frac{2}{\mu\gamma\omega_2}} \tag{D.24}$$

This length can then be taken as an effective depth of penetration of the electromagnetic field and as a measure of the skin effect. If the conductor thickness exceeds this length, only the skin layer is utilized. This conclusion is borne out by cases 2 and 4 which reduce to cases 1 and 3 when $\alpha a > 1$. Introducing δ from Eq. (D.24) into Eq. (D.20b), we find that the approximate expression for α given by Eq. (D.21) is valid as long as $\delta \ll \tau$.

Finally we want to investigate the flow of power into the secondary conductor in terms of the Poynting vector. The only relevant component, the z component

$$-\langle N_z \rangle = \operatorname{Re}\,[\bar{E}_y \bar{H}_x^*] \tag{D.25}$$

can be obtained for the various cases by introducing the appropriate values of $\bar{E}_y$ and $\bar{B}_x$. For instance in case 1 we have, from Eqs. (D.8),

$$-\langle N_z \rangle = \mathrm{Re}\left[\frac{\alpha|\bar{E}_0|^2 e|^{(\alpha+\alpha^*)z}|}{j\omega_e\mu}\right] \tag{D.26}$$

and in case 3 we have, from Eq. (D.15),

$$-\langle N_z \rangle = \mathrm{Re}\left[\frac{j\omega_e\mu|\bar{K}_1|^2 e|^{(\alpha+\alpha^*)z}|}{\alpha}\right] \tag{D.27}$$

If we introduce the characteristic impedance of the secondary circuit which in both cases is

$$\frac{\bar{E}_y}{\bar{H}_x} = \frac{j\omega_e\mu}{\alpha} = \bar{Z}_c \tag{D.28}$$

we can write for the density of power flowing through the surface of the conductor at $z = 0$

$$-\langle N_z \rangle_0 = \mathrm{Re}\left[\frac{|\bar{E}_0|^2}{\bar{Z}_c}\right] \tag{D.29}$$

for case 1 and

$$-\langle N_z \rangle_0 = \mathrm{Re}\,[\bar{Z}_c|\bar{K}_1|^2] \tag{D.30}$$

for case 3. This power density represents the power transferred from the primary to the secondary per-unit surface of the gap and is therefore an indication of the performance of the converter. We shall now see that the converter will exhibit a radically different performance, depending on whether the magnetic Reynolds number is low and Eq. (D.20*a*) is satisfied, or high and Eq. (D.20*b*) is satisfied.

When the impressed magnetic field is only slightly perturbed by the armature reaction and Eq. (D.20*a*) holds, we can expand $1/\alpha$ as

$$\begin{aligned}\frac{1}{\alpha} &= \frac{1}{\sqrt{(\pi/\tau)^2(1 + j\mu\gamma S v_s \tau/\pi)}} \\ &= \frac{\tau}{\pi}\left(1 - \frac{j}{2}\mu\gamma S v_s \frac{\tau}{\pi}\right) + \cdots\end{aligned} \tag{D.31}$$

so that the characteristic impedance becomes,

$$\bar{Z}_c = \frac{\omega_e\mu\tau}{\pi}\left(\frac{1}{2}\mu\gamma S v_s \frac{\tau}{\pi} + j\right) \tag{D.28a}$$

This impedance can be represented in conformity with Figs. 9.5 and 10.8 as the combination of a large secondary resistance,

$$\frac{R_2'}{S} = \frac{1}{\gamma(\tau/2\pi)S}$$

in parallel with a magnetizing reactance $\mathfrak{X}_m = \mu v_s$. This means that according to Eq. (7.21) the gap has an effective length $g = \tau/\pi$, and, according to Eq. (9.2), the conductor has an effective thickness $a = \tau/2\pi$. Introducing this approximation for $\bar{Z}_c$ and taking into account Eq. (D.20a), then Eq. (D.29) for the case of impressed $\bar{E}$ reduces to

$$-\langle N_z \rangle_0 = \frac{1}{2} \frac{\gamma S v_s}{\omega_e} |\bar{E}_0|^2 = \frac{\tau}{2\pi} \gamma S |\bar{E}_0|^2 \qquad \text{(D.29a)}$$

and Eq. (D.30) for the case of impressed K reduces to

$$\begin{aligned} -\langle N_z \rangle_0 &= \frac{1}{2} \left(\frac{\tau}{\pi}\right)^2 \mu^2 \omega_e \gamma S v_s |\bar{K}_1|^2 \\ &= \frac{1}{2} \left(\frac{\tau}{\pi}\right)^3 \mu^2 \omega_e^2 \gamma S |\bar{K}_1|^2 \qquad \text{(D.30a)} \end{aligned}$$

We observe that when B_z is practically constant across the conductor and the approximate Eq. (D.28a) holds, the imaginary part of $\bar{Z}_c$ is constant and independent of the slip. Also from Eqs. (D.29a) and (D.30a) it appears that the power transferred to the rotor, and therefore the electromagnetic force, is proportional to the slip. This condition then corresponds to the portion of the stable branch of the force-speed characteristic where S is small. We thus find, as expected, that at low values of slip, when the skin effect is negligible, large-gap and narrow-gap motors perform alike. In all cases the locus of primary and secondary current is the arc of a circle.

When, instead, the skin effect is appreciable and Eq. (D.20b) holds, the characteristic impedance becomes

$$\bar{Z}_c = \frac{1}{1+j} \frac{\omega_e \mu}{\sqrt{\mu \gamma S \pi v_s / 2\tau}} = \frac{1+j}{2} \omega_e \mu \delta = \sqrt{\frac{j\omega_e \mu}{\gamma S}} \qquad \text{(D.28b)}$$

This characteristic impedance indicates that the regime prevailing in the slip range where Eq. (D.21) applies ($\delta \ll \tau$ and $\delta \ll a$) is completely different from the one studied so far. Indeed we find that the impedance of the secondary circuit:

1. Has equal values for the resistive and reactive parts independently of the speed.
2. Is independent of the pole pitch τ and, therefore, for a given primary frequency ω_e, is independent of the number of pole pairs p and the synchronous speed v_s.
3. Cannot be represented in terms of a finite number of lumped parameters, but only in terms of an infinite transmission line with parameters $Z_{\text{series}} = j\omega_e \mu$ and $Y_{\text{shunt}} = \gamma S$, as indicated in Fig. D.2.

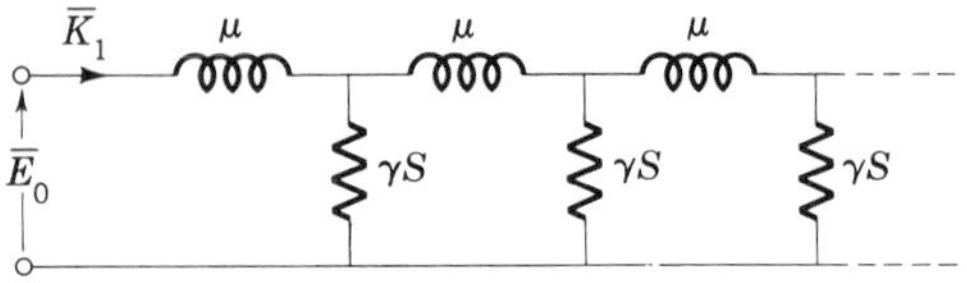

Fig. D. 2

In this case the power density becomes

$$-\langle N_z \rangle_0 = \frac{|\bar{E}_0|^2 \sqrt{S}}{\sqrt{2\omega_e \mu/\gamma}} \tag{D.29b}$$

for the case of impressed $\bar{E}$ and

$$-\langle N_z \rangle_0 = \frac{|\bar{K}_1|^2}{2} \sqrt{\frac{2\omega_e \mu}{\gamma}} \frac{1}{\sqrt{S}} \tag{D.30b}$$

for the case of impressed $\bar{K}$. We thus observe that the limiting cases of an ideal voltage source and an ideal current source are distinguished by inverse functional dependence of the power on the slip. In both cases the dependence is weak because of the square root. It is then to be expected that in the intermediate case of a practical converter the power transferred to the secondary circuit should be rather constant over a wide range of speeds. This explains the flat characteristic of Fig. 10.14.

A comparison of the equations for the power density brings to light very important guiding principles for the design. From Eqs. (D.29*a*) and (D.30*a*) we learn that when the converter is designed so as to satisfy steady-state (low S) performance specifications, maximum power density is obtained when we choose τ as large as possible and therefore a large radius and a small number of poles. This is particularly true in the case of small servocomponents which are fed by high-impedance sources, because for a given frequency the power output increases as the cube of the pole pitch. When instead the converter is designed on the basis of its starting performance (high S), then we see from Eqs. (D.29*b*) and (D.30*b*) that the electric-power input in the secondary conductor is independent of τ and therefore of the radius and the number of poles. This is the reason why, when linear accelerators are built with constant slip and variable pole pitch, not only is the power dissipated at low velocities less than in the constant-pitch construction, but also the power converted is larger.

INDEX